◎ Harden's

LONDON
Restaurants 2022

Take your dining to the next level

Enjoy benefits at the UK's Best Restaurants

Join today at hardens.com

© Harden's Limited 2021

ISBN 978-1-9160761-2-9

British Library Cataloguing-in-Publication data:
a catalogue record for this book is available from
the British Library.

Printed in the UK by CPI Books

Assistant editors: Bruce Millar, Antonia Russell

Harden's Limited
Missionworks, 41 Iffley Road, London W6 0PB

Would restaurateurs (and PRs) please address
communications to 'Editorial' at the above address,
or ideally by email to: editorial@hardens.com

CONTENTS

RATINGS & PRICES

Ratings

Our rating system does not tell you – as most guides do – that expensive restaurants are often better than cheap ones! What we do is compare each restaurant's performance – as judged by the average ratings awarded by reporters in the survey – with other similarly-priced restaurants. This approach has the advantage that it helps you find – whatever your budget for any particular meal – where you will get the best 'bang for your buck'.

The following qualities are assessed:

F — Food
S — Service
A — Ambience

The rating indicates that, *__in comparison with other restaurants in the same price-bracket__*, performance is…

5 — Exceptional
4 — Very good
3 — Good
2 — Average
1 — Poor

Prices

The price shown for each restaurant is the cost for one (1) person of an average three-course dinner with half a bottle of house wine and coffee, any cover charge, service and VAT. Lunch is often cheaper. With BYO restaurants, we have assumed that two people share a £7 bottle of off-licence wine.

__NOTE: All details are subject to change at no notice, especially post-Covid. Please call to verify.__

__Map reference__ – *shown immediately after the telephone number.*

__Full postcodes__ – *for non-group restaurants, the first entry in the 'small print' at the end of each listing, so you can set your sat-nav.*

__Website, Twitter__ – *shown in the small print, where applicable.*

__Last orders time__ – *listed after the website (if applicable); Sunday may be up to 90 minutes earlier.*

__Opening hours__ – *unless otherwise stated, restaurants are open for lunch and dinner seven days a week.*

__Credit and debit cards__ – *unless otherwise stated, Mastercard, Visa, Amex and Maestro are accepted.*

__Dress__ – *where appropriate, the management's preferences concerning patrons' dress are given.*

HOW THIS GUIDE IS WRITTEN

Celebrating our 30th edition!

This guide is based on our 30th annual survey of what 'ordinary' diners-out think of London's restaurants. This year, the total number of reporters in our combined London/UK survey, conducted mainly online, numbered 3,500, and, between them, they contributed 30,000 individual reports.

COVID-19 effects on the survey

Last year our annual national diners' poll could not run. This year, it did run. But, due to the closure of restaurants until late spring, the survey ran later in the year than normal; over a shorter time period (so we could publish before year-end).

In generating 60% of our usual amount of reports, this was an excellent result in a year when the poll could only run for half the normal amount of time. This up-to-date diners' feedback allows us to maintain the authoritative snapshot of how restaurants are faring for which the guide has become known. And, with the trade in such a state of flux, everyone needs a guide right now just to have half a chance of keeping up with the relentless reinvention, resilience, rescues, reverses and rapidity of change evident in the restaurant scene.

How intelligent is AI?

At a time when the credibility of online reviews and influencer posts are under ever-more scrutiny, there is an ever-greater need for trusted sources such as the Harden's annual national diners' poll. In particular, the active curation by humans that we provide. For – while obviously folks can attempt to stuff the Harden's ballot too – our high degree of editorial oversight, plus our historical data about both the restaurants and those commenting, makes it much harder to cheat. In this way Harden's can socially source restaurant feedback, but – vitally – curate it carefully. It is this careful curation that provides extra 'value-added' for diners.

How we determine the ratings

In general, ratings are arrived at statistically. We create a ranking akin to football leagues, with the most expensive restaurants in the top league and the cheaper ones in lower ones. Any restaurant's ranking *within its own particular league* determines its ratings. This year, we have allowed ourselves a little more scope than normal for editorial judgement. The prime aim is to guide the reader, and – in these bizarre times – latitude to 'read the runes' seems sensible.

How we write the reviews

The tone of each review and the ratings are guided by the ranking of the restaurant concerned, derived as described above. At the margin, we may also pay regard to the balance of positive votes (such as for 'favourite restaurant') against negative ones (such as for 'most overpriced'). To explain why an

TAKE YOUR DINING TO THE NEXT LEVEL

PLATINUM
MEMBER

Love good food?
Join the club!

entry has been rated as it has, we extract snippets from user comments ("enclosed in double quotes"). On well-known restaurants, we receive several hundred reports, and a short summary cannot do individual justice to all of them. What we seek to do – *without any regard to our own personal opinions* – is to illustrate key themes in the collective feedback.

How do we find our reporters?

Anyone can take part. Register now at www.hardens.com if you have not already done so! In fact, we find that once people have taken part, they often continue to do so. Consequently, many people who complete the survey have done so before. With high repeat-participation, the end-result is really more the product of a very large and ever-evolving panel, or jury, than a random 'poll'.

Wouldn't a random sample be better?

That's a theoretical question, as there is no obvious way, still less a cost-efficient one, to identify a random sample of the guests at each of, say, 5,000 establishments across the UK, and get them to take part in any sort of survey. People steeped in statistical market research tend be most keen on this idea. Other folks accept that having someone stand with a clipboard at Oxford Circus asking random people their opinion on Le Gavroche is unlikely to glean useful data.

Do people ever try to stuff the ballot?

Of course they do! Sometimes with the aid of social media agencies. Many rogue entries are weeded out every year. But stuffing the ballot is not as trivial a task as some people seem to think: the survey results throw up clear natural voting patterns against which unfair 'campaigns' tend to stand out.

Aren't inspections the best way to run a guide?

This was the traditional model. And chefs in particular often tout this form of recognition. And, doubtless the inspection model has its strengths. But a prime weakness is that it is so expensive it precludes too many visits. Take its most famous exponent: Michelin. The tyre man doesn't claim to visit each entry listed in its guide annually. Even once! And who are its inspectors? Often catering professionals, whose tastes may be at odds with the natural customer base. On any entry of note, however, Harden's typically has somewhere between dozens and hundreds of reports annually from the folks who keep the restaurant in business. We believe that such feedback, carefully analysed, is far more revealing and accurate than an occasional 'professional' inspection.

SURVEY MOST MENTIONED

These are the restaurants which were most frequently mentioned by reporters. (Last year's position is given in brackets.) An asterisk* indicates the first appearance in the list of a recently opened restaurant.

1	Core by Clare Smyth (7)
2	Scott's (5)
3	Chez Bruce (3)
4	J Sheekey (1)
5	Le Gavroche (2)
6	The Wolseley (8)
7	The River Café (12)
8	La Trompette (10)
9	Brasserie Zédel (9)
10	The Cinnamon Club (25)

11	Noble Rot (21)
12=	Gauthier Soho (11)
12=	A Wong (16)
14	Sams Riverside*
15	Above at Hide (14)
16	Gymkhana (13)
17	Clos Maggiore (4)
18	Bocca di Lupo (17)
19	The Five Fields (31)
20	Medlar (36)

21	Pied à Terre (34)
22	Bentley's (30)
23	Galvin La Chapelle (22)
24	Elystan Street (40)
25	The Ritz (28)
26	Andrew Edmunds (19)
27	La Poule au Pot (27)
28	The Ivy (15)
29	Gordon Ramsay (29)
30	Dastaan (-)

31	The Delaunay (20)
32	Mere (-)
33	Trinity (24)
34	Cornerstone (-)
35	Bibendum (-)
36=	Trishna (35)
36=	Murano (33)
36=	Rick Stein (-)
39	Hélène Darroze, The Connaught Hotel (-)
40	Benares (-)

SURVEY NOMINATIONS

Top gastronomic experience

1. Core by Clare Smyth (1)
2. Le Gavroche (2)
3. Chez Bruce (4)
4. La Trompette (5)
5. The Five Fields (10)
6. The River Café (-)
7. Elystan Street (-)
8. Scott's (-)
9. A Wong (-)
10. Above at Hide (9)

Favourite

1. Chez Bruce (1)
2. La Trompette (5)
3. Core by Clare Smyth (-)
4. The Wolseley (9)
5. Bocca di Lupo (-)
6. The River Café (4)
7. Elystan Street (-)
8. Gauthier Soho (6)
9. The Ritz (-)
10. Rules (-)

Best for business

1. The Wolseley (1)
2. Hawksmoor (Group) (2)
3. The Delaunay (3)
4. Brasserie Zédel (-)
5. Le Gavroche (-)
6. Scott's (6)
7. Galvin La Chapelle (8)
8. The Dining Room, The Goring Hotel (5)
9. Coq d'Argent (10)
10. 45 Jermyn St. (-)

Best for romance

1. Clos Maggiore (1)
2. La Poule au Pot (2)
3. Andrew Edmunds (3)
4. Le Gavroche (6)
5. Mere (-)
6. The Five Fields (-)
7. The Ivy (-)
8. Café du Marché (8)
9. The Ritz (10)
10. Chez Bruce (4)

Best breakfast/brunch

1 The Wolseley (1)
2 Dishoom (2)
3 Côte (6)
4 The Delaunay (4)
5 Granger & Co (8)
6 Megan's (-)
7 Caravan (3)
8 Breakfast Club (9)
9 The Ivy Grills & Brasseries (5)
10 Hawksmoor EC2 (10)

Best bar/pub food

1 Harwood Arms (1)
2 The Anchor & Hope (2)
3 Bull & Last (-)
4 Canton Arms (5)
5 The Eagle (-)
6 The Drapers Arms (7)
7 The Red Lion & Sun (-)
8 The Carpenter's Arms (-)
9 The Windmill (-)
10 The Anglesea Arms (3)

Most disappointing cooking

1 Oxo Tower (1)
2 Gordon Ramsay (6)
3 Dinner by Heston Blumenthal (-)
4 Kanishka (-)
5 Hélène Darroze, The Connaught Hotel (-)
6 La Trompette (-)
7 Nutbourne (-)
8= Rick Stein (-)
8= The Wallace (-)
10 Huo (2)

Most overpriced restaurant

1 The River Café (1)
2 Sexy Fish (4)
3 Dinner by Heston Blumenthal (-)
4 The Chiltern Firehouse (-)
5 Gordon Ramsay (2)
6 Oxo Tower (3)
7 Alain Ducasse at The Dorchester (-)
8 Wiltons (-)
9 Hélène Darroze, The Connaught Hotel (-)
10 Rules (-)

SURVEY HIGHEST RATINGS

FOOD

SERVICE

£100+

FOOD	SERVICE
1 Da Terra	1 Endo at Rotunda
2 Endo at Rotunda	2 The Five Fields
3 Core by Clare Smyth	3 Core by Clare Smyth
4 La Dame de Pic London	4 Aulis London
5 Five Fields	5 Kitchen Table

£75–£99

FOOD	SERVICE
1 Nobu, Metropolitan Hotel	1 Sale e Pepe
2 Anglo	2 Portland
3 Dinings (Group)	3 Cambio de Tercio
4 St John Smithfield	4 Otto's
5 Scully	5 Noizé

£60–£74

FOOD	SERVICE
1 Behind	1 Sams Riverside
2 A Wong	2 Behind
3 Carousel	3 Carousel
4 Sabor	4 Randall & Aubin
5 Palomar	5 Lorne

£45–£59

FOOD	SERVICE
1 50 Kalò di Ciro Salvo	1 The Wet Fish Café
2 The Wet Fish Café	2 Darjeeling Express
3 FENN	3 Noble Rot Soho
4 Kricket	4 Babur
5 Kiln	5 Paladar

£44 or less

FOOD	SERVICE
1 Dastaan	1 Bubala
2 Bubala	2 Kaffeine
3 Roti King	3 Dastaan
4 Tayyabs	4 Paradise Hampstead
5 Silk Road	5 Bao (Group)

AMBIENCE

1. Endo at Rotunda
2. Sketch (Lecture Rm)
3. Kitchen Table
4. Da Terra
5. Hutong

1. Bob Bob Ricard
2. Petersham Nurseries
3. Rules
4. Min Jiang
5. J Sheekey Atlantic Bar

1. Brunswick House Café
2. Behind
3. Carousel
4. The Wolseley
5. Sams Riverside

1. Noble Rot Soho
2. The Wet Fish Café
3. Masala Zone
4. José
5. Bar Douro

1. Mercato Metropolitano
2. Bubala
3. Bao (Group)
4. Dastaan
5. Kaffeine

OVERALL

1. Endo at Rotunda
2. Da Terra
3. Core by Clare Smyth
4. Kitchen Table
5. Pied à Terre

1. Cornerstone
2. St John Smithfield
3. Chez Bruce
4. Bob Bob Ricard
5. Portland

1. Behind
2. Carousel
3. Sams Riverside
4. Randall & Aubin
5. Sabor

1. The Wet Fish Café
2. 50 Kalò di Ciro Salvo
3. Masala Zone
4. Noble Rot Soho
5. Darjeeling Express

1. Bubala
2. Dastaan
3. Mercato Metropolitano
4. Bao (Group)
5. Monmouth Coffee

SURVEY BEST BY CUISINE

These are the restaurants which received the best average food ratings (excluding establishments with a small or notably local following).

Where the most common types of cuisine are concerned, we present the results in two price-brackets. For less common cuisines, we list the top three, regardless of price.

For further information about restaurants which are particularly notable for their food, see the area overviews starting on page 262.

British, Modern

£60 and over
1. Core by Clare Smyth
2. Anglo
3. Ormer Mayfair
4. The Clove Club
5. Five Fields

Under £60
1. The Wet Fish Café
2. FENN
3. Noble Rot Soho
4. The Eagle
5. 12:51

French

£60 and over
1. La Dame de Pic London
2. Pied à Terre
3. The Ninth London
4. LPM
5. Le Gavroche

Under £60
1. Provender
2. Café du Marché
3. Bellanger
4. Brasserie Zédel
5. Mon Plaisir

Italian/Mediterranean

£60 and over
1. Da Terra
2. Murano
3. Clarke's
4. Bocca di Lupo
5. Luca

Under £60
1. Anima e Cuore
2. Osteria Tufo
3. 500
4. Mercato Metropolitano
5. Bancone

Indian & Pakistani

£60 and over
1. Jamavar
2. Amaya
3. Trishna
4. Brigadiers
5. Gymkhana

Under £60
1. Dastaan
2. Kricket
3. Masala Zone
4. Babur
5. Darjeeling Express

Chinese

£60 and over

1 A Wong
2 Hunan
3 Min Jiang
4 Yauatcha
5 Hakkasan

Under £60

1 Mandarin Kitchen
2 Silk Road
3 Yming
4 Singapore Garden
5 Master Wei

Japanese

£60 and over

1 Endo at Rotunda
2 Nobu, Metropolitan Hotel
3 Dinings
4 Roka
5 Zuma

Under £60

1 Takahashi
2 Jin Kichi
3 Kanada-Ya
4 Sushi Murasaki
5 Tonkotsu

British, Traditional

1 St John Smithfield
2 Goring Hotel
3 The Ritz

Vegetarian

1 Farmacy
2 Mildreds
3 The Gate

Burgers, etc

1 MeatLiquor
2 Patty and Bun
3 Burger & Beyond

Pizza

1 50 Kalò di Ciro Salvo
2 Antica Pizzeria da Mi…
3 Sacro Cuore

Fish & Chips

1 Toff's
2 The Sea Shell
3 Olympus Fish

Thai

1 Kiln
2 Smoking Goat
3 Farang

Steaks & Grills

1 The Guinea Grill
2 Lurra
3 Smith's Wapping

Fish & Seafood

1 Behind
2 Cornerstone
3 Prawn on the Lawn

Fusion

1 Da Terra
2 Scully
3 Sollip

Spanish

1 Sabor
2 José
3 Barrafina

THE RESTAURANT SCENE

Two for one

Because no publication was possible last year, we present below two years' statistics in a single 'lump'. See pages 21-26 for the underlying detail.

Given the limited extent to which restaurants were open from Spring 2020–Spring 2021, it doesn't seem unrealistic to count ventures since our 2020 edition as new. Many launches missed the usual PR and full power of word of mouth in this period, due to lockdown closures and other distractions.

Record closures, record churn, but still there's faith in London

Over the two-year period since the last guide, there are 293 newcomers in this year's edition (so, annualised, the equivalent of 147 debuts per year).

On a straight-average annualised basis, this level of openings is the 8th-best year we have recorded; and in the middle of the range of 107–200 recorded in the last ten years.

Closures, however, have been at record levels (especially if one were to account for the mass closures across larger chains which are not historically included in our figures).

Including restaurants which are temporarily closed, closures stand at 125 on an annualised basis. This compares with 2018's chart-topping 117 and the 113 recorded in the 2004 guide, which resulted from the savage hit the trade took as a result of the second Gulf war and SARS epidemic.

If one excludes those temporarily closures and focuses just on so-far-confirmed permanent closures, the picture would seem a fraction rosier. In this case, the annualised figure would be 109 – a little below those previous highs. But, to leave this number unadjusted for temporary closures seems unrealistic. Restaurant-owners are keen to PR their openings, but do nothing to promote their closures. So, it seems likely that – despite our best fact checking efforts – a few restaurants we believe to be open have quietly closed. Some counted as 'temporarily closed' may actually have gone for good. And it is worth repeating that our indie-focused statistics omit the mass closures at chains such as Byron, GBK, PizzaExpress and Wahaca (all with entries in the guide). If these were included, then net growth could be negative.

Animal spirits

And yet, despite these caveats and the apocalyptic business backdrop to this year's edition, there is a definite feeling that London has weathered the storm better than might have been expected. Not even during WWII did pubs actually have to close. Yet a massive contraction has been avoided and openings of superb quality continue to come to market. Although the government should have done far, far more to help restaurants with rent difficulties, kudos to Rishi Sunak for the furlough scheme. Without it, the result would have been meltdown. And respect, too, to the trade in general, which was dealt an awful hand. In their tenacity, creativity, and sheer bloody mindedness, many operators clung on where less enterprising folks would have called it a day.

Of course, not all of the brave new recent openings are post-pandemic bets. A large backlog of pent-up projects has been working its way through the system. One new five-star hotel in central London prepared to launch five times over the pandemic! It only finally did so in September 2021.

Back in the present, there appears to be no shortage of folks prepared to bet on a London comeback. Despite all the talk of a new era – where life is lived in pyjamas via Zoom from a rural barn – armies of investors are betting on the capital.

Indeed, property development has continued throughout the pandemic. In both the business and the residential sector nowadays, a 'signature' restaurant (or two) is de rigeur for any new project. The favourable terms granted to up-and-coming restaurateurs in the early days of such schemes have been a growing feature of London's restaurant scene. This boost has helped undercut the corrections that generic over-supply would otherwise typically bring.

In a similar vein, a September 2020 change to local planning regulations (scrapping the old A3 use class) has further expanded the supply of sites for budding restaurateurs and lowered barriers to entry into the market

So, while it has become fashionable for operators to say that a fall-out was long past due, there is, in fact, a continuing enthusiasm to crank up openings nevertheless.

Trends that are here to stay

The rise of the 'makeaway' was an emblem of lockdown. As restaurants have reopened, a perhaps surprisingly large amount of demand has remained. People are loath to give up the habit, it seems. And numerous restaurateurs who have found the flexibility to meet demand continue to do so. It makes them money and spreads their brand.

Along with the ongoing rise of computer-based ordering, it is another victory for technology from those tough times.

Staff shortages are one, new, very unwelcome development: one that seems unlikely to go away any time soon. They are the biggest existential threat to the restaurant industry in a generation and may create greater long-term damage than the pandemic. The London restaurant industry in the last 20 years has often been buoyed along by the hard graft of young Europeans. Anecdotal feedback suggests that native workers are in no hurry to replace them. When this guide began 31 years ago, it was common to hear restaurateurs bemoan their inability to expand due to the difficulty of finding good staff. Sadly those times have come again.

THE RESTAURANT SCENE

On the rise: Japan... and Africa

After new Modern British (66) openings, Japanese cuisine was the most popular for newcomers this edition, accounting for 23 of the debuts (just beating Italian cuisine which was the designation for 22).

Having been a rarity when we first launched our guide, Japanese dishes are becoming fully integrated into UK food culture. One recent signpost of this trend is a new dedicated sushi menu introduced at London's oldest French restaurant, L'Escargot. Such a move would have seemed outré just a few years back: nowadays it barely rated mention.

With five openings, it may be that African and Afro-Caribbean cuisine is now coming of age in London. For decades, few people could name any African restaurant other than the grungy basement of the now-relocated Africa Centre in Covent Garden. But the recent arrivals of restaurants like Akoko, Antillean, Chuku's, Chishuru and Tatale – to join the likes of Ikoyi and Stork – represent a striking break from the past.

WIll the trend be like the 'nouvelle Indian' revolution of the late '90s? At that time a 'posh Indian' was still a contradiction in terms. African cuisines do not have the heritage of a curry house on every corner. to draw on as Indian cuisine does and did. Yet, it feels like London may again sit at the forefront of a trend to take a family of cuisines mostly celebrated for their 'humble homespun qualities' (as Jimi Famurewa put it in *The Standard*) and reposition their flavour palette as the basis for luxury openings globally.

When it comes to the location of new openings, Central London asserted its traditional dominance, accounting for 102 arrivals. In the 'burbs, East London confidently led the way (with 60 openings). Trailing behind came South London (with 49) and West London (46). As usual, North London took the bottom slot (with just 35 newcomers).

Prices remain above-inflation

The average price of dinner for one at establishments listed in this guide is £64.14 (c.f. £59.28 two years previously). Prices have risen by an annualised rate of 4.0% in the past two years. This rate remains above the general annual inflation rate of 3.2% for the 12 months to August 2021.

The rise is most marked amongst pricey restaurants (over £100 per head). In this group, the annualised growth is a whopping 8.8%.

This situation feels reminiscent of the early 1990s, when luxury restaurants aimed to protect their margins against diminishing footfall. Ultimately, that trend reversed as restaurants tried to put bums on seats through lower pricing. In that vein, it is worth noting that promotional lunch menus are excluded from our figures. So watch out for bargain menus at the most expensive establishments!

OPENINGS & CLOSURES

The listings below relate to the period from Autumn 2019 to Autumn 2021. This information is provided on a best-efforts basis, with the important caveat that the industry remains in a seldom-seen state of flux. The pattern of restaurants shifting their status between being open, temporarily closed and permanently closed remains highly unusual.

With the data we publish below and in the 'Restaurant Scene' section, we do not aim to track large, branded chains. Where we know of openings or closures amongst members of such groups, these are shown in the lists but excluded from the final tallies shown.

Openings (292)

A Slice of Blue *(E5)*
Acre *(NW6)*
Akoko *(W1)*
Al Mare *(SW1)*
The Alma *(SE19)*
Amazonico *(W1)*
Amethyst *(W1)*
Ampéli *(W1)*
Andanza *(SE1)*
Antica Pizzeria da Michele *(W1)*
Antillean *(SE1)*
Apothecary *(EC2)*
Arabica KX *(N1)*
L'Artigiano *(SW10)*
At Feast *(NW8)*
Attawa *(E8)*
Ave Mario *(WC2)*
Ayllu *(W2)*
Le Bab *(EC1, E8)*
Baccala *(SE1)*
Bad Vegan *(NW1)*
Bancone *(W1)*
Bando Belly *(SE15)*
Bao Noodle Shop *(E2)*
Bar des Prés *(W1)*
Bar La Rampa *(W1)*
Baraka *(EC2)*
Barboun *(EC2)*
Base Face Pizza *(W6)*
Behind *(E8)*
Bellefields *(SW9)*
Bermondsey Larder *(SE1)*
BiBi *(W1)*
Bibo by Dani García *(EC2)*
Big Fernand *(SW7)*

Big Jo Bakery *(N7)*
Bindas Eatery *(W1, W12)*
Bisushima *(WC2)*
Black Bear Burger *(SW9)*
The Black Book *(W1)*
Blacklock *(WC2)*
Bleecker Burger *(W12)*
Bobo Social *(SE17)*
Borough Market Kitchen *(SE1)*
Il Borro *(W1)*
Brat at Climpson's Arch *(E8)*
The Broadcaster *(W12)*
Trattoria Brutto *(EC1)*
Bund *(N2)*
Burger & Lobster *(EC2)*
Buvette *(W11)*
Cafe Bao *(N1)*
Cafe Cecilia *(E8)*
Café Deco *(WC1)*
Carmel *(NW6)*
Casa do Frango *(EC2)*
Casacosta *(SW6)*
Cavita *(W1)*
Ceru *(W2)*
Cha Cha x Sister Jane *(W10)*
Chameleon *(NW1)*
The Cheese Barge *(W2)*
Chick 'n' Sours *(E1)*
La Chingada *(SE8)*
Chishuru *(SW9)*
Chucs *(SW1 x2)*
Chuku's *(N15)*
Cin Cin *(W1)*
Cincinnati Chilibomb *(EC2)*
Cinder *(NW3)*
The Clarence Tavern *(N16)*

OPENINGS & CLOSURES

Club Mexicana Taqueria *(WC2)*
Colette *(SW10, SW19)*
Colonel Saab *(WC1)*
The Connaught Grill *(W1)*
Copper Chimney *(W12)*
CORD *(EC4)*
The Crossing *(SW13)*
Darjeeling Express *(WC2)*
The Duke of York *(N1)*
Dulwich Lyceum *(SE21)*
Dumpling Shack x F…*(E14)*
The Dusty Knuckle *(N4)*
East West *(NW5)*
Eataly *(EC2)*
Ekstedt at The Yard *(SW1)*
El Ta'koy *(WC2)*
Eldr at Pantechnicon *(SW1)*
Elliot's *(E8)*
Epic Pies *(EC4)*
Erev *(SE1)*
The Farrier *(NW1)*
Fat Badger *(TW10)*
Fatt Pundit *(WC2)*
FENN *(SW6)*
Fiend *(W10)*
Figo *(E20)*
Firebrand *(EC1)*
Flat Iron *(SE1, W1)*
Florattica *(EC3)*
Forza Wine *(SE15)*
14 Hills *(EC3)*
Frank's *(SW1)*
Galvin Bistrot & Bar *(E1)*
Ganymede *(SW1)*
Giannino Dal 1899 *(W1)*
The Good Plot *(W11)*
Goods Way *(N1)*
Gunmakers *(W1)*
Hackney Coterie *(E8)*
Halo Burger *(EC2)*
Hankies *(W2, SW1)*
Hannah *(SE1)*
Harrods Social *(SW1)*
Haugen *(E20)*
The Hawk's Nest *(W12)*
Heddon Yokocho *(W1)*
Heritage *(SE21)*
Homestead *(E14)*

Hoppers *(N1)*
Hot May Pot Pot *(SW3)*
Hot Stone *(N1, W1)*
Humble Chicken *(W1)*
The Hunter's Moon *(SW3)*
Huo *(SW10)*
Il Teatro della Carne *(W1)*
Imad's Syrian Kitchen *(W1)*
INO *(W1)*
Isola by San Carlo *(W1)*
Italian Greyhound *(W1)*
Ivy Asia *(SW3, W1, EC4)*
The Ivy Victoria *(SW1)*
Jiji *(N1)*
Joan *(E1)*
Jolie *(SW10)*
José Pizarro at the RA *(W1)*
Junsei *(W1)*
Kalimera *(N8)*
Kanada-Ya *(W5)*
Kibou London *(SW11)*
Kolamba *(W1)*
Kudu Grill *(SE15)*
L'Oscar Restaurant *(WC1)*
Lahpet *(WC2)*
Larry's *(SE15)*
The Light Bar *(E1)*
Liv *(SW1)*
London Stock *(SW18)*
Louie *(WC2)*
Lucky & Joy *(E5)*
Lyon's *(N8)*
Madera *(W1)*
The Maine Mayfair *(W1)*
Maison Francois *(SW1)*
Mallow *(SE1)*
Mama Shelter *(E2)*
Manteca *(EC2)*
Manthan *(W1)*
Maroush Park Royal *(NW10)*
Maru *(W1)*
Maya *(EC2)*
Megan's *(N1, W8)*
Mei Mei *(SE1)*
The Melusine *(E1)*
Mike's Peckham *(SE15)*
MiMi Mei Fair *(W1)*
Mio Yatai *(E2)*

Los Mochis *(W8)*
Molly's Café *(E2)*
Morena *(SW1)*
Morso *(NW10)*
Mr Ji *(W1)*
Muse *(SW1)*
My Neighbours the Dumplings *(E9)*
Naifs *(SE15)*
Nakanojo *(SW3)*
Native at Browns *(W1)*
Nebula Pizza *(E2)*
NEST *(E9)*
1947 London *(W1)*
No 35 Mackenzie Walk *(E14)*
Noble Rot Soho *(W1)*
Nobu Portman Square *(W1)*
NoMad London *(WC2)*
The Nook *(N1)*
Nue Ground *(SW4)*
116 at the Athenaeum *(W1)*
One Hundred Shoreditch *(E1)*
123V *(W1)*
Only Food and Courses *(SW9)*
Oren *(E8)*
Other Side Fried *(SW9)*
Ottolenghi *(W1)*
The OWO *(SW1)*
Oxeye *(SW11)*
Ozone Coffee Roasters *(E2)*
Padella Shoreditch *(EC2)*
Pali Hill *(W1)*
Panton Yokocho *(SW1)*
Park Row *(W1)*
Parlour, Gt Scotland Yd *(SW1)*
Parlour, The Ned *(EC2)*
Party Store Pizza *(SW4)*
Pascor *(W8)*
Passyunk Avenue *(E20)*
Pastaio *(W12)*
El Pastor Soho *(W1)*
Patri Ealing *(W5)*
Patty and Bun *(W1)*
Peachy Goat *(SE24)*
Peckham Cellars *(SE15)*
The Pem *(SW1)*
Pergola on the Wharf *(E14)*
The Perry Hill *(SE6)*

Philippe Conticini *(NW1)*
The Phoenix *(W12)*
Piazza Italiana *(EC2)*
Pino *(W8)*
Pivot *(WC2)*
Pizza Pilg… *(EC2, SW1, W12, NW1)*
Pizzeria Mozza *(W1)*
Planque *(E8)*
The Plimsoll *(N4)*
PLU *(NW8)*
Poster Bar at the RA *(W1)*
Prairie Fire *(W12)*
The Prince of Wales *(W6)*
Queens of Mayfair *(W1)*
RAW - Fish & Cocktails *(W1)*
Republic *(W4)*
Rita's Soho *(W1)*
Roketsu *(W1)*
Roof Gdn, Pantechnicon *(SW1)*
Royale *(E3)*
Rudy's *(W1)*
Rudy's Vegan Diner *(N1)*
Sachi at Pantechnicon *(SW1)*
Saint Jacques *(SW1)*
Sam's Café *(NW1)*
Santo Remedio *(EC2)*
Satay Street Cafe *(E1)*
Savoy, River Restaurant *(WC2)*
Scott's On The River *(TW9)*
The Sea, The Sea *(E8)*
SeaSons *(W1)*
Sessions Arts Club *(EC1)*
Showaken *(SW1)*
Sidechick *(W1)*
The Silver Birch *(W4)*
Six by Nico *(W1, E14)*
Skal Nordic Dining *(N1)*
Slice *(SE1)*
So LA *(W1)*
Sollip *(SE1)*
St Clair *(SW4)*
Stanley's *(SW3)*
Sticks'n'Sushi *(W1)*
Straits Kitchen *(EC3)*
Street Burger *(EC4, WC2, N1, W8, SE10, WC2)*
Sucre London *(W1)*
Sumi *(W11)*

OPENINGS & CLOSURES

Sunday in Brooklyn *(W2)*
Sushi on Jones *(N1)*
Sushi Revolution *(SW9)*
Sushi Show *(E2)*
Sussex *(W1)*
Sycamore Vino Cucina *(WC2)*
Taka Marylebone *(W1)*
Talad *(SW10)*
Tandoor Chop House *(W8)*
Tatale *(SE1)*
Tattu London *(WC2)*
Tavernaki *(W11)*
Tavolino *(SE1)*
Tendril *(W1)*
Tila *(SE8)*
TOKii *(W1)*
Toklas *(WC2)*
Tomahawk Steakhouse *(N1)*
Tonkotsu *(SE15, EC2)*
Townsend *(E1)*
Trawlerman's Fish Bar *(N1)*
Truffle *(W1)*
Turnips *(SE1)*
Turul Project *(N15)*
28-50 Chelsea *(SW3 x2, WC2)*
400 Rabbits *(SE27, SE24)*
26 Grains *(SE1)*
Vergine Maria *(W5)*
Volta do Mar *(WC2)*
VyTA *(WC2)*
Water House Project *(E2)*
The Watermans *(TW9)*
West 4th *(SW6)*
Whitcomb's *(WC2)*
Wild Tavern *(SW3)*
Wildflower *(NW1)*
Wright Brothers *(EC2)*
Wulf & Lamb *(W1)*
Yard Sale Pizza *(SE19)*
Zahter *(W1)*
081 Pizzeria *(SE15)*
Zia Lucia *(SW18, SW12, E1)*

Closures (217)

Addomme *(SW2)*
Aleion *(N10)*
Ametsa *(SW1)*
Anarkali *(W6)*
Andina *(E2, W11)*
Arlo's *(SW12, SW11)*
Atari-Ya *(W5)*
Alyn Williams *(W1)*
Baba G's *(NW1)*
BabaBoom *(N1)*
Babette *(SE15)*
Baltic *(SE1)*
Baptist Grill, L'Oscar *(WC1)*
Bar Boulud *(SW1)*
Beef & Brew *(N1, NW5)*
Belvedere Restaurant *(W8)*
Bernardi's *(W1)*
Bibimbap *(EC3, W1)*
Bistro Mirey *(SW6)*
Bistro Vadouvan *(SW15)*
Black Roe *(W1)*
Blanchette East *(E1)*
Bleeding Heart *(EC1)*
Blixen *(E1)*
Bodean's *(SW17, EC1)*
Bonnie Gull *(W1 x2)*
Boulestin *(SW1)*
Breddos Tacos *(W1)*
Bryn Williams at Somerset House *(WC2)*
Bubbledogs *(W1)*
Bucket *(W2)*
Bumpkin *(E20)*
Bumpkin *(SW7)*
by Chloe *(SE1, SE10, W1, WC2)*
Café del Parc *(N19)*
Café Monico *(W1)*
Cambridge Street *(SW1)*
Camillo Benso *(W1)*
Camino Bankside *(SE1)*
Cantina Laredo *(WC2)*
Le Caprice *(SW1)*
Catford Constitutional Club *(SE6)*
Le Cellar *(EC1)*
Ceru *(W1)*
Charlotte's *(W4, W5)*
Chipping Forecast *(W1, W11)*
Chit Chaat Chai *(SW4)*

Chucs Serpentine (W2)
Cigala (WC1)
CôBa (N7)
Corazón (W1)
Counter Culture (SW4)
Craft London (SE10)
Cub (N1)
Da Giua (EC1)
The Dairy (SW4)
Dandy (SE1)
Darjeeling Express (W1)
Department of Coffee and
Social Affairs (EC1)
Dip & Flip (SW17)
Dokke (E1)
Duddell's (SE1)
Dum Biryani (W1)
E&O Chelsea (SW3)
Emilia's Crafted Pasta (E1)
Emilia (W1)
Ethos (W1)
Fancy Crab (W1)
Fish in a Tie (SW11)
Flank (SW1)
Forza Win (SE15)
Four Legs at The Compton
Arms (N1)
Freak Scene (W1)
The Frog Hoxton (N1)
Fucina (W1)
Galvin, Athenaeum (W1)
Galvin HOP (E1)
Garden Room (WC2)
Geales (W8)
Gezellig (WC1)
The Gilbert Scott (NW1)
The Greenhouse (W1)
Guglee (NW6, NW3)
Hai Cenato (SW1)
The Halal Guys (WC2)
Harlequin (SW6)
Harry Morgan's (NW8)
Hello Darling (SE1)
Henrietta Bistro (WC2)
Hix (W1)
Hix Oyster & Chop Hs (EC1)
Homeslice (W1)
Hot Stuff (SW8)
Hubbard & Bell (WC1)
Ichi Buns (W1)

Indian Accent (W1)
Jacob the Angel (WC2)
Jidori (E8, WC2)
Jones Family Project (EC2)
Kaspar's Seafood and Grill,
The Savoy Hotel (WC2)
Kerbisher & Malt (W6)
Kuku Riku (NW1)
Kym's by Andrew Wong (EC4)
Kyseri (W1)
Lagom at Hackney Church
Brew Co. (E8)
Lamberts (SW12)
Lido Café, Brockwell (SE24)
Linden Stores (N1)
Lino (EC1)
Little Kolkata (WC2)
Loyal Tavern (SE1)
Lucknow 49 (W1)
Lupita (E1)
Lupita West (W8)
Mac & Wild (EC2, W1)
Made in Italy James St (W1)
Maroush (W2 x 2, W1)
maze Grill (W1)
MEATliquor (WC1)
Melabes (W8)
Merchants Tavern (EC2)
Meza (SW17)
Mimo (SE1)
The Modern Pantry (EC1)
Moio (N16)
Monsieur Le Duck (EC1)
Mother (SW11)
Nanashi (EC2)
Native (SE1)
Neptune (WC1)
Next Door (SE22)
Nobu Berkeley (W1)
Northbank (EC4)
Oldroyd (N1)
108 Garage (W10)
OOTY (W1)
El Parador (NW1)
Petit Pois Bistro (N1)
Piebury Corner (N7, N1)
Pisqu (W1)
Pizzicotto (W8)
Plot (SW17)
Polpo (EC1, W1, WC2, SW3, W11)

OPENINGS & CLOSURES

Pomona's *(W2)*
The Portrait, National Portrait Gallery *(WC2)*
Princi *(W1)*
Pucci Mayfair *(W1)*
Quirinale *(SW1)*
Rambla *(W1)*
Raoul's Café *(W9)*
Rasa *(W1)*
Rasa Travancore *(N16)*
Red Rooster *(EC2)*
The Rex Whistler Restaurant, Tate Britain *(SW1)*
Rib Room *(SW1)*
Rivington Grill *(SE10)*
Rochelle Canteen at the ICA *(SW1)*
Roe *(SW9)*
Roganic *(W1)*
Rossopomodoro *(SW18,W1)*
Roux at Parliament Sq *(SW1)*
Royal China *(W2)*
Sakagura *(W1)*
Sanxia Renjia *(SE8)*
Sapori Sardi *(SW6)*
Sardine *(N1)*
Season Kitchen *(N4)*
Siren *(SW1)*
Smoke & Salt *(SW9)*
Snaps & Rye *(W10)*
The Square *(W1)*
StreetXO *(W1)*
Sub Cult *(EC2)*
Suksan *(SW10)*
Tell Your Friends *(SW6)*
Terroirs *(WC2)*
Texture *(W1)*
The Yard *(SW1)*
tibits *(W1, SE1)*
Tom Simmons *(SE1)*
Tom's Kitchen *(SW3)*
The Tramshed *(EC2)*
Tredwell's *(WC2)*
Two Lights *(E2)*
Union Street Café *(SE1)*
Vanilla Black *(EC4)*
Verdi's *(E1)*
VQ *(W11, SW4, NW1)*
Wild Food Cafe *(WC2)*
Workshop Coffee at The

Pilgrim *(W2)*
Wright Brothers *(E1,W1)*
Xier *(W1)*
XR *(W1)*
XU *(W1)*
Yen *(WC2)*
Yum Bun *(EC2)*
Zelman Meats *(W1)*

Temporarily Closed (33)

Closed as we go to press, but expected to reopen.

L'Amorosa
Bao & Bing *(W1)*
The Betterment *(W1)*
Bleeding Heart Tavern *(EC1)*
Boisdale of Bishopsgate *(EC2)*
Boulevard Theatre *(W1)*
Bund *(N2)*
Chick 'n' Sours *(E8)*
Il Convivio *(SW1)*
Don Bistro and Bar *(EC4)*
Dragon Castle *(SE17)*
Edera *(W11)*
Eneko *(WC2)*
Ella Canta *(W1)*
Gallery Mess *(SW3)*
Gopal's of Soho *(W1)*
Gridiron *(W1)*
K10 *(EC1, EC3)*
Laurent at Cafe Royal *(W1)*
The Lore of the Land *(W1)*
Malabar *(W8)*
Mam *(W11)*
Manna *(NW1)*
Michael Nadra *(W4)*
Momo *(W1)*
Moncks of Dover Street *(W1)*
Onima *(W1)*
Other Naughty Piglet *(SW1)*
Palatino *(EC1)*
Park Terrace, *(W8)*
Les Platanes *(W1)*
Simpsons in the Strand *(WC2)*
Wild Rice & Mamasan *(W1)*

DIRECTORY

Comments in "double quotation marks" were made by reporters.

A Cena TW1 £55 3 3 3
418 Richmond Road   020 8288 0108   1–4A

This smart Italian in St Margaret's (owned and run by English chef Tom Rowlandson) wins consistently good ratings across the board, and has a solid following from nearby and beyond. It's also handy for those making a full day out of the rugby just up the road at Twickers. / TW1 2EB; www.acena.co.uk; @acenarestaurant; Tue-Sat 10 pm, Sun 2 pm; closed Tue-Thu L closed Sun D, closed Mon; booking max 6 may apply.

A Slice of Blue E5 NEW £28 3 3 3
43 Lower Clapton Road   020 8533 3301   14–1B

In gentrifying Clapton – this 'pizza pub' (on the former site of The Elephant's Head) is the creation of the founders of two pizza multiples: Santa Maria (Pasquale Chionchio & Angelo Ambrosio) and Firezza (Edin Basic). Craft beers and live music complete the offering. / E5 0NS; www.asliceofblue.com/; @asliceofblue; Mon-Thu midnight, Fri & Sat 1 am, Sun 11 pm; closed Mon-Fri L.

A Wong SW1 £63 5 5 3
70 Wilton Rd   020 7828 8931   2–4B

"The second Michelin star was well deserved" at Andrew Wong's Pimlico superstar – the survey's No.1 Chinese, and, since January 2021, the first Chinese restaurant outside China to reach such a level. Success has come quickly – it doesn't seem like yesterday (it was 2012) that he opened this comparatively simply decorated fixture on the site of his parents' former restaurant, Kym's (and he recently announced that the search is on for a new, grander home). With its "inspired" and "strikingly varied textures and flavours" ("stunning wagyu tart with peas…", "featherlight dumplings…", "legendary custard buns that justify Jay Rayner's enthusiasm!") the kitchen demonstrates "extraordinary ways of handling Chinese cuisine"; its output includes some "really interesting dishes from different regions in China". And on the service front, "his friendly and professional team bring it all together with style and professionalism". "A true gastronomic adventure!" / SW1V 1DE; www.awong.co.uk; @a.wong_londonuk; Tue-Sat 10 pm; closed Sun & Mon; credit card required to book.

The Abbeville SW4 £52 3 3 3
67-69 Abbeville Rd   020 8675 2201   11–2D

This stylish modern gastropub in Clapham's 'Abbeville Village' scores well across the board, and is especially "good value when they have one of their frequent deals on". Marks for the food would be higher still "but it's not 100% reliable as an over-achiever". / SW4 9JW; www.theabbeville.co.uk; @threecheerspubs; Mon-Thu, Sat 10.30 pm, Sun 9.30 pm; closed Fri.

The Abingdon W8 £70 3 3 4
54 Abingdon Rd   020 7937 3339   6–2A

This unusually chic gastropub in a Kensington backstreet (champagne buckets on the bar) is a "locals' favourite" for good reason, having entertained them in style and fed them well for almost 25 years. The bright interior is particularly striking, with red-leather booths adding an element of privacy. / W8 6AP; www.theabingdon.co.uk; @theabingdonw8; Mon-Sun 10 pm.

Abu Zaad W12 £35 3 3 3
29 Uxbridge Rd   020 8749 5107   8–1C

An evocative tiled interior adds to a visit to this cheap 'n' cheerful Syrian café, near the north end of Shepherd's Bush Market – a handy place for a fresh fruit juice and affordable mezze meal. / W12 8LH; www.abuzaad.co.uk; @abuzaaduk; Mon-Sun 10 pm; no Amex.

Acre NW6 NEW
Lonsdale Road   07821 392930   1–2B
Thomas Straker (who grew up on a smallholding in Herefordshire) has stints at Elystan Street and Casa Cruz on his CV and – after a residency at Carousel refining his menu – is set to launch this Queen's Park newcomer in the last quarter of 2021. Produce from Britain and inspiration from the Mediterranean are the guiding principles for cooking – from an open kitchen and with much of it wood-fired – that's 'more simple than fine dining'. / NW6 6RA; www.acre.london; Tue-Sun 10 pm.

Adams Café W12   £39   3 4 3
77 Askew Rd   020 8743 0572   8–1B
"Extremely tasty and good-value food" have cemented this Shepherd's Bush veteran's reputation as a "lovely local" over the past 32 years. Run by Frances and Abdel Boukraa, it serves standard greasy-spoon grub during the day and reopens at 7pm, transformed into a Maghrebi specialist serving Tunisian tagines, couscous and other delights. / W12 9AH; www.adamscafe.co.uk; @adamscafe; Mon-Sat 10 pm; closed Mon-Sat L, closed Sun; Booking evening only.

Addie's Thai Café SW5   £37   4 2 2
121 Earl's Court Rd   020 7259 2620   6–2A
"Very well-priced Thai street food" has kept this Earl's Court canteen buzzing for the best part of 25 years. (It was "sorely missed while restaurants were closed, but at least there was eventually a take-away option!".) / SW5 9RL; www.addiesthai.co.uk; Mon-Sun 10 pm; closed Mon & Tue, Sun L; no Amex.

The Admiral Codrington SW3   £59   3 3 4
17 Mossop St   020 7581 0005   6–2C
A long-standing watering-hole for the Chelsea set (immortalized in the 1980s style bible, The Sloane Rangers Handbook), off eternally chic Brompton Cross: the Cod is "not too pretentious or posey", and serves "good honest pub grub" – albeit of a quality not found in your average backstreet boozer. / SW3 2LY; www.theadmiralcodrington.co.uk; Mon-Sat 9.30 pm, Sun 4 pm; closed Sun D; No trainers.

Afghan Kitchen N1   £32   3 3 2
35 Islington Grn   020 7359 8019   9–3D
This small, sparse café on Islington Green is one of the longest-running entries in our guide. Nothing fancy, but check it out for a quick bite (simple curries and rice) that's interesting and won't break the bank. / N1 8DU; Tue-Sat 11 pm; closed Sun & Mon; cash only; no booking.

Aglio e Olio SW10   £48   3 3 2
194 Fulham Rd   020 7351 0070   6–3B
"No-frills" Italian near Chelsea and Westminster hospital that's "consistently good without being flashy". The "menu doesn't change much, but the kitchen knows what it's doing, including the excellent pasta dishes". Top Tip: "the zabaglione is to die for". / SW10 9PN; www.aglioeolio.co.uk; Mon-Sun 11 pm.

Akira at Japan House W8   £79   3 3 3
101-111 Kensington High Street   020 3971 4646   6–1A
"This showcase of Japanese culture" – an upmarket restaurant within the Japanese government's Japan House cultural centre in Kensington's former Derry & Toms department store building – "delivers an on-the-whole good dining experience", which includes "beautiful food, beautifully presented and it's all delicious". The main caveat is that it is "a little pricey" Top Tip: "the sake menu is worthy of the cultural centre". / W8 5SA; www.japanhouselondon.uk; @japanhouseldn; Tue-Sun 11 pm; closed Sun & Mon.

Akoko W1 NEW   £140   4 4 4
21 Berners Street   020 7323 0593   5–1A

After three years of planning and during the torrid times of October 2020, Aji Akokomi launched his Fitzrovian homage to West African 'jollof' cuisine – mixing Nigerian, Ghanaian and Senegalese influences into an ambitious tasting menu format. Not a man to be easily deflected, he emerged from the pandemic and departure of his initial star-chef (William Chilila) to win post-lockdown raves from The Standard's Jimi Famurewa in June 2021: "agog at the sumptuousness of it all… Akoko's triumph is to re-energise tradition with a flash of modernity, to draw out the sophistication, elegance and undulating flavour complexity of food that, when it isn't ignored, is mostly celebrated for its humble, homespun qualities". Our early survey feedback was scarcely less upbeat, and it's on that basis that we've rated it. / WIT 3LJ; akoko.co.uk; @akokorestaurant; Wed-Sat 11 pm; closed Wed-Fri L, closed Mon & Tue & Sun.

Al Duca SW1   £63   3 2 2
4-5 Duke of York St   020 7839 3090   3–3D

This "good-value classic Italian in the heart of St James's" gets "extremely busy at lunchtime" – which is not surprising, given that a two-course lunch costs less than £20. But it's more than just a cheap option: "the food is surprisingly tasty and well-presented – much better than we could have expected". / SW1Y 6LA; www.alduca-restaurant.co.uk; Mon-Sat 10 pm; closed Sun.

Al Mare,
Jumeirah Carlton Tower Hotel SW1 NEW   £90
Cadogan Pl   020 7858 7250   6–1D

Sign of the times – it's out with the steak of Olde England (The Rib Room, RIP, has gone) and in with Med seafood at this reopened super-lux five star off Sloane Street. Head chef is Italian native Marco Calenzo who joined the hotel from not-very-Italian Zuma. We are promised a convivial gastronomic experience, taking guests on a journey between the French Riviera and Northern Italy. Features include a theatre kitchen, private dining room and al fresco dining. / SW1; www.jumeirah.com/en/stay/london/the-carlton-tower; Mon-Sat 10.30 pm, Sun 10 pm.

Alain Ducasse at The Dorchester W1   £221   2 3 3
53 Park Lane   020 7629 8866   3–3A

Alain Ducasse made headlines in May 2021 by parting company with Dorchester Collection's Hôtel Plaza Athénée in Paris, but he maintains his relationship with this, his UK flagship. Despite holding three Michelin Stars, our mixed survey feedback has always questioned the Tyre Men's assessment here. On the plus-side, there are advocates who say Jean-Philippe Blondet's cuisine is "always fabulous", and is supported by "glorious wine" and staff "who really know what they are doing". On the minus side, though, it's hard to ignore the very large number of reporters for whom the experience is wildly "overpriced", and the almost complete absence of support for Michelin's notion that this is really one of London's top five dining rooms. / W1K 1QA; www.alainducasse-dorchester.com; Wed-Sat 9.30 pm; closed Sat L, closed Mon & Tue & Sun; Jacket required.

Albertine W12   £56   3 3 5
1 Wood Lane   020 8743 9593   8–1C

This "cosy wine bar favourite", off Shepherd's Bush Green, stands out against the modernity of Westfield shopping centre across the road. "You always feel at home here" – "the wines are interesting, with new things to try and discover", while "the food is simple but so good". It's now owned by chef Allegra McEvedy, who bought it a few years ago in memory of her mother, who founded it in the 1970s. McEvedy kept the business afloat under lockdown by switching to wine-and-meal deliveries. / W12 7DP; albertine.london; @albertineLDN; Thu-Sat midnight; closed Thu-Sat L, closed Mon-Wed & Sun; no Amex.

The Alfred Tennyson Pub Belgravia SW1   £71   323

10 Motcomb Street   020 7730 6074   6–1D

Definitely a "pub/restaurant" rather than a gastroboozer – this stylishly appointed four-storey venue in one of Belgravia's smartest streets earns consistently strong ratings for the meals served in its airy first-floor dining room. / SW1X 8LA; thealfredtennyson.co.uk; @TheTennysonSW1; Mon-Thu 11.30 pm, Fri & Sat midnight, Sun 10.30 pm; Take bookings all week via phone and/or online.

Ali Baba NW1   £30   322

32 Ivor Pl   020 7723 5805   2–1A

No feedback this year on this small, quirky dining room behind a take-away, off the top end of Baker Street. We're prepared to bet it hasn't changed, though, as it's been family-run since 1979. For the flavour of Egypt – not just the food, the whole not-particularly-polished experience – worth a visit. / NW1 6DA; alibabarestaurant.co.uk; @alibabalondon; Mon-Sun 10 pm; cash only; booking online only.

Allegra E20   334

The Stratford, 20-22 International Way   020 3973 0545   14–1D

"A bit of the West End in E20" – this stylish contemporary dining room sits on the seventh floor of a hotel/apartments tower, with an interior fit-out by the Copenhagen design team behind Noma, and boasts a terrace with views of the City skyline. Ex-Chiltern Firehouse head chef Patrick Powell uses high-quality British dishes to create what fans say is "by far the best cuisine in the Westfield Stratford area". / E20 1GQ; www.allegra-restaurant.com; Wed-Sat 11 pm; closed Wed & Thu L, closed Mon & Tue & Sun.

The Alma SE19 NEW   £50   324

95 Church Road   020 8768 1885   1–4D

"A huge enclosed garden" (where eating under the canopy was a boon during the post-lockdown months) is a feature at this newly revivified Crystal Palace pub, whose gentrified nature is hinted at by the florist in its courtyard. Chef David Yorkston helps it "punch above its weight" foodwise with some "really tasty" dishes that were strongly plugged by Grace Dent in an adulatory May 2021 review. Any negatives? One disastrous visit was reported service-wise (which has echoes in a few online reviews). / SE19 2TA; thealmapub.com; Thu-Sun 5 pm.

Amaya SW1   £90   533

Halkin Arcade, 19 Motcomb St   020 7823 1166   6–1D

Perhaps "the best and coolest Indian restaurant in London" (if you have deep pockets) – this slick Belgravian provides "beautifully presented, utterly delicious" small plates from its "wonderfully original menu" (fans are "not sure it's really Indian in a purist sense, but more a top, modern Indian grill on its own terms"). It is "expensive but provides real value" – "I've rarely tasted such terrific flavours in India, and never in the UK". / SW1X 8JT; www.amaya.biz; @theamaya_; Sun-Wed 9.30 pm, Thu-Sat 10 pm; closed Mon L.

Amazonico W1 NEW   £90   334

10 Berkeley Square   020 7404 5000   3–3B

"A great atmosphere and amazing food" dazzle fans of this "fun", "see-and-be-seen" late-2019 sibling to Madrid's celeb-haunt of the same name, famous for its lushly forested interior (think Rainforest Cafe, but without the animals or kids), which occupies the former Allied Irish Bank building in Berkeley Square. On the downside, though, prices for its luxurious sushi, seafood and charcoal grills verge on "astronomical". / W1J 6EF; Mon-Sun 11 pm.

The American Bar SW1 £82

The Stafford, 16-18 Saint James's Place   020 7493 0111   3–4C

This St James's institution is a survivor of the American bars which sprang up in grand hotels throughout Europe from the 1920s, and serves a Med-inspired brasserie menu. It has retained a vast collection of flags and mementos over the years, and the adjacent cobbled courtyard (where there's a summer BBQ) "is a gem – perfect for relaxed business gatherings or a friendly meal". / SW1A 1NJ; thestaffordlondon.com/the-american-bar; @StaffordLondon; Mon-Sun 11 am; Take bookings all week via phone and/or online.

Amethyst W1 NEW

52 Stratton Street   3–3C

Carlo Scotto has left the well-liked Xier (RIP) to launch in September 2021 this small but ambitious new venture. A 24-cover site housed in a former Caffe Nero just by Green Park Station – its menus span from a three- and four-course offering at lunch, with six- and 15-course tasting menus at dinner. / W1J 8LN; www.amethystdining.com; Mon-Sat 11 pm.

L'Amorosa W6 £58

278 King St   020 8563 0300   8–2B

"The Chiswick High Road is not exactly a destination, but L'Amorosa is". Andy Needham's "superb neighbourhood Italian", near Ravenscourt Park, is particularly known for its pasta and offers "great value for the quality of cooking". Apparently, water damage through the roof in September 2020 added insult to injury during the pandemic, but a reopening in autumn 2021 is promised, complete with a full refurb. We have rated it on the basis of plus ça change… / W6 0SP; www.lamorosa.co.uk; @LamorosaLondon.

Ampéli W1 NEW £63

18 Charlotte Street   020 3355 5370   2–1C

"Lovely contemporary Greek" inspired by the modern wine-focused restaurants of Athens – and with a high-quality list created by a Greek Master of Wine. Photographer Jenny Pagnoni opened this agreeable newcomer on Charlotte Street's 'restaurant row' in January 2020. It features "interesting" dishes inspired by the Eastern Mediterranean generally, not just Greece (with lots emerging from the Josper oven), from a chef trained in Tel Aviv. The mezzanine is the best dining spot (rather than the ground floor bar or basement). / W1T 2LZ; www.ampeli.london; Thu-Sat, Wed 10 pm; closed Wed L, closed Mon & Tue & Sun.

Amrutha SW18 £30

326 Garratt Lane   020 8001 4628   11–2B

"The atmosphere is basic (it's not a date place) but there's a reason devoted fans keep going back" to Arvin Suntaramoophy and Shyam Kotecha's 'little vegan soul-food lounge' in Earlsfield: "delicious curries and fantastic, charming service make for a great meal out with friends or family". / SW18 4EJ; www.amrutha.co.uk; Tue-Sat 10 pm, Sun 9 pm; closed Tue-Fri L, closed Mon.

The Anchor & Hope SE1 £58

36 The Cut   020 7928 9898   10–4A

"The ultimate gastropub" – this Southwark "pioneer of quality pub dining" missed out this year, by the narrowest whisker, on re-taking the crown as being London's No.1 favourite hostelry in our annual diner survey. The gutsy, honest food is "top-notch every time" and – even though no longer viewed as achingly cutting edge – comes "at sensible prices, and with good beer and wine to go with it". Service is "super-nice", and all-in-all it's just "a great, laid-back place to relax". Best of all for some folks, they "now accept reservations!" / SE1 8LP; www.anchorandhopepub.co.uk; @AnchorHopeCut; Tue-Sat 10.30 pm, Mon 11 pm, Sun 3 pm; closed Mon L closed Sun D; no Amex; no booking.

Andanza SE1 NEW   £86
66 Weston Street   020 7967 1972   10–4C
A former bookies' shop houses this new tapas and pintxos bar in Bermondsey, run by the owners of The Rose pub across the street. Head chef Paulina Irzyk was senior sous chef at Marylebone's Lurra for six years. 'Andanza' means luck (or fate) in Spanish – here's wishing it the best as it opened at a dire time in December 2020. Too little feedback as yet for a rating, but such as we have is very upbeat. / SE1 3QJ; www.andanza.co.uk; Mon-Sun 11 pm; booking online only.

The Andover Arms W6   £53   2 3 4
57 Aldensey Rd   020 8748 2155   8–1B
"A pearl of a pub" in a cute Hammersmith backstreet – much less foodie than the Anglesea Arms about five minutes away, but the epitome of a true local, and "with one of the finest pints of Fullers to be had anywhere". "Pub-standard food is produced with style and care", if no huge culinary pretentions. "A winner!". / W6 0DL; www.theandoverarms.com; @theandoverarms; Mon-Sun 11 pm; Take bookings all week via phone and/or online.

Andrew Edmunds W1   £65   3 3 5
46 Lexington Street   020 7437 5708   4–2C
"Romance oozes out of the walls here!" at what is – for many Londoners – "the ultimate date- night venue": a "very intimate" ("fantastic eavesdropping possibilities!"), "historic" Dickensian townhouse that's "old-school Soho and very welcome for it". The "simple food" is "well-priced", but the unbeatable "attraction is the superb wine list that's probably the best value in London", with "gentle markups that lure you into some wonderful bottles at great prices"; "totally lovable" and "always a joy!". / W1F 0LP; www.andrewedmunds.com; @AndrewEdmunds46; Mon-Sun 10.30 pm; no Amex; booking max 6 may apply.

Angelina E8   £56   4 4 3
56 Dalston Lane   020 7241 1851   14–1A
"Amazing, very clever combination of tastes" infuse some "wonderful fusion dishes presented by knowledgeable staff" at this Italian-Japanese fusion haunt in Dalston. The 4-course and 10-course omakase and kaiseki menus (so chef's choice throughout) are available lunch and dinner. / E8 3AH; angelina.london; Mon-Fri 10 pm, Sat 10.30 pm, Sun 3.30 pm; closed Mon-Fri L closed Sun D; No shorts.

Angie's Little Food Shop W4   £47   3 2 2
114 Chiswick High Road   020 8994 3931   8–2A
Angie Steele's Chiswick café again gets a big thumbs-up, including from the local yummy mums, for its brunch treats, cakes and other simple, healthy-ish fare. / W4 1PU; www.angieslittlefoodshop.com; Mon & Tue, Sun 5 pm, Wed-Sat 10.30 pm; closed Mon & Tue, Sun D.

Angler, South Place Hotel EC2   £104   4 3 3
3 South Pl   020 3215 1260   13–2A
"Paradise for anyone who loves fish and seafood", this "first-class 7th-floor" restaurant "with a lovely terrace" near Broadgate is a champion of the D&D London stable – "and the views of the City only make it more exciting". "Chef Gary Foulkes works closely with all the best suppliers in the UK and it shows in the quality and freshness of every dish". Top Tip: "the mackerel tartare with oyster cream is not to be missed". / EC2M 2AF; www.anglerrestaurant.com; @Angler_London; May need 8+ to book.

The Anglesea Arms W6 £62 4 4 4

35 Wingate Rd 020 8749 1291 8–1B

"The Anglesea delivers on all fronts" – with its "glorious gastropub fare", "great wine list", "very friendly service" and "good local vibe"; and it's regularly ranked as one of London's better hostelries. Its quiet location, in a leafy sidestreet near Ravenscourt Park (with small outside terrace) adds further to its appeal. What's more, "they make that extra effort. Why can't more pubs be like this?". / W6 0UR; www.angleseaarmspub.co.uk; @_AngleseaArmsW6; Mon-Sat 10 pm, Sun 9 pm; closed Mon-Thu L; cards only; no booking.

Anglo EC1 £82 5 3 2

30 St Cross Street 020 7430 1503 10–1A

"Superbly original cooking" showcasing British ingredients is the hallmark of Mark Jarvis's "unshowy, minimalist little restaurant" in Farringdon. Structured around a tasting menu of nine small plates, the "food is about as locally sourced as you can get – sometimes foraged less than a stone's throw from the restaurant". "The flavour combinations and contrasts are exceptional, and every dish is beautifully plated and presented", with due attention paid to minimising waste and reviving traditional techniques such as pickling and fermenting. (Note, "while still under the guiding hand of Mark Jarvis, Anthony Raffo nowadays cooks as head chef"). / EC1N 8UH; www.anglorestaurant.com; @AngloFarringdon; Tue-Sat 8.30 pm; closed Sun & Mon; booking max 6 may apply.

Anima e Cuore NW1 £58 5 3 2

129 Kentish Town Rd 07590 427171 9–2B

"All it's cracked up to be" – Mustapha Mouflih's tiny but dynamic Italian restaurant and gelato bar in Kentish Town delivers "exceptional value". "The homemade pasta is a revelation, and is cooked with invention" alongside other "amazing" dishes. "It's all a bit cramped and hectic in spite of the extension". / NW1 8PB; www.animaecuore.co.uk/; @animaecuoreuk; Tue-Sat 11 pm, Sun & Mon 8 pm.

Anjanaas NW6 £30 3 3 2

57-59 Willesden Lane 020 7624 1713 1–1B

For "genuine Keralan delights", beat a path to this "little gem" in Kilburn, which puts "more care and subtlety into its spicing than most Indian restaurants". "It isn't a fancy Michelin-starred Mayfair basement or Chelsea townhouse, but it's cheap and all about individual flavours, not just a spice variation on the same curry base" – "so each sauce tastes different and fresh". / NW6 7RL; www.anjanaas.com; Mon, Wed & Thu 10.30 pm, Fri & Sat 11 pm, Sun 10 pm; closed Tue.

Annie's W4 £65 3 3 4

162 Thames Rd 020 8994 9080 1–3A

"Such a good neighbourhood spot" – Lorraine Angliss's cosy diner has been a feature of Strand-on-the-Green for approaching two decades now. Not every dish turns out super-exciting, but it makes a good choice for a chilled brunch or other relaxed get-together. / W4 3QS; www.anniesrestaurant.co.uk; @annieschiswick; Tue-Sat 11 pm, Sun 9 pm; closed Tue-Fri L, closed Mon.

The Anthologist EC2 £52 2 2 2

58 Gresham St 0845 468 0101 10–2C

This large bar-restaurant, near the Guildhall, isn't going to win any culinary awards, but is a very versatile venue that's conveniently located: "a good fallback in the City for decent if unspectacular food and a nice atmosphere. The staff are friendly and it's turned into our office standby". / EC2V 7BB; www.theanthologistbar.co.uk; @theanthologist; Mon-Wed 11 pm, Thu & Fri midnight, Sun 5 pm; closed Sun D, closed Sat.

Antillean SE1 NEW £60
74 Blackfriars Rd   020 3011 4449   10–4A
Out goes the Polish vodka and in comes the jerk chicken, oxtail curry and flying fish at this Waterloo site, opened in summer 2021. For over a decade, this intriguing former Georgian factory (a coachbuilding works) traded as Baltic (RIP). But it's now in the hands of Michael Hanbury, who is aiming to highlight an evolved form of Jamaican cuisine. A rum library and cocktails too – Whispering Death anyone? / SE1; antillean.co.uk; Mon-Sat 11 pm; closed Sun.

AOK Kitchen W1 £86   ③②④
52-55 Dorset Street   020 3889 9400   2–1A
"Wonderfully fresh, tasty and simple flavours" stand out at this health-conscious Marylebone two-year-old, which has a decidedly pretty interior in the upstairs restaurant (there's a bakery below). Dietary requirements are celebrated rather than being grudgingly catered for, so there are no refined sugars in the cooking, along with limited dairy and gluten. The owner, Kelly Landesberg, is the daughter of Gary, chairman of the Arts Club in Mayfair. / W1U 7NQ; www.aokkitchen.co.uk; Wed & Thu 9 pm, Fri & Sat 9.30 pm, Sun 8 pm; closed Mon & Tue.

Apothecary EC2 NEW
36 Charlotte Road   020 7060 5335   13–1B
On the sizable Shoreditch site that was Merchant's Tavern (RIP), this mid-2021 newcomer is nowadays a 130-cover Japanese izakaya, with more of an emphasis on drinking (and DJs) than of old. It comes complete with open kitchen and robata counter, serving skewers, sushi and steamed buns to soak up the hot or cold sake, beers and cocktails. / EC2; apothecaryeast.co.uk; Wed-Sun 8.30 pm.

Applebee's Fish SE1 £74   ③③②
5 Stoney St   020 7407 5777   10–4C
"Once an old-fashioned chippy, it has upped its game effectively now that Borough Market has become fashionable" and nowadays is a more stylish café in this foodie enclave, where a plate of simply prepared fish or seafood makes for the perfect al fresco lunch. Top Tip: "the Applebee's prawn and fish wrap is one of the best things to eat in London". / SE1 9AA; www.applebeesfish.com; @APPLEBEESFISH; Mon-Wed 10 pm, Fri & Sat, Thu 11 pm, Sun 6 pm; no Amex.

Apulia EC1 £60   ②②②
50 Long Ln   020 7600 8107   10–2B
"Satisfying home-style southern Italian cooking, including a good-value daily fixed-price menu", is the draw at this "bright and friendly little restaurant opposite Smithfield market" – "conveniently close to the Barbican" – which offers "decent value for the area". / EC1A 9EJ; www.apuliarestaurant.co.uk; @apulia_london; Mon-Fri 11.30 pm; closed Sat & Sun.

aqua kyoto W1 £84   ②②④
240 Regent St (entrance 30 Argyll St)   020 7478 0540   4–1A
"Rooftop views of central London" are a highlight of this nightclubby Japanese venue, whose large outside terraces can come as a surprise for somewhere so close to Oxford Circus. It's in the same HK-based group as Aqua Shard, and also has a rooftop neighbour, Aqua Nueva, if you prefer Spanish food. It's not a particularly foodie choice, but is sometimes noted for its "good sushi". / W1B 3BR; www.aqua-london.com; @aquakyotolondon; Sun-Thu 10 pm, Sat, Fri 10.15 pm.

Aqua Shard SE1 £112 2 2 4

Level 31, 31 St Thomas St   020 3011 1256   10–4C

"Fabulous views, a great atmosphere and an interesting fusion menu" were more in focus in commentary this year on this sexily located venue, near the top of The Shard. Unsurprisingly, it is sometimes still seen as being *"overpriced"*, but this was less of a complaint this year. Options here also include brunch and unlimited sandwiches and cakes for afternoon tea. / SE1 9RY; www.aquashard.co.uk; @aquashard; Mon-Sun 10.30 pm.

Aquavit SW1 £93 3 3 2

St James's Market, 1 Carlton St   020 7024 9848   4–4D

"The wonderful menu transports diners to Scandinavia" at this large and starkly stylish unit in the glossy St James's Market development, near Piccadilly Circus – an offshoot of Swedish superchef Emma Bengtsson's garlanded New York original. Ratings are solid, if not quite reaching the feverish excitement levels achieved in Manhattan. / SW1Y 4QQ; www.aquavitrestaurants.com; @aquavitlondon; Tue-Sat 10 pm; closed Sun & Mon; cash only; Take bookings all week via phone and/or online.

Arabica £57 3 3 2

7 Lewis Cubitt Walk, N1   020 3747 4422   9–3C **NEW**
3 Rochester Walk, SE1   020 3011 5151   10–4C

"Very good quality food" from across the Middle East – along with *"especially great spiced cocktails"* – is on the menu at this permanent Borough Market venue and its two-year-old King's Cross offshoot in the Aga Khan Centre building, a stone's throw from Coal Drops Yard. Self-taught chef James Walters has developed the business gradually over 20 years, from a stall selling Levantine snacks at markets and festivals via a regular Borough Market presence that graduated to a glass-fronted sit-down restaurant in 2014. He is looking to expand further. / www.arabicalondon.com.

The Araki W1 £389 5 4 4

Unit 4 12 New Burlington St   020 7287 2481   4–3A

"The team that took over from Matsuhiro Araki is outstanding", and under Marty Lau this Mayfair nine-seater continues to deliver *"stunning sushi, immaculately served and presented"*. When the maestro moved on in 2019, Michelin not only removed all three stars, but completely deleted the restaurant from its database – a fantastic example of the capriciousness of its decision-making and the partial nature of its ultimate listings. As a result, this Mayfair venue inspires very much less attention and feedback than once it did, but it can still deliver *"a meal you're likely to remember for the rest of your life"* (even if the same can be said about the price tag…). / W1S 3BH; the-araki.co.uk; Tue-Sun 8.30 pm; closed Tue-Sun L, closed Mon; no Amex; No shorts.

Arcade Food Theatre WC1

103-105 New Oxford Street   020 7519 1202   5–1A

After a bit of a false start, new partners JKS restaurants are to help resuscitate this food court offering by Centrepoint in November 2021. Originally it opened about eight months before the pandemic, and never really found its mojo. The new format still incorporates eight different kitchens, but there is to be a novel streamlined ordering system allowing dishes from multiple kitchens in a single order. All this plus various other innovations, such as a new counter for coffee, sarnies and cakes. / WC1A 1DB; www.arcade-london.com; Mon-Sun 4.30 pm; closed Mon-Sun D.

Ark Fish E18 £49 3 3 2

142 Hermon Hill   020 8989 5345   1–1D

"Fresh fish cooked well" is the mantra at this South Woodford chippy with a proud tradition of doing things properly. The current owners sold up their successful west London chippies after almost 30 years five years ago, but 'fell in love' with the Ark and returned to the trade in late 2019. *"Everyone is so friendly, it feels like you're visiting relatives"*. / E18 1QH; www.arkfishrestaurant.co.uk; @ArkfishLondon; Tue-Thu 9.45 pm, Fri & Sat 10.15 pm, Sun 8.45 pm; closed Mon; no Amex; no booking.

Arros QD W1 £101 ②②❸
64 Eastcastle Street 020 3883 3525 3–1D
He has three Michelin stars back in Alicante, but Quique Dacosta's two-floor two-year-old just north of Oxford Street is a more middle-market affair, with an extensive menu of meat, fish and vegetarian dishes whose most obvious Hispanic features are a large collection of paellas. Feedback was mixed this year, though. Some reporters had wonderful meals, but others found it "just too pricey for what it was… lovely interior, but the dishes fell a bit flat". / W1W 8NQ; www.arrosqd.com; @ArrosQD; Tue-Sat 11 pm, Sun 3 pm; closed Sun D, closed Mon.

L'Artista NW11 £47 ②❹❸
917 Finchley Rd 020 8731 7501 1–1B
Tucked into the railway arches by Golders Green tube, this family-friendly trattoria has been a linchpin of local life for as long as anyone can recall. "The pizzas and pasta are better than average, but nothing very special. What makes this place buzz is the charming service and the reasonable prices. I've been coming here since I was a teenager, and the fact that it is still going, and is always full and buzzy, must say something!". / NW11 7PE; www.lartistapizzeria.com; Mon-Sun midnight.

Artusi SE15 £49 ❹❸❸
161 Bellenden Rd 020 3302 8200 1–4D
This "tiny and impeccable" Italian in Peckham "punches well above its weight", thanks to a team who "really put the effort in". Star billing goes to the "fresh pasta to die for", but there's "flavour in every dish", and locals count themselves "so lucky to have it". Named after the 19th-century doyen of Italian cuisine, Pellegrino Artusi, it's also something of a "hipster heaven – check out the beard count!". / SE15 4DH; www.artusi.co.uk; @artusipeckham; Wed & Thu 9.30 pm, Fri & Sat 10 pm, Sun 4 pm; closed Wed L closed Sun D, closed Mon & Tue.

Asakusa NW1 £36 ❹❸②
265 Eversholt St 020 7388 8533 9–3C
Limited, but still enthusiastic feedback on this well-established Japanese fixture, near Mornington Crescent tube. It changed owners a couple of years ago, but on most indications its sushi and other traditional fare mean it is still worth a visit. / NW1 1BA; asakusa.has.restaurant; Mon-Sat 11.30 pm; closed Mon-Sat L, closed Sun.

Assaggi W2 £70 ❸❹❸
39 Chepstow Pl 020 7792 5501 7–1B
"A firm favourite", this unusual venue on the first floor of a Notting Hill pub has served "classic Italian food of the highest quality" for over 25 years, and for a good part of that period was often hailed as London's top Italian. Over time, it has lost some of its former brio and no longer earns quite such stellar ratings as once it did. But no big critiques are made, and there's still lots of appreciation for its "excellent food and personable service". / W2 4TS; www.assaggi.co.uk; @Assaggi3; Tue-Sat 10 pm; closed Sun & Mon; no Amex.

At Feast NW8 NEW £26
49 St John's Wood High Street 020 3989 7800 9–3A
Wholesome family fare with an eco-friendly twist is the promise of this new all-day arrival on St John's Wood High Street – open from breakfast onwards and incorporating a child-friendly cookery school. The menu leans heavily on its plant-based associations. / NW8 7NJ; atfeast.com; Sun & Mon 6 pm, Tue-Sat 10 pm; closed Sun & Mon D.

Atari-Ya £47 ❸❸②
20 James St, W1 020 7491 1178 3–1A
75 Fairfax Road, NW6 020 7328 5338 9–2A
"A sushi bar in a shop" may not sound appealing, but these cafés operated by a Japanese food importer – in Ealing, Swiss Cottage, Golders Green and Marylebone – provide fresh, "clean-tasting" sushi, and they're "good-value". / www.sushibaratariya.co.uk.

The Atlas SW6 £52 434

16 Seagrave Rd   020 7385 9129   6–3A

This "gem of a gastropub" with a "huge secluded terrace garden" (much enlarged in recent years), a short walk from West Brompton tube, has earned its spurs over more than two decades, serving a "terrific" menu of Mediterranean-style dishes alongside the steaks and Sunday roasts you might expect from its classic Victorian appearance. There's a good list of wines with a bias to Italy and "some of London's finest real ale". / SW6 1RX; www.theatlaspub.co.uk; @theatlasfulham; Mon-Sat 11 pm, Sun 10.30 pm; closed Mon-Thu L.

Attawa E8 NEW £20 332

6 Kingsland High Street   020 7254 1236   14–1A

Opening in mid-2020 into the storm of early lockdown, this Dalston Indian serves modern Punjabi food prepared by Arbinder Duggal, a semi-finalist on MasterChef: The Professionals in 2019. It's named for the owners' home village in north India and serves recipes sourced from friends and family in the area. One early reporter's take: "interesting and delicious small plates to start, main courses not quite as good. But friendly service and nice ambience make this a welcome addition to the local restaurant scene". / E8 2JP; attawa.co.uk; Tue-Sun 10 pm; closed Tue-Sun L, closed Mon.

Augustine Kitchen SW11 £55 443

63 Battersea Bridge Rd   020 7978 7085   6–4C

This "lovely French neighbourhood bistro" just south of Battersea Bridge is very much a labour of love for chef-patron Franck Raymond – he named it after his grandmother, and the "excellent" cuisine is inspired by his boyhood home at Evian on Lake Geneva. Reporters are agreed that it's "very good value and enjoyable". / SW11 3AU; www.augustine-kitchen.co.uk; @augustinekitchen; Tue-Sat 9 pm; closed Sun & Mon.

Aulis London W1 £178 554

16a St Anne's Court   020 3948 9665   4–1D

"Blown away by the food!" – Simon Rogan's only restaurant in the capital is a "small, intimate chef's table experience, with six diners per seating": "an oasis of calm and elegance". When it first opened a few years ago, they only told you where it was after you had booked, but in recent times they have become much less 'secret squirrel' about its location off a Soho alleyway. It has also recently ditched its single-offering, all-in £195 per head format (which included all food and drinks) in favour of a more conventional £125 per head tasting menu, with various drinks offerings. "With just half a dozen customers, it offers an excellent chance to chat with fellow diners and the fabulous chefs and hear the story of the food". "The chefs do a great job of preparing and hosting at the same time", and the food is "exceptional and original". "Three hours speed by in a jiffy". This year's only complaint? – "the ground hazelnut topping could have benefitted from being slightly coarser!". / W1F 0BF; aulis.london; @AulisSimonRogan; Tue-Sat 11.30 pm; closed Tue-Thu L, closed Sun & Mon.

Authentique Epicerie & Bar NW5 £47 333

114-116 Fortess Road   020 3609 6602   9–2C

This three-year-old hybrid wine bar/shop/restaurant in Tufnell Park celebrates the produce of the French-speaking world, with "delicious wines by the glass" backed up by a "small but very good menu". Chef Kathy Bonus, who grew up between Bordeaux, Paris and Guadeloupe, prepares regular tasting menus focused on 12 different regional cuisines, and there are always cheese and charcuterie boards to nibble at the bar. More than 700 wines and 75 craft beers (not all of them from Belgium) are kept in stock. / NW5 5HL; authentique-epicerie.com; @AuthentiqueLDN; Tue-Sat 11 pm, Sun 8 pm; closed Mon; Take bookings all week via phone and/or online.

Ave Mario WC2 NEW £53

15 Henrietta Street 5–3C

Undaunted by the pandemic, Big Mamma (the French group behind smash hits Gloria and Circolo Popolare) opened this huge – 7,000 square feet and 295 covers – newcomer in June 2021. Set over two floors, with two outside terraces, it's in the same over-the-top vein as its siblings, this time aiming for a 'cheeky interpretation of the Church'! Apparently that means a bar decorated with 3,500 bottles, and a mirrored basement for events. As with its siblings, the cooking (how did we nearly forget?!) majors on Italian dishes (lots of pasta and pizza) featuring loads of cream, the must-Instagram dishes in this case being a mega stracciatella and chocolate ice cream cake. It opened too late for any survey feedback, but Jimi Famurewa of The Standard diagnosed "sequel bloat and a brand getting slightly lost in the sauce of its own success". "All the subtlety of a Swarovski-encrusted fist" and food that's "a touch Nonna's Gone to Iceland". / WC2E 8QG; www.bigmammagroup.com/en/trattorias/ave-mario; @bigmammagroup; Sun-Wed 10.30 pm, Thu-Sat 10.45 pm.

L'Aventure NW8 £80 3 4 4

3 Blenheim Terrace 020 7624 6232 9–3A

"Still going strong" after 41 years – chef-patronne Catherine Parisot's "lovely and atmospheric" hideaway in St John's Wood remains first choice for a "romantic" date for many reporters. "The classically French menu hasn't changed in years", but regulars aren't complaining – "Catherine is a wonderful host" and they've "never had a bad meal": this is a place that "keeps its high standards for cooking and service, and keeps its customers". / NW8 0EH; www.laventure.co.uk; Mon-Sat 11 pm, Sun 2.30 pm; closed Sat L closed Sun D.

The Avenue SW1 £65

7-9 St James's Street 020 7321 2111 3–4D

Despite its size, this large D&D Group operation in St James's has attracted limited feedback in recent years. In early September 2021 (as we were heading to press), after a period of closure, its website promised a reopening 'with some very exciting changes'… / SW1A 1EE; www.avenue-restaurant.co.uk; @avenuestjames; Tue-Sat 9.30 pm, Sun 5 pm; closed Sun D, closed Mon.

Aviary EC2 £64 2 3 4

10th Floor, 22-25 Finsbury Square 020 3873 4060 13–2A

"Stunning views of the City from the roof terrace" add glamour to this 10th floor eyrie overlooking Finsbury Square, and with a large outside terrace. The cooking is decent, service "affable" and "people-watching those attracted by Insta-friendly high-end hotel restaurants is an added bonus – or detraction depending on your mood!". / EC2A 1DX; aviarylondon.com; @AviaryLDN; Mon-Sun midnight.

Awesome Thai SW13 £36 3 3 2

68 Church Rd 020 8563 7027 11–1A

"This family-run Thai" is a popular choice in Barnes for its "wonderful welcome" and proximity to the Olympic Studios indie cinema across the road. "The odd curry can be a bit erratic, but overall it's an excellent local". / SW13 0DQ; www.awesomethai.co.uk; Fri & Sat, Mon-Thu 10.30 pm, Sun 10 pm; closed Mon-Thu L.

Ayllu W2 NEW £30

25 Sheldon Square 020 7286 9458 7–1C

Hidden beneath Smith's Bar & Grill in the Paddington Basin development – a spring 2020 Peruvian newcomer named for the Ayllu community of the Inca Empire, and serving Peruvian-Japanese fusion dishes and cocktails. / W2 6EY; ayllu.co.uk; Mon-Sat 11 pm, Sun 10.30 pm.

BabaBoom SW11 £37 3 3 2
30 Battersea Rise   07809 903181   11–2C

"Always delicious and very reasonably priced" – fans of this kebab-focused street-food concept in Battersea say it's equally *"lovely to eat in or take away"*. It lost its Islington branch during the pandemic, but should endure as it has backing from many of 'the great and the good' (including Gumtree founder Mike Pennington and ex-Nando's chief executive David Niven). / SW11 1EE; www.bababoom.london; @bababoomlondon; Mon, Wed & Thu, Sun 7.30 pm, Fri & Sat 8.15 pm.

Babur SE23 £54 5 4 3
119 Brockley Rise   020 8291 2400   1–4D

With its *"extraordinary modern take on Indian cuisine with a British slant"*, this unsung food hero of the south London suburbs is *"worth the trek"* to Forest Hill – *"it's not easy to find but don't miss it"*. A local hit for 36 years now, it's *"a major cut above your standard Indian"*, and boasts *"surprising, inventive and unfailingly delicious food, impeccably charming staff, and a Dal Makhni I travel 150 miles twice a year to eat"*. *"The chefs are artists with a rabbit"* – evidence of their *"particular talent with game that surprises and delights in equal measure"*. / SE23 1JP; www.babur.info; @BaburRestaurant; Mon-Sun 11 pm; No shorts; Take bookings all week via phone and/or online.

Baccala SE1 NEW £46 3 4 3
Unit B3, 194-204 Bermondsey Street   0207 407 5514   10–4D

Italian seafood and wine (available by the glass) is the simple but high-quality format of this November 2019 opening – a bar, restaurant and shop next door to the area's long-established 'Pizarro'. Ex-Four Seasons chef Moreno Polverini presides over an offering ranging from a conventional if modernised Italian à la carte to a five-course 'seafood feast' for £85. It's rated on limited early feedback, all of it positive. / SE1 3TQ; www.baccalalondon.co.uk; Tue-Sat 10 pm; closed Sun & Mon; No bookings.

Bacco TW9 £65 3 3 2
39-41 Kew Rd   020 8332 0348   1–4A

"The best Italian in the area", say fans of this *"buzzy"* trattoria and bar on Richmond's main drag, which now has *"a new covered terrace, a legacy of lockdown"*. The *"dishes are imaginative"*, the *"service always welcoming"*, and there's *"a reasonably priced all-Italian wine list"*. Very handy for the Orange Tree Theatre – and Richmond station. / TW9 2NQ; www.bacco-restaurant.co.uk; @BaccoRichmond; Tue-Sat 10 pm; closed Sun & Mon; No shorts.

Bad Vegan NW1 NEW
Buck Street Market, 198 Camden High Street   9–3B

Tom Kerridge's involvement (in partnership with Mark Emms) made it 100% likely this summer 2021 opening, on the top of Buck Street Market, would attract attention. It's 'bad' in that many dishes (e.g. beef brisket 'taternator') are not vegan! – anything with red packaging is for meat- eaters (leaf-eaters, green of course). In an early August 2021 review, Kate Samuelson of The Week was upbeat, branding it *"a mightly alternative"* to KFC and McDs. Then again, she also noted that: *"our meal, which included three portions of food, two milkshakes and two beers, came to about £50"* – so you'd kind of hope for a pretty major step up… / NW1 8QP; www.bad-vegan.com; @badveganuk; Tue-Sat 11 pm.

Bageriet WC2 £19 4 2 2
24 Rose St   020 7240 0000   5–3C

"Would you find better in Stockholm?" – the Swedish buns at this tiny Covent Garden coffee house are *"deliciously authentic"*. *"Serious coffee at a decent strength, and as for the cakes… well, just leave space in your schedule for an exercise class after eating one"*. *"The only issue is the very limited space of eight seats – at least 50% of the time you can't get in!"*. / WC2E 9EA; www.bageriet.co.uk; @bagerietlondon; Mon-Fri 7 pm; closed Sat & Sun; No bookings.

Bala Baya SE1 £68 3️⃣2️⃣2️⃣
Old Union Yard Arches, 229 Union Street   020 8001 7015   10–4B
A "great take on modern Israeli cooking" – ex-Ottolenghi chef Eran Tibi
creates "brilliant dishes inspired by the buzzing food markets in Tel Aviv" at
this all-day venue on two levels in a Southwark railway arch. Top Tip: "love
the shakshuka, a Sunday morning treat". / SE1 0LR; balabaya.co.uk; @bala_baya;
Mon-Thu, Sat & Sun 10 pm, Fri 10.15 pm.

Balady NW11 £25 3️⃣2️⃣2️⃣
750 Finchley Road   020 8458 2064   1–1B
"Reliably good falafels and hummus" top the bill at this kosher joint in
Temple Fortune. The interior is "stark and fluorescent-lit, with an excess of
Formica – but the falafels are worth it". Top Tip: "go for the wraps over the
pitta". / NW11 7TH; Sun-Thu 11 pm, Fri 5 pm, Sat midnight; closed Sat L closed Fri D.

Balthazar WC2 £84 2️⃣2️⃣3️⃣
4 - 6 Russell Street   020 3301 1155   5–3D
"Comfortable and inviting" – this glam-looking offshoot of the famous
Manhattan joint (brought to Covent Garden by NYC founder Keith McNally,
and nowadays owned by Richard Caring's Caprice Holdings) features decent
"brasserie-style" cooking. But even those fans who say (slightly ambitiously)
that "it's a place to see and be seen" note that it's "not as good as the NYC
namesake" and can feel a little "robotic", especially as "staff can struggle
with the volume of people". / WC2B 5HZ; www.balthazarlondon.com;
@balthazarlondon; Mon-Sun 11 pm.

Bancone £52 4️⃣4️⃣3️⃣
10 Lower James Street, W1   020 3034 0820   4–3C NEW
39 William IV Street, WC2   020 7240 8786   5–4C
"For a quick Italian meal in the West End", you will struggle to better this
award-winning duo of "beautiful" pasta-bars, off Trafalgar Square and in
Soho's Golden Square, where the "gorgeous fresh pasta" is notably
"excellent value". To be fair, the odd reporter does feel the cooking is
"serviceable rather than spectacular", but the vast majority say the dishes
are "to die for". "Friendly staff get high marks" too, as does the "fantastic
buzz". / www.bancone.co.uk.

Bando Belly SE15 NEW £27
Unit 606 Peckham Levels, 95a Rye Lane   1–4D
One of the few early 2021 newcomers (at which time it was delivery only) –
this 'soul food fusion' newcomer operates out of the Peckham Levels. The
aim? – 'a bold and culturally relevant brand to disrupt the traditionally Euro-
centric and often whitewashed London food scene'. This translates into
hearty spicy scoff – Trinidadian Bara Tacos (fried bread with a chickpea
filling), Philly Banh Mi Cheesesteaks… deep-fried Oreos. / SE15 4ST;
www.bandobelly.com; @bandobelly; Thu-Sat 10.30 pm, Sun 9 pm; closed
Mon & Tue & Wed.

Bang Bang Oriental NW9 £55 2️⃣2️⃣2️⃣
399 Edgware Road   no tel   1–1A
"Quality varies" at this "shed with flavours galore (some are awesome, some
awful)" – a vast foot court in Colindale. But it's certainly a "unique offering",
and if you're a lover of Asian cuisines it will repay a visit out of curiosity, if not
always more. Top Tip – "Four Seasons, Hakka Village and Coconut Tree are
among the more consistent performers". / NW9 0AS;
www.bangbangoriental.com; @BANGBANGOFH; Sun-Thu 10 pm, Fri & Sat 10.30 pm.

Bánh Bánh £46 3️⃣3️⃣2️⃣
46 Peckham Rye, SE15   020 7207 2935   1–4D
326 Coldharbour Lane, SW9   020 7737 5888   11–2D
The Nguyen family run this duo of no-nonsense Vietnamese cafés in
Peckham Rye and Brixton – well-rated all-round for their tasty scoff: soups,
salads, rolls and other simple dishes. / www.banhbanh.com; @BanhBanhHQ.

Banners N8 £52 ☑☒☒
21 Park Rd 020 8348 2930 1–1C

Juliette Banner's "lively unpretentious place" in Crouch End celebrates its 30th anniversary this year, basking in the "relaxed vibe" it provides regulars, who keep coming back for the "interesting cheap menu" of world food. It "can be clamorous, but in a good way – and the food couldn't be more child-friendly". Top Tip: you can book 'Bob Dylan's table', the very spot where the Nobel Prize-winning beatnik bard dined during his legendary 1993 visit to Crouch End. / N8 8TE; www.bannersrestaurant.com; @https://banners-restaurant.com/?share=twitter&nb=1; Sun-Thu 9.30 pm, Fri & Sat 10.30 pm; no Amex.

Bao £42 ☒☒☒
31 Windmill St, W1 020 3011 1632 5–1A
53 Lexington St, W1 07769 627811 4–2C
4 Pancras Square, N1 9–3C **NEW**
13 Stoney Street, SE1 020 3967 5407 10–4C
1 Redchurch Street, E2 13–1B **NEW**
Netil Market, 13-23 Westgate Street, E8 no tel 14–2B

"The bao are just so good" at these "charming" and stylish Taiwanese cafés, whose eponymous steamed buns filled with "brilliant" and "magnificent" Asian flavours have been a sensation since their first opening at Netil Market in London Fields in 2013. There are now six venues, the most recent of which have branched out in new directions: Café Bao at King's Cross, serving an East Asian take on Western classics, such as chicken XO Kiev and baked ham hock congee pie, and Bao Noodle Shop, on the former site of Andina in Shoreditch, which is inspired by old-school Taiwanese beef noodle shops. / baolondon.com; @bao_london.

Baozi Inn £32 ☒☒☒
24 Romilly Street, W1 020 7287 3266 5–3A
25 Newport Court, WC2 020 7287 6877 5–3B
34-36 Southwark Street, SE1 020 8037 5875 10–4C

An "excellent" Chinese menu wins a small but dedicated fan club for Wei Shao's slightly disparate group of eateries. Most prominent nowadays is its three-storey, 120-cover flagship near Borough Market. There's also the Chinatown original (no reservations), whose main options include baozi, dumplings, wonton and noodles, and a Soho site serving northern Chinese street food, plus all-day dim sum. (There's also a stall at Market Halls Victoria.) / baoziinn.com.

Bar des Prés W1 **NEW** £108 ☒☒☒
16 Albemarle Street 020 3908 2000 3–3C

On the Mayfair site of Indian Accent (RIP), this chic May 2021 newcomer is the first London outpost of Gallic TV chef Cyril Lignac, who owns four Parisian restaurants. Unlike his St Germain venture of the same name – which serves only raw food to soak up the cocktails – here at this 100-seater (with ground floor and basement) you can find luxurious hot bites: e.g. scallops with caramelised miso, Madras curried crab, or satay fillet steak. There are also nearly 250 wines and cocktails. Early reporters acclaim this as an "amazing and really original" venue, but even they can find it "overpriced" (a slight echo of the views of the Guardian's Grace Dent, who judged it 'a not-very-good restaurant'). / W1S 4HW; bardespres.com; Mon-Sun 11 pm; No shorts.

Bar Douro SE1 £46 ☒☒☒
Arch 25b Flat Iron Square, Union St 020 7378 0524 10–4B

"Love it" – eating at this Portuguese tapas bar near Borough Market is "always a thoroughly enjoyable experience – especially outside in summer". It's a tiny, atmospheric place serving big flavours, the result of "top-quality ingredients and execution" backed up by "a comprehensive Portuguese wine list". / SE1 1TD; www.bardouro.co.uk; @bardouro; Tue-Sat 10.30 pm, Sun 9 pm; closed Tue-Thu L, closed Mon; booking max 4 may apply.

Bar Esteban N8   £57   3 3 3
29 Park Rd 020 8340 3090 1–1C

"A lively tapas spot popular with the locals" – if you are up Crouch End way, this well-established Spanish restaurant is one of the better wining and dining venues in the 'hood. / N8 8TE; www.baresteban.com; @barestebanN8; Mon-Sat 10 pm; closed Mon-Sat L, closed Sun; booking max 8 may apply.

Bar Italia W1   £37   2 3 5
22 Frith St 020 7437 4520 5–2A

"Great people-watching" helps make this characterful 24-hour Italian institution the beating heart of Soho, especially after midnight. Founded in 1949 and still owned by the Polledri family, its first customers were Italian waiters from the area's restaurants needing a caffeine hit. If you find yourself stressing about the "indifferent service", chill! – it's all part of the experience. / W1D 4RF; www.baritaliasoho.co.uk; @TheBaristas; Mon-Fri 5 am, Sat & Sun midnight; no booking.

Bar La Rampa W1 NEW
8 Market Place 020 3840 5555 3–1C

Near Oxford Circus, on a site that briefly saw Sweet Chick (RIP) hatch and go – this summer 2021 newcomer aims to import vintage Cuban style to the centre of the West End, and David Ellis in a complimentary review for The Evening Standard describes it as a 'fairytale of 1950s Havana'. A sibling to Kol and Casa do Frango – it features Cuban small bites overseen by the TATA eatery folks, and puts a big emphasis on cocktails. / W1W; barlarampa.com; Fri & Sat 11 pm, Sun-Thu 10.30 pm.

Baraka EC2 NEW   £42
Unit 4, 1 Finsbury Avenue 020 3984 3030 13–2A

In a quiet, pedestrianised square in the City's sprawling Broadgate development – near Broadgate Circle – this January 2020 arrival occupies a swishly decorated unit, and has a large terrace outside for a warm day. The rustic Anatolian cuisine – much of it on the open-flame mangal – is cosily at odds with all the surrounding modernity, and is washed down with a more metropolitan selection of cocktails. / EC2M 2PF; barakarestaurant.co.uk; Mon-Sat 11.30 pm, Sun 10 pm.

The Barbary WC2   £66   5 4 4
16 Neal's Yard 5–2C

"Fantastic food and a great countertop dining experience" are twin highlights of Layo and Zoe Paskin's casual younger sibling to The Palomar in Neil's Yard, where inspired North African-inspired tapas are served at the bar in a vibey, intimate space. In autumn 2021, it will expand into the adjacent site that was formerly their posh coffee and light bite stop, Jacob the Angel (which they are relocating). 'The Barbary Next Door' will, we gather, be a place 'you can pop by for a coffee, chilled beer or glass of wine' as much as a meal. / WC2H 9DP; www.thebarbary.co.uk; @barbarylondon; Tue-Fri 11 pm, Sat 9 pm; closed Tue, Wed L, closed Sun & Mon; no booking.

Barboun EC2 NEW   £74
61-67 Great Eastern Street 020 3995 3622 13–1B

With its swish, spacious metropolitan styling, this 100-seater brasserie on one of Shoreditch's main drags does little to advertise the fact that it's part of the Hart Shoreditch Hotel London (part of the Curio Collection by Hilton), which opened in early 2020. Knowing this helps explain the slightly over-plush styling – at odds with the strenuously hip neighbourhood – and also the wilfully un-corporate menu: inspired by the flavours of Levantine coastal towns (Levantine weekend brunch is a feature). Early reports are too limited for a rating, but all-round very good. / EC2A 3HU; www.barboun.com; @BarbounL; Mon-Sun 11 pm.

La Barca SE1 £82 3 3 3
80-81 Lower Marsh   020 7928 2226   10–4A

This "family-owned Italian restaurant" is a well-known landmark behind Waterloo Station "that feels like it hasn't changed in 50 years" – it even "seems the same staff has been there" since its 1970s opening. But "they're friendly and cheerful" and ensure this is "the place to go after performances at the Old Vic", almost opposite – as thespians including Sir Ian McKellen, Robert De Niro and Al Pacino have done in the past. / SE1 7AB; www.labarca-ristorante.com; Mon-Sat 10.30 pm; closed Sat L, closed Sun; Booking max 12 may apply.

Barrafina £65 4 4 5
26-27 Dean Street, W1   020 7813 8016   4–1D
10 Adelaide St, WC2   020 7440 1456   5–4C
43 Drury Lane, WC2   020 7440 1456   5–2D
Coal Drops Yard, N1   0207 440 1486   9–3C

"As brilliant as ever… and being able to book is a big bonus!!" – the Hart Bros' recreations of Barcelona's Cal Pep are "still going strong"; and with the Drury Lane branch – Barrafina Mariscos – now dedicated to seafood. "Sitting at the bar is just so intimate": "it's fun to watch all the prep" and "watching the chefs at work simply makes you want to order more of the superb tapas". "This is the food that made lockdown so hard. The food you can't cook yourself… the courgette flower a crispy, yet unctuously delicious, dirty cheesy and honey- dripping delight, and the oh so, so, so oozingly fabulous tortilla with prawns and peppers". And "the people watching is fabulous" too. One warning flag though. The ratings slipped a fraction this year, alongside the odd comment that "while it's very good on a good day, consistency can be an issue"; or that "what once seemed almost impossibly daring now feels more familiar and comfy". Still, for most folks, it's plain "terrific". Top Tip – at all branches, not just Mariscos, "the fish is fantastic". / www.barrafina.co.uk.

Barrica W1 £56 3 3 3
62 Goodge St   020 7436 9448   2–1B

"A wonderful menu with a good choice of tapas to suit all tastes" again wins recommendations for this buzzy and good-value bar on Goodge Street. / W1T 4NE; www.barrica.co.uk; @barricatapas; Tue-Sat 10.30 pm; closed Tue, Wed L, closed Sun & Mon.

Base Face Pizza W6 NEW £35 3 3 3
300 King Street   020 8617 1092   8–2B

What a backstory! Jazz musician Tim Thornton lost his income in the pandemic and, with the help of his wife, sold pizza to bring in cash. Being in West London, it was (naturally!) from a special, low-GI mix for the bases, alongside some upscale toppings (Stichelton blue cheese, crispy cured pig cheek, etc). And now he's opened his own pizza caff, opposite King Street W6's Tesco Metro, on a site that was formerly Piate (RIP). Most reports are out-and-out raves: "it rocks" thanks to its "delicious toppings and great ingredients". / W6; www.basefacepizza.com; @base.face.pizza; Tue-Sat 10 pm, Sun 5 pm; closed Tue-Sat L closed Sun D, closed Mon.

Bears Ice Cream W12 £7 3 3 2
244 Goldhawk Road   020 3441 4982   8–1B

There's only one flavour of (Icelandic) ice cream at this small Shepherd's Bush gelateria and it's quite "pricey". Kids love it, though, because of the huge variety of "amazing toppings". / W12 9PE; www.bearsicecream.co.uk; @bears_icecream; Mon-Sun 8.30 pm; cards only; No bookings.

Beast W1 £117 ②②②
3 Chapel Pl   020 7495 1816   3–1B
"We went for the 'Beast Experience' and once we added cocktails and service we ended up spending over £200 per head! A nice meal but certainly not worth the money" – typical feedback over the years on this candle-lit surf 'n' turf extravaganza, just off Oxford Street. To be fair, the website kind of hints what you are in for ('The Beast Is Inside You. From the dawn of its very existence it has searched land and sea to feast. Craving the extravagance of nature's finest flesh. Relentlessly drawn to flame and fire. Behold you are the Beast…'). / W1G 0BG; www.beastrestaurant.co.uk; @beastrestaurant; Mon-Sat 11 pm; closed Mon-Thu L, closed Sun; May need 7+ to book.

The Begging Bowl SE15 £50 ③③③
168 Bellenden Rd   020 7635 2627   1–4D
Celebrating its tenth anniversary this year, this Peckham crowd-pleaser was an early proponent of "genuinely spiced" Thai street food in the capital, and works hard to stay ahead of the pack. Co-owner Jane Alty fell for Thai food while working in the kitchen at David Thompson's Nahm (long RIP), and makes regular trips to Bangkok to source recipes and ingredients. These days they take bookings – removing the irritation of waiting in the pub opposite for a table. / SE15 4BW; www.thebeggingbowl.co.uk; @thebeggingbowl; Tue-Sat 10 pm, Sun 4 pm; closed Tue-Thu L closed Sun D, closed Mon; booking online only.

Behind E8 NEW £72 ⑤④④
20 Sidworth Street   14–2B
"You can see why this won a Michelin star in 20 days" – Andy Beynon's Hackney newcomer set a new record when it opened in October 2020, a short stroll from London Fields. Previously Jason Atherton's development chef, his stylish, industrial-ish space is focused on a chef's table with all 18 seats overlooking the kitchen: *"a great place to get up and personal with the chefs"*. *"Watching the chefs put together the dishes is a pleasure given their quiet, efficient and impressively clean-cut working practices"*; and the main man himself comes over as being very *"approachable and personable"*. From your perch, you sample a 12-course tasting menu focused on sustainable seafood. *"Andy is seriously knowledgeable about fish cookery and delivers brilliant fish dishes and accompanying wines over the many courses"*, and all at *"a reasonable price"*. Next door is a wine bar and bottle shop. / E8 3SD; www.behindrestaurant.co.uk; Tue-Sat 11 pm; closed Tue, Wed L, closed Sun & Mon; booking online only.

Bellamy's W1 £63 ③④④
18-18a Bruton Pl   020 7491 2727   3–2B
"The epitome of civility" – former Annabel's MD Gavin Rankin's establishment Mayfair brasserie is *"so reliable you cannot fault it"*. Such is its blue blooded credentials that the Queen – who is never seen in restaurants – has dined here twice. Foodwise, there's some *"very deft cooking"* and *"always something of interest on the menu – but it won't blow your socks off"*. Prices for both food and the French-only wine list are – perhaps surprisingly – *"very reasonable"*, especially if you choose the *"excellent table d'hôte"* menu (two courses for £25). / W1J 6LY; www.bellamysrestaurant.co.uk; @https://twitter.com/bellamysmayfair?lang=en; Mon-Fri 10.30 pm, Sat 11.30 pm; closed Sat L, closed Sun; Jacket required.

Bellanger N1 £57 **3** **4** **5**
9 Islington Grn 020 7226 2555 9–3D

Corbin & King's "perfect local brasserie", "with outside seating by Islington Green", was reopened as a rare bonus from the pandemic. (Having decided pre-Covid that the venue wasn't working for them, C&K then found themselves unable to off-load the site due to the downturn, so decided to revisit their decision to close it). "Islington really needs this place, and they've found their feet at last", "with a menu that is rather less focused, but still works for brunch, lunch or dinner". "It was pure comfort to be able to come back to Bellanger, as it had been sorely missed, and going back felt like a warm hug!". / N1 2XH; www.bellanger.co.uk; @BellangerN1; Mon & Tue, Sun 10 pm, Wed-Sat 11 pm.

Bellefields SW9 NEW £52
9 Stockwell Avenue 020 7846 8540 11–1D

Ex-Bonnie Gull chef James Mathieson heads up this post-lockdown 2021 newcomer, located on the ground floor of Brixton's Design Store, and owned by Squire & Partners – a family-run architectural practice. It incorporates a cobblestone courtyard for alfresco dining – on the menu, Mediterranean dishes 'from the Aegean and Balearics to the Levantine basin'. / SW9 9SY; bellefields.com.

Belmond Cadogan Hotel (Tea Lounge) SW1 **2** **3** **4**
75 Sloane Street 020 7048 7141 6–2D

"Superb dishes, presented wonderfully" win praise for the afternoon tea served in the stylish lounge of this deluxe hotel on Sloane Street (where Oscar Wilde was arrested in 1895 after losing a libel case). Prices, though, are too "aggressive" for some tastes. / SW1X 9SG; www.belmond.com/hotels/europe/uk/london/belmond-cadogan-hotel/; @belmond; Mon-Sun 10.30 pm.

Benares W1 £101 **4** **4** **4**
12a Berkeley Square House, 020 7629 8886 3–3B

"Returning to form following the departure of Atul Kochhar" – this "stunning" first-floor venue on Berkeley Square won renewed kudos this year under new executive chef Sameer Taneja. The "top-notch" Indian cuisine – "perfectly presented and fantastically flavoursome" – has achieved "a well-deserved return to Michelin star status" and service is "just as impressive – attentive and super-friendly". / W1J 6BS; www.benaresrestaurant.co.uk; @benaresofficial; Tue-Sat 10.30 pm, Sun 9.30 pm; closed Mon; No trainers; Take bookings all week via phone and/or online.

Bentley's W1 £94 **3** **2** **2**
11-15 Swallow St 020 7734 4756 4–4B

Richard Corrigan's 100-year-old veteran, down a cute lane a short walk from Piccadilly Circus, remains one of London's best-known destinations, with "drinks and nibbles on the heated terrace" ("a godsend during the lockdown era") as a precursor to sampling the "classic" fish and seafood provided either in the lively ground-floor seafood bar ("lush oysters") or more stately first floor (think lobster Newburg, Dover sole). Satisfaction levels remain high, but the pressures of the times have weighed a little on ratings: even a fan noting the "brilliant food" also spoke of "rising prices" and "value that's not quite what it was". Most reports, though, remain a resounding thumbs-up: "my favourite… you're guaranteed to have a happy time". / W1B 4DG; www.bentleys.org; @bentleys_london; Mon-Sat 11 pm, Sun 10 pm; booking max 8 may apply.

Berber & Q £57 **4**|**3**|**4**
Arch 338 Acton Mews, E8   020 7923 0829   14–2A
Exmouth Market, EC1   020 7837 1726   10–1A
*"Fabulous starters and dips with full-on heat and unmissable shawarma
(both meat and vegetarian)" is the run-down on Josh Katz's Tel Aviv-meets-
North Africa grill in Exmouth Market. Here and at his original venue from
2015, a Haggerston railway arch, Katz and his team conjure up a "reliably
great range of quality melanges" – he's not fussy about where he'll find
ideas and ingredients (the Balkans, Turkey, Iraq, Iran and Yemen are all
mentioned on his menus). It's all very more-ish – "so good I went twice in
one week!".*

Berenjak W1 £64 **4**|**3**|**3**
27 Romilly Street   020 3319 8120   5–2A
*"What a find" – Kian Samyani mines his Iranian background at this Soho
three-year-old, to create "exceptionally tasty kebabs and mezze, a cool vibe
and bread baked fresh from the oven right before your eyes". The food may
not be "entirely authentically Persian" (for a start, many prime ingredients are
British), but it can be "exceptional" and the "menu is interesting". Top Tip:
"sit at the bar and watch the guys at work to heighten your appetite".
/ W1D 5AL; berenjaklondon.com; Mon-Sat 11 pm; closed Mon-Thu L, closed Sun.*

Bermondsey Larder SE1 **NEW** £21 **3**|**4**|**3**
153-157 Tower Bridge Road   020 7378 6254   10–4D
*"A great team and food ethos" won praise for The Dairy in Clapham (RIP),
and when the pandemic forced its closure, Robin and Sarah Gill found their
crew a new Bermondsey berth within a recently opened 'aparthotel' called
Bermonds Locke. Otherwise, the aim was to maintain its hip style and
"skilful small-plate cooking", and they seem to be on the way to succeeding:
in an October 2020 review, Jimi Famurewa found that "something born from
frantic necessity can still be a vessel for pure, boundless joy" that "blazes
with a rare confidence and immense likeability". Our early reporters were a
bit more measured but still upbeat: "ate outside on a bit of a windswept
patio: but the food and service were great!". / SE1 3LW;
www.thedairybermondsey.com; Thu-Sat, Wed 10 pm, Sun 4 pm; closed Wed L closed
Sun D, closed Mon & Tue.*

The Berners Tavern W1 £102 **2**|**2**|**5**
10 Berners St   020 7908 7979   3–1D
*"The most sensational-looking dining room" – a "so lively" ("far too loud"?)
converted banking hall in Ian Shrager's Edition hotel – overshadows Jason
Atherton's food at this fashionable Fitzrovia haunt. Fans do hail cooking they
say is "lovely", but it "miscues" too often for comfort, and its harshest critics
now place it "essentially at gastropub level". Even critics, though, suspect the
place will "carry on pulling people in". / W1T 3NP; www.bernerstavern.com;
@bernersTavern; Tue-Sat 10 pm, Mon 10am, Sun 4 pm; closed Mon D.*

Bertie Blossoms W10 £44
323 Portobello Road   020 3960 1293   7–1A
*This expensively refurbished Ladbroke Grove pub quietly opened in late
summer 2019 – when we added it to the website it already had over 20k
followers on Instagram, which can be explained by its backing... some guy
called Ed Sheeran. Early reports of the diverse menu suggest that Ed's
lyricism hasn't infused the cooking with any magic – quite the contrary – but
that his upbeat style is more evident in its party vibe. / W10 5SY;
www.bertieblossoms.co.uk; @BertieBlossoms; Wed-Sat 11 pm, Sun 5 pm; closed
Wed & Thu L closed Sun D, closed Mon & Tue.*

Best Mangal £44 **3 4 2**
619 Fulham Rd, SW6   020 7610 0009   6–4A
104 North End Rd, W14   020 7610 1050   8–2D
This pair of "genuine Turkish" grills in Fulham "faithfully reproduce the correct flavours, smells and textures" required by kebab-lovers. Their "great shish kebabs are full of flavour, served beautifully with an accompaniment of rice and salad" – "always reliable for a delicious dinner". (Note, there is also a business called "1996 Best Mangal" at 66 North End Road – similar, but not reviewed here). / www.bestmangal.com.

The Betterment W1 **3 4 3**
The Biltmore, 39-44 Grosvenor Square   020 7629 9400   3–2A
Jason Atherton's Social Company oversees the all-day, brasserie-style operation at this luxury Mayfair hotel, which opened a couple of years ago. In particular, "it's a good set-up for business, with well-spaced tables". At the time of writing, it is still 'temporarily closed', but according to its website reopening is imminent. / W1K 2HP; lxrhotels3.hilton.com/lxr/biltmore-mayfair/dine/; Thu-Sun, Wed 10 pm; closed Mon & Tue.

Bibendum SW3 £145 **4 3 4**
81 Fulham Rd   020 7589 1480   6–2C
"Claude Bosi is really nailing it with his classic French cuisine" ("wonderful flavours and very refined…" with "a complexity that is astounding") in this "very special" first-floor dining room, in South Kensington's iconic Michelin Building. Shaking off the pandemic chaos of the past year, scores here have actually gone from strength to strength, and criticism is most notable by its absence. And the room itself – perhaps the late Sir Terence Conran's finest contribution to London's restaurant scene – is a major draw, especially at lunchtime, with its "gorgeous, bright and spacious" interior, not to mention the "epic wine list". "A fantastic all-rounder". / SW3 6RD; www.bibendum.co.uk; @bibendumltdSW3; Wed-Sat 9.45 pm; closed Mon & Tue & Sun; booking max 12 may apply.

Bibendum Oyster Bar SW3 £84 **3 4 4**
Michelin House, 81 Fulham Road   020 7581 5817   6–2C
"You can't fault" this luxurious seafood bar in the foyer of Chelsea's historic Michelin garage: an offshoot of Claude Bosi's upscale restaurant upstairs. It's a "lovely setting, with original ceramic depictions of Michelin tyre car racing victories from the 1900s". The food – from a small menu that nowadays includes cooked dishes alongside the crustacea – is "exceptional", although it comes at "shocking prices". / SW3 6RD; www.bibendum.co.uk; @bibendumrestaurant; Wed-Sun 9.45 pm; closed Wed & Thu L, closed Mon & Tue; no booking.

BiBi W1 NEW £60
42 North Audley Street   020 3780 7310   3–2A
A new autumn 2021 arrival in the JKS stable of market-leading Indians – Trishna, Gymkhana, Brigadiers – a high-end project, this time on the Mayfair site that used to be Truc Vert (long RIP). Chef Chet Sharma leads the kitchen, which is to showcase upmarket modern Indian cuisine and the flavours of South Asia, using the best ingredients. / W1K 6ZR; www.bibirestaurants.com; Tue-Sat 10.30 pm; closed Tue-Thu L, closed Sun & Mon.

Bibimbap Soho W1 £37 **3 2 2**
11 Greek St   020 7287 3434   5–2A
Soho canteen plus City take-away, which scores high marks for its trademark bibimbaps (rice with a topping). Its Fitzrovia branch is no more, and its City 'to go' option has moved from Leadenhall Market to near Cannon Street. / W1D 4DJ; www.bibimbapsoho.com; @bibimbapsoho; Wed-Sat 10 pm; no Amex.

Bibo by Dani García EC2 NEW £70
Mondrian Hotel, 45 Curtain Road   020 3146 4545   13–1B
On the site of Red Rooster (RIP) within the The Curtain Hotel (RIP), comes this 120-seat August 2021 newcomer within the newly opened Mondrian Shoreditch, decked out in rural Spanish style (and including a 'Spanish Courtyard' seating 20). Whether the name chef, Andalusian Dani Garcia, will spend much time here we don't know, but he already has Bibos in Madrid, Marbella, Cádiz and Doha, so maybe not. Some of his signature dishes will be on the menu (for example, oxtail ravioli) alongside international hotel staples. / EC2; www.sbe.com/restaurants/bibo/shoreditch; Mon-Sun 11 pm.

Big Easy £67 3️⃣2️⃣3️⃣
12 Maiden Ln, WC2   020 3728 4888   5–3D
332-334 King's Rd, SW3   020 7352 4071   6–3C
Crossrail Pl, E14   020 3841 8844   12–1C
"Great lobster and huge quantities of meat" are the order of the day at this American-style crabshack and BBQ, a King's Road, Chelsea fixture for 31 years, and its more recent offshoots in Covent Garden and Canary Wharf. With the in-house blues and rock bands, they're ideal party venues for the whole family – "my children were vastly impressed by location, food, view – everything!". / www.bigeasy.co.uk; @bigeasytweet.

Big Fernand SW7 NEW £26
39 Thurloe Place   020 3031 8330   6–2C
The famous Parisian 'hamburgé' brand with over 55 branches in France and the Middle East quietly opened a London site at the start of 2020: a return to the capital after a failed attempt at colonisation which ended in 2014. A civilised venue in Francophile South Kensington (north of the tube), it serves nine types of burger along with excellent frites and looks set to carve a niche in the capital's crowded marketplace for burger joints. / SW7 2HP; www.bigfernanduk.com; @BigFernand_UK; Sun-Thu 10.30 pm, Fri & Sat 11 pm.

Big Jo Bakery N7 NEW £25
318-326 Hornsey Road   020 3915 6760   9–1D
In September 2020, the Jolene (Primeur, Westerns Laundry) team opened a spin-off between Finsbury Park and Holloway: a sizeable eat-in café overlooking the street with floor-to-ceiling windows and serving pâtisserie, salads and a selection of pizza and pizza fritta (deep-fried calzone). / N7 7HE; www.bigjobakery.com; Tue-Sun 10 pm; closed Mon.

Bindas Eatery £43
5 Princes Street, W1   020 7495 1705   4–1A NEW
Westfield White City, W12   020 7495 1705   1–3B NEW
After winning a mentorship in a pop-up competition at Westfield White City Shopping Centre in 2018, Mehak Kansal brought this bricks-and-mortar operation to Mayfair in October 2020. 'Bindas' – Punjabi for without limitations and inhibitions – here translates into eclectic decor and a varied selection of street food. No feedback as yet, but they must be doing something right, as a second site is on the cards.

Bistro Union SW4 £60 3️⃣2️⃣3️⃣
40 Abbeville Rd   020 7042 6400   11–2D
"A lovely little restaurant to have on one's doorstep", this 'Abbeville Village' outpost of Adam Byatt's Trinity – up the road in Clapham Old Town – may lack its big sister's star quality, "but the food never disappoints". / SW4 9NG; www.bistrounion.co.uk; @BistroUnion; Wed-Sat 8.30 pm, Sun 4 pm; closed Wed L closed Sun D, closed Mon & Tue; booking max 8 may apply.

Bisushima WC2 NEW   £50
Page8 Hotel, 8 Saint Martin's Place   020 3879 9403   5–4C
With magnificent central views from its two roof terraces, this big (6,000 sq ft with 190 covers) and glam new venue opened at the start of December 2020 and occupies the entire sixth floor of the new Page8 Hotel, just off Trafalgar Square. Sergey Men and Ruslav Ugarov run the operation, which features a wide range of sushi, sashimi, caviar and cocktails. No survey feedback as yet, but having poked our nose around the corner it certainly looks the part. / WC2N 4JH; bisushima.com; Tue-Thu midnight, Fri & Sat 1 am; closed Tue-Thu L, closed Sun & Mon.

Black Bear Burger   £11   5 3 3
11-13 Market Row, SW9   020 7737 3444   11–2D NEW
Boxpark Shoreditch, 2-10 Bethnal Green Road, E1   no tel   13–2B
"OMG! that's what you call a burger!" – fans of this Brixton Market Row and Boxpark Shoreditch operation insist that their patties – dry-aged beef served with cheese, bacon, onion jam and garlic mayo – are "mind-blowing". "Side dishes are great, too". Founders Liz and Stew launched five years ago after working ski seasons in Whistler, Canada – haunt of black bears. / blackbearburger.com; @BlackBearBurger.

The Black Book W1 NEW   £37   2 3 4
23 Frith Street   020 7434 1724   5–2A
"No better place to unwind with a great bottle of wine in central London", say early fans of this new (since September 2020) heart-of-Soho hideaway: a cosy, underground haunt that was previously known as Trade (a members-only club for those in the hospitality industry) and which was relaunched by the same team as a 'boutique late-night wine bar' and restaurant that's open to all. Master sommeliers Gearoid Devaney and Xavier Rousset stock a walk-in Coravin cellar with well-priced fine wines sold by the glass. The menu is simple stuff – charcuterie, cheese, steak, some tapas-y sharing plates – but really comes into its own in the wee hours as the place is open till 1am early in the week and 3am at weekends. "Small mark-ups on the 'black book' wine list with both classics and under the radar gems, plus great cocktails and decent food means it's worth venturing into this basement hangout". / W1D 4RR; blackbooksoho.co.uk; @blackbooksoho; Tue, Wed 1 am, Thu-Sat 3 am; closed Tue-Sat L, closed Sun & Mon.

Black Dog Beer House TW8   £58   4 3 3
17 Albany Road   020 8568 5688   1–3A
This "cracking boozer in Brentford" has "a most original and well-executed gastropub menu" including a bar-snacks list of 31 Iberian tinned fish or seafood choices, served with grilled sourdough. There's "good real ale", with surprises from Fearless Nomad, a one-barrel nano-brewery in the garden, and a "strong wine list" featuring an unfiltered Sicilian white on tap. "Great service and vibe" come courtesy of Pete Brew (yes, really) and Ash Zobell, who launched it from the ashes of the former Albany Arms in 2018. / TW8 0NF; www.blackdogbeerhouse.co.uk; @blackdogbeerhse; Mon, Thu 8.45 pm; closed Tue, Wed, Fri & Sat & Sun.

The Black Horse KT2   £45   3 3 3
204 London Road   020 3637 6199   11–2A
Five minutes' walk from Norbiton station, "a great local" (dating from 1893) which was revivified in recent times by Hippo Inns with a quality food offering including "a fabulous Sunday roast". "Well worth a visit if in the local area". / KT2 6QP; www.blackhorsekingston.co.uk; @blackhorseKT2; Mon-Sat 10 pm, Sun 9 pm.

Black Radish SW19 — £74 — 4 5 3
28 Ridgway   020 8617 3960   11–2B

"*Super food, inventiveness and friendly staff – and it's local!*" – this Wimbledon Village two-year-old wins raves from locals who feel they don't have to step out of their hood to eat top-notch cuisine. Young chef Toby Cartwright (who trained at Coworth Park under John Campbell) offers a no-choice set meal only, so his team can get the best out of special ingredients – which is fine, since "*every dish balances different elements perfectly, and the personal service is exceptional*". Its closest nearby rival is White Onion, round the corner in the High Street: is a theme developing? / SW19 4QW; www.blackradishsw19.com; @BlackRadishSW19; Tue-Sat 11.30 pm; closed Tue-Fri L, closed Sun & Mon.

Blacklock — £50 — 4 4 4
24 Great Windmill St, W1   020 3441 6996   4–3D
Henrietta Street, WC2   5–3D **NEW**
28 Rivington Street, EC2   awaiting tel   13–1B
13 Philpot Lane, EC3   020 7998 7676   10–3D

"*If you love good quality, flavourful meat, you'll love Blacklock*" – this brilliant small chain wins a massive thumbs-up for its "*unique, simple but tasty menu*" incorporating steaks and chops, with "*excellent side dishes (not usual for a steak place and a pleasant change)*" and a growing veg-friendly selection. "*The Blacklock at Home boxes they sold during lockdown (and thankfully continue to sell now) are fantastic!*". In late 2019 they announced a fourth, Covent Garden branch – as of August 2021 no opening date as yet. / theblacklock.com; @BlacklockChops.

Blanchette W1 — £62 — 4 3 3
9 D'Arblay St   020 7439 8100   4–1C

"*Great French food in a relaxed setting*" makes this "*cosy*" Soho bistro a magnet for London diners wanting a taste of Belle Epoque Paris. Launched in 2013 by three brothers and named after their mother, the establishment "*consistently delivers to a high standard*". A sister venue in Brick Lane has closed down. / W1F 8DS; www.blanchettesoho.co.uk; @blanchettesoho; Mon-Thu 9 pm, Fri & Sat 9.30 pm, Sun 7.30 pm.

Blandford Comptoir W1 — £66 — 3 3 3
1 Blandford Street   020 7935 4626   2–1A

"*Wonderful wines*" – from an "*amazing list, especially for Rhône Valley*", with many "*excellent vintages by the glass*" – top the billing at this "*classy*" (if "*slightly cramped*") five-year-old Marylebone wine bar from Xavier Rousset, once the youngest-ever Sommelier of the Year. It's backed up by "*well-produced food with French influences and a modern twist*". / W1U 3DA; blandford-comptoir.co.uk; @BlandfordCompt; Tue-Sat 10 pm; closed Sun & Mon; no Amex.

Bleecker Burger — £24 — 4 2 1
205 Victoria St, SW1   no tel   2–4B
The Balcony, Westfield White City, W12   020 3582 2930   1–3B **NEW**
Unit B Pavilion Building, Spitalfields Mkt, E1   07712 540501   13–2B
Bloomberg Arcade, Queen Victoria Street, EC4   awaiting tel   10–3C

"*Juicy, tasty, moreish*" – New Yorker Zan Kaufman's "*great dirty burgers*" are, say fans, "*the best I have tasted anywhere*". Starting out from a van 10 years ago, she has graduated to five permanent sites including the biggest yet, at Westfield White City, which has an all-female management team. With the Bloomberg Arcade branch in the City closed during the pandemic, the brand linked up with Deliveroo to open three delivery-only kitchens in Battersea, Bermondsey and Canary Wharf. / www.bleecker.co.uk; @bleeckerburger.

Bleeding Heart Bistro EC1 £60 3 3 5
Bleeding Heart Yard 0207 2428238 10–2A

"In an out-of-the-way, historic courtyard in Farringdon" – where the terrace is a major draw in summer – this "delightful and atmospheric" Gallic brasserie continues to fly the flag for the Bleeding Heart brand. (Its grander, older sibling, in a nearby basement, closed in the pandemic. As of October 2021, future plans are not yet clear, although it seems likely a resurrection at some point may be on the cards). "Classic French dishes" are charmingly served at "fair prices", the "evocative atmosphere makes it a romantic place" and the dependable wine selection continues to make it a favoured option for expense account types. / EC1N 8SJ; www.bleedingheart.co.uk; @bleedingheartyd; Mon-Sat 10.30 pm; closed Sat L, closed Sun; Booking max 12 may apply.

Bleeding Heart Tavern EC1 £45 3 3 3
Bleeding Heart Yard 02072428238 10–2A

On the fringe of the City, this large tavern is part of the well-known eateries grouped around Bleeding Heart Yard, all under common ownership. A "decent-all-round and handy standby", it was in particular "a perfect place to meet people for the elusive business meetings that could take place between lockdowns". Reported by Google as 'Temporarily closed' in October 2021, we have rated it on the basis that – as the Square Mile picks up – its return is likely. / EC1N 8SJ; www.bleedingheart.co.uk; @bleedingheartyd; Mon-Fri 10.30 pm; closed Sat & Sun; Take bookings all week via phone and/or online.

Blue Boar Pub SW1
Conrad London St James, 22-28 Broadway 020 3301 1400 2–3C

The arrival of Sally Abé from Fulham's stellar Harwood Arms has majorly upped the cred of this recently relaunched pub-restaurant – one of four eateries set to open in summer 2021 in a newly refurbished Westminster hotel (see also The Pem). In line with her time in Fulham, Sunday roasts are a big feature, as are Scotch eggs and other ribsticking British fare. Some early feedback is positive, but too limited for a rating. / SW1H 0BH; www.hilton.com/en/hotels/loncoci-conrad-london-st-james/dining/.

Bluebird SW3 £89 2 3 4
350 King's Road 020 7559 1000 6–3C

Given the size and prominence of this huge D&D London landmark on Chelsea's main drag – the conversion of a beautiful 1920s car showroom – it's astounding how little feedback it inspires. Such as we have is all positive this year, though. / SW3 5UU; www.bluebird-restaurant.co.uk; @bluebirdchelsea; Sun & Mon 11 pm, Tue-Fri midnight, Sat 1 am.

Bob Bob Ricard W1 £81 2 4 5
1 Upper James Street 020 3145 1000 4–2C

"What a sexy dining room!" – the "all-booth seating" at Leonid Shutov's extravagant Soho venue (each with its own 'Push for Champagne' button) "makes you feel like you're in your own carriage of the Orient Express" and is perfect for "date night and important romantic celebrations" (and also for a lighthearted business meal). Even if the "luxurious" Russian-British cuisine (caviar and Beef Wellington are highlights) strikes some as a tad "overpriced", most reporters also feel it's "absolutely delicious". In 2019, Shutov launched a £25m sibling Bob Bob Cité on the third floor of the City's Cheesegrater. It inspired mixed reports and in October 2021 relaunches under the Bob Bob Ricard brand, after tweaks to the decor bringing it closer to the Soho original. In EC3, the menu will have a Russian-French leaning. / W1F 9DF; www.bobbobricard.com; @BobBobRicard; Jacket required.

BOB's Lobster SE1 £59 3 4 3
Unit 71, St Thomas Street 020 7407 7099 10–4C

"For that lobster craving when in London... which surprisingly does not need a bank robbery" – head to this railway arch near London Bridge station (or seek out the *"glimmering and rather plush-looking food truck/van"* on the corner of Bedale Street and Borough High Street). It's *"a really fun and tasty meal"*: the *"crab stack and lobster rolls are delicious"* and *"you don't feel as though you are eating from a mobile food operation – the brioche is warm and buttery, the sauce moreish and the lobster is good quality"*. / SE1 3QX; www.bobslobster.com; @BOBs_Lobster; Tue-Sat 11.30 pm; closed Sun & Mon.

Bobo Social SE17 NEW £62
23 Sayer Street 020 7636 9310 1–3C

Former Charlotte Street fixture Bobo Social has – since July 2020 – found a new home near Elephant & Castle. 'Out there' burger combos are still the main menu mainstay, washed down with a selection of cocktails, although the tasteful white decor is arguably at odds with the stonking tastes delivered on the plate (peanut butter burger with truffle fries, anyone?). / SE17 1FY; bobosocial.com; @BoboSocial; Mon-Sun 11.30 pm; cards only.

Bocca di Lupo W1 £66 5 3 3
12 Archer St 020 7734 2223 4–3D

"Absolutely oozing with regional Italian flavours" – the *"exceptional"*, *"gutsy"* small plates at Jacob Kenedy's *"perennial favourite"* near Piccadilly Circus earn it a ranking in London's Top 40 most-mentioned restaurants. His menu remains *"very innovative"*, with many offbeat dishes and *"novel takes"* on more familiar ones. (*"You really can come here and slowly explore the entire wonder of Italian cuisine, from Piedmont to Sicily!"*). *"Really superb value too for such a central Theatreland location"* including *"a top Italian wine list, with many bargains"*. *"Chic"*, yet quite tightly packed, many regulars' favourite perch is by the open kitchen: *"a stool at the chef's counter is my happy place!"*. (*"Excellent home delivery boxes"* also feature in many reports). / W1D 7BB; www.boccadilupo.com; @boccadilupo; Mon-Sat 11 pm, Sun 9.30 pm; booking max 10 may apply.

Bocconcino Restaurant W1 £100 2 3 3
19 Berkeley St 020 7499 4510 3–3C

"Up-market (loud) Italian" in a prime Mayfair location with swish styling and and a large menu incorporating relatively affordable pizzas as well as more substantial classic dishes. The experience is generally well-rated but, valuewise, prices can seem to verge on the *"stratospheric"* for what is delivered. / W1J 8ED; www.bocconcinorestaurant.co.uk; @BocconcinoUK; Mon-Sat 12.30 am, Sun 10.30 pm.

Boisdale of Belgravia SW1 £84 2 2 3
15 Eccleston Street 020 7730 6922 2–4B

Ranald MacDonald's clubby Scottish-themed Belgravian has been around for decades and was an early exponent of carefully sourced British ingredients, particularly steaks and other meaty fare (Aberdeenshire beef, Highland venison, …). It also has the virtue of an unusually strong wine list and one of London's best selection of whiskies, not to mention a terrace dedicated to smoking Cuban cigars. Unsurprisingly, it's most recommended as a business location for clubbable males, but the Courtyard garden and regular live jazz help broaden its appeal. Complaints are few, other than that a meal here can prove *"expensive"*. / SW1W 9LX; www.boisdale.co.uk/belgravia; @boisdale; Mon-Sat 11 pm, Sun 4 pm; closed Mon, Sat L closed Sun D.

Boisdale of Bishopsgate EC2 £83 322
Swedeland Court, 202 Bishopsgate   020 7283 1763   10–2D
This Caledonian-themed branch of the Belgravia-based chain comprises a ground-floor wine bar and basement restaurant, with echoes of the mothership in its meaty menu, quality wine list and business-friendly set-up. It is still "temporarily closed" as we go to press in September 2021, but we've listed it on the basis that it is likely to re-open as the City gets its mojo back. / EC2M 4NR; www.boisdale.co.uk; @Boisdale; Mon-Fri 11 pm; closed Sat & Sun.

Boisdale of Canary Wharf E14 £66 334
Cabot Place   020 7715 5818   12–1C
"An evening out – in style" is oft-reported at the Docklands branch of Ranald Macdonald's Belgravia haunt, dedicated to the high life with a Scottish twist – with whisky, cigars and nightly jazz and soul courtesy on occasion of house music patron Jools Holland. It also proved itself an "absolute stalwart as the go-to place for those still going to the office through lockdown". Top Tip: "the haggis pizza is a must!". / E14 4QT; www.boisdale.co.uk/canary-wharf; @boisdaleCW; Tue, Wed 11 pm, Fri & Sat 2 am, Thu 1 am, Sun midnight; closed Tue-Sat L, closed Mon.

Bombay Brasserie SW7 £80 332
Courtfield Road   020 7370 4040   6–2B
"Solid and reliable", plush Indian veteran in South Kensington that celebrates its 40th anniversary this year, and still earns consistently made marks for its cooking. Now owned by Taj Hotels, it has a spacious glassed-in terrace and spruced-up decor, although some long-time regulars preferred it "when the atmosphere was more Indian Raj". / SW7 4QH; www.bombayb.co.uk; @BBSW7; Mon-Sat 11 pm, Sun 10.30 pm; closed Mon L.

Bombay Bustle W1 £67 433
29 Maddox Street   020 7290 4470   3–2A
This "lively new-generation small-plates Indian" in Mayfair gives its nearby upmarket stablemate, Jamavar, a real run for its money. "The food's amazing – try the broccoli" with 'tomato dust' and cheese. "With so many fine Indian restaurants to choose from, a favourite's not easy – but BB is the place I return too most regularly". Top Tip: "the early-bird set menu is absolutely delicious and great value". / W1S 2PA; www.bombaybustle.com; @BombayBustle; Mon-Sat 10.30 pm, Sun 9.30 pm.

Bombay Palace W2 £62 543
50 Connaught St   020 7723 8855   7–1D
"Finger-lickin' delicious"; this "long-standing beacon of the Indian restaurant industry", est 1983, provides plush surroundings "tucked away from the commotion of Marble Arch". The cuisine is "authentic and of consistently great quality" – both "upscale and gratifyingly plentiful" – while "brilliant service and staff" ensure that "every visit is immensely gratifying". / W2 2AA; www.bombay-palace.co.uk; @bombaypalaceW2; Mon-Thu 9.30 pm, Fri-Sun 10 pm; closed Mon-Thu L.

Bone Daddies £44 333
Nova, Victoria St, SW1   no tel   2–4B
30-31 Peter St, W1   020 7287 8581   4–2D
46-48 James St, W1   020 3019 7140   3–1A
Whole Foods, Kensington High St, W8   020 7287 8581   6–1A
24 Old Jamaica Road, SE16   020 7231 3211   10–4D
The Bower, 211 Old Street, EC1   020 3019 6300   13–1A
"Super ramen" constitutes "a top meal at a great price" at these Japanese-style fast-food bars. In early 2021, the brand opened on Putney High Street in a former branch of Byron and later announced 'Wing Daddies' (a virtual chicken wing delivery option at all its London stores). / www.bonedaddies.com/restaurant/bermondsey/.

Bonoo NW2 £56 443
675 Finchley Road   020 7794 8899   1–1B
"Authentic, delicious food in a friendly welcoming environment" scores high grades for this family-run Indian in Child's Hill, where fans say "you couldn't ask for more!". / NW2 2JP; www.bonoo.co.uk; @bonoohampstead; Mon-Sun 10.30 pm; closed Mon-Sun L.

Boqueria £55 333
192 Acre Ln, SW2   020 7733 4408   11–2D
278 Queenstown Road, SW8   020 7498 8427   11–1C
These "delightful, laid-back, buzzy local tapas bars" provide a "well curated selection" of Hispanic small plates at their two venues in Battersea and Clapham. "Helpful staff" and "good value for money" seal the deal – "Acre Lane (Clapham) needs more places like this". / www.boqueriatapas.com; @BoqueriaTapas.

Il Bordello E1 £52 333
Metropolitan Wharf, 70 Wapping Wall   020 7481 9950   12–1A
"Huge portions and great Italian family vibes" have ensured this Wapping trattoria has remained a "real neighbourhood favourite" for more than 20 years. The "very large portion sizes" mentioned by almost every reporter mean only one thing: bring your hungriest, greediest teenagers along. / E1W 3SS; www.ilbordello.com; Mon-Sat 11 pm, Sun 10.30 pm; closed Mon L.

Borough Market Kitchen SE1 NEW £66
Jubilee Place   10–4C
Never known to stand still in its 800-year history, Borough Market has expanded again. Hot on the heels of its home delivery service (www.goodsixty.co.uk/borough-market) is this new food hall, just off Winchester Walk, which features 13 permanent fitted kitchens and a further 10 pop-up stalls – a crucible for young brands that are going places. Current incumbents include Applebee's Fish stall, Brindisa Kitchen, Juma Kitchen, the phenomenal Mei Mei, and Rudie's Jerk Shack. / SE1 9AG; Mon-Wed 10 pm, Thu-Sat 11.30 pm, Sun 6 pm; closed Sun D.

Il Borro W1 NEW
15 Berkeley Street   020 3988 7717   3–3C
Originally set to open in summer 2020, this Tuscany-via-Dubai import – part of an international group – set a new record for rent on its new Mayfair home: the 11,000 square foot, two-floor site vacated by Nobu Berkeley (RIP) with 220 covers. Finally open now from September 2021, it's one of a number of very high-end Italians to have opened in Mayfair in recent years: here, with produce and wine from the 700-acre Tuscan estate of the same name. / W1J 8DY; ilborrotuscanbistro.co.uk; Tue-Sat 1 am, Sun 4.45 pm.

The Bow Wine Vaults EC4 £45 334
10 Bow Church Yd   020 7248 1121   10–2B
"A stalwart for lunches in the City", this "unpretentious" venue in "lovely Bow Lane by the famous church" has "kept its standards up" for 35 years. The outdoor seating was a major attraction during the pandemic restrictions, and prices are "very reasonable" for the area, while "the boisterous tables make it easy to have confidential chats without being overheard". / EC4M 9DQ; Sun-Thu 9 pm, Fri & Sat 21.30 pm.

Boxcar Baker & Deli W1 333
7a Wyndham Place   020 3006 7000   2–1A
This all-day Marylebone deli/café starts the day at breakfast time and thereafter serves a range of pastries, salads, quality sandwiches and some more substantial dishes, winning praise despite "high prices, even for this posh neighbourhood", for "good, quality fare". / W1H 1PN; boxcar.co.uk; @boxcarbaker; Mon-Sun 4 pm; closed Mon-Sun D.

Boxcar Bar & Kitchen W1 £53 **4** **4** **3**
23 New Quebec St 020 3006 7000 2–2A
"Really good burgers at very reasonable prices" used to win praise for this "cool" Marylebone butcher, deli and steakhouse (sibling to The Lighterman et al). We've rated it for its pre-pandemic performance, but it remains closed as we go to press in September 2021, so change may be afoot at some time in the future. / W1H 7SD; boxcar.co.uk; @BoxcarLondon; Tue-Sat 10 pm; closed Sun & Mon.

Brackenbury Wine Rooms W6 £54 **2** **3** **3**
111-115 Hammersmith Grove 020 3696 8240 8–1C
A "big terrace on Hammersmith Grove" draws a steady crowd to this "reliable local", whose "buzzy atmosphere and interesting wine list" make it "a good place for meeting friends" (including for "coffee and pastries" at its adjoining deli). The menu offers a good range from small plates to full meals: but while most reporters see it as a "reliable local", there is the odd dissenter who feels "if it were run better, it could be brilliant not average". / W6 0NQ; winerooms.london/brackenbury; @Wine_Rooms; Mon-Sat midnight, Sun 11 pm.

Bradley's NW3 £63 **2** **2** **2**
25 Winchester Rd 020 7722 3457 9–2A
Simon and Jolanta Bradley's neighbourhood restaurant in Swiss Cottage has provided a professional experience for more than 30 years, with modern European cooking that's a cut above what might be expected in its backwater location. Ratings are undercut by one or two reporters who see "room for improvement". But there's no doubting its "reasonable pre-theatre menu" is particularly useful for visitors to the nearby Hampstead Theatre. / NW3 3NR; www.bradleysnw3.co.uk; @bradleysnw3; Tue-Sat , Sun 2.30 pm; closed Tue-Sat L closed Tue-Sun D, closed Mon.

Brasserie Blanc £62 **2** **2** **3**
"Classic French cuisine at reasonable prices" sums up the aim of superchef Raymond Blanc's "jolly" mid-market brasseries (which sometimes suffer by comparison with his temple to haute cuisine, Le Manoir aux Quat' Saisons). At their best, they provide "an overall pleasant dining experience" that's "solid and dependable". At their worst, the experience is "middle-of-the-road" going on "mass-produced". The South Bank branch opposite the Festival Hall is "a great place", while venues in the City, Chancery Lane and riverside Hammersmith are also usefully located. Another 10 are scattered across other English cities. / www.brasserieblanc.com.

Brasserie of Light W1 £73 **2** **2** **2**
400 Oxford Street 020 3940 9600 3–1A
"Big, busy, brassy and tightly packed, like an Ivy on steroids!" – Richard Caring's brasserie on the first floor of Selfridges is designed first and foremost to be "eye-catching" and "fun", and "the grand Pegasus by Damien Hirst adds to the glamour". But while the "so-so" food is "better than expected" for some diners – "ideal for ladies after a hard day's shopping" – the "glitz"-first approach is becoming more grating to others; especially those who discern an ever-more "impersonal" ("get 'em in, then chuck 'em out") approach. "I've eaten at Selfridges' restaurants for decades and this one reflects where the store is moving – flash, loud and expensive…"; "it's always full and lively, I suppose you could say – frequented mostly by people who like to dine surrounded by lots of music and noise". / W1A 1AB; www.brasserie-of-light.co.uk; Mon-Sat midnight, Sun 11 pm.

Brasserie Zédel W1 £47 ②③⑤
20 Sherwood St 020 7734 4888 4–3C

"What a setting!" This *"improbably glamorous and huge"* destination – *"well-located"* just seconds from Piccadilly Circus – occupies a *"magnificent"* Grade I listed basement, whose gorgeous Beaux Arts / Art Deco interiors date from the 1930s. That it is, for many reporters, *"the nearest thing in the UK to an authentic Parisian brasserie (reminiscent of La Coupole in Montparnasse)"* is entirely by design as that is just what Corbin & King were aiming for when they established it in 2012. The brasserie fare – *"good, safe, formulaic and French"* – doesn't typically set the world on fire, but was rated more highly than ever this year and is *"amazing value for money in the heart of London's West End"*, making the venue *"a favourite go-to when in town"*. *"If you stick with the cheaper dishes and daily specials you will get as close to a bargain as you are likely to get in this area"*. Try to squeeze in a cocktail in the super-atmospheric bar. Or make an evening of it: *"the cabaret show is not to be missed"*. / W1F 7ED; www.brasseriezedel.com; @brasseriezedel; Mon-Sat 11 pm, Sun 10 pm.

Brat E1 £85 ⑤④③
First Floor, 4 Redchurch Street no tel 13–1B

"Superb, unadorned cooking", cooked on an open wood fire – *"the quality of meat and fish is magnificent"* not least the *"truly memorable turbot"* (for which the place is named) – continues to inspire adulatory reviews for Tomos Parry's *"unassuming but cool first-floor dining room"*, above Shoreditch's Smoking Goat. *"If you want dark and moody, with glowing lights in the background and a roaring fire in the corner of the room, this is the place! You get pared down surroundings offset by outstanding food"*. *"I could easily just eat the bread as a meal: this place is really that good!"* See also Brat at Climpson's Arch. / E1 6JJ; www.bratrestaurant.com; @bratrestaurant; Mon-Sun 10.30 pm.

Brat at Climpson's Arch E8 NEW £94 ④②②
Climpson's Arch, 374 Helmsley Place 020 7254 7199 14–2B

What started as a residency during the 2020 pandemic – when Tomos Parry's Shoreditch HQ was deemed unsuitable for social distancing – was confirmed as a permanent venture in January 2021. Situated in a courtyard, and covered with a marquee-type structure, cooking with fire is still central to the cuisine here: e.g. roasted game rice, whole grab with hay butter, grilled mushrooms and wood-fired breads. (Parry originally cooked here from 2013-2015, so he has history on this site.) *"The food is way better than the casual surroundings would suggest: cooking almost everything on charcoal produces wonderful flavours"*. But even some who applaud the *"outstanding"* results can still find it too pricey, given *"friendly but random"*, *"café-style service"* and humble surroundings. / E8 3SB; bratrestaurant.com/climpsons-arch/; Mon-Sun 10 pm; closed Mon-Thu L.

Bravi Ragazzi SW16 £20 ⑤②②
2a Sunnyhill Road 020 8769 4966 11–2D

"Exceptional" sourdough pizza has won a more-than-local fanclub for Andrea Asciuti's Streatham pitstop. He branched out this year with a second opening, 081 Pizzeria at Peckham Levels, see also. / SW16 2UH; www.braviragazzipizzeria.co.uk; Mon-Sun 10.30 pm.

Brawn E2 £75 ⑤③③
49 Columbia Road 020 7729 5692 14–2A

Next to Columbia Road flower market, this East End outpost of the Caves du Pyrène group is *"the perfect neighbourhood restaurant"* – albeit one which attracts custom from far and wide for its *"benchmark small plates"* of Mediterranean food and *"clever wine list with lots of natural/biodynamic options"*. It remains *"very hip"* after a dozen years, *"always buzzing"* with *"delicious dishes from Ed Wilson's kitchen, served by knowledgeable and friendly staff"* in a *"lovely light-filled room"*. / E2 7RG; www.brawn.co; @Brawn49; Wed-Sat, Tue 10.30 pm; closed Tue L, closed Sun & Mon; Take bookings all week via phone and/or online.

Bread Street Kitchen EC4 £75 2 2 3
10 Bread Street 020 3030 4050 10–2B

If it were not for Gordon Ramsay's involvement, we would likely ignore this big warehousey venue, in a large mall next to St Paul's. If you work in one of the local money factories and are fairly cost-insensitive, its interior is agreeable and it suits less formal business entertaining (or even a family meal); but as ever, it achieves very limited and mixed feedback overall. Still, the GR Holdings crew must think the idea's got legs, as they have created a sub-brand – Bread Street Café – first opening Ealing in late 2021 and aimed at relaxed, all-day family dining. / EC4M 9AJ; www.gordonramsayrestaurants.com/bread-street-kitchen; @breadstreet; Mon-Wed midnight, Thu-Sat 1 am, Sun 9 pm.

Breakfast Club £46 3 3 3
33 D'Arblay St, W1 020 7434 2571 4–1C
2-4 Rufus St, N1 020 7729 5252 13–1B
31 Camden Pas, N1 020 7226 5454 9–3D
12-16 Artillery Ln, E1 020 7078 9633 13–2B

"I admit I was a bit skeptical when I tried Breakfast Club for the first time. It seemed small, a little understated and how differentiated can breakfast be? Luckily they proved me wrong!". So "don't be put off by external appearances" at these busy and "cool" cafés, where you get a "proper breakfast" from a "good choice of UK or global options". "I don't know that I'd stand outside for an hour plus as some folks do, but the early bird gets the Chorizo Hash here!". / www.thebreakfastclubcafes.com; @thebrekkyclub; SRA-Food Made Good – 3 stars.

Breddos Tacos EC1 £46 3 2 2
82 Goswell Road 020 3535 8301 10–1B

"The real deal!", say fans of this ten-year-old tacos brand, which has various pitches around town, as well as this permanent taqueria in Clerkenwell, serving small plates alongside margaritas and mezcals. / EC1M 7AH; www.breddostacos.com; @breddostacos; Tue-Sat 10.30 pm; closed Sun & Mon; no booking.

Briciole W1 £62 3 2 2
20 Homer St 020 7723 0040 7–1D

"Genuine" Italian cooking is on the menu at this Marylebone trattoria and deli, where the "excellent pasta makes up for punishingly high noise levels when the place is busy". It has outlasted Latium, the now-closed Fitzrovia restaurant it was spun out from. / W1H 4NA; www.briciole.co.uk; @briciolelondon; Mon-Sat 10.30 pm, Sun 10.15 pm.

Brick Lane Beigel Bake E1 £82 4 1 1
159 Brick Ln 020 7729 0616 13–1C

"Well worth the queue", this legendary Brick Lane bakery – a rare survivor of Whitechapel's historic Jewish community – produces as many as 20,000 beigels a week for the hungry crowd that lines up, 24 hours a day, to devour them stuffed with salt beef, lox, cream cheese or chopped herring. Why? They are so, so cheap! Other Jewish deli classics are available including onion platzels and cheesecake, and everything is "great value for money". Top Tip: 'beigel' is the correct European spelling, to be pronounced as in 'Einstein'; 'bagel' is the American version. / E1 6SB; bricklanebeigel.co.uk; @BeigelBake; Mon-Sun midnight; cash only; No bookings.

Brigadiers EC2 £67 **5 4 4**
Bloomberg Arcade, Queen Victoria Street   020 3319 8140   10–3C
"Magnificent" Indian scoff (and surprisingly good value considering the
location) has quickly earned a stellar reputation for this "superb" venue in
the City's Bloomberg Arcade (from JKS, "the same group as Trishna,
Gymkhana etc"). It's a "noisy" venue with plentiful TV screens showing sport
and is a haven for "meat-lovers" – all of which gives it a decidedly male feel.
But it "oozes fun", and even detractors who find it "slightly excessively 'City'"
– and "about as authentic as Kim Kardashian" – concede that "there's no
doubt the food and drink can't be beaten". / EC2R; brigadierslondon.com/;
@brigadiersldn; Mon-Sat 11 pm; closed Sun.

Bright E8 £84 **4 4 3**
Netil House, 1 Westgate Street   020 3095 9407   14–2B
"Hipster dining at its very best, free of the pretentious flourishes and stuffy
formalities of fine dining" – that's the renown of this semi-industrial space in
London Fields, from the same team as P Franco and Peg, whose features
include a carefully curated wine list and nowadays also an outside terrace. Its
ratings were taken down a notch this year, though, by the odd report of
"bland" results. / E8 3RL; www.brightrestaurant.co.uk; Wed & Thu 11.30 pm, Fri-Sun
midnight; closed Wed & Thu L, closed Mon & Tue.

The Bright Courtyard W1 £77 **3 2 2**
43-45 Baker St   020 7486 6998   2–1A
The food still rates well at this modern Chinese, although the office-block
setting near Marylebone's Portman Square generates very little enthusiasm.
/ W1U 8EW; www.lifefashiongroup.com; @BrightCourtyard; Mon-Sat 11.30 pm, Sun
10.30 pm.

Brinkley's SW10 £68 **2 2 3**
47 Hollywood Rd   020 7351 1683   6–3B
A "fun atmosphere" and "wide wine list that's almost at cost prices" ensure
that John Brinkley's Chelsea-set haunt remains "a perfect place for an
afternoon to float away", or a "summer's evening in the conservatory". The
food "won't set the world alight", but that's never been the point. There are
now spinoffs in the Wandsworth Bridge Road and on the edge of
Wandsworth Common. / SW10 9HX; www.brinkleys.com; @BrinkleysR; Mon-Sat
11.30 pm, Sun 11 pm.

Brinkley's Kitchen SW17 £60 **3 3 3**
35 Bellevue Rd   020 8672 5888   11–2C
This "smart neighbourhood restaurant" is a popular spot for evening rendezvous or Sunday lunches overlooking Wandsworth Common (a few doors
from local star Chez Bruce). "The food is good eclectic modern bistro fare –
but you don't go for the food, you go for the feel-good atmosphere and the
convenience". It is an offshoot of John Brinkley's Chelsea-based group, and his
excellent wine selection is also a feature here. / SW17 7EF; www.brinkleys.com;
@BrinkleysR; Mon-Sat 11.30 pm, Sun 11 pm.

The Broadcaster W12 **NEW**
101 Wood Lane   020 4549 7420   1–2B
At the entrance to the old TV Centre (near Westfield's John Lewis and White
City tube), this spangly new pub is from the same Open House stable as
King's Cross's glossy Lighterman and is very similar in concept: a striking,
four-floor new-build whose most striking feature is a pergola roof top with
panoramic views. The food offering – all in modern pub style – will vary
between floors, with the first floor more a sit-down dining room and with bar
snacks and BBQ on the top floor. / W12 7FA; Mon-Sun 4 pm.

Brook House SW6 £62 3︎2︎3︎
65 New King's Road   020 7371 5283   11–1B
"Charming, neighbourhood gastro-boozer, with a delightful view", overlooking Fulham's Eel Brook Common: the latest venture from Mark Dwyer, the former royal equerry and mentor to Prince Harry, who sold his three nearby pubs, the Sands End, Cross Keys and Brown Cow, five years ago for a rumoured £10m. / SW6 4SG; brookhousefulham.com; Tue-Thu 11 pm, Fri & Sat midnight, Sun 5 pm; closed Tue L closed Sun D, closed Mon; cards only.

Brookmill SE8 £44 3︎3︎3︎
65 Cranbrook Road   020 8333 0899   1–4D
There's *"always good food to be had"*, including *"fabulous steak"*, at this *"lively"* and cleverly modernised Victorian pub with beer garden in Deptford, part of a small 'indie' chain in southeast London. / SE8 4EJ; www.thebrookmill.co.uk; @thebrookmillpub; Mon & Tue 9 pm; closed Mon & Tue L, closed Wed-Sat & Sun.

The Brown Dog SW13 £61 3︎2︎3︎
28 Cross Street   020 8392 2200   11–1A
A *"good neighbourhood gem"* tucked down a side street in Barnes's 'Little Chelsea' conservation zone, the Dog was taken over by a new team during lockdown, who have *"nudged it towards the bistro end of the gastroboozer spectrum"*. The food is definitely a grade or two better as a result, although it's *"less inviting for a couple of pints at the bar"* – which makes it a *"big favourite among Barnes ladies who lunch, who bring their men and children along at weekends"*. There's also a hip pizza-and-ice cream shack, the Doghouse, in the back yard. / SW13 0AP; www.thebrowndog.co.uk; @browndogbarnes; Wed-Sat 10 pm, Sun 6 pm; closed Wed L closed Sun D, closed Mon & Tue.

Brown's Hotel,
The Drawing Room W1 £77 3︎4︎4︎
Albemarle St   020 7493 6020   3–3C
"Lots of space and lovely surroundings" help recommend this classic British hotel's plush lounge to its many fans. Though not as famous as the nearby Ritz Palm Court, fans have long acclaimed it for what they claim is *"the best afternoon tea in London!"*. / W1S 4BP; www.roccofortehotels.com; @Browns_Hotel; Mon-Sun 8 pm; No trainers.

Brunswick House Café SW8 £66 3︎2︎5︎
30 Wandsworth Rd   020 7720 2926   11–1D
"Housed in an architectural antiques emporium" in a Georgian mansion overlooking the traffic of Vauxhall Cross, with a dining room *"full of chandeliers and vintage finds"*, this *"quirky"* venue has a *"one-of-a-kind atmosphere"* that makes it *"one of the most fun places to eat"*. *"The food is always interesting"*, too, courtesy chef Jackson Boxer (also behind Orasay in Kensington) – *"even if the odd dish is a little bonkers"*. Overall it's a *"unique restaurant punching way above its weight"*, and *"a jolly night out is always guaranteed"* (especially if, as from September 2021, you enjoy some of the wine evenings or live jazz recently introduced in the cellars of the building). / SW8 2LG; www.brunswickhouse.london; @BrunswickHse; Wed-Sat, Tue 9.45 pm, Sun 3.45 pm; closed Tue L closed Sun D, closed Mon.

Trattoria Brutto EC1 NEW £45
35-37 Cowcross Avenue, Smithfield Market   10–1A
On the Smithfield site that was most recently Mark Hix's Chophouse (RIP) – and which has a recent history of meaty destinations – ex-Polpo supremo, Russell Norman continues in a somewhat similar vein with the launch of this modern Italian venture in September 2021. The Tuscan cuisine will make a feature of Bistecca alla Fiorentina alongside many homemade pasta dishes and is inspired by the simple, neighbourhood restaurants of Florence. Russell even purchased a 1980s electric typewriter of the same make as one of the restaurants he visited in Italy for maximum authenticity when it came to the feel of the menu. / EC1A 9PS; msha.ke/brutto; Tue-Sat 11 pm; closed Sun & Mon.

Bubala E1 £43 **4 4 3**
65 Commercial Street 020 7392 2111 13–2C
*"Tel Aviv café food of gourmet quality and with strong, delicious flavours" is
to be had at this Middle Eastern three-year-old, near Spitalfields. Staff are
"so welcoming" and it is "a find" in particular for non meat-eaters: "one of
the tastiest and best-priced vegan feasting menus I've ever had!". / E1 6BD;
www.bubala.co.uk; Mon-Sat 11 pm; closed Sun.*

The Builders Arms SW3 £61 **3 3 3**
13 Britten St 020 7349 9040 6–2C
*This lovely 200-year-old pub in a Chelsea backstreet serves a very decent
menu (including "child-friendly" options) and is thriving follow a smart refurb
under the ownership of Rupert Clevely's Hippo Inns for the second time – in
2010 he sold it to brewer Youngs as part of Geronimo Inns. / SW3 3TY;
www.thebuildersarmschelsea.co.uk; @BuildersChelsea; Mon-Thu 11 pm, Fri & Sat
midnight, Sun 10.30 pm; no booking.*

The Bull N6 £61 **2 3 3**
13 North Hill 020 8341 0510 9–1B
*"Enormous portions" – "cooked to order from a menu with a good variety"
– and beer brewed in-house by the Gorgeous Brewery "out the back" can be
found at this handsome old Highgate pub. "Waiting staff are helpful" and
it's "a family- and dog-friendly place". / N6 4AB; thebullhighgate.co.uk;
@Bull_Highgate; Mon-Thu 9 pm, Fri & Sat 10 pm, Sun 5 pm; closed Sun D.*

Bull & Last NW5 £73 **3 3 3**
168 Highgate Rd 020 7267 3641 9–1B
*This "reliably brilliant gastropub" beside the Heath in Kentish Town is
"hugely popular" for good reasons – its "well-crafted food and well-kept
beers, warm service and comfortable surroundings", which are "just the job
after a cold stomp on Hampstead Heath". It seems to have taken in its
stride a long closure for a major refurb, including the addition of six
bedrooms, coming back "better than ever". / NW5 1QS;
www.thebullandlast.co.uk; @thebullandlast; Mon-Thu 11 pm, Fri & Sat midnight, Sun
10.30 pm; closed Fri & Sat D.*

Bund N2 NEW £34
4-5 Cheapside, Fortis Green 020 8365 2643 1–1B
*East Finchley tube is the closest to this November 2019 newcomer, north of
Muswell Hill – a contemporary, neighbourhood Pan Asian, trendily presenting
a mix of southeast Asian cuisines – "great Asian dishes which isn't just
limited to the stalwarts". / N2 9HP; bundrestaurant.co.uk; Thu-Sun 10 pm; closed
Thu-Sun L, closed Mon & Tue & Wed.*

Burger & Beyond E1 £49 **4 3 2**
147 Shoreditch High Street 020 3848 8860 13–1B
*This minimalist Shoreditch independent attracts superlatives for its burgers,
sides and funky drinks. While the eat-in diner is standalone, the business is
expanding via a delivery-only kitchen in Wandsworth and a nationwide
meal-kit operation, also rated "amazing – one of the best". Top Tip: "the
truffle fries". / E1 6JE; burgerandbeyond.co.uk; @burgerandbeyond.co.uk/shoreditch;
Mon-Thu 10 pm, Fri & Sat 11 pm, Sun 9.30 pm; closed Mon-Wed L.*

Burger & Lobster £66 **3 2 2**
Harvey Nichols, 109-125 Knightsbridge, SW1 020 7235 5000 6–1D
26 Binney St, W1 020 3637 5972 3–2A
29 Clarges St, W1 020 7409 1699 3–4B
36 Dean St, W1 020 7432 4800 5–2A
6 Little Portland St, W1 020 7907 7760 3–1C
18 Hertsmere Road, E14 020 3637 6709 12–1C
40 St John St, EC1 020 7490 9230 10–1B
52 Threadneedle Street, EC2 020 7256 9755 10–2C NEW
Bow Bells Hs, 1 Bread St, EC4 020 7248 1789 10–2B
"Both the burgers and the lobster rolls attract long queues for a reason –

they are very good", agree fans of this 10-year-old surf 'n' turf chain that has expanded to nine branches across the capital and a growing list around the world. "Prices are up sharply since launch though, so they're not quite the value they once were" – nor are they as straightforward, with the initial flat price of £20 morphing into a more conventional menu of burgers and assorted seafood. The value offer now is in the "stunning lobster rolls, which have redefined for me and others how lobster should best be served" – so "stick to the lobster for good quality at a reasonable price". The chain and its equally American-style stablemate Goodman steakhouses were founded and are still owned by Moscow-based Misha Zelman. / www.burgerandlobster.com; @Londonlobster.

Busaba £56 3️⃣2️⃣3️⃣
This modern Thai-fusion chain still wins solid ratings for its "great food from an ever-changing menu", but lack of feedback suggests waning enthusiasm for its nine sites across London. Founded in 1999 by Alan Yau as a follow-up to Wagamama, his global smash hit, it was forced to close its branches outside the capital a few years ago. / www.busaba.com; @busabaeathai.

Butlers Wharf Chop House SE1 £81 2️⃣2️⃣4️⃣
36e Shad Thames 020 7403 3403 10–4D
Known for its "great view" of nearby Tower Bridge and menu of British carnivore classics ("it serves what it says: meat, meat, meat, with limited veggie choice)" – this D&D venue was conceived by the late Sir Terence Conran as part of his 1990s 'Gastrodrome' food complex. A typical assessment of the food is that results are "OK for work purposes, but expensive". A big plus in the era of outdoor dining was that the terrace is "comfortable and warm" even in cooler months, thanks to "heaters that really work!". / SE1 2YE; www.chophouse-restaurant.co.uk; @BWChophouse; Mon-Sat 10 pm, Sun 9 pm.

Buvette W11 NEW £48 3️⃣3️⃣4️⃣
9 Blenheim Crescent 020 7229 8398 7–1A
"A recent addition to Notting Hill – the London branch of an NYC original" – this cute 'gastrothèque' breezed into town in December 2020 via other spin-offs in Paris and Tokyo. In early reports, it's best supported for its breakfast and brunch potential (from 8am, with croques, and scrambled egg also available on the later all-day menu), but – as the name hints – the long list of wines, beers, cocktails, cidres and other imbibements forms much of the offering. / W11 1NN; ilovebuvette.com/eat-drink-london-location; Mon-Sun 11 pm.

Byron £41 1️⃣2️⃣2️⃣
The jury is still out on whether this once-trailblazing posh burger chain deserves to be saved, and indeed whether saving it is feasible. Having undergone a CVA in 2018, in June 2020 the chain brought in the administrators, who sold the brand to new owners Calveton. In the process, it lost 31 restaurants and 651 workers, leaving only 20 of Byron's 51 branches open. In May 2021, it opened its first new branch in five years on the Wembley retail park and soon after announced a new CEO. Meanwhile our reporters are in two minds about the whole situation. Even fans can find it "formulaic" although they feel "it's everything you need from a burger joint without trying too hard". Critics, though, find "there's not much to commend" in its current performance: "dreadful". / www.byronhamburgers.com.

C&R Café W1 £32 4️⃣3️⃣2️⃣
3-4 Rupert Court 020 7434 1128 4–3D
It's "nothing special to look at, down an alleyway" in Chinatown, but "you must go here for the fantastic Malaysian food" – including "the best Singapore laksa ever". This family-run diner was established in 1998, serving classic Malaysian-Chinese dishes including nasi goreng and beef rendang. (Its former sibling in Westbourne Grove became a Japanese izakaya before closing down during the pandemic.) / W1D 6DY; www.cnrcaferestaurant.com; Sun-Thu 10 pm, Fri & Sat 11 pm.

Cabotte EC2 £71 4 5 4
48 Gresham St 020 7600 1616 10–2C

"A great restaurant in the heart of the City of London" is a very rare thing, and one its adherents are happy to shout about. "Owned and run by two Master Sommeliers" – Xavier Rousset and Gearoid Devaney – it boasts a "superb Burgundy-centric wine list", supported by a "limited but very well cooked menu" from chef Edward Boarland, and "welcoming, unfussy service with a smile". "It's one of the best bets in the City and people are catching on". Top Tip: "the amazing tarte tatin to share". / EC2V 7AY; www.cabotte.co.uk; @Cabotte_; Mon-Fri 10 pm; closed Sat & Sun.

The Cadogan Arms SW3 £51
298 King's Road 020 3148 2630 6–3C

The PR for this newly relaunched King's Road pub says it's a 'much-loved institution', but we hadn't heard of it before its mid-2021 relaunch. Still, it's got a prime Chelsea location; it's got a fine restored interior (dating from 1838); and it's got strong backing, with investors led by Dominic Jacobs of The Running Horse Mayfair and Jyotin, Karam & Sunaina Sethi, of JKS Restaurants. The culinary team has splendid form too – Kitchen Table's James Knappett is collaborating with chef Alex Harper, who has The Ledbury and The Harwood Arms on his CV. / SW3 5UG; thecadoganarms.london.

Cafe Cecilia E8 NEW
Canal Place, 32 Andrews Road 0203 478 6726 14–2B

Down by the canal in Hackney, this new café is part of the new WME8 development. Opened in August 2021, it's the work of Dubliner Max Rocha (an ex-River Café chef and son of Irish fashion designer John Rocha) who has run a series of supper clubs in recent years. Breakfast (with Guinness bread and potato cake advertising his origins) is served from 9am, then it's on to fairly simple lunches (onglet and chips, rabbit tagliatelle…), with dinner opening promised for later in 2021. / E8 4RL; www.cafececilia.com; Wed-Sun 3.30 pm; closed Mon & Tue.

Café Deco WC1 NEW £51 3 2 2
43 Store Street 020 8091 2108 2–1C

Bloomsbury greasy spoon that's been artfully transformed into a simple bar and modern bistro by the team behind 40 Maltby Street, with Anna Tobias (P Franco, Rochelle Canteen) at the stoves. It was launched in December 2020 and won a big thumbs-up from Guardian reviewer Grace Dent, who – while noting that it "looks a bit like a sandwich shop with lofty aspirations" – found "finely judged, nicely eccentric cooking with a strong undercurrent of country-house living". Our early feedback is limited but similarly upbeat. / WC1E 7DB; www.cafe-deco.co.uk; Tue-Sat 9.30 pm; closed Sun & Mon; no Amex.

Café du Marché EC1 £54 3 3 5
22 Charterhouse Sq 020 7608 1609 10–1B

"A magic wand of romance is waved as you enter!" at this "seductive Gallic number" – "a classic little bistro", "tucked away down a cobbled lane in Clerkenwell" and occupying "cosy", ancient-feeling premises. In the early nineties it was one of London's better-known destinations, but nowadays it feels like "very much a hidden gem". Foodwise – "who said the classics can't be fun?"; its traditional offering delivers "consistently tasty food and an interesting little wine list". "The brilliant chaps playing live jazz in the corner on many evenings add much to the charm, character and ambience of the place". / EC1M 6DX; www.cafedumarche.co.uk; @cafedumarche; Mon-Sat 10 pm; closed Sat L, closed Sun.

Café in the Crypt, St Martin in the Fields WC2 £31 ②②**4**
Duncannon St   020 7766 1158   2–2C

For a "relaxed" bite in the West End, remember the charming "self-service" crypt of St Martin-in-the-Fields. It's basic scoff (soups, salads, daily hot dishes), but quick, well-priced, of decent quality and the setting is very characterful. / WC2N 4JJ; stmartin-in-the-fields.org/cafe-in-the-crypt; @smitf_london; Mon-Sat 6 pm, Sun 5 pm; closed Mon-Sun D; no Amex; May need 5+ to book.

Cafe Murano £70 ②**3**②
33 St James's St, SW1   020 3371 5559   3–3C
34 Tavistock Street, WC2   020 3535 7884   5–3D
36 Tavistock St, WC2   020 3371 5559   5–3D
184 Bermondsey Street, SE1   020 3985 1545   10–4D

Angela Hartnett's chain continues to split opinion in our annual diners survey. To their very many fans, these comfortable and well-located Italians (in Covent Garden, St James's, and now also in Borough) are a real "favourite" thanks to their "buzzy" atmosphere, staff who are "always friendly and helpful" and their "wonderful" trattoria food ("gutsy peasant-type dishes, including good pasta"). Even fans, though, can feel that "prices are only just about OK for the quality" and harsher sceptics just feel they "trade on the Murano name" with a formula that's just too "unimaginative". / www.cafemurano.co.uk.

Café Spice Namaste E16 £69
1-2 Lower Dock Walk, Royal Dock   020 7488 9242   12–1D

"I've been going to this unique Indian restaurant for the last 15 years and it always hits the spot for authentic Indian food" – that's the kind of loyalty inspired by Cyrus and Parvin Todiwala's well-known destination, which – when it had to close mid-pandemic – received the support of a crowdfunded appeal to secure its survival. In truth, the "outdated" old building was "looking tired", though it was buoyed up by an excellent welcome and Parsi and Goan-inspired cuisine that was regularly "exceptional". In late 2021, a re-opening is planned in a shiny new location in the distant Royal Docks, a short walk from Gallions Reach DLR station, five minutes' travel-time from Canary Wharf. / E16 2GT; www.cafespice.co.uk; @cafespicenamast.

Caffè Caldesi W1 £73 ②②②
118 Marylebone Ln   020 7487 0754   2–1A

"Just a delight" – this long-running Italian in a "nice location" on a Marylebone corner has spun out into a cookery school and a string of cookbooks from Tuscan-born chef Giancarlo Caldesi. But praise for its cooking was more reserved this year, with some feeling it is rather "standard and underwhelming" – maybe it's simply just too pricey. / W1U 2QF; www.caldesi.com; Mon-Sat 10.30 pm, Sun 4.30 pm; closed Sun D.

Cakes and Bubbles W1 £70 **3**4**4**
Hotel Cafe Royal, 10 Air St   020 7406 3310   4–4C

"I love the signature cheesecake… if only it came in a bigger size!". Albert Adria (pastry chef at one time at his brother Ferran's famous El Bulli) is the name behind this swish café on Regent's Street (now with an outside terrace too). For a blow-out sweet and glass of fizz, it's not cheap but well-rated. / W1B 4DY; www.cakesandbubbles.co.uk/; Mon-Sun 10 pm.

The Camberwell Arms SE5 £57 **4**3**3**
65 Camberwell Church St   020 7358 4364   1–3C

"Ever popular and always delicious" – this "absolutely fantastic" Camberwell gastropub has earned a reputation almost equal to that of its famous south London stablemate, the Anchor & Hope. It's a "great local spot" – "busy but welcoming" – "with generally excellent and ambitious food (we've had the occasional less successful plate, but the success rate is high)". / SE5 8TR; www.thecamberwellarms.co.uk; @camberwellarms; Tue-Sat 11 pm, Sun 5 pm; closed Sun D, closed Mon; Take bookings all week via phone and/or online.

Cambio de Tercio SW5 £75 444
161-163 Old Brompton Rd 020 7244 8970 6–2B
"Abel [Lusa] and his team have created one of London's best neighbourhood restaurants" at this Spanish specialist in the Old Brompton Road. The food is consistently *"fantastic"* *"(if pricey)"*, while service and ambience are also *"excellent"*. Since launching in 1995 – well before the boom in Hispanic cuisine – they have maintained impressively high scores, building *"a justifiably loyal clientele"*. / SW5 0LJ; www.cambiodetercio.co.uk; @CambiodTercio; Tue-Sat 11.30 pm, Sun & Mon 11 pm.

Camino £59 332
3 Varnishers Yd, Regent Quarter, N1 020 7841 7330 9–3C
2 Curtain Road, EC2 020 3948 5003 13–2B
15 Mincing Ln, EC3 020 7841 7335 10–3D
"You can't knock a place that does good morcilla" – and for *"great food that won't break the bank"*, the *"consistently high standards"* at this small Hispanic group win it a small but enthusiastic following. The Bankside branch closed since our last edition, leaving the King's Cross original, plus Shoreditch and Monument. / www.camino.uk.com.

Campania & Jones E2 £59 433
23 Ezra St 020 7613 0015 14–2A
"Outside tables in Columbia Road" help lend an air of rusticity to this former cowshed off Columbia Road Flower Market. The culinary focus is on the south of Italy, and with pasta made daily (including to buy retail), the thrust of our feedback: *"what's not to like?"*. / E2 7RH; www.campaniaandjones.com; Tue-Sat 11 pm, Sun 7 pm; closed Mon.

Canto Corvino E1 £72 333
21 Artillery Lane 020 7655 0390 13–2B
"A delight" – this modern Italian *"off the beaten track"* by Spitalfields Market offers *"tasty, well-presented food"* in a *"great atmosphere"* – and the *"pasta dishes are some of the best in the City"*. There's also an impressive list of wines, from the Italian regions and elsewhere. / E1 7HA; www.cantocorvino.co.uk; @cantocorvinoE1; Tue-Sat 9 pm; closed Sat L, closed Sun & Mon.

Canton Arms SW8 £50 433
177 South Lambeth Rd 020 7582 8710 11–1D
"A stand-out for a distinctive pub meal" (*"as you'd expect from the same stable as the Anchor & Hope"*) – an *"intriguing seasonal menu"* that's *"always different and surprising"* (*"watermelon gazpacho, anyone?"*) from chef Trish Hilferty helps keep this Stockwell boozer in our diners' Top 5 bars and pubs – *"it's no surprise Fergus Henderson is a regular"*. *"It's a proper pub, where you're as welcome for a pint as you are for a four-hour lunch (and Charlie the landlord kept it as a genuine centre of the community even during lockdown)"*. *"They have interesting tipples too made in situ"*. / SW8 1XP; www.cantonarms.com; @cantonarms; Tue-Sat 2.30 pm; closed Tue-Sat D, closed Sun & Mon; no Amex; no booking.

Caractère W11 £86 443
209 Westbourne Park Road 020 8181 3850 7–1B
"The food is the centrepiece" at Emily Roux (daughter of Michel) and her husband Diego Ferrari's (former head chef of Le Gavroche) *"gem tucked away in Notting Hill"*, which has established a strong foodie following. *"The French/Italian theme to the cooking works well"*, delivering *"strong flavours with a light touch"* from *"an interesting menu whose dishes are a little out of the ordinary"*. Service is *"fabulous and personal"* too, which helps make for *"a very special meal out"* in this comfortable, *"cosy"* space. *"Surely it's getting a star some time soon?"* / W11 1EA; www.caracterestaurant.com; Tue-Sat 9.45 pm; closed Sun & Mon; Take bookings all week via phone and/or online.

Caraffini SW1 £71 3 4 3
61-63 Lower Sloane St   020 7259 0235   6–2D
"An old mate who you love to see!" – this *"civilised"*, *"comfortable"* and *"buzzy"* Italian, south of Sloane Square, remains a huge favourite, and even though its heartland is Chelsea residents, fans come here from all points of the compass. "It is still the staff who make the place" – "everyone is greeted so enthusiastically" – but the "old-fashioned Italian cooking" is "always of a high standard" too (and there's also a "nice outside terrace"). / SW1W 8DH; www.caraffini.co.uk; Mon-Sat 10.30 pm; closed Sun.

Caravaggio EC3 £61 3 2 2
107-112 Leadenhall St   020 7626 6206   10–2D
A *"great standby for a business lunch"* – this stately but *"buzzy"* City Italian (declared open in 1996 by Luciano Pavarotti no less) is a well-known expense-accounter haven and wins solid all-round ratings for its *"excellent"* standards. Celebrate your return to the office with their new bottomless bubbles offer! / EC3A 4DP; www.caravaggiorestaurant.co.uk; Mon-Fri 10 pm; closed Sat & Sun.

Caravan £60 2 2 2
Yalding House, 152 Great Portland Street, W1   020 3963 8500   2–1B
1 Granary Sq, N1   020 7101 7661   9–3C
30 Great Guildford St, SE1   020 7101 1190   10–4B
11-13 Exmouth Mkt, EC1   020 7833 8115   10–1A
22 Bloomberg Arc, Queen Victoria St, EC4   020 3957 5555   10–3C
"OK I guess, but could be so much better" is an increasingly common view on this once-groundbreaking chain, where the feeling that *"it seems to have gone off a bit"* is most prevalent at the well-known Granary Square branch, which risks becoming *"a cheerless, so-so, fast-turnaround experience"*. At its best, though – mostly to be found at the EC1 original, with its *"great outside seating area and very relaxed atmosphere"* – the group remains popular for its *"innovative and delicious breakfasts"*: *"great sharing plates"* and *"something for everyone"* (which includes *"a good set of vegan and vegetarian alternatives"*). / www.caravanonexmouth.co.uk; @CaravanResto.

Carmel NW6 NEW
Lonsdale Road   1–2B
Coming in October 2021, from the team behind Berber & Q (Josh and Paul Katz and Mattia Bianchi) – a big sister restaurant in Queen's Park. The newcomer is to be more of an all-day operation, starting from breakfast, with an offering that evolves through the day. Seating will incorporate communal tables and a counter facing the open kitchen, where – as at its siblings – much of the cooking will be over a wood fire, delivering food (including flatbreads) with bold flavours from the Eastern Med and North Africa; there will also be a list of 60 wines curated by Bianchi. / NW6 6RR; www.carmelrestaurant.co.uk.

Carousel W1 £71
71 Blandford St   020 7487 5564   3–1A
"Innovative guest chefs from around the world", but also with gigs from local stars ("went solo on James Knappett night – how can they provide that level of cooking for £95, when he's normally £250+!") have won a major reputation for Ed and Ollie Templeton's one-of-a-kind revolving-residency venue. In August 2021, they announced they are on the move, closing their Marylebone site and taking over three Georgian townhouses on Fitzrovia's Charlotte Street. The expansive site will also house Carousel's own wine bar (open throughout the day), as well as a ten-seater incubator for new concepts and longer-term residencies, and separate spaces dedicated to private dining, workshops and events. / W1U 8AB; www.carousel-london.com; @Carousel_LDN; Tue-Sat midnight; closed Sun & Mon.

The Carpenter's Arms W6 £60 3|3|3
91 Black Lion Ln 020 8741 8386 8–2B
"Tucked away" in a backstreet off Hammersmith's St Peter's Square, this "top-end gastropub" is "a great place to chill out and eat better-than-average pub food", especially in summer when the "glorious, spacious back garden" really comes into its own. Even a reporter who – unusually – said the food "didn't quite hit the mark" thought the experience was "good value and well worth a return". / W6 9BG; www.carpentersarmsw6.co.uk; Mon-Fri 9 pm, Sun 6.30 pm; closed Sat; cards only.

Casa do Frango £49 4|3|4
32 Southwark Street, SE1 020 3972 2323 10–4C
3 King John Court, EC2 020 7654 3020 14–1B NEW
This "buzzy" yearling serves "tasty Portuguese tapas" and "grilled chicken, done to perfection" in the Algarve style, over charcoal with piri-piri seasoning. "Don't eat too much – the desserts are delicious as well", led by pastel de nata and a thick chocolate mousse. The Green Room is a 'secret' cocktail bar, and there's now a second branch with a large terrace between Great Eastern Street and Commercial Street in Shoreditch. / www.casadofrango.co.uk.

Casa Fofó E8 £73 5|4|4
158 Sandringham Road 020 8062 2489 14–1B
"Such a shame I moved from Hackney, so this fabulous place is no longer within walking distance!". Ex-Pidgin chef Adolfo de Cecco's "eclectic" cuisine is focused on a "chef-delivered tasting menu" and provides food that's "always interesting with wonderful flavours". Aside from all the "innovation", "the service offers that wonderful mixture of professionalism and friendliness which makes it such an enjoyable evening". / E8 2HS; www.casafofolondon.co.uk; Wed-Sun 9.30 pm; closed Wed-Fri L, closed Mon & Tue; no Amex.

Casa Pastór & Plaza Pastór N1 £73 3|2|3
Coal Drops Yard 020 7018 3335 9–3C
"Reliably magnificent" Mexico City-style street food has arrived in Coal Drops Yard, courtesy the Hart Bros' El Pastor brand, a big hit when it launched at Borough Market five years ago. The adjoining Plaza Pastór is the outdoor (but covered) branch. The "authentic" tortillas are freshly made every morning at the outfit's tortilleria in Bermondsey, using Mexican corn. / N1C 4AB; www.tacoselpastor.co.uk; @Tacos_El_Pastor; Tue-Thu 11 pm, Fri & Sat midnight, Sun 8 pm; closed Tue-Thu L, closed Mon.

Casacosta SW6 NEW
461-465 North End Road 020 3848 6830 6–4A
Roberto Costa – the man behind Macellaio RC – has reformatted his site near Fulham Broadway. Previously Ardiciocca (RIP), he relaunched it as this Italian deli and delivery company in October 2020. It incorporates a simple restaurant (lasagna, meatballs, veggie burger...), entered through a 'secret door' at the back of the shop. / SW6 1NZ; www.casacosta.co.uk; @casacostauk; Mon-Sat 9 pm, Sun 6 pm.

Casita Andina W1 £57
31 Great Windmill Street 020 3327 9464 4–3D
In July 2020, Martin Morales's original Redchurch Street branch shut up shop and has moved to this new, much larger 3,000 sq ft flagship on Commercial Street E1, which opened in May 2021. It's a seven-days-a-week operation with 80 covers and a pisco bar. No survey feedback as yet, but the hope is that it continues the excellent ceviches and other sunny Latino fare of its former location. / W1F 9UE; www.andinalondon.com/casita; @CasitaAndina; Mon-Thu 11 pm, Fri & Sat 11.30 pm, Sun 10 pm.

Casse-Croute SE1 £67 443
109 Bermondsey St   020 7407 2140   10–4D

"Splendid French food in a tiny bistro" that *"feels as near to Paris as is possible"* has made this Bermondsey fixture a hit with fans of old-school Gallic cuisine – the chalked-up daily menu is studded with such classics as escargots, canette de Châlons and millefeuille vanille. It's *"slightly tight for room"*, though, so do book. / SE1 3XB; www.cassecroute.co.uk; @CasseCroute109; Mon-Sat 11 pm, Sun 5 pm; closed Sun D.

Cavita W1 NEW
55 Wigmore Street   3–1A

Mexican-born star chef Adriana Cavita completes her pop-up at the Dorchester Rooftop to open her first permanent London venture in November 2021: a 70-cover site with an open-fire kitchen, communal dining (hosted by Adriana herself) and a chef's table (plus a basement mezcaleria with its own street entrance). The cuisine is Mexican (obvs). / W1U 1PU; www.cavitarestaurant.com; Thu-Sat 9 pm, Sun 3 pm.

Cay Tre £47 333
42-43 Dean St, W1   020 7317 9118   5–2A
301 Old St, EC1   020 7729 8662   13–1B

This Vietnamese duo in Soho and Hoxton are a good bet for *"hugely tasty"* and *"great-value"* southeast Asian food. Founder Hieu Trung Bui has been a major force in popularising Vietnamese cuisine in the capital for 20 years; he also owns Viet Grill in Shoreditch and the three Keu delis, specialising in 'banh mi' (stuffed baguettes). / www.caytrerestaurant.co.uk; @CayTreLondon.

Cecconi's £94 224
19-21 Old Compton Street, W1   020 7734 5656   5–2A
5a Burlington Gdns, W1   020 7434 1500   4–4A
58-60 Redchurch Street, E2   020 3841 7755   13–1C
The Ned, 27 Poultry, EC2   020 3828 2000   10–2C

"A table at the bar is always fun" at the original Cecconi's – a sophisticated Italian brasserie, tucked away off Bond Street, which in particular is brunch central – *"a comfortable place to have your coffee, eggs and Sunday Times… and to people-watch"*. As ever here, though, it can all seem too pricey: a case of *"style over substance"*, or somewhere that's *"fine… but just fine"*. And then there's the question of judging the less commented-on brand extensions embarked on by owners Soho House. None of them inspire a huge volume of feedback but it's all good, be it for the outlet at the City's Ned Hotel, the *"always enjoyable"* neighbourhood spot in Shoreditch, or the Soho pizzeria (*"always a great buzz"*). / cecconis.co.uk.

Celeste at The Lanesborough SW1 £131 225
Hyde Park Corner   020 7259 5599   6–1D

For sheer grandeur, it's hard to match this sweeping, spacious chamber, to the rear of this five-star landmark on Hyde Park Corner, where head chef Giuseppe Strippoli produces a luxurious series of menus – from about £90 per head – in a classic modern European style. For these troubles, he holds a Michelin star, although the venue generates relatively little feedback in our diner survey, amidst some ongoing concerns that *"whilst a very good standard, pricing can seem OTT in comparison with other top hotels"*. In fact, it – and the nearby 'Withdrawing Room' – are more heartily recommended for a push-the-boat-out afternoon tea, which comes with a piano accompaniment at weekends in Celeste. / SW1X 7TA; www.oetkercollection.com/hotels/the-lanesborough/restaurants-bars/restaurants/celeste/; @TheLanesborough; Mon-Sun 10 pm; No shorts; Take bookings all week via phone and/or online.

Cent Anni SW19 £55 **3 3 3**
33 High Street   020 3971 9781   11–2B
"An uncomplicated menu" of "lovely Italian food" – "efficiently served, in a friendly atmosphere" – is the verdict on this large (100 seats) three-year-old in Wimbledon Village. "While not designed as specifically family-friendly, the staff are very welcoming and it works just fine" with kids – and there is plenty of pizza and pasta to choose from. / SW19 5BY; centanni.co.uk; Mon-Sat 11 pm, Sun 10.30 pm.

Ceru £38 **4 4 4**
7-9 Bute St, SW7   020 3195 3001   6–2C
13 Queensway, W2   020 7221 2535   7–2C **NEW**
"Innovative and delicious Lebanese/Middle-Eastern cooking" has firmly established Barry and Patricia Hilton's nattily decorated modern bistro in the 'Petit France' enclave close to South Kensington's museums. "It's great to see them back in action – they've tweaked the menu and the food is even more delicious". "Fabulous service, too". The venture started out with a series of pop-ups, and a second bistro that started off in Soho transferred to Queensway in summer 2021. / www.cerurestaurants.com; @CeruLondon.

Ceviche £66 **4 3 4**
17 Frith St, W1   020 7292 2040   5–2A
Alexandra Trust, Baldwin St, EC1   020 3327 9463   13–1A
The "delicious" Peruvian flavours at Martin Morales's "atmospheric and reliable" cantina in Soho "set those taste buds on fire" – and "the pisco sours are great". The restaurant celebrates its 10th anniversary this year (while its stablemate Andina has relocated from Shoreditch to Spitalfields). Top Tip: "the Don Ceviche is an absolute must". / www.cevicheuk.com; @cevicheuk.

Cha Cha x Sister Jane W10 **NEW** £45
36 Golborne Road   020 3866 0543   7–1A
Burnt oranges, creams and walnut decor (from groovy designers Sella) aim to evoke the '70s at this retro Notting Hillbilly store, where a bite in the ground-floor restaurant is a warm up for browsing the vintage-style clothing from Sister Jane above. The funky, Latin-American inspired bites are created by ex-Chiltern Firehouse chef Kai Rykowski, and the Cha Cha team runs a bar on the rooftop, too. (Cha Cha also operates at Mayair's Mercato Metropolitano, and used to have a bar in Maida Vale, now RIP). / W10 5PR; www.sisterjane.com/; Mon 6 pm; closed Mon D, closed Tue-Sat & Sun.

Chameleon NW1 **NEW** £41
One Marylebone, 1 Marylebone Road   020 7101 4924   9–4B
'One Marylebone' – an event space run by One Events – occupies the former Grade I listed Holy Trinity Church (designed by Sir John Soane). It is morphing for the time being into more of a conventional restaurant operation. The starting point came in May 2021 with a 'Tel Avivian sharing-style outdoor restaurant' from Isreali chef (and ex-NYC's Alenbi) Elior Balbur, set in nine individual greenhouses. Other features will include a tented garden lounge, silent cinema, 'magical wellness sessions', weekend market, fitness centre, dance classes, gallery and private members' club. On a June 2021 visit, The Sunday Times's Marina O'Loughlin raved: "stellar", "thrilling", "considered", "irresistible". / NW1 4AQ; chameleon.london; Wed-Sat 11 pm, Sun 6 pm; closed Wed-Fri L closed Sun D, closed Mon & Tue; Jacket required; Take bookings all week via phone and/or online.

Charlie at Brown's, Brown's Hotel W1 £93 3 4 3

Albemarle Street   020 7493 6020   3–3C

Chef-director Adam Byatt (of Clapham's exceptional Trinity) is the latest incumbent of this splendidly traditional panelled chamber in one of Mayfair's landmark hotels, which has seen a succession of occupants come and go over the years. On its 2019 launch it inspired up-and-down press critiques, but all our (admittedly limited) feedback in the current survey was very complimentary about Matthew Starling's modern European cuisine, and in September 2021 a long-time maître d' at Le Caprice, Jesus Adorno, joins the team to add further sparkle. / WIS;
www.roccofortehotels.com/hotels-and-resorts/browns-hotel/restaurants-and-bars/charlies /; @Browns_Hotel; Mon-Sat 10 pm, Sun 4 pm; closed Sun D.

The Cheese Barge W2 NEW £36 2 3 3

Sheldon Square   07862 001418   7–1C

"Bit of a one-trick pony… but we knew that!". Not satisfied with opening a cheese bar and the world's first cheese conveyor belt, Matthew Carver has taken his theme one step further: a barge – hand-crafted in Somerset no less – to create a two-storey, 40-cover restaurant with outside terrace permanently moored in Paddington Basin and officially launched (after two previous attempts) in June 2021. Its honest British dishes incorporate many small producer cheeses, and feedback suggests results are dependable, with the Guardian's Grace Dent reporting 'cheesy stupefaction… silly, but fun'. / W2 6HY; www.thecheesebar.com/paddington; @thecheesebarldn; Tue-Sat 11 pm, Sun 6.15 pm; closed Sun D, closed Mon.

Chelsea Cellar SW10 £51 4 4 4

9 Park Walk   020 7351 4933   6–3B

This "lovely little basement local", hidden behind an "easy-to-miss entrance" near Chelsea & Westminster Hospital, serves "excellent Italian fare at acceptable prices" in a usually expensive part of town. There's also "a fantastic assortment of wine", and the real clincher is that it doesn't cost an arm and a leg to buy it. Top tip: "a delicious burrata to start, followed by fantastic pasta is a real winner". / SW10 0AJ; www.thechelseacellar.co.uk; @chelseacellar; Tue-Sat 11.30 pm; closed Tue-Sat L, closed Sun & Mon.

Chez Bruce SW17 £95 5 4 3

2 Bellevue Rd   020 8672 0114   11–2C

"The kind of restaurant that makes you want to celebrate more often" – Bruce Poole's south London legend was voted London's favourite by our diners for the 16th year running. Reflecting its neighbourhood appearance and location (by Wandsworth Common), it is "as near to a home-from-home as a luxury London restaurant can be", while features noted in feedback over many years have been its "honest and ungimmicky" approach, "unpretentious staff", "lack of crazy prices" and the fact that it "never lets you down" (also, to be fair, that the interior is "slightly cramped"). The deceptively simple modern British cuisine (for the last 10 years from head chef Matt Christmas) is in a similar vein: the menu – "always full of dishes you really want to eat" – "has a good mixture of classics and seasonal, more modern dishes" and "the pared-back flavour combinations allow the nuances of each ingredient to be identified and savoured". "We leave with a smile on our face every time". / SW17 7EG; www.chezbruce.co.uk; @ChezBruce; Tue-Thu 9.15 pm, Fri & Sat 9.30 pm, Sun 9 pm; closed Mon.

Chez Elles E1 £61 4 4 4

45 Brick Ln   020 7247 9699   13–2C

"Like a rip in the fabric of space-time, transplanting a perfect Paris bistro to Brick Lane" – just the job for a quick French onion soup or plate of snails. / E1 6PU; www.chezellesbistroquet.co.uk; @chezellesbistro; Tue-Sat 10.30 pm; closed Tue, Wed L, closed Sun & Mon.

Chicama SW10 £75 3 2 3
383 King's Road   020 3874 2000   6–3C
"Bursting with fresh, clean flavours", the "amazing" seafood at this "buzzy" King's Road outfit has converted many to the delights of ceviche and other "delicious" Peruvian specialities in recent years. It is an offshoot of Pachamama in Marylebone. / SW10 0LP; www.chicamalondon.com; @chicamalondon; Mon-Sun 11 pm; Take bookings all week via phone and/or online.

Chick 'n' Sours £47 3 3 3
1 Earlham Street, WC2   020 3198 4814   5–2B
62 Upper Street, N1   020 7704 9013   9–3D
14 Artillery Passage, E1   020 8106 1149   13–2C **NEW**
390 Kingsland Rd, E8   020 3620 8728   14–2A
"I'm completely addicted to the unique blend of fried chicken with a range of light and fresh, or even rich and unctious, Asian flavours!" say fans of these pit stops in Haggerston and Covent Garden. "Takeaways were a revelation during lockdown – the delicious chicken burgers travel pretty well". A third branch in Spitalfields was still 'temporarily closed' due to Covid-19 in September 2021. / www.chicknsours.co.uk; @chicknsours.

Chilli Cool WC1 £38 4 2 1
15 Leigh St   020 7383 3135   2–1D
"A basic restaurant with many fiery dishes" – this student-friendly canteen in Bloomsbury is known for its good prices and lip-tingling Sichuan noodle dishes. / WC1H 9EW; www.chillicool.co.uk; Mon-Sun 10 pm; no Amex.

The Chiltern Firehouse W1 £101 1 2 3
1 Chiltern St   020 7073 7676   2–1A
"A place to be a guest, not the host!" – this splashy Marylebone scene still attracts "the smart set" on account of its gorgeous decor and "stunning gardens", but over half of reports on it are votes as London's most overpriced restaurant. "The food takes second place to the venue", while service – though friendlier than in its heyday – "can at times be rather amateurish". All in all, it's "a pleasant enough place, but £80 a head for a one-course Sunday brunch is a bit much. More than a bit much, in fact…". / W1U 7PA; www.chilternfirehouse.com; Mon-Sat 10.30 pm, Sun 10 pm.

China Tang, Dorchester Hotel W1 £100 3 3 4
53 Park Ln   020 7319 7088   3–3A
Although the late Sir David Tang's recreation of Art Deco-era Shanghai in the basement of this famous five-star continues to inspire mention of its 'arm-and-a-leg' prices, even those who noted its "eye watering expense" this year thought a trip here was "worth it". In fact, reporters have become more appreciative in recent years of its classic Cantonese offering, which includes dim sum at both lunch and dinner (the best bet for keeping the bill manageable). In the afternoon, there is also the option of a Cantonese Afternoon Tea. If you want to check it out, start with a cocktail in the superbly evocative bar. / W1K 1QA; www.chinatanglondon.co.uk; @ChinaTangLondon; Thu-Sun 11 pm; closed Mon & Tue & Wed.

La Chingada SE8 **NEW** £14 5 4 3
206 Lower Road   020 7237 7448   12–2B
If you live in Surrey Quays – or go bonkers for Mexican cuisine – consider a diversion to this small hole in the wall (take away and just a few stools). The pay-off is particularly authentic tacos, tortillas and other Mexican scoff: one early report says it's "outstanding" and The Standard's Jimi Famurewa said it was 'One of the most exhilarating food discoveries of the year'. / SE8 5DJ; lachingada.co.uk; Tue-Sat 10 pm, Sun 9 pm; closed Mon.

Chishuru SW9 NEW   **£45**   4 4 3
Unit 9 Market Row   07960 002150   11–2D
"Wow! What amazing, punchy and exciting food" – 'contemporary West African cuisine with a foundation of age-old recipes and techniques', using British ingredients, is the promise at Nigerian-born Adejoké 'Joké' Bakare's August 2020 newcomer in Brixton's Market Row. It's the new forever home of her supperclub, which won the Brixton Kitchen competition in 2019. Early feedback says it's "highly recommended: the tiny room is very basic, but that means nothing gets in the way of enjoying the wonderful hospitality of the owner and her team!". / SW9 8LB; www.chishuru.com; @chishuru; Tue-Sat 10.30 pm; closed Tue-Thu L, closed Sun & Mon.

Chisou   **£72**   3 2 2
22-23 Woodstock Street, W1   020 7629 3931   4–1A
31 Beauchamp Pl, SW3   020 3155 0005   6–1D
"Absolutely spot-on sushi" tops the bill at this "upmarket, though friendly" pair in Mayfair and Knightsbridge, where "the food is absolutely at a level you would expect in Japan". "Perfectly fresh raw fish, light and crunchy tempura, great wine with attentive and flexible service" make the Mayfair original "a reliable choice just off the fray of Oxford Street". / www.chisourestaurant.com.

Chook Chook SW15   4 3 3
137 Lower Richmond Road   020 8789 3100   11–1B
"A great addition to the Lower Richmond Road" – numerous Putney residents are heartily enthusiastic about this September 2019 addition and it's become "a favourite Indian that can always be relied upon". / SW15 1EZ; chookchook.uk; Mon-Thu 10.30 pm, Fri & Sat 11 pm, Sun 10 pm; closed Mon-Fri L.

Chotto Matte W1   **£79**   4 3 4
11-13 Frith St   020 7042 7171   5–2A
Loud and lively late-night Nikkei (Peruvian-Japanese fusion) haunt that's "a great spot for watching Soho" – and the food is "awesome" too. "You have to book in advance because it's usually very full". For a more wallet-friendly option earlier in the day, order a bento box with "a little bit of everything – highly recommended". In September 2021 the brand announced a second branch in Marylebone Village, to open in January 2022. / W1D 4RB; www.chotto-matte.com; @ChottoMatteLDN; Mon-Sat 1.30 am, Sun midnight.

Chriskitch N10   **£44**   4 3 3
7a Tetherdown   020 8411 0051   1–1C
An August 2021 Insta post saying 'we're hiring' helps inspire confidence that this neighbourhood fixture in Muswell Hill – known for its "fantastic selection of cakes", brunches and other interesting salads and snacks – is soon to return after a long period of closure during the pandemic. (On that basis, we've maintained its rating on our guesstimate that it will continue as before). / N10 1ND; www.chriskitch.com; @chriskitchfood; Sat-Mon 5 pm, Tue-Fri 6 pm; closed Sat-Mon & Tue-Fri D; May need 3+ to book.

Christopher's WC2   **£89**   2 2 3
18 Wellington St   020 7240 4222   5–3D
A Covent Garden mansion that once housed a bordello is now the "beautiful setting" for an all-day American restaurant and cocktail bar of 30 years' standing. It tends to fly under the radar these days, although is still "great for pre- or post-theatre", but its steaks and martinis are overshadowed by the "amazing pancake and French toast options" served for brunch until 4pm, which are "totally delicious" – and "the pecan pie is to die for!". / WC2E 7DD; www.christophersgrill.com; @ChristophersWC2; Tue-Thu midnight, Fri & Sat 1.30 am, Sun 5 pm; closed Sun D, closed Mon; May need 6+ to book.

Chucs £94 2 3 4
25 Eccleston Street, SW1   020 3827 3000   2–4B NEW
65 Lower Sloane Street, SW1   020 3827 2999   6–2D NEW
31 Dover St, W1   020 3763 2013   3–3C
97 Old Brompton Road, SW7   020 8037 4525   6–2B
226 Westbourne Grove, W11   020 7243 9136   7–1B

Aiming for a taste of La Dolce Vita lifestyle, these retro-glam Italian cafés and restaurants mostly occupy the same sites as the eponymous clothing brand, and deliver classic casual Italian menus mixing pizza and pasta (both typically over £20 a plate) with both more and less substantial dishes. A brief involvement with Zaha Hadid's Serpentine restaurant has ended, but a new, sixth branch debuted in July 2021 in the heart of St John's Wood (on the site of a former Côte). With 84 covers, it's the largest outlet to-date and opens all day from breakfast. / www.chucsrestaurants.com.

Chuku's N15 NEW £31
274 High Road   1–1D

"Chop, chat, chill" is the motto at this much-reviewed February 2020 newcomer – a family-owned homage to Nigerian cuisine in an upbeat, pink-walled 35-seater in Seven Sisters (Tottenham). It's the crowd-funded forever home of brother and sister team Emeka and Ifeyinwa Frederick, serving big-flavoured West African dishes in a tapas format, washed down with gluggable cocktails and an Afrobeats soundtrack. / N15 4RR; www.chukuslondon.co.uk; @chukusLDN; Thu-Sat 10.30 pm, Sun 8 pm; closed Thu & Fri L, closed Mon & Tue & Wed.

Church Road SW13 £60 4 4 3
94 Church Road   020 8748 0393   11–1A

"A great neighbourhood site (it was Sonny's, RIP for many years) that just keeps getting better and better" – this linchpin Barnes restaurant was refitted and relaunched in late 2019 (under the same owner, Rebecca Mascarenhas, who is still in partnership here with chef Phil Howard) and has subsequently "emerged strongly from the pandemic". "Phil Howard and his team have taken this place to an entirely different level" and – even if "prices are a little high" – regularly produce "fabulous" modern British cuisine in a more ambitious and accomplished vein than the neighbourhoody experience of the Sonny's of old. "No need to open Hammersmith Bridge to get to central London now for those of us in SW13!". / SW13 0DQ; www.churchroadsw13.co.uk; Wed-Sat 10.30 pm, Sun 9.30 pm; closed Wed-Sat L, closed Mon & Tue.

Churchill Arms W8 £44 3 3 4
119 Kensington Church St   020 7792 1246   7–2B

A landmark on Ken Church Street for generations (it claims Sir Winston's grandparents as regulars in the 1800s) – one feature of this flower-bedecked pub is a dining annex that's served "generous portions of delicious Thai curry at surprisingly low prices" for the best part of 30 years. "Dining among a mass of indoor plants and knick-knacks completes the experience". / W8 7LN; www.churchillarmskensington.co.uk; @ChurchillArmsW8; Mon-Sat 11 pm, Sun midnight.

Chutney Mary SW1 £84 3 3 3
73 St James's Street   020 7629 6688   3–4D

The "creative menu, intriguing spices and beautiful interior" ensure this "outstanding" St James's restaurant remains at the forefront of "excellent modern Indian food" – "despite increasingly stiff competition". "Moving from Chelsea five years ago did not diminish the appeal – in fact, the decor is more glamorous and the food more refined than ever" – although one or two reporters question whether it's still "worth the prices". / SW1A 1PH; www.chutneymary.com; @RealIndianFood; Sun-Wed 9.30 pm, Thu-Sat 10 pm; closed Mon L.

Chutneys NW1 £23 3 3 2
124 Drummond St   020 7388 0604   9–4C

"The dosas are always tasty and good value" at this cheap 'n' cheerful café in the 'Little India' near Euston station, which has made a feature of an 'all-you-can-eat' vegetarian lunch buffet for many moons now. / NW1 2PA; www.chutneyseuston.uk; Mon-Sun 11 pm; no Amex; May need 5+ to book.

Ciao Bella WC1 £50 3 3 4
86-90 Lamb's Conduit St   020 7242 4119   2–1D

This *"robust and lively"* Bloomsbury fixture, which celebrates its 40th anniversary next year, *"feels like you're really in Italy"* with its *"great food and atmosphere"* – and it *"can't be beaten for cheap and cheerful"*. *"I had my 40th here just before lockdown – a long table for 30 people – and it was wonderful"*. It's a *"fun, noisy place, ideal for a group of friends, not a date"* – although nobody told Boris Johnson, who wooed Jennifer Arcuri here over chips and red wine when he was mayor of London. / WC1N 3LZ; www.ciaobellarestaurant.co.uk; @CiaobellaLondon; Mon-Sat 10.45 pm, Sun 10.30 pm.

Cibo W14 £59 4 4 3
3 Russell Gdns   020 7371 6271   8–1D

"Always good for a special occasion" – this family-run Italian between Olympia and Holland Park has maintained the highest standards for more than 20 years – and shows little sign of relaxing into veteran status. Still a *"slick operation in terms of food presentation and service"*, it is a *"really lovely place to eat, with good-quality food and wine"*. / W14 8EZ; www.ciborestaurant.net; Mon-Sat 9.45pm; closed Mon-Sat L, closed Sun.

Cigalon WC2 £51 3 4 4
115 Chancery Lane   020 7242 8373   2–2D

You dine in an airy former auction room with a glass ceiling at this legal-land restaurant in Chancery Lane, whose brief is *"delicious"* Provençal cuisine and a *"wine list full of wonderful surprises"* – many of them from the South of France or Corsica. The set menus offer *"very good value"* for the quality and locality, and a downstairs cocktail bar, Baranis, has indoor pétanque to transport you to the Riviera. Founded in 2010, it is part of Pascal Aussignac's Club Gascon group. / WC2A 1PP; www.cigalon.co.uk; @cigalon_london; Tue-Fri 9.45 pm; closed Mon, Sat & Sun.

Cin Cin W1 NEW £36
21a Foley St   020 7436 0921   2–1B

The 25-seat terrace of this small Fitzrovia corner site – previously Bonnie Gull (RIP) – opened first at this April 2021 newcomer: the first spin-off from the well-known Brighton duo of the same name. The outside is actually a bigger space than the tightly packed 20-seat interior, open a month or so later. No survey feedback as yet, but Marina O'Loughlin from The Sunday Times gave its 'topically brief' menu (four choices for each course) from chef Jamie Halsall a thumbs-up. / W1; www.cincin.co.uk/london/; @cincinuk; Tue-Sat 11.30 pm; closed Sun & Mon; No shorts.

Cincinnati Chilibomb EC2 NEW £19
26 Curtain Road   07910 010210   13–2B

Tim Brice, aka 'Captain Chilli', bravely launched London's first dedicated Cincinnati-style chili restaurant in February 2021. It occupies the small (40 seats) former Shoreditch premises of Rök (RIP). Part of the vogue for Americana-driven menus, Tim has developed a chili-filled brioche 'bombshell' for his new venture. Each batch is three days in the making and – the coup de grâce – you inject your Chilibomb with a syringe of chili-infused oil to get the level of heat that you desire. No survey feedback as yet, but The Telegraph's William Sitwell declared it: *"nuts, but if you feel the need for a mad, crazy time and enjoy the catharsis of blowing your head off, your table awaits"*. / EC2A 3NY; www.cincinnatichilibomb.co.uk; Tue-Sat 11 pm; closed Sun & Mon.

Cinder NW3 NEW £63 3 2 2
66 Belsize Lane 020 7435 8048 9–2A

"A tiny new kid on the block" – this Belsize Park newcomer from chef Jake Finn has 16 seats inside matched by a similar number outside. *"All the food is cooked over wood flames"* on a Josper grill, with influences from lots of sunny countries all over the world (including Peru, Japan, Italy, France and Greece). Not all locals are dazzled *("not as hot as reported")*, but most say results are *"fabulous"* – *"everything tastes good and shares well, delicious lamb, beef, bream, and lots of delicious veggie plates"*. / NW3 5BJ; www.cinderrestaurant.co.uk; Tue-Sat 10 pm, Sun 3 pm; closed Sun D, closed Mon; cards only.

Cinnamon Bazaar WC2 £54 4 3 4
28 Maiden Lane 020 7395 1400 5–4D

"Amazing Indian street food", *"in a fun, vibrant environment"* – this Covent Garden café provides *"a cheaper alternative to the other Cinnamon restaurants"*, with *"lots of small contemporary Indian dishes"* that mirror the quality of its pricier stablemates. There's a *"great early-evening set menu"* for theatre- and opera-goers. / WC2E 7NA; www.cinnamon-bazaar.com; @Cinnamon_Bazaar; Mon-Sun 11 pm; Take bookings all week via phone and/or online.

The Cinnamon Club SW1 £79 3 3 4
Old Westminster Library, Great Smith St 020 7222 2555 2–4C

"Amazing surroundings in the old Westminster Library, a stone's throw from the Houses of Parliament", provide a *"very stately"* backdrop to a meal at Vivek Singh's acclaimed venue – still one of London's best-known and most impressively located destinations. *"Start with cinnamon-based cocktails"* in the bar and then progress to the *"gourmet-level"* cuisine, which has *"flavour packed into every morsel"*. Amongst quibbles this year was the odd dish that *"lacked zip"* and a feeling that all the grandeur can feel *"sterile"*. But the final verdict – *"this is true high-end Indian dining"*. / SW1P 3BU; www.cinnamonclub.com; @cinnamonclub; Mon-Sat 11 pm; closed Sun; No trainers; booking max 14 may apply; SRA-Food Made Good – 2 stars.

Cinnamon Kitchen £62 3 2 2
4 Arches Lane, SW11 020 3955 5480 11–1C
9 Devonshire Sq, EC2 020 7626 5000 10–2D

Vivek Singh's *"interesting and innovative"* Indian duo still inspire their numerous fans with *"delicious"* Indian dishes; and the EC2 branch also has the benefit of a *"lovely 'outside' space"* (in fact within a large atrium) that's *"unexpected"* given its Square Mile location. Its three-year-old sibling is within the new Battersea Power Station complex. Even some fans, though, have found both locations *"less interesting that they were"* of late, with incidents of *"atrocious"* service a particular drag on the general mood. Hopefully, this is a temporary post-pandemic blip – the historic performance here has been consistently good. / www.cinnamon-kitchen.com; @CinnamonKitchen.

Circolo Popolare W1 £55 3 3 4
40 Rathbone Square 5–1A

"More fun per pound (£) than anywhere else in London". Big Mamma group's *"completely mad"* Fitzrovian is long on ambience and – so long as you don't mind consuming a week's worth of cream in one sitting – *"so much the better for it"*, especially if you want to record the outsize plates of simple Italian scoff on Instagram. Even spoilsports who feel *"the food doesn't really warrant the queue and the hype"* feel that *"the overall experience is pleasant and it's not bad value for money given the location"*. / W1T 1HX; www.bigmammagroup.com/en/trattorias/circolo-popolare; @bigmammagroup; Mon-Thu 10.45 pm, Fri & Sat 11 pm, Sun 10.30 pm.

Citro N6   3 3 2
15A Swain's Lane   07840 917586   9–1B
Family-run "cheap 'n' cheerful" Highgate Italian that majors in pizza and pasta plus a variety of small dishes. "Went in for a quick bite and have gone back many times since as care is taken with small details". In summer, "eating outside in the sunshine is a real treat". / N6 6QX; www.eatcitro.com; Tue-Sat 10 pm, Sun 5 pm; closed Tue L closed Sun D, closed Mon.

City Barge W4   £68   3 3 3
27 Strand-on-the-Green   020 8994 2148   1–3A
"On a summer's day, the outside riverside tables are delightful" at this consistently well-rated gastropub overlooking the Thames at Strand-on-the-Green, Chiswick. "And on a cold/wet day, the dining room is pretty good, too!". / W4 3PH; www.citybargechiswick.com; @citybargew4; Mon-Fri 10 pm, Sun 9 pm, Sat 10.30 pm.

City Social EC2   £109   3 3 3
Tower 42 25 Old Broad St   020 7877 7703   10–2C
"The views of London from Tower 42 are spectacular", and there's plenty more to please visitors to Jason Atherton's 24th-floor City venue – not least "a great menu of outstanding food, knowledgeable staff and consistency in delivery". Given the location, a large slice of the clientele is inevitably engaged in business entertaining – but that does not mean it's inferior to stablemates further west. Says one fan: "We think this is better than Pollen Street, JA's flagship restaurant in Mayfair". / EC2N 1HQ; www.citysociallondon.com; @CitySocial_T42; Tue-Sat 9.30 pm; closed Sat L, closed Sun & Mon; booking max 4 may apply.

The Clarence Tavern N16 NEW   £34
102 Stoke Newington Church Street   020 8712 1188   1–1C
Great news for Stoke Newington: in March 2020, the Anchor & Hope team took over and stripped back this Grade II listed boozer (once known as The Daniel Defoe but now reverting back to the older name that's literally written in stone on the walls). It comes complete with a terrace, beer garden and basement wine bar. With chef Harry Kaufman (formerly of Great Queen Street, RIP) at the stoves, this has the makings of a major neighbourhood asset. / N16 0LA; www.clarencetavern.com; @clarenceN16; Tue-Sat 11 pm, Sun 5 pm; closed Tue L closed Sun D, closed Mon.

Clarette W1   £87   3 3 3
44 Blandford St   020 3019 7750   3–1A
"A fabulous wine list" is the highlight one would hope for at this Marylebone venture – a pub converted by part of the family which owns Château Margaux. Fifty wines are served by the glass and there's an extensive list of directly sourced Château Margaux wines. Feedback says the food – a mixture of French and Mediterranean dishes – is "wonderful", too. / W1U 7HS; www.clarettelondon.com; @ClaretteLondon; Tue-Sat 11 pm, Sun 6 pm; closed Tue, Wed L, closed Mon.

Claridges Foyer & Reading Room W1   3 4 4
49 Brook Street   020 7107 8886   3–2B
A "real must-go", this deluxe Mayfair hotel offers "glamour personified" (and "a famous face or two") alongside "afternoon tea as it should be" – "no gimmicks, just all you would expect in a stunning location" that makes you feel "far from the madding crowd". "While top-end in pricing, it's worth it to enjoy the serenity of this exquisite room and super-efficient, yet easy and friendly service". / W1K 4HW; www.claridges.co.uk/; @ClaridgesHotel; Mon-Sun 10 pm.

Clarke's W8 £95 544
124 Kensington Church Street   020 7221 9225   7–2B

"Have never had a bad meal over the 30 years I have eaten here!". "You feel spoilt and well treated" at Sally Clarke's Kensington HQ, established in 1984 – she was a very early exponent of Californian-influenced cuisine in London, a formula she has stuck by ever since with *"forever outstanding dishes from seasonal produce"* (*"fresh-tasting and beautifully prepared"*). Opinions differ on the understated decor, which is *"a bit cold"* for some tastes, but *"calm and relaxing to others"*. In any case the *"lovely and helpful"* staff add further vim to the experience. / W8 4BH; www.sallyclarke.com; @SallyClarkeLtd; Tue-Sat 10 pm; closed Sun & Mon; booking max 8 may apply.

The Clifton NW8 £64 333
96 Clifton Hill   020 7625 5010   9–3A

This *"really outstanding local"* in St John's Wood was once a royal hunting lodge frequented by the future King Edward VII for assignations with the actress Lillie Langtry. Saved from developers four years ago, it was relaunched as a *"dog-friendly pub"* with food well above average gastroboozer standard. / NW8 0JT; www.thecliftonnw8.com; @thecliftonnw8; Mon-Sun 10 pm.

Clipstone W1 £83 443
5 Clipstone Street   020 7637 0871   2–1B

"Assured and friendly service" is a particular plus at Will Lander and Daniel Morgenthau's *"low-key"* but engaging corner site in Fitzrovia, whose *"informal"* but professional approach suits it to a simple business lunch but also to a *"perfect, relaxed and unstuffy"* meal with friends. There was the odd quibble about creeping prices this year, but practically all reports are of *"inventive and surprising"* cuisine that's *"always seasonal, unpretentious and utterly delicious"*. Interesting wine options too (including reasonable corkage and the option to purchase and take home). / W1W 6BB; www.clipstonerestaurant.co.uk; @clipstonerestaurant; Tue-Sat 9.45 pm, Sun 8.45 pm; closed Mon.

The Clock N8 N8 £35
59 The Broadway   020 8347 8861   1–1C

In the heart of Crouch End, this modern bar/brasserie (which opened in early 2019) offers an affordably priced selection of modern European dishes plus bar bites. Too limited feedback for a rating, but all of it enthusiastic. / N8 8DT; www.theclockn8.com; Tue-Thu 10.30 pm, Fri & Sat 11 pm, Sun 6 pm; closed Tue-Thu L closed Sun D, closed Mon; Take bookings all week via phone and/or online.

Clos Maggiore WC2 £87 225
33 King St   020 7379 9696   5–3C

"The perfect way to a loved one's heart" – this *"oasis of calm and tranquillity amid the hustle and bustle of Covent Garden"* yet again tops our annual diners' poll as London's No 1 spot for romance. *"The best tables are in the conservatory"* – *"intimate, elegant and florally stunning"* – which is *"like being whisked away to a beautiful spot in the countryside"* (but don't despair if you don't nab one of the prime slots as there are also may *"soft, dark and secluded"* tables elsewhere). Another *"star attraction is the wine list of biblical proportions"*, showcasing its *"brilliant"* and *"fairly priced"* cellar. In prior years, we have always said the food and service are surprisingly good for somewhere with so many other competing attractions, and many reports do still laud its *"very good modern British cuisine"*. There's no glossing over a big slide in ratings here though this year. No single complaint was to the fore, standards just weren't rated as excellently as usual. Hopefully a blip. / WC2E 8JD; www.closmaggiore.com; @Clos_Maggiore; Wed-Sun 10 pm; closed Mon & Tue; No shorts.

The Clove Club EC1 £186 544

Shoreditch Town Hall, 380 Old St   020 7729 6496   13–1B

"Still at the top of their game" – Daniel Willis, Johnny Smith and chef Isaac McHale's famous trailblazer within Shoreditch's monumental old town hall put in a very assured survey performance this year. The odd report did query the *"astronomical pricing"*, even while acknowledging that a meal here is *"a great occasion"*. But for the most part there was nothing but veneration for the *"top service and evolving tasting menu"*: *"intense flavours from the hands of an artist"* twinned with *"an amazing wine pairing"* (and a non-alcoholic matching drinks option is also available). / EC1V 9LT; www.thecloveclub.com; @thecloveclub; Mon-Sat 11 pm; closed Mon L, closed Sun; SRA-Food Made Good – 1 stars.

Club Gascon EC1 £133 433

57 West Smithfield   020 7600 6144   10–2B

An *"ever-changing menu"* mining the culinary delights of southwest France has kept Pascal Aussignac and Vincent Labeyrie's Smithfield institution at the forefront of London's dining scene for more than 20 years. Hugely influential, they pioneered the now ubiquitous small tasting plates and focus on regional cuisines. *"We've been coming for years and are rarely disappointed"* is a typical comment. They serve very well-chosen regional wines, too, and *"did brilliant take-away during lockdown"*. / EC1A 9DS; www.clubgascon.com; @club_gascon; Tue-Sat 9.30 pm; closed Tue-Sat L, closed Sun & Mon; No shorts; Take bookings all week via phone and/or online.

Club Mexicana Taqueria WC2 NEW £35 443

35 Earlham Street   5–2C

"Great-tasting tacos… you don't even realise the food is vegan!" – This meat-free Mexican has (after a series of pop-ups, and a big line in delivery) found a permanent home in a pink-painted unit (with outside seats too) at Soho's Kingly Court, and is already winning high praise from reporters: *"the meal totally sated us and the 'fake meat' was amazingly good"*. They also have a stall in Covent Garden's Seven Dials Market. / WC2H 9LD; www.clubmexicana.com; @clubmexicana; Mon-Sat 10 pm, Sun 9 pm.

The Coach EC1 £61 222

26-28 Ray Street   020 3954 1595   10–1A

"Lovely", converted 1790 pub in a *"quiet street in Farringdon"* – with an *"unexpectedly beautiful dining room upstairs"* and a *"garden out the back"* – that makes the perfect setting for its menu of *"classic"* dishes. But marks have dropped sharply amid grumbles of *"inconsistency"* following the departure of highly rated Henry Harris, the ex-Racine chef who launched The Coach as chef-director of Harcourt Inns. / EC1R 3DJ; www.thecoachclerkenwell.co.uk; @thecoachldn; Mon-Sat 11 pm, Sun 4 pm; closed Sun D.

Coal Office N1 £76 444

2 Bagley Walk   020 3848 6085   9–3C

"Every morsel is delicious" at this well-pitched three-year-old, on the edge of the new King's Cross dining quarter – the work of Israeli celeb chef Assaf Granit (founder of London's Palomar and Barbary, plus equally hot venues in Israel and Paris). Fitted out by Tom Dixon (whose offices are adjacent), its *"wonderful Middle Eastern flavours and lively Tel Aviv vibe"* draw an appreciative crowd: *"boy was it worth it – such interesting flavours and perfectly executed"*. / N1C 4PQ; coaloffice.com; @coaloffice; Mon-Sat 11 pm, Sun 10.30 pm; closed Mon-Sun L.

Coal Rooms SE15 £66 4 4 4
11a Station Way 020 7635 6699 1–4D

"What a superb place": the old goods rooms and booking hall of Peckham Rye station – lending the enterprise "a touch of Victorian elegance" – repurposed five years ago as a modern restaurant serving "tasty and beautifully presented European dishes, with thoughtful and attentive staff, brilliant cocktails and a good wine list". "If only we'd retained and re-used more of these buildings". Top Tip: "the best toilets in south London". / SE15 4RX; www.coalroomspeckham.com; @coalrooms; Wed-Sat 11 pm, Sun 6 pm; closed Sun D, closed Mon & Tue.

The Coal Shed SE1 £70 3 3 3
One Tower Bridge 020 3384 7272 10–4D

Surprisingly limited, but all round very good, feedback on this London sibling to a Brighton original, where steaks, Sunday roasts and BBQ feasts are the mainstays of the menu. It's a good-looking contemporary venue too, convenient for the new Bridge Theatre. / SE1 2AA; www.coalshed-restaurant.co.uk; @TheCoalShed1; Tue-Sat 11 pm, Sun 8 pm; closed Tue, Wed L, closed Mon.

Colbert SW1 £62 2 2 3
51 Sloane Sq 020 7730 2804 6–2D

"A very fashionable location on Sloane Square" complete with outside terrace guarantees a steady crowd and "great people-watching" at Corbin & King's classic café-brasserie – bang next-door to the Royal Court Theatre – and its "delightful" faux-period decor goes a long way in this corner of Chelsea, where flâneurs and ladies-about-town gather en masse. Never C&K's best performer, it was better rated this year, but even so "the food can vary – it's usually good, but occasionally bad". Oft nominated as a good place to start the day, it's a "great venue for meeting business associates over breakfast". / SW1W 8AX; www.colbertchelsea.com; @ColbertChelsea; Tue-Sat 10.30 pm, Sun & Mon 10 pm.

Colette
315 Fulham Road, SW10 020 7351 6817 6–3B NEW
77 High Street Wimbledon, SW19 020 3668 3700 11–2B NEW

'A taste of rural France on the Fulham Road' is the promise at this 'gourmet traiteur' in Chelsea: an early 2020 newcomer where dishes (to go or for delivery within 4 miles) are designed for reheating at home and prepared by Chris Hill, who most recently worked as a senior sous chef at The Ritz. It's owned by Dimitri and Mira Plaquet, of a high-quality Belgian food group called La Villa Lorraine. They must be doing something right, as in mid 2021 they launched a second store in Wimbledon. / colette.co.uk.

La Collina NW1 £70 3 2 3
17 Princess Rd 020 7483 0192 9–3B

"One of London's nicest garden restaurants for a warm summer evening" is to be found at this 10-year-old independent at the foot of Primrose Hill (hence the name), which serves a "well-presented menu" of Piedmontese dishes. / NW1 8JR; www.lacollinarestaurant.co.uk; @LacollinaR; Wed-Sat 10 pm, Tue 9.30 pm, Sun 9 pm; closed Tue L, closed Mon; booking max 8 may apply.

The Collins Room SW1 £122 3 3 4
The Berkeley Hotel, Wilton Place 020 7107 8866 6–1D

"The Pret a Portea champagne afternoon tea was my highlight of 2021! Phenomenal!" – Each year, the team at The Berkeley produce a new, fashion-themed afternoon tea and – if you can afford the hefty price tag – it's an AbFab experience ('…the 2021/22 collection debuts with Donatella Versace's ocean-themed cocktail dress, reimagined as a coconut dacquoise and mango confit, encased with exotic fruit mousse and topped with a sugar starfish'). Results are "incredible, a perfect balance between tartness and sweetness: my mouth is literally watering as I remember it. Huge amounts of delicious sandwiches followed by an inventive afternoon tea spread and unlimited choices of teas and coffees. I can't wait to go back!". / SW1X 7RL; www.the-berkeley.co.uk/restaurants-bars/collins-room; @TheBerkeley; Mon-Sun 10 pm.

Le Colombier SW3 £84 3 3 3
145 Dovehouse Street 020 7351 1155 6–2C

"I love it because it reminds me of when I lived in France!" – Didier Garnier's *"good, old-fashioned brasserie"* occupies a tucked-away Chelsea corner in a cute, well-situated backstreet, and is particularly *"popular with a local upmarket clientele"*, who are forgiving of the fact that it's *"a bit packed and noisy"* and a little *"expensive"* for somewhere not aiming to produce culinary fireworks. Selling points are its *"traditional French-bourgeois"* menu, *"elegant"* decor, *"attentive and professional service"* (with le patron much in evidence), and an *"extensive wine list"* (which, unlike the food, *"is not at Chelsea prices at all"*). / SW3 6LB; www.le-colombier-restaurant.co.uk; Mon-Sat 10.30 pm, Sun 10 pm.

Colonel Saab WC1 NEW
Holborn Hall, 193-197 High Holborn 020 3004 0004 5–1D

Will this Autumn 2021 newcomer finally dispel the curse of Holborn Town Hall? It's a potentially magnificent but serial graveyard site that's so far seen off Shanghai Blues, Burger & Lobster and most recently Gezellig (RIP). This 'progressive Indian Restaurant' is the first London venture of entrepreneur Roop Partap Choudhary, and culinary inspiration will come from his property Hotel Noor Mahal in Karnal (north of Delhi). / WC1V; www.colonelsaab.co.uk/; Mon-Sat 12.30 am, Sun 11 pm.

Colony Grill Room, Beaumont Hotel W1 £101
The Beaumont, 8 Balderton Street, Brown Hart Gardens 020 7499 9499 3–2A

This luxurious Art Deco hotel near Selfridges with its 1920s NYC-style grill room underwent a major refurbishment during the lockdowns to emerge in August 2021 with a lighter, slightly more colourful look (with striking new murals and banquettes now in deep-red leather). Chef Ben Boeynaems oversees the cooking, which focuses on shellfish, grills, steaks and tableside salads. / W1K 6TF; www.colonygrillroom.com; @ColonyGrillRoom; Mon-Sat 9.30 pm, Sun 2.30 pm; closed Sun D.

Comptoir Gascon EC1 £65 3 2 3
63 Charterhouse St 020 7608 0851 10–1A

"The duck burger is sublime and the triple-cooked duck-fat chips are moreish" at this offshoot of nearby Club Gascon, which offers a more informal venue for simpler but similar cuisine from SW France. We've rated it on the basis of its consistent pre-pandemic performance, as it remains closed as of September 2021 while the team waits for folks to return to their offices around Smithfield. / EC1M 6HJ; www.comptoirgascon.com; @ComptoirGascon; Tue-Fri 9.30 pm; closed Mon, Sat & Sun.

Le Comptoir Robuchon W1 £127 4 4 3
6 Clarges Street 020 8076 0570 3–4C

With the passing of Joel Robuchon and closure of Covent Garden's L'Atelier de Robuchon (RIP), this newish (late 2019) Mayfair venture is the main London torch-bearer for this famous French gastronomic name (see also 'Le Deli Robuchon' on Piccadilly, but it's of no huge culinary ambition). The dining room – with a gorgeous marble bar running down one side, and tables with banquette seating down the other – is very fine and grand and already winning fans as a prime *"business"* choice. The luxurious modern French dishes are of high quality, with many echoes of L'Atelier (but perhaps a little simpler and less expensive), and a good proportion of early reporters acclaim this as their best meal of the year. / W1J 8AE; www.robuchonlondon.co.uk; Tue-Sat 11 pm; closed Tue, Sat L, closed Sun & Mon.

Con Gusto SE18   £54   3 4 4
No 1 Street   020 8465 7452   12–2D
"Everything you could wish for in a local", say fans of this quirky Italian, in a tiny but characterful former guards' room in the grounds of the old Woolwich Arsenal. "High-quality food is freshly prepared in an amazing setting with friendly, professional staff. A joy!". / SE18 6GH; www.congusto.co.uk; @ConGustoTweets; Tue-Sun 9.30 pm; closed Tue-Sun L, closed Mon.

The Connaught Grill W1 NEW   £125
Carlos Place   020 7107 8852   3–3B
Although it is branded under the famous 'Connaught Grill' name – which ran from 1955-2000 and was presided over for 26 of those years by the legendary Michel Bourdin – this new dining room, which opened in early 2020, is a total break from the past. With Hélène Darroze occupying the Grill's old site, this reincarnation inhabits former private rooms elsewhere on the ground floor. John Heah's sleek design for the interior – with much bespoke woodwork – is a world away from the 'period piece' decor of the former grill. The same could also be said of NYC chef Jean-Georges Vongerichten's menu, much of it produced from the rotisserie and a wood-burning grill. Where, in days of yore, you might have enjoyed Consommé 'Prince of Wales', followed by Médaillons de Cailles 'Belle Epoque', you can now have Sashimi, followed by Wagyu Beef Fillet. / W1K 2AL; www.the-connaught.co.uk/restaurants-bars/the-connaught-grill; @TheConnaught; Mon-Sun 11 pm.

Il Convivio SW1   £62   3 3 3
143 Ebury St   020 7730 4099   2–4A
"Fairly modern in style", this Belgravia Italian of over 20 years' standing has a "pleasant" ambience and typically provides a civilised safe haven within striking distance of Victoria. We have rated it on the basis of its consistent pre-pandemic performance and the assumption that it will reopen: as we go to press in September 2021, it remains 'temporarily closed'. / SW1W 9QN; ilconvivio.co.uk/; Mon-Sat 11 pm; closed Sun.

Coopers Restaurant & Bar WC2   £61   3 4 3
49 Lincoln's Inn Fields   020 7831 6211   2–2D
This independent fixture in legal-land (near the LSE) is a long-running staple of the area – welcoming, "always good value", and with some interesting picks and bin-end deals on the wine list. / WC2A 3PF; www.coopersrestaurant.co.uk; @coopers_bistro; Mon-Fri 8.30 pm; closed Sat & Sun; no booking.

Copper & Ink SE3   £85   5 4 3
5 Lee Road   020 3941 9337   1–4D
"A perfect little bistro-style place" in Blackheath, offering "fine dining and run by MasterChef runner-up Tony Rodd": "the £45 tasting menu is the best-value five-course meal in London", they say: "prawns as big as your fist, lovely venison cookery and a £35 wine pairing – what more can you want on date night?". / SE3 9RQ; www.copperandink.com; @copperink; Wed-Sat 11.30 pm; closed Mon & Tue & Sun.

Copper Chimney W12 NEW   £39
South Terrace, Westfield London, Ariel Way   020 8059 4439   1–3B
Founded by JK Kapur in 1972 in Bombay, Copper Chimney has 15 restaurants in five Indian cities and chose a unit on Westfield London's main restaurant row (the South Terrace) for its first UK branch. If you're in the mall, this is one of its better eating options – feedback is still too limited though to suggest you should cross postcodes to try it out. / W12 7GA; www.copperchimney.uk; Sun-Thu 10 pm, Fri & Sat 10.30 pm; Take bookings all week via phone and/or online.

Coq d'Argent EC2 £95 22**3**
1 Poultry 020 7395 5000 10–2C

This "swish rooftop restaurant in the City" from D&D London is "always an impressive venue to take people, with good food and great views". It sits at the top of No 1 Poultry, a dramatic modern building that featured in the James Bond sequence during the London Olympics opening ceremony, and has a "great outdoor space for warm evenings". But beware: what's "great for a good business lunch" – "mainly corporate credit cards" – can be a shock for the self-funded: "didn't check to see if there was a set lunch… painful!". / EC2R 8EJ; www.coqdargent.co.uk; @CoqdArgent1; Mon-Sat 9.45 pm; closed Sat L, closed Sun; booking max 10 may apply.

Coqfighter W1 £28 5**3**2
75 Beak Street 020 7734 4001 4–2C

"Oh-so-dirty chicken, that is actually fresh and crispy and so so moreish" ("soooo tasty, the green chilli chicken burger is fab!") wins continued praise for this finger-lickin' group, which operates out of Shoreditch Boxpark and various take-away and delivery locations, as well as this Soho forever home. "Service is casual… it feels like it's deliberately trying to be a dive!". / W1F 9SS; www.coqfighter.com; @Coqfighter; Mon-Sat 10 pm, Sun 9 pm.

Cora Pearl WC2 £67 **3**3**3**
30 Henrietta Street 020 7324 7722 5–3C

"Cosily atmospheric", with a "stylish theatrical ambience", this little sister of Kitty Fisher's in Shepherd Market (both are named after historical courtesans) is "particularly welcome in Covent Garden". There's a "delicious short menu" of "sophisticated British comfort food", and "efficient but personal service which creates a warmish glow". Top Tips: "the chips are to die for" and the kitchen "does rose veal like nowhere else". / WC2E 8NA; www.corapearl.co.uk; @corapearlcg; Tue-Sat 10 pm, Sun 3.30 pm; closed Sun D, closed Mon.

CORD EC4 NEW
85 Fleet Street 10–2A

Originally scheduled to open in March 2020 – the 125th anniversary of the opening of Cordon Bleu in Paris – this new City-based outpost of the famous culinary institute includes a 90-cover restaurant (whose offering will include a £25 set-lunch menu, delivered in 90 minutes) and 30-cover café (selling posh pastries). The site is Le Cordon Bleu's second in London (the other is in Bloomsbury) and will, of course, also offer courses and training to stressed investment bankers, whose souls can be soothed by whisking up a quick soufflé. / EC4Y 1AE; www.cordrestaurant.co.uk; Mon-Fri 11 pm; closed Sat & Sun.

Core by Clare Smyth W11 £130 5**5**4
92 Kensington Park Rd 020 3937 5086 7–2B

"Where's a fourth Michelin star when you need one?" – Clare Smyth's "world-class" Notting Hill luminary offers "a supreme gastronomic experience" and now dominates our diners' poll, topping not just votes as top gastronomic experience, but also the most-mentioned restaurant this year: an incredible achievement for somewhere charging top dollar. "From the moment you walk in to the moment you leave, everything is perfect", but "despite being in the top echelons of restauration, everyone is so friendly and unstuffy" and "Clare and head chef Jonny Bone always make time to say 'hi' from the kitchen doorway". The service (led by Rob Rose) is so smooth and slick "it's almost like a ballet" and "Gareth Ferreira's ability to pair wines is also exceptional". When it comes to the cuisine itself, the third Michelin star awarded in January 2021 was "well-warranted and overdue" thanks to the "unsurpassed levels of sophistication, technical expertise, and the sheer culinary pleasure of the majestic tasting menu". Dishes are "consistently bursting with flavour" ("I have never been so excited by a potato dish!") and "look like works of art"; while "vegetarians and pescatarians are clearly no *afterthought". "After two cancellations for Covid restrictions I finally made it… well worth the money!". / W11 2PN; www.corebyclaresmyth.com; Tue-Sat 10 pm; closed Tue, Wed L, closed Sun & Mon; Take bookings all week via phone and/or online.*

Cork & Bottle WC2 £58 2 3 5
44-46 Cranbourn St 020 7734 7807 5–3B

This extremely cosy and characterful, 50-year-old wine cellar off Leicester Square provides "an unbeatable variety of wine at all price points" – "and you can usually get a seat despite the central location". "The food's not bad, either" – including the famous cheese & ham pie that has been on the menu since 1978, selling almost a million portions. Will Clayton has carried on where legendary founder Don Hewitson left off, and has expanded into branches in Hampstead (now closed) and Bayswater. / WC2H 7AN; www.thecorkandbottle.co.uk; @corkbottle1971; Wed-Sat 11.30 pm; closed Wed & Thu L, closed Mon & Tue & Sun; no booking D.

Corner Room E2 £52 3 3 3
Patriot Sq 020 7871 0461 14–2B

"No fuss, not a lot of choice but solid food and good-value wine list" – that's the deal at this 30-cover, bistro-esque venue, in a light-filled room on the first floor of Bethnal Green's Town Hall Hotel. / E2 9NF; www.townhallhotel.com/dining/corner-room; Mon ; closed Mon D, closed Tue-Sat & Sun.

Cornerstone E9 £83 5 5 4
3 Prince Edward Road 020 8986 3922 14–1C

"Tom Brown is a genius with fish cooking" and his Scandi-chic venture with open kitchen in the hipster-central environs of Hackney Wick station provides dishes that are "exploding with flavour and full of originality (the sea bream tartare with miso-ponzu dressing and chilli oil was astonishing!)". The place has "such a chilled vibe as well" – "it's great to watch the open kitchen during service" and the atmosphere is "not in the least pretentious", thanks to service that's particularly "friendly and expert". "My daughter and I went for her 21st and my 59th – amazing!". / E9 5LX; cornerstonehackney.com; @Cornerstone_h_w; Wed-Sat, Tue 9 pm; closed Tue L, closed Sun & Mon.

Corrigan's Mayfair W1 £117 3 3 3
28 Upper Grosvenor St 020 7499 9943 3–3A

"Excellent cooking with top-quality ingredients" inspires numerous fans of Irish celeb chef Richard Corrigan's Mayfair HQ, just off Park Lane, whose guiding principle is that of a modernised hunting lodge, focused on "traditional" British and Irish cuisine, including beef from the carving trolley. Naturally it doesn't come cheap, but the experience was consistently highly rated this year. / W1K 7EH; www.corrigansmayfair.com; @CorriganMayfair; Wed-Sat, Tue 10.30 pm; closed Tue L, closed Sun & Mon; Booking max 12 may apply.

Côte £63 2 2 2
"It won't blow you away, but is still adequate and reasonably competitively priced" remains the upbeat view on this ubiquitous high street chain, whose "bistro-style" offering still has a surprisingly large fanbase (including those with kids in tow). Its ratings are entering the danger zone, though, as it passes from private equity owner to owner – the latest having purchased it out of administration in October 2020. One sceptic notes: "my favourite chain is going from hero to zero under the new ownership, and heading down the same path as Café Rouge and Strada before it". / www.cote.co.uk.

The Cow W2 £64 3 3 3
89 Westbourne Park Rd 020 7221 0021 7–1B

"Still a top fish stew and the atmosphere is as good as ever", say fans of Tom Conran's Irish-themed gastropub on the Notting Hill/Bayswater border, known for its seafood, Guinness and good craic. It's become much less commented-on, however, in recent years. / W2 5QH; www.thecowlondon.co.uk; @TheCowLondon; Mon-Sat 10.30 pm, Sun 9.30 pm; no Amex.

Coya £90 **3 3 4**
118 Piccadilly, W1   020 7042 7118   3–4B
Angel Court, 31-33 Throgmorton St, EC2   020 7042 7118   10–2C
"Cool music adds to the brilliant vibe for a fun night out" at this "romantic" Peruvian duo in Mayfair and near the Bank of England. The cuisine (charcoal-grilled meat and seafood, plus tacos and Nikkei sashimi) is well-rated, as is the "comprehensive and interesting world-wide wine list", although some diners find their enthusiasm dampened by "silly prices". The concept, developed by Anglo-Indian chef Sanjay Dwivedi, has expanded in recent years to Paris, Monaco, Mykonos and moneyed hot-spots in the Middle East. / www.coyarestaurant.com.

The Crabtree W6 £50 **3 3 4**
Rainville Road   020 7385 3929   11–1A
"Local pub in a super setting on the Thames" just along from the River Café, with a spacious interior, large garden and cute riverside terrace. The food's not especially gastro, but well-realised and dependable. One caution – the tranquil garden by the river can have a very different atmosphere on busy summer weekends or Fulham match days at nearby Craven Cottage. / W6 9HA; www.thecrabtreew6.co.uk; @thecrabtreew6; Mon-Sat 11 pm, Sun 10.30 pm.

Crate Brewery and Pizzeria E9 £35 **3 2 4**
7, The White Building, Queens Yard   020 8533 3331   14–1C
Chilled microbrewery haunt across the canal from the Olympic Park (near Hackney Wick Station) whose waterside terrace is a big plus in summer. The pizza and brews are fair value, and it has a lovely, hip vibe… meaning, though, that it gets busy and service can at times be swamped. / E9 5EN; www.cratebrewery.com; @cratebrewery; Sun-Thu 11 pm, Fri & Sat 1 am.

Crocker's Folly NW8 £54 **4 4 4**
23-24 Aberdeen Pl   020 7289 9898   9–4A
The unique combination of a "beautiful venue" – an ornate late-Victorian pub built in the mistaken expectation that a railway terminus would arrive in St John's Wood – and "wonderful Lebanese food" from the Maroush Group has made this unlikely destination one of the higher-rated restaurants in north London. / NW8 8JR; www.maroush.com/restaurant/crockers-folly/; @crockersfolly; Mon-Sun midnight; Take bookings all week via phone and/or online.

The Crooked Well SE5 £56 **3 3 3**
16 Grove Ln   020 7252 7798   1–3C
With its jazzy decor, this handsome-looking Camberwell gastropub with large outside seating area is worth discovering – "a gem in the very truest sense", with a high-quality menu (which typically includes a "fantastic pie option"). / SE5 9SY; www.thecrookedwell.com; Tue-Sat 9.30 pm; closed Tue L, closed Sun & Mon; no Amex; booking max 6 may apply.

The Crossing SW13 **NEW**
73 White Hart Ln   020 8392 1617   11–1A
After a significant refurb (about £400k), this sweet pub on White Hart Lane – fka The Tree House – has been relaunched by hospitality operator Christian Arden. There's a new outside terrace (complete with its own pizza oven), while the food offering includes a charcuterie selection and a number of mains from the flame-fired bespoke rotisserie grill in the garden. / SW13; www.thecrossing-barnes.co.uk; Tue-Sun 5 pm.

**The Crystal Moon Lounge,
Corinthia Hotel London SW1** £97 **3 4 4**
Whitehall Place   020 7321 3150   2–3C
"Exquisite delicacies" from a "creative pastry department whose inventions not only tick the box for visual impact but also taste delicious" win numerous fans for this glossy five-star's stylish lounge (where you eat under a two-ton chandelier). "Superb" and "unhurried" service, too. / SW1A 2BD; www.corinthia.com/en/hotels/london/dining/afternoon-tea; @CorinthiaLondon; Mon-Sun midnight.

Cubé W1 £120
4 Blenheim Street   020 7165 9506   3–2B
Upscale Japanese three-year-old, which includes a sushi counter, restaurant and 'hideaway' bar and bills itself as serving 'modern Japanese tapas and sushi dishes to the heart of Mayfair'. The evening omakase at the counter is its top attraction: appetisers, chef's daily special of 10 kinds of nigiri sushi and 1 temaki roll, plus a dessert for £88. It doesn't attract much in the way of survey feedback, but it gives a promising impression. / W1S 1LB; www.cubemayfair.com; @c_u_b_e___; Mon-Sat 11 pm.

The Culpeper E1 £60 3️⃣2️⃣3️⃣
40 Commercial St   020 7247 5371   13–2C
A "really beautiful spot, with a great buzz" – this handsome old boozer on a Spitalfields corner has been cleverly refurbished as a multi-storey venue with a spectacular rooftop garden, chic bedrooms, impressive first-floor dining room and "good gastropub food". / E1 6LP; www.theculpeper.com; @theculpeper; Mon-Thu 11 pm, Fri & Sat midnight, Sun 6 pm; closed Sun D; SRA-Food Made Good – 3 stars.

Cut + Grind N1 £42 3️⃣3️⃣3️⃣
The Urbanest Building, 25-27 Canal Reach   020 3668 7683   9–3C
"Brilliant burgers charmingly served in a student-friendly hang-out" – that's the deal at this indie four-year-old, which is located at the northern end of the new developments near King's Cross. / N1C 4DD; www.cutandgrindburgers.com; @cngburgers; Sun-Thu 9 pm, Fri & Sat 10 pm.

Cyprus Mangal SW1 £47 3️⃣2️⃣2️⃣
45 Warwick Way   020 7828 5940   2–4B
This Turkish-Cypriot grill has established a strong local following around Pimlico in the past 15 years, notably for kebabs fans rate as "simply the best". / SW1V 1QS; www.cyprusmangal.co.uk; @cyprus_mangal; Sun-Thu midnight, Fri & Sat 1 am.

Da Mario SW7 £49 3️⃣3️⃣4️⃣
15 Gloucester Rd   020 7584 9078   6–1B
This "bustling and busy Italian very close to the Albert Hall" is a "fantastic little place", where "children are always very welcome and well looked after" and the "food is good, especially the pasta dishes". "It makes the most of its connection with Princess Diana", who would bring Princes Wills and Harry here to lunch on pizza. / SW7 4PP; www.damario.co.uk; Mon-Sun 11.30 pm.

Da Mario WC2 £68 2️⃣3️⃣3️⃣
63 Endell St   020 7240 3632   5–1C
This "nice, intimate, friendly Italian restaurant" in Covent Garden makes you feel "as if you were in Italy". The retirement of the family that ran it for years seems to have had little effect on the menu of basic trattoria classics, "reasonably priced wines and smiling welcome". / WC2H 9AJ; www.da-mario.co.uk; Wed-Sat 11.30 pm, Sun 9 pm; closed Mon & Tue.

Da Terra, Town Hall Hotel E2 £179 5️⃣4️⃣4️⃣
8 Patriot Square   020 7062 2052   14–2B
Chef Rafael Cagali's "take on Brazilian food with a fresh and fine-dining perspective is absolutely sublime" – one of London's most culinarily exciting – at this East End three-year-old: the worthy successor on this site in Bethnal Green's old Town Hall that's also housed The Typing Room and Viajante. The setting is "characterful", "the open kitchen gives you a great view of the kitchen" and it's "brilliant to be served by the chefs" ("allowing you to really understand the restaurants' focus and philosophy"). "What other Michelin place allows you to add your own chillies to a fish curry so you spice it to your liking? Bread is a course in its own right: a large lump of roasted bone

marrow with three different butters that you could just live off and be happy. A short but interesting beer list means you can keep costs down if you don't fancy wine". / E2 9NF; www.daterra.co.uk; @DaTerra_London; Fri & Sat, Wed & Thu 9 pm; closed Wed & Thu L, closed Mon & Tue & Sun; booking online only.

Daddy Bao SW17 £33 4 3 3
113 Mitcham Road   020 3601 3232   11–2C
Tooting's contribution to the bao boom, this "friendly, fast-paced small restaurant offers excellent Taiwanese food", with exotic cocktails to accompany the steamed buns. It is part of Frank Leung's growing chain, alongside Mr Bao in Peckham and Master Bow in Westfield Shepherd's Bush. / SW17 9PE; www.daddybao.com; Tue-Thu, Sun 9.45 pm, Fri & Sat 10.45 pm; closed Tue-Fri L, closed Mon.

Daffodil Mulligan EC1 £75 3 4 3
70-74 City Road   020 7404 3000   13–1A
Just south of Silicon Roundabout, this two-year-old Irish bar/restaurant is backed by a crack team of London's most famous Irish foodies – chef Richard Corrigan, plus Green & Fortune's John Nugent and King's Place owner Peter Millican. Its small plates cooked over open fire are interesting and well-realised – even a reporter who considers the place "expensive" concedes that "otherwise it is very good indeed". / EC1Y 2BJ; www.daffodilmulligan.com; @DaffyMulligans; Wed-Sat, Tue 10 pm; closed Tue L, closed Sun & Mon.

Dalloway Terrace, Bloomsbury Hotel WC1 £78 2 3 4
16-22 Great Russell St   020 7347 1221   2–1C
This "delightful" hotel terrace (with fully retractable roof) takes its name from a Virginia Woolf novel, and provides a rare peaceful haven in busy central London – "honestly, everything's that's been said about this beautiful place is true!". "Service is attentive", and the venue is perfect for a "lovely afternoon tea catching up with friends". It can seem a little "chichi and pricey generally, although the brunch set menus are decent value". / WC1B 3NN; www.dallowayterrace.com; @DallowayTerrace; Mon-Wed 11 pm; closed Thu-Sat & Sun.

La Dame de Pic London EC3 £133 5 4 3
10 Trinity Square   020 7297 3799   10–3D
"Spectacular setting and superb cuisine" – not, in truth, what you might expect in a "plush" five-star popular with City expense-accounters, but what is delivered by the Pic family's admirable dining room, within the majestic building that was once the HQ of the Port of London Authority. "The cookery is on another level – it's beguiling and enchanting with perfume-like layers of aromas and flavours that show the most delicate touch and incredible execution": some of the most highly rated in London. Service, meanwhile, is "refined" but "friendly" and the grand setting "manages to feel relaxed and modern whilst being a temple of excellence". The bill is gargantuan, but nobody seems to mind. / EC3N 4AJ; ladamedepiclondon.co.uk; @FSTenTrinity; Thu-Sat 9 pm; closed Mon-Wed & Sun; No shorts; Take bookings all week via phone and/or online.

Daphne's SW3 £87 2 2 3
112 Draycott Ave   020 7589 4257   6–2C
This "romantic" Italian near Brompton Cross dates back to Chelsea's 'Swinging Sixties', when it was founded by Richard Burton's agent, Daphne Rye, and was still swinging two decades later as one of Princess Di's hangouts. Nowadays, impressions vary between sceptics who fear it's lost its mojo ("riding on its reputation from many years ago") and a loyal majority for whom it's "old-school but consistently good". / SW3 3AE; www.daphnes-restaurant.co.uk; @DaphnesLondon; Mon-Sat 11 pm, Sun 10.30 pm.

Daquise SW7 £57 **3** **3** **3**
20 Thurloe St   020 7589 6117   6–2C
"The antidote to noisy, sterile London eating", this "wonderfully different" old-world Polish institution near South Ken tube "feels like it has been here forever, because it has". Since 1947, to be precise, but it's certainly a "lovely time-warp – you can imagine it's still 1962", in the Cold War era when Christine Keeler and Roman Polanski had assignations here. More recent regulars have included the late restaurant critic AA Gill, and they're all drawn back by the "never-changing menu" of robust Polski classics. / SW2 2LT; www.daquise.co.uk; @daquise_london; Tue-Sun 11 pm; closed Mon; no Amex.

Darby's SW11 £78 **3** **3** **4**
3 Viaduct Gardens Road, Embassy Gardens   020 7537 3111   11–1D
"Rich and flavourful" food and a "buzzy atmosphere" help earn a thumbs-up for Dublin-born Robin Gill's NYC-inspired oyster bar and grill that provides a home-from-home for staff at the new US Embassy at Nine Elms nearby. It's a "classy outfit, all very slick", and "the meat hanging room is quite the spectacle". Gill made his name down the road in Clapham with The Dairy, Counter Culture and Sorella. / SW11 7AY; www.darbys-london.com; @robingillchef; Wed, Fri & Sat 10 pm, Thu 3 pm, Sun 4 pm; closed Wed L closed Thu & Sun D, closed Mon & Tue.

Darjeeling Express WC2 NEW £60 **4** **5** **2**
2a Garrick Street   020 7287 2828   5–3C
"So charismatic" TV-chef Asma Khan's meteoric rise continues with the autumn 2020 opening of a "beautiful", new, 120-seat flagship (to take over from her old Soho premises) on the prominent Covent Garden site that once housed a large Carluccio's. The kitchen is still all-female, and "there is so much love and gratitude in the room for Asma and her team" and their "home-style but brilliantly flavoursome concoctions" (from £3.50 snacks in the deli to a £95 tasting menu in the restaurant). Top Tip – "try the lunch/brunch chilli cheese toastie or keema toastie". / WC2E 9BH; www.darjeeling-express.com; @Darjeelingldn; Wed-Sat 9.30 pm; closed Mon & Tue & Sun; cards only.

The Dartmouth Castle W6 £58 **3** **4** **4**
26 Glenthorne Rd   020 8748 3614   8–2C
Three minutes' walk from downtown Hammersmith, this characterful pub – sibling to The Atlas in Earl's Court – is worth knowing about for its dependable cooking, atmospheric style and lovely outside terrace. / W6 0LS; www.thedartmouthcastle.co.uk; @DartmouthCastle; Mon-Fri 10 pm, Sat & Sun 9.30 pm; closed Mon L.

Darwin Brasserie EC3 £77 **3** **3** **5**
1 Sky Garden Walk   033 3772 0020   10–3D
"The excitement of the view before and after the meal" is clearly the main draw to this all-day brasserie at the top of the City's Walkie-Talkie Tower – so "the very good food and service" are "a pleasant surprise: I was expecting corporate fare". / EC3M 8AF; skygarden.london/darwin; @SG_Darwin; Mon-Wed 9 pm, Fri-Sun 10.30 pm, Thu 10 pm; closed Mon L.

Dastaan KT19 £43 **5** **5** **3**
447 Kingston Rd   020 8786 8999   1–4A
"Ewell is now a foodie destination; everyone should come to be enlightened here once!" – Sanjay Gour and Nand Kishor's "truly outstanding Indian in the 'burbs" has "a frontage and decor that don't reflect its quality" but is "worth a long detour, be it to eat in or take away". Few restaurants elicit such enthusiasm, which is inspired by the "always welcoming front of house team" and "wholly original dishes, which are far away from the usual predictable Indian fare". "The level of flavour and the divine balance of spices in every dish puts Dastaan on a pedestal above just about every other

Indian restaurant in the country, even those charging twice the price for finer dining!" Top Tip – "Their lamb chops are unbeaten!". / KT19 0DB; dastaan.co.uk; @Dastaan447; Tue-Sat 10.30 pm, Sun 9.30 pm; closed Tue-Fri L, closed Mon; Booking weekdays only.

Davies and Brook, Claridge's Hotel W1 £160 **3** **3** **3**

49 Brook Street 020 7107 8848 3–2B

"First class cooking" – "the presentation of every dish was stunning!" – helps win lofty praise for star NYC-chef Daniel Humm's régime at this "elegant but relaxed dining room in the centre of Mayfair", which he took over in autumn 2019. Our overall assessment is made a tad more guarded though by the significant minority, who – while acknowledging its high quality – still consider it "overpriced". / W1K 4HW;
www.claridges.co.uk/restaurants-bars/davies-and-brook/; Tue-Sat 9 pm; closed Sun & Mon.

Daylesford Organic £66 **2** **2** **2**

44b Pimlico Rd, SW1 020 7881 8060 6–2D
6-8 Blandford St, W1 020 3696 6500 2–1A
76-82 Sloane Avenue, SW3 awaiting tel 6–2C
208-212 Westbourne Grove, W11 020 7313 8050 7–1B

The four London farm shop/cafés – in Brompton Cross, Notting Hill, Pimlico and Marylebone – supplied by Lady Bamford's organic farm offer a reassuring taste of life in the Cotswolds. They serve "pleasant café food, but some of the prices are too much". / www.daylesfordorganic.com.

Dean Street Townhouse W1 £71 **2** **3** **4**

69-71 Dean St 020 7434 1775 4–1D

This all-day brasserie from the Soho House group – on home territory in the heart of Soho – is "a great 'go-to' place" and serves "the best breakfast in the area" (fittingly, since it is attached to a hotel). "The atmosphere is brilliant" and overall it's "a really fun place to spend a few hours, although the food isn't as good as it likes to think". / W1D 3SE;
www.deanstreettownhouse.com; @DeanStTownhouse; Mon-Thu midnight, Fri & Sat 1 am, Sun 11 am; closed Sun D.

Decimo WC1 £91 **3** **3** **5**

The Standard, 10 Argyle St 020 3981 8888 9–3C

Dramatic views of St Pancras, triple-height ceilings and funky 1970s-style decor – not to mention the red glass-walled lift on the side of the hotel to shoot you up to the tenth floor – all add to the "slick and sexy" appeal of Peter Sanchez-Iglesias's dining room, whose vibey style demands a swift order from the extensive cocktail list. All reports agree the Spanish/Mexican plates are "very good" too, as you'd hope from a London sibling to Bristol's incredible Casamia. One or two diners struggle to ignore the lofty prices (£16 for a margarita), leading to the odd "style over substance" impression, but on most accounts it's worth the indulgence for the fun and glamour of a trip. / WC1H 9JE; www.decimo.london; Wed & Thu 1 am, Sat, Fri 2 am; closed Wed-Fri L, closed Mon & Tue & Sun.

Defune W1 £82 **4** **4** **2**

34 George St 020 7935 8311 3–1A

This Marylebone veteran claims to be the longest-serving Japanese restaurant in London, and wins high ratings for its "consistent" classics, ranging from sushi to teppanyaki. Food writer and chef Simon Hopkinson was for many years a regular here, although it tends to fly under the radar these days. / W1U 7DP; www.defune.com; Mon-Sat 11 pm, Sun 10.30 pm.

Dehesa W1 £65 2️⃣2️⃣3️⃣
25 Ganton Street   020 7494 4170   4–2B
This "lovely little" spot with an "atmospheric terrace" off Carnaby Street has a strong reputation for its interesting combination of Spanish and Italian tapas. Ratings have slipped since its sale by the Salt Yard Group a few years ago – it's "not quite what it once was, having lost its edge among a sea of Spanish excellence – but not bad!". / W1F 9BP; www.saltyardgroup.co.uk/dehesa; @DehesaSoho; Mon-Sat 11 pm, Sun 9 pm.

Delamina £46 3️⃣3️⃣3️⃣
56-58 Marylebone Lane, W1   020 3026 6810   3–1A
151 Commercial Street, E1   020 7078 0770   13–2B
"Really interesting food combinations from the Levant" make self-taught chef Limor Chen and husband Amir's stripped-down Shoreditch and Marylebone venues worthwhile additions to London's "Middle East-with-a-twist" dining scene. It's "another of the small-plate trends with the now-familiar land, sea, earth menu – but packed with flavour". A natural choice for veggies and vegans, too. / www.delaminaeast.co.uk; @DelaminaKitchen.

The Delaunay WC2 £60 2️⃣4️⃣4️⃣
55 Aldwych   020 7499 8558   2–2D
"They get all the important things right and the room is lovely and welcoming" at Corbin & King's slightly less showy but equally "slick and professional" sibling to The Wolseley, just off Aldwych. It, too, is in the style of a continental grand café, and while its Mitteleuropean cooking "is not the most exciting in the world", its comforting style somehow captures "an authentic taste of Old Vienna in the golden days". Perhaps it "lacks something for the price you pay", but it attracts little in the way of harsh critiques. In particular, "it never lets you down" for business entertaining; and also "just works for breakfast, be it personal or professional" ("really indulgent, it feels like a real treat to sit in one of the spacious booths"). "Delicious strudel and other delights served with great coffee" also make it an afternoon favourite, and there's also Delaunay Counter – "a wonderful coffee place next to the main restaurant". / WC2B 4BB; www.thedelaunay.com; @TheDelaunayRest; Mon-Sat 10.30 pm, Sun 5.15 pm; closed Sun D.

Delfino W1 £60 3️⃣3️⃣3️⃣
121a Mount St   020 7499 1256   3–3B
This Mount Street fixture proves that you can still find "solid Italian home-style food" in the heart of Mayfair – all the favourites including pizza, pasta and tiramisu. In proper Italian style, there's a "great atmosphere", too. / W1K 3NW; www.delfinomayfair.com; Mon-Sun 10.30 pm.

Delhi Grill N1 £31 3️⃣3️⃣2️⃣
21 Chapel Mkt   020 7278 8100   9–3D
"Top Indian food at reasonable prices, with plenty of vegan options" again wins praise for this Punjabi 'dhaba' (roadside food stall) in Islington's Chapel Market. / N1 9EZ; www.delhigrill.com; @delhigrill; Mon-Sat 10.30 pm, Sun 10 pm; cash only.

Le Deli Robuchon W1 £43 3️⃣3️⃣3️⃣
83 Piccadilly   020 8076 0564   3–4C
Following closure of L'Atelier de Joel Robuchon and the death of the man himself, this Picadilly café is now one of two London ventures opened in late 2019 by the group he founded. It's all very chic and continental, but you don't come here for culinary adventure – but to buy or snack on everyday staples (lots of tempting patisserie and viennoiserie, lasagna, club sandwich, Caesar salad…). / W1J 8JA; www.robuchonlondon.co.uk; Mon-Sat 7 pm, Sun 6 pm.

Delicatessen NW3 £66 3 2 2
46 Rosslyn Hill 020 7700 5511 9–2A

"A varied menu" of sharing plates and burgers sits alongside more ambitious dishes at this modern Middle Eastern restaurant in Hampstead, whose *"great atmosphere, excellent food and rustic decor"* create an *"enjoyable"* experience. / NW3 1NH; delicatessen.company; Sun-Thu 11 pm; closed Fri & Sat.

Din Tai Fung £35 3 3 3
Centre Point, Tottenham Court Road, WC1 awaiting tel 5–1A
5-6 Henrietta Street, WC2 020 3034 3888 5–3D

"Makes me feel as if I'm back in Asia" – this *"busy and large"* Covent Garden *"canteen"* is the first London outlet of an *"international chain specialising in dumplings"*, founded in Taiwan 50 years ago. *"In Bangkok, in Manila, in Singapore, this is mall food"* – and after the launch here newbies were *"not sure the PR hype was warranted"* with *"better in Chinatown"*. Still, for *"top soup dumplings"* (xiao long bao) and *"consistent dim sum"* it does win lots of votes – *"and if children get bored they can watch the chefs making the dumplings in the kitchens"*. / www.dintaifung-uk.com.

The Dining Room,
The Goring Hotel SW1 £107 4 5 4
15 Beeston Pl 020 7396 9000 2–4B

Just behind Buckingham Palace (and where the Middleton family stayed before Wills and Kate were wed) – this posh five-star was built by Otto Goring in 1910 and has been run since 2005 by his great grandson Jeremy Goring. With its peerless service and *"very well spaced"* tables, it's the perfect bastion for traditionalists and an excellent choice for a *"pricey but classy"* old-school experience. The main dining room's cuisine has moved with the times, but is still in a fairly traditional mould well-suited to *"formal family lunches or business"*. Another attraction is one of the best breakfasts in town. Head to the adjoining lounges for *"afternoon tea at its best"*: *"beautifully made cakes and sandwiches, and just a special and lovely experience"*. / SW1W 0JW; www.thegoring.com; @TheGoring; Mon-Sat 9.30 pm, Sun 9 pm; No jeans; booking max 8 may apply.

Dinings £87 5 3 2
22 Harcourt St, W1 020 7723 0666 9–4A
Walton House, Walton St, SW3 020 7723 0666 6–2C

"An always-exciting menu, incredible food combinations and superb ingredients" remain points in common for this *"fantastically inventive"* duo of modern Japanese restaurants in Marylebone and Chelsea (*"we thought the original was exceptional until we tried this one too…"*). Branded in common, the owners – who formerly worked together in W1 – increasingly operate independently, with Tomonari Chiba in Marylebone and Masaki Sugisaki steering SW3. Both premises retain an aesthetic that some find *"too cool"*. The Marylebone original is on two floors, of which the bar upstairs is sometimes preferred. Chelsea is in a quiet mews, and has a courtyard garden that comes into its own in summer. / dinings.co.uk.

Dinner by Heston Blumenthal SW1 £144 2 2 1
Mandarin Oriental, 66 Knightsbridge 020 7201 3833 6–1D

Some *"stunning"* meals (*"you just can't beat the tipsy cake!"*) are still reported at Heston Blumenthal's Knightsbridge outpost, but the feeling that it's losing its way is stronger than ever. Despite a menu shake-up in 2020 (a shift away from its increasingly stale menu of Ye Olde English dishes to a more mainstream 'Edible History' menu), its ratings continue to disappoint across the board. The chief complaint is that it's *"so overpriced and overhyped"*, not helped by its bizarrely high rating from Michelin (who are asleep at the wheel on this one, presumably because they don't want to upset Heston by downgrading it). Too often reporters have *"no idea how this place got two stars"*, saying that *"whilst technically the dishes aren't wrong, for the most part they are utterly pedestrian. We paid £660 for 2 for lunch with 5 glasses of wine between us. Off the top of my head, I can think of 20*

*restaurants in the capital alone that are more interesting and better value".
And it's not as though the hotel-style dining room provides much in the way
of compensation, either: "like sitting in an airport lounge… just with even
less personality…".* / SW1X 7LA; www.dinnerbyheston.com; @dinnerbyheston;
Mon-Thu 9 pm, Fri-Sun 9.30 pm.

Dip & Flip £37 3 2 2
87 Battersea Rise, SW11   no tel   11–2C
62 The Broadway, SW19   no tel   11–2B
*"Delicious" gravy is, according to fans, more than a gimmick at this duo of
burger cafés in Battersea and Wimbledon, where thin-sliced West Country
beef is served with lashings of savoury goodness. (The Tooting branch closed
in late 2019).* / www.dipandflip.co.uk; @DipFlippo.

Dirty Burger £37 3 2 2
86 The Broadway, SW19   020 3859 1122   11–2B
Arch 54, 6 South Lambeth Rd, SW8   020 7074 1444   2–4D
13 Bethnal Green Rd, E1   020 7749 4525   13–1B
*This once-thriving burger brand from Nick Jones's Soho House group has
been reduced to a single branch, under the arches in Vauxhall, and a
supporting role at stablemate Chicken Shop in St John's Wood. Fans reckon
it's "good for when you're in a hurry" – perhaps they should hurry, while it's
still there.* / www.eatdirtyburger.com.

Dishoom £49 3 4 5
22 Kingly St, W1   020 7420 9322   4–2B
12 Upper St Martins Ln, WC2   020 7420 9320   5–3B
The Barkers Building, Derry Street, W8   awaiting tel   6–1A
Stable St, Granary Sq, N1   020 7420 9321   9–3C
7 Boundary St, E2   020 7420 9324   13–1B
*"The new Covent Garden branch of Dishoom is spectacular and the food is
still ace" – our poll's most commented-on chain continues to win
overwhelmingly rapturous reviews. It helps that the "very different" Indian
menu is a winner: "super-tasty" and "excellent value", with the "out-of-the-
box" breakfast options a particular fave rave ("have a bacon naan and a
cup of chai, and the world feels a better place"). But, actually, the stand-out
feature is the "always buzzing and fun" atmosphere at its individually
designed branches; and post-lockdown, WC2 took the wraps off a successful
makeover, which mines the heritage of Bombay theatres and early Bollywood
talkies. It helps that service is "slick", from "courteous and attentive staff
who never push what they want to sell". The catch? "painful and lengthy
queues" for walk-ins which have, if anything, worsened since they introduced
reservations in all locations.* / www.dishoom.com; @Dishoom.

Diwana Bhel-Poori House NW1 £30 4 2 2
121-123 Drummond St   020 7387 5556   9–4C
*"This long-standing institution" – "the first bhel poori house in Drummond
Street" (the 'Little India' enclave behind Euston station) – offers "authentic
and tasty vegetarian Indian street food for not much dosh". There are "no
surprises" here, and the "basic, very simple decor and pine furniture" are
"unchanged in decades" – all part of the timewarp appeal to its legion of
long-term habitués.* / NW1 2HL; www.diwanabph.com; @DiwanaBhelPoori; Mon-Sat
10 pm, Sun 9 pm; no Amex; May need 10+ to book.

Donostia W1 £59 4 4 3
10 Seymour Pl   020 3620 1845   2–2A
*"Top tapas" wins fans for this small Basque outfit – along with nearby Lurra,
one of a pair inspired by the pintxo bars of San Sebastian (Donostia in
Basque) under the same ownership near Marble Arch. "The room is lovely, at
the front by the bar or in the window", although it can be "a bit noisy".*
/ W1H 7ND; www.donostia.co.uk; @DonostiaW1; Wed-Sat 10 pm; closed Wed-Sat L,
closed Mon & Tue & Sun; booking max 8 may apply.

Double Standard WC1 £55 3 4 4
The Standard, 10 Argyle St 020 3981 8888 9–3C

A top find bang opposite King's Cross: this comfy, stylish bar at the foot of the Standard Hotel – complete with '70s-tastic soundtrack and decor – is, in particular, "a great choice for brunch, with a super, large outdoor courtyard and terrace, plus lovely and very helpful staff". "The cocktails are great too!". (There is also an adjoining, more moody space called Isla).
/ WC1H 8EG; www.standardhotels.com/london/features/standard_london_isla; Mon-Sun 11 pm; closed Mon-Sun L.

Dragon Castle SE17 £45 3 3 3
100 Walworth Rd 020 7277 3388 1–3C

"Deservedly popular seven days a week" is – in normal times – our assessment of this large South London Chinese, near Elephant & Castle, which has a vast Cantonese menu, and where dim sum is a top attraction. In July 2021, the restaurant told us via email: "we are reopening, but we haven't got a date set in stone just yet". Although still 'temporarily closed' in October 2021, we have rated it on the assumption that it will be business as usual when it does finally re-open. / SE17 1JL; www.dragoncastlelondon.com; @Dragoncastle100; Mon-Sun 11 pm.

The Drapers Arms N1 £60 3 3 4
44 Barnsbury Street 020 7619 0348 9–3D

"Comfort food with modern twists" which "make it different from the usual pub fare", plus "one of the best-priced wine selections in London", explain the enduring success of this early-Victorian Islington gastroboozer. Licensee Nick Gibson "is a gem", and leads an "attentive front of house team" who ensure that "every dish is a pleasure". "Only drawback is that it can get far too busy and noisy". / N1 1ER; www.thedrapersarms.com/; @DrapersArms; Mon-Sat 10.30 pm, Sun 8.30 pm; no Amex.

Dropshot Coffee SW19 £20 3 4 4
281 Wimbledon Park Road 07445 673405 11–2B

"There's always a queue" at this Southfields independent coffee shop – "on the route to Wimbledon tennis (hence the name)" – which "beats the numerous nearby chains by a long way". "Thank God for the coffee – and for their delicious brunches after reopening". / SW19 6NW; dropshotcoffee.co.uk; Mon-Sun 5 pm.

The Drunken Butler EC1 £118 4 4 4
20 Rosebery Avenue 020 7101 4020 10–1A

"Completely unique and hugely enjoyable" – Yuma Hashemi offers modern European cuisine from a tasting menu of his choice (for £85 or £135 at the chef's table) at this Clerkenwell three-year-old. Except on Sundays, when there's a traditional Persian feasting menu that celebrates his heritage. / EC1R 4SX; www.thedrunkenbutler.com; @SYumaHashemi; booking online only.

The Duck & Rice W1 £69 3 3 3
90 Berwick St 020 3327 7888 4–2C

This modern mashup of a gastropub with Chinese cuisine in Berwick Street, Soho, earns solid ratings for its "very good food in the bar and also in the more formal restaurant". But, by comparison to the standards of creator Alan Yau's previous mega-hits, including Wagamama and Hakkasan, some can find it "a bit disappointing overall". / W1F 0QB; www.theduckandrice.com; @theduckandrice; Tue-Sat 11 pm, Sun 9 pm; closed Tue, Wed L, closed Mon.

Duck & Waffle EC2 £92 2️⃣2️⃣3️⃣
110 Bishopsgate, Heron Tower 020 3640 7310 10–2D

"You go for the lovely views" from the 40th floor of the City's Heron Tower when you visit this "loud and crowded" hang-out; and also for the fact that you can eat at any hour due to its 24/7 service. Opinions on the cooking are up-and-down, however, although the "the signature duck & waffle is decent enough and probably the best value", and "the cocktails are good". One hazard: "at least half the diners devote most of their attention to taking photos for their Instagram account". / EC2N 4AY; www.duckandwaffle.com; @DuckandWaffle; Mon-Sun 6 am.

The Duck Truck E1 £16 5️⃣4️⃣2️⃣
Lamb Street 07919 160271 13–2B

"A little truck in the centre of the city serving nothing but duck and chips": parked up permanently at Spitalfields Market, it's "the Nando's of duck!" – "delicious and very affordable", providing "generous portions of very good duck, plus excellent duck-fat-fried fries and slaw". "If I worked locally, I wouldn't be able to fit into my suit after coming here every day!". / E1 6EA; www.theducktruck.com; @TheDuckTruck1; Mon-Fri 4 pm, Sat & Sun 5 pm; closed Mon-Sun D.

Ducksoup W1 £76 3️⃣3️⃣3️⃣
41 Dean St 020 7287 4599 5–2A

The vibe might seem very loose at this rackety Soho bar, but the Italian-North African small plates are "surprisingly filling and delicious". There's also an "adventurous walk through the natural wine list" and the opportunity to select music from the vinyl selection. / W1D 4PY; www.ducksoupsoho.co.uk; @ducksoup; Wed-Sat, Tue 10.30 pm, Sun 5 pm; closed Tue L closed Sun D, closed Mon; Take bookings all week via phone and/or online.

The Duke of Richmond E8 £55 3️⃣2️⃣3️⃣
316 Queensbridge Road 020 7923 3990 14–1A

This three-year-old Dalston/Haggerston gastroboozer from chef Tom Oldroyd (of Oldroyd, Islington) serves serious food in beautiful surroundings – and the mix seems to work: "where else can you have fresh oysters while watching the Euros?". "The burger here is great – but the crab chip butty is also a must", so "prepare to get your hands messy!". / E8 3NH; www.thedukeofrichmond.com; @dukeofrichmond_; Mon-Thu 11 pm, Fri & Sat 9.30 pm, Sun 8 pm; closed Mon-Thu L; Take bookings all week via phone and/or online.

The Duke of Sussex W4 £67 2️⃣2️⃣3️⃣
75 South Pde 020 8742 8801 8–1A

A classic Victorian tavern by Acton Green Common with "lovely pub food you can rely on" from a Spanish tapas-style menu, served in a "beautiful dining room" at the rear, leading out to a small garden. As a bonus for local families, it's notably "good with kids". / W4 5LF; www.thedukeofsussex.co.uk; @thedukew4.

The Duke of York N1 NEW £28
33 Downham Road 020 3137 2539 14–2A

After a spell as Beef & Brew (RIP), this corner pub in Haggerston complete with outside terrace re-launched in winter 2019 in a more pub-like format, with a menu that headlines pizza (with miscellaneous small plates providing backing tracks). The decor sympathetically updates the traditional boozer format, with its tiled floors, bare brick walls and foliage. / N1 5AA; thedukeofyorkpub.com; Mon-Sat 11.30 pm, Sun 11 pm.

Dulwich Lyceum SE21 NEW £53
7 Croxted Road 020 8670 5837 1–4D

Sibling to Peckham Bazaar, John Gionleka's relatively recent Dulwich arrival (which opened in October 2019) focuses – like its sibling – on cooking over a grill. Despite the theatrical connotations of the 'Lyceum' name, this moniker is chosen to chime with its interesting East Mediterranean cuisine, not its premises (which are of a smartish neighbourhood joint, not any kind of venue-conversion). / SE21 8SZ; www.dulwichlyceum.com; @DulwichLyceum; Tue-Sat 11 pm; closed Tue-Sat L, closed Sun & Mon.

Dumpling Shack x Fen Noodles E14 NEW £8 5 3 2
The Collective, 20 Crossharbour Plaza 12–1C

"Pleasingly chewy and slippery noodles…", "excellent dumplings…", "strong, spicy and well-balanced flavours…" – this Isle of Dogs takeaway and delivery outlet a short walk from Crossharbour DLR is worth the pilgrimage despite its "weird location as the in-house restaurant of an aparthotel, where it feels like you're eating in their lobby…?!" The formula combines John & Yee Li's two street-food businesses in Spitalfields with the ultimate aim of a bigger opening in London Fields. The press have raved (Jimi Famurewa in the Standard hailed "some of the best contemporary Chinese food I have ever, ever had"… "delirious command of flavour and fun"). / E14 9YF; www.dumplingshack.co.uk; @DumplingShack; Mon & Tue 6 pm, Wed-Fri 6.30 pm, Sat 5 pm, Sun 4.30 pm; closed Sat & Sun D.

Dumplings' Legend W1 3 2 2
16 Gerrard St 020 7494 1200 5–3A

"Legendary dumplings served with typical Chinatown efficient service" – help this central fixture live up to its name for most reporters, making it a top dim sum favourite for many. To a minority, though, the experience is "sterile and inauthentic". / W1D 6JE; www.dumplingslegend.com; Mon-Sun midnight.

Durbar W2 £40 3 2 2
24 Hereford Rd 020 7727 1947 7–1B

A "local gem" off Bayswater's Westbourne Grove which celebrates its 65th anniversary this year – this "classic tandoori" is "one of London's oldest Indian family-run restaurants" and "never disappoints". Popular for its "warm welcome" and "great flavours at a reasonable price". / W2 4AA; www.durbartandoori.co.uk; Wed-Sun 5 pm; Booking evening only.

Dynamo £50 3 3 3
200-204 Putney Bridge Rd, SW15 020 3761 2952 11–2B
16-18 Ritherdon Road, SW17 020 8767 3197 11–2C

"Great pizza in a cycle-themed restaurant", alongside high-energy breakfast and brunch, washed down by decent coffee, fuel the peloton that passes through Putney on the way to and from Richmond Park – "what's not to like?". The branch in Balham closed down in 2020. / www.the-dynamo.co.uk; @WeAreTheDynamo.

The Dysart Petersham TW10 £80 3 3 4
135 Petersham Road 020 8940 8005 1–4A

"By far the best restaurant in the Richmond area", this superior Arts & Crafts pub on the edge of Richmond Park is "a lovely place for a special occasion", boasting a "beautiful room, lovely attentive staff and top-quality ingredients". The fan club is overwhelmingly local, but chef Kenneth Culhane's "well thought-out and presented" cuisine is winning wider recognition, including a coveted star from the French tyre-makers. / TW10 7AA; www.thedysartpetersham.co.uk; @dysartpetersham; Fri & Sat, Wed & Thu 8.30 pm; closed Wed & Thu L, closed Mon & Tue & Sun.

E Mono NW5 £21 4|3|2
285-287 Kentish Town Road 020 7485 9779 9–2B
"It is simple and basic", but this family-run Turkish fixture in Kentish Town (named for the original Victorian sign on its building) is renowned locally for "utterly delicious and authentic" kebabs. "Well worth a visit, even after so many years" – "it is what cheap and cheerful is all about". / NW5 2JS; emonoturkishrestaurant.co.uk; Mon-Sun 11 pm; No bookings.

E&O W11 £70 3|3|3
14 Blenheim Crescent 020 7229 5454 7–1A
"Delicious fresh Asian food" – a 'greatest hits' selection from dim sum and sushi via Thai green curry and crispy duck with pancakes to black cod in miso – once gave this "buzzy" Notting Hill haunt major profile, and it remains a "real favourite local". Perennially accused of "style over substance", most reporters actually view it as "good value considering the quality". Its Chelsea sibling closed during the pandemic. / W11 1NN; www.eandolondon.com; Mon-Sat midnight, Sun 10 pm; booking max 6 may apply.

The Eagle EC1 £57 4|2|4
159 Farringdon Rd 020 7837 1353 10–1A
"It may be the original gastropub but there's no resting on its laurels" – 30 years since founding chef David Eyre chalked up a blackboard menu and launched a revolution, this Farringdon institution still serves up "tasty rustic food and great beer – what more could you want?". The Mediterranean-leaning menu "changes daily", and the "quality of produce is only heightened by how it is cooked". It's also "very reasonably priced, with a fun and lively atmosphere – all a gastropub should be". / EC1R 3AL; www.theeaglefarringdon.co.uk; @eaglefarringdon; Mon-Sat 10.30 pm, Sun 5 pm; closed Mon-Fri L closed Sun D; no Amex; no booking.

East West NW5 NEW £43
135 Fortess Road 020 3302 5300 9–1C
Adding Indian spicing to pasta and crispy Italian pizza explains the name of Devinder Singh's Tufnell Park venue, which opened in Spring 2020. Early bird feedback suggests it's a concept that 'has legs'. / NW5 2HR; eastwestlondon.com; Tue-Sat 10 pm; closed Tue-Sat L, closed Sun & Mon.

Eat Tokyo £35 3|2|2
16 Old Compton St, W1 020 7439 9887 5–2A
50 Red Lion St, WC1 020 7242 3490 2–1D
27 Catherine St, WC2 020 3489 1700 5–3D
17 Notting Hill Gate, W11 020 7792 9313 7–2B
169 King St, W6 020 8741 7916 8–2B
14 North End Rd, NW11 020 8209 0079 1–1B
628 Finchley Rd, NW11 020 3609 8886 1–1B
This veteran group has served up "authentic Japanese food" – "always fresh, tasty and beautifully presented" – for four decades, at its half-dozen "basic" (ignore the "tired" decor) but "extremely reliable and good-value" London diners. They "never disappoint", with "consistently excellent sashimi and sushi, using really high-quality fish". Venues stretch from Hammersmith via Notting Hill to Soho, Covent Garden and Holborn, while the Golders Green branch adds shabu-shabu to the menu. The group also operates Tonkotsu-ya Ramen on Bond Street. Top Tip: "miso eel is very good". / www.eattokyo.co.uk.

Eataly EC2 NEW £48 3 2 2
135 Bishopsgate   07966 544965   10–2D
The Square Mile continues to up its foodie credentials with the recent arrival of this "excellent Italian food emporium" near Liverpool Street "with a range of bars and restaurants within". Eataly was founded in 2004 by entrepreneur Oscar Farinetti and now has 35 megastores worldwide, including in Tokyo and New York. It finally opened here in London in May 2021, and very early days survey feedback on 'Terra', its pizza and pasta restaurant, was upbeat: "it has a small menu of handmade pastas, wood-fired pizzas, and also specialises in different types of mozzarellas. The food was very good. Service was friendly and the setting busy and buzzy".
/ EC2M 3YD; www.eataly.co.uk; Mon-Sat 11 pm, Sun 10 pm.

Edera W11 £66 3 3 3
148 Holland Park Ave   020 7221 6090   7–2A
Limited but good all-round feedback on this smart neighbourhood Italian in Holland Park, whose menu features some interesting Sardinian dishes. 'Temporarily closed' as we go to press, we have rated it on its historical performance and hope of a reopening some time soon. / W11 4UE; www.edera.co.uk; Mon-Sun 11 pm.

Ekstedt at The Yard,
Great Scotland Yard Hotel SW1 NEW
Great Scotland Yard   020 7925 4700   2–3C
With the September 2021 arrival of Swedish star chef Nicklas Ekstedt, this five-star Hyatt off Whitehall is continuing its creative, north European theme with this "godfather of wood-fired cooking" stepping into the shoes of The Yard by Robin Gill (RIP). It will feature Ekstedt's "old Nordic" cuisine, which sees seasonal ingredients cooked over wood-grills in a (very) open kitchen. / SW1A; www.ekstedtattheyard.com; Tue-Sat 10.30 pm; closed Tue-Sat L, closed Sun & Mon.

Ekte Nordic Kitchen EC4 £53 3 2 2
2-8 Bloomberg Arcade   020 3814 8330   10–3C
"Cheap and cheerful Nordic food" (by City standards), with "fast service and a straightforward menu", has arrived in the Bloomberg Arcade from Danish-born restaurateur Soren Jessen (of the City's No.1 Lombard Street). There's a "very interesting selection of dishes – not just meatballs" – with a good range of smørrebrød (Danish open sandwiches). / EC4N 8AR; www.ektelondon.co.uk; @ektelondon; Mon-Sat 9.30 pm; closed Sun.

El Pastor £47 3 3 4
Brewer Street, W1   020 3092 4553   4–3C NEW
7a Stoney Street, SE1   no tel   10–4C
"A fun spot in Borough Market" – the original "buzzing" branch of the Hart Bros' Mexican duo wins praise for its "tasty tacos", "packed with smoky flavour and a good punch of heat", although even fans often note that it feels "a little pricey for what it is". In June 2021 (after our survey had concluded), a striking new Soho flagship was launched using the space vacated by Hix (RIP), comprising an 86-cover ground floor (terrazzo tiles, muted walls, chandeliers and hanging plants) and 60-cover basement ('Mezcaleria El Colmillo,' named after the nightclub Sam and Crispin Hart ran in the '90s and '00s in Mexico City).

El Ta'koy WC2 NEW
3 Henrietta Street   5–3D

In the basement of the large Covent Garden townhouse development that houses Pivot (see also), this autumn 2021 newcomer marks the return of former Asia de Cuba chef Luis Pous. Here, he will import a street-food operation along the lines of his ventures in Miami, New York and Riyadh. We can expect culinary influences from 'the islands of Hawaii and the Pacific rim, all the way down to South America and a hint of the Caribbean'. Not much you can't put on that menu! Dishes will include tacos, lumpias (akin to spring rolls) and 'guacapoke' – guacamole with poke toppings, alongside Tiki-themed cocktails. / WC2E 8LU; el-takoy.com/.

Eldr at Pantechnicon SW1 NEW   £77   3 3 4
19 Motcomb Street   020 7034 5422   6–1D

In the gobsmackingly impressive redevelopment of Belgravia's gracious Georgian Pantechnicon building – which opened in summer 2020 – this second-floor newcomer is the venue's most grown-up restaurant space. The name means 'fire' in Old Norse, giving some clue as to the main cooking method – with pickling and foraging inspirations much present – and early reports laud some "wonderfully prepared Nordic dishes". For less foodie fidelity, but more fun, head upstairs to the "stunning Roof Garden" (see also). / SW1X; www.pantechnicon.com; Tue-Sat 10 pm, Sun 4 pm; closed Sun D, closed Mon.

Ella Canta W1   £94
InterContinental London Park Lane, Park Lane   020 7318 8715   3–4A

Mexico City chef Martha Ortiz was creating a good reputation for her street-food-inspired menu at this venture, within a large hotel right on Hyde Park Corner. 'Temporarily closed' as we go to press: a call to the hotel in September 2021 showed no fixed time had been set for a re-opening. / W1J 7QY; www.ellacanta.com; @ellacantalondon; Mon-Thu 1 am, Fri 2 am, Sat 4 pm, Sun 6 pm; closed Fri, Mon-Thu L closed Sat & Sun D.

Elliot's   £65   3 3 4
12 Stoney St, SE1   020 7403 7436   10–4C
121-123 Mare Street, E8   020 3302 5252   14–2B NEW

This ten-year-old Borough Market favourite has a "lovely lively ambience" and makes good use of its location to source "excellent, fresh" ingredients for its "delicious Italian-accented small plates" and "tasty seafood". A pioneer purveyor of natural wines in London, it also champions cooking with wood, both on the grill and in the oven that produces "top-class sourdough pizzas". A sibling opened in Mare Street, Hackney, in July 2021. / www.elliots.london; @elliotslondon.

Elystan Street SW3   £96   4 4 3
43 Elystan Street   020 7628 5005   6–2C

"Full of bright, light flavours" – and from a superbly imaginative, "fresh and varied menu" – Phil Howard's "splendid" 'flexitarian' cuisine continues to delight and inspire at this Chelsea five-year-old, in a chichi backstreet. "No expense accounters here – just real people spending their own money on wonderful food in a really friendly contemporary environment", and with notably "attentive but unobtrusive" staff. Its ratings blipped slightly this year, and even a diner reporting his best meal of the year felt it was "struggling to find its rhythm, as so many places are post-lockdown". More typically, though, diners "are thrilled to come back here" – "during the lockdowns, he kept us going with civilized, assemble-at-home meals, but the reopening has made us realize what a master he is. Carry on!!!". / SW3 3NT; www.elystanstreet.com; @elystanstreet; Mon-Thu 2145 pm, Fri & Sat 10.30 pm, Sun 4 pm; closed Sun D.

The Empress E9 £54 **3 3 3**
130 Lauriston Rd   020 8533 5123   14–2B
A famous Sunday lunch destination by Hackney's Victoria Park – this classic mid-Victorian tavern with exposed brickwork serves up ambitious gastropub meals with "great casual professionalism". There's a different cut of steak on the menu every day, and "good Hackney beer" on tap. / E9 7LH; www.empresse9.co.uk; @E9TheEmpress; Tue-Sat 10 pm, Mon 10.30 pm, Sun 9 pm; closed Mon L; no Amex.

Endo at Rotunda W12 £276 **5 5 5**
White City, 101 Wood Lane   020 3972 9000   1–2B
"A gastronomic triumph teamed with great theatre makes for an unforgettable night out", at Endo Kazutoshi's "educational, luxurious, cosseting and extremely fun" experience: a 16-seater on the rooftop of the former BBC TV Centre in Shepherd's Bush. "Endo is a huge character and his sushi is the best in London". "To see the food prepared, learn about the ingredients and experience impeccable Japanese service is brilliant, and the added showmanship of Endo-san just makes the whole thing unforgettable". "The eye-watering price makes this an occasional treat", but those with sufficiently deep pockets say it's "definitely worth the spend": "best meal I've ever had… still thinking about it on a daily basis!". / W12 7FR; www.endoatrotunda.com; Tue-Sat 11 pm; closed Tue-Sat L, closed Sun & Mon; booking online only.

Enoteca Turi SW1 £79 **3 5 3**
87 Pimlico Road   020 7730 3663   6–2D
"Putney's loss a few years ago became Chelsea's gain", and Giuseppe and Pamela Turi's long-established gem has shone even more brightly in its new location, providing "sophisticated Italian dining at its best". "The premises are not huge, but cleverly laid out so you don't feel crammed". And "the fact that so many Putney loyalists are willing to make the longer journey to eat here is testament to how good the food and service are". "Flavours are always spot-on" (and "their truffle menu is a gastronomic highlight"). "But it's the wine list that blows you away": "superbly curated by Guiseppe" and offering a "serious voyage through Italy but one that's fair value. You can drink well at a very reasonable price… or go mad and take out an extra mortgage!". / SW1W 8PH; www.enotecaturi.com; @EnotecaTuri; Mon-Sat 10 pm; closed Sun; No trainers; booking max 8 may apply.

The Enterprise SW3 £69 **2 3 4**
35 Walton St   020 7584 3148   6–2C
This "friendly local" is as smart as its Walton Street regulars in a very soigné corner of Chelsea, providing "solid" service and "good food" – at prices that probably exclude it from the definition of a pub (it's akin to a club for regulars). / SW3 2HU; www.theenterprise.co.uk; Mon-Sat 10.30 pm, Sun 10 pm; closed Mon-Fri L.

Epic Pies EC4 NEW £36
53-55 Carter Lane   020 7236 0721   10–3B
The name says it all about this new 'Britisserie' (an 'authentic British patisserie'), which opened on a corner site near St Paul's in December 2019. Owners Daniel Jobsz and his mum honed their classic pie-making skills at markets, festivals and pop-ups from 2015 before they found the site, which incorporates a small courtyard. Full English breakfasts (in a tart, of course), plus epic mash and a good list of beers and other drinks complete the formula. / EC4V 5AE; www.epicpies.co.uk; @EpicPiesUK; Tue-Fri 9.30 pm; closed Mon, Sat & Sun.

Erev SE1 NEW   **£38**
Borough Market Kitchen, Jubilee Place, Winchester Walk   10–4C
*'Tel Aviv Market Food' is the promise at Shuk (a stand in Borough Market)
and this 2020 creation – an evening supperclub in a nearby covered
marquee – builds on the formula with less fast-foody modern Israeli dishes
of a quality that belies the picnic-in-a-tent vibe. / SE1 1TL;
www.shuklondon.com/; @LondonShuk; Mon-Sat 4.30 pm; closed Mon-Sat D, closed
Sun.*

L'Escargot W1   **£92**   3 3 4
48 Greek Street   020 7439 7474   5–2A
*"A beautiful interior from another era and a lovely, unhurried, relaxing
experience" underpin the period appeal of Brian Clivaz and George Pell's
Soho veteran – London's oldest French restaurant, they say (est 1927). The
introduction of a sushi and cocktail menu is a recent innovation, alongside a
French menu the charm of which is its traditional style: snails in garlic butter,
lobster bisque, chateaubriand…. It doesn't attract as many reports as once it
did, but fans say "a romantic evening spent here is utter perfection". (For
those up Aldeburgh way, it now has a country sibling too, L'Escargot sur
Mer). / W1D 4EF; www.lescargot.co.uk; @LEscargotSoho; Tue-Sat 10 pm; closed
Sun & Mon.*

Estiatorio Milos SW1   **£109**   3 2 4
1 Regent St   020 7839 2080   4–4D
*A "glamorous feel that befits the location in St James's" – complete with
white marble from mountains near Athens! – infuses this "buzzy" and
"noisy" London outpost of Costas Spiladis's ritzily international Greek
seafood chain. The "nosebleed prices for its delicious fresh fish" do nothing
to deter the crowd – "it's a big restaurant, but whenever I go there isn't an
empty table". The centrepiece is a counter display of "super fish" – "perfect
for the choosing side of things with people who know what they're talking
about". Top Tip: "the lunchtime menu is a real bargain". / SW1Y 4NR;
www.estiatoriomilos.com/; @Milos_London; Mon-Sun 11 pm.*

Evelyn's Table at The Blue Posts W1   **£106**   5 5 3
28 Rupert Street   07921 336010   4–3D
*Star chef Luke Selby (former head chef of Hide), together with brothers
Nathaniel and Theo, now runs this intimate 10-seat counter experience in
the cellar of the 275-year-old Blue Posts pub in Chinatown, which melds a
love of British produce, Japanese techniques and classic French training.
We've rated it on limited but outstanding initial feedback and the
impossibility of getting a table – bookings are released on the first of every
month, at midday. / W1D 6DJ; www.theblueposts.co.uk/evelyns-table/; Tue-Sat 11 pm;
closed Tue-Sat L, closed Sun & Mon; Take bookings all week via phone and/or online.*

Everest Inn SE3   **£47**   3 2 2
41 Montpelier Vale   020 8852 7872   1–4D
*This "good-value Nepalese restaurant" in Blackheath Village wins plaudits
for its "excellent" curries and Himalayan specialities including momo –
steamed dumplings filled with meat or vegetables. Service is not always up
to scratch. / SE3 0TJ; www.everestinn.co.uk; @Everestinn; Tue-Sun 10 pm; closed
Tue-Fri L, closed Mon.*

Fallow at 10 Heddon Street W1 £95 4 4 4
10 Heddon Street   07785 937900   4–3B

"Classy and talented cooking, with a sustainable bent (that doesn't overshadow enjoyment)" has made a smash hit out of Jack Croft and Will Murray's extended residency at this well-known site, off Regent Street, which has previously been the launch pad for a series of impressive extended pop-ups (Leach & Carter, Pacific). Despite opening at a tricky time (they took over here in autumn 2020) it inspires tons of favourable reports, lauding its *"incredible small plates"* (*"triumphant corn ribs"*, *"rich and moreish mushroom parfait"*, with *"cod's head as a particular favourite"*). The contemporary interior is stylish enough, but in good weather head for the terrace. / W1B 4BX; www.fallowrestaurant.com; @FallowRestaura1; Mon-Sat 11 pm, Sun 8 pm; Credit card deposit required to book.

La Famiglia SW10 £72 2 2 3
7 Langton Street   020 7351 0761   6–3B

"Little has changed" in five decades at this *"old established Italian"* – in a plush enclave off King's Road Chelsea – which, with its gorgeous garden, has hosted celebrities as diverse as Princess Margaret and Jack Nicholson over the years. It *"continues to please"* a clientele of loyalists – *"what's in a name? I've been coming for 25 years, since my children were a year old and had tubetti in a high chair – and it's still a lovely place to go with the family"*. Nevertheless, the ratings have for years now suggested that *"standards are slipping and prices going up"* – *"it's still the right side of OK, but only just"*. For those inclined to nostalgia, one 70s survival might justify a visit – *"the sweet trolley"*! / SW10 0JL; www.lafamiglia.co.uk; @lafamiglia_sw10; Mon-Fri 10.45 pm, Sat 10.45pm, Sun 9.30 pm.

Farang N5 £48 4 3 3
72 Highbury Park   020 7226 1609   9–1D

"Thai food with wonderful spicing" – *"truly authentic flavours"* – *"is not to be missed"* at this new-wave Southeast Asian pop-up-turned-permanent in Highbury. Seb Holmes has developed the project from a market stall to some prominence in five years, and now serves only a nine-course tasting menu in the *"lovely light and spacious environment"* of the former San Daniele (RIP). *"The takeaway versions worked really well during lockdown, too"*. Top Tip: *"the not-to-be-missed roti bread"*. / N5 2XE; www.faranglondon.co.uk; @farangLDN; Wed-Sat 9 pm; closed Mon & Tue & Sun; no Amex; Take bookings all week via phone and/or online.

Fare EC1 £56 3 3 3
11 Old Street   020 3034 0736   13–1A

With its chic take on simple Italian food, this three-year-old near Silicon Roundabout, where Clerkenwell meets Shoreditch, *"has become a favourite pizzeria"* in the area – *"although their other food is just as good"*, including home-made pasta. *"The Saturday afternoon special with pizza and cocktails is very good value"*. / EC1V 9HL; farelondon.com/; @Farebarcanteen; Mon-Sun 10 pm.

Farmacy W2 £65 4 4 4
74 Westbourne Grove   020 7221 0705   7–1B

"I don't normally like vegan food but this was just fine" – Camilla Fayed's 'sun to soil' venture in Bayswater was again solidly well reviewed this year. / W2 5SH; www.farmacylondon.com; @farmacyuk; Mon-Sun 10 pm; SRA-Food Made Good – 2 stars.

The Farrier NW1 NEW £50
Camden Market, Chalk Farm Road   020 8092 4100   9–2B
On the former Camden Market site of Proud Cabaret, this April 2021 newcomer is the market's first-ever pub (yes, really!) and occupies a Grade II listed space that once housed stables (lots of vaulted brick ceilings and bare brick walls). Not only does it have the handy feature of a hidden courtyard with fire pit, but also locally brewed beers and rustic British fare from Ash Finch (ex-The Langham and Wild Honey). / NW1 8AH; www.thefarriercamden.com; cards only.

The Fat Badger TW10 NEW
15-17 Hill Rise   01423 505681   1–4A
The Gladwin family (owners of Shed, Rabbit, Nutbourne, Sussex) are opening their fifth venture in late 2021, supplied by the family farm and vineyard in Sussex: a new bar/restaurant just off Richmond's high street on a site that was once GBK. We are promised 'distinct countryside luxe-style, serving modern farm-to-fork food in an atmospheric, sprawling space overlooking the Richmond riverside'. / TW10 6UQ; www.thefatbadger-restaurant.com; Mon-Sun 4 pm.

Fatt Pundit £61   3 3 2
77 Berwick Street, W1   02072877900   4–1C
6 Maiden Lane, WC2   020 7836 8883   5–3D NEW
Chinese-Indian Hakka cuisine incorporating some interesting ingredients (crab, rabbit, venison) help inspire enthusiastic (if limited) feedback for this Soho two-year-old. In late 2021, a sibling will open on a former Polpo site in Covent Garden featuring a new cocktail offering and unusual wines from organic producers across the globe.

Fenchurch Restaurant, Sky Garden EC3 £91   3 3 4
20 Fenchurch St   033 3772 0020   10–3D
"Amazing views" from the 37th floor of the Walkie Talkie Tower are backed up by "delicious and beautiful food" from chef Michael Carr at this "well-presented" City destination. Upmarket caterers Rhubarb have worked commendably hard to ensure the venue offers more than just a "great location". / EC3M 3BY; skygarden.london/fenchurch-restaurant; @SG_SkyGarden; Tue, Wed, Sun 11 pm, Fri & Sat 2 am, Mon 6 pm, Thu midnight; closed Mon D; booking max 7 may apply.

FENN SW6 NEW £57   5 4 3
194 Wandsworth Bridge Road   020 7371 9888   11–1B
"If you live anywhere near Fulham you have to go!" and discover this "recognition-worthy" newcomer – which looks like "a proper local, but serves star-quality food". The team behind Hackney's Nest (Luke Wasserman, Toby Neill and Johnnie Crowe) crossed town to open this 30-seater venture plus terrace, first launching it as Harlequin (RIP) then redoing it as Fenn. "The location is not ideal" given "the continuous traffic you get on Wandsworth Bridge Road", but "the wonderful food and wines more than make up for seeking it out". Chef Joe Laker, ex-Anglo, is at the stoves, and his "stunning and creative" but unponcey British cooking inspires raves: "every plate is wonderfully crafted" and there's "an interesting wine list full of surprises", all delivered by "a charming, helpful young team". "The tasting menu is certainly worth it – as otherwise it would be too hard to choose!". / SW6 2UF; fennrestaurant.co.uk; Tue-Sat 9.30 pm; closed Tue, Wed L, closed Sun & Mon.

Fez Mangal W11 £28   5 4 3
104 Ladbroke Grove   020 7229 3010   7–1A
This "highly recommended" Turkish grill in Ladbroke Grove has earned top marks in our survey for its "delicious food" over several years now and its "great value" is thanks in part to the BYO policy. An extension added a few years back means you don't have to queue too long for a table. / W11 1PY; www.fezmangal.com; @FezMangal; Mon-Sun 11.30 pm; no Amex.

Fiend W10 NEW £55
301 Portobello Road   020 3971 8404   7–1A

Chris Denney, chef at the excellent but now defunct 108 Garage (RIP), launched this curiously named spot on the Notting Hill site that was formerly Santo (RIP) site in July 2021 (after our survey had concluded). You eat on the ground floor with views to the open kitchen (and there's also a basement bar), with the option of either à la carte or a 6-course tasting menu. The cuisine is in a similar, creative modern European vein to what was offered at 108. / W10 5TD; www.fiend-portobello.com; Tue-Thu midnight, Fri & Sat 1 am; closed Tue-Thu L, closed Sun & Mon.

50 Kalò di Ciro Salvo WC2 £45   5 4 3
7 Northumberland Avenue   020 7930 9955   2–3C

"Utterly delicious Neapolitan-style pizza" – the highest rated in town – is to be found here, where you'd least expect it – bang in the middle of the West End, just off Trafalgar Square. Neapolitan master pizza-slinger Ciro Salvo's UK offshoot occupies a huge, "buzzy and lively" space in a hotel with its own entrance. 50 Kalò signifies 'good dough' in Napolitano, and Salvo's secret is ultra-high hydration and long fermentation for a super-light crust. / WC2N 5BY; www.xn–50kal-yta.it/index.php; Mon-Thu midnight, Fri & Sat 12.30 am, Sun 11 pm.

Figo E20 NEW £34
17 Endeavour Square, Westfield Avenue   020 8075 9899   14–1D

By the Stratford entrance to the Olympic park, this all-day Italian restaurant and café arrived in autumn 2019 and has since spawned a couple of Essex-based spin-offs. The space – with big windows – is modern, but the food is traditional: arancini, pasta, pizza from the oven... / E20 1JN; figorestaurant.co.uk; @Figo_Restaurant; Mon-Sun 11 pm.

Fink's Salt and Sweet N5 £53   3 4 3
70 Mountgrove Road   020 7684 7189   9–1D

"A lovely local coffee shop" in Highbury – this four-year-old majors on "tasty fresh bread/pastries and delicious coffee" and "also sells a nice range of deli bits/wines etc". The same team have opened a second site on nearby Gillespie Road. / N5 2LT; finks.co.uk; @FinksLondon; Mon-Sun 4 pm; closed Sun D; cards only; No bookings.

Firebrand EC1 NEW 3 3 3
84 Rosebery Avenue   020 7683 0326   10–1A

Solid ratings for the Neapolitan-inspired scran at these vaguely retro, wood-fired sourdough pizza cafés in Marylebone and Clerkenwell, which also serve a range of Italian wines, cocktails and craft beers. / EC1R 4QY; www.firebrandpizza.co.uk; @firebrand_pizza; Fri & Sat 10.30 pm, Tue-Thu 10 pm.

Fischer's W1 £60   2 2 4
50 Marylebone High Street   020 7466 5501   2–1A

With its "glorious interior", Corbin & King's "buzzy Viennese" all-day café in Marylebone is "a lovely, nostalgic and comforting experience", which – even if it is "a bit pricey" nowadays – "presses all the buttons" if you are hankering for schnitzel Holstein, breakfast gröstls, rye sandwiches and the like. "I love this place and missed my Austrian holidays this year, so the food reminds me of those missed trips". / W1U 5HN; www.fischers.co.uk; @FischersLondon; Sun & Mon 9.30 pm, Tue-Sat 10 pm.

Fish Central EC1 £39   3 3 2
149-155 Central St   020 7253 4970   13–1A

This Greek-Cypriot Clerkenwell veteran has offered consistently "good-quality and good-value" fish for more than half a century, evolving beyond the basic fish'n'chips to encompass a range of seafood dishes plus grilled meat, along with a wine list and cocktails. Handily, it's within easy walking distance of the Barbican arts centre. / EC1V 8AP; www.fishcentral.co.uk; @fishcentral1968; Mon-Thu, Sat 10.30 pm, Fri 11 pm; closed Sun.

fish! SE1 £73 **4**3**3**
Cathedral St   020 7407 3803   10–4C

"The fish and shellfish is so fresh and perfectly cooked" at this glass-and-steel venue *"in the buzzing environment of Borough Market"*. Founded in 1999, it has continued to prosper with the expansion of the foodie market. / SE1 9AL; www.fishkitchen.co.uk; @fishborough; Mon-Sat 9.30 pm, Sun 3 pm.

Fishers SW6 **3**2**3**
19 Fulham High Street   02073715555   11–1B

"The standard is consistently high" for *"quality fresh fish"* at this well-known chippy and seafood restaurant, visible to anyone stuck in the traffic trying to get over Putney Bridge. / SW6 3JH; www.fishersfishandchips.co.uk/; Mon-Sun 10.30 pm.

Fishworks £72 2**2**2
7-9 Swallow St, W1   020 7734 5813   4–4C
89 Marylebone High St, W1   020 7935 9796   2–1A
2-4 Catherine Street, WC2   020 7240 4999   5–3D

"Thoroughly reliable, good fresh fish at sensible prices for London" justifies a trip to this trio of seafood bistros in some of the capital's most expensive areas – Covent Garden, Marylebone and Swallow Street (just a step from Piccadilly Circus). The cooking may not be hugely exciting, but *"they do pretty standard fish dishes very well"* – *"including excellent cod and chips"*. Each branch has an in-store fishmonger, so you can pick up something extra to cook at home. / www.fishworks.co.uk.

Fiume SW8 £76 **3**2**4**
Circus West Village, Sopwith Way   020 3904 9010   11–1C

"Good food" from eminent southern Italian chef Francesco Mazzei and a *"spectacular terrace with views over the river"* are the calling cards of this spacious D&D London venue near Battersea Power Station. On a sunny day, though, lunch on the terrazzo can witness *"the whole riverside teeming with building workers from the huge power station site on their lunch break"*. / SW8 5BN; fiume-restaurant.co.uk; @FiumeLondon; Mon-Sat 10 pm, Sun 9 pm.

The Five Fields SW3 £163 **554**
8-9 Blacklands Ter   020 7838 1082   6–2D

Taylor Bonnyman's *"exceptional"* Chelsea heavyweight (one of the survey's Top 40 most mentioned restaurants, and the winner of Harden's London Restaurant Awards' Top Gastronomic Experience in 2019) provides an un-showy but luxurious experience that's hard to better. It's very consistent all-round. His and head chef Marguerite Keogh's thoughtful cuisine is *"not too heavy and perfectly judged"*, using *"own-grown seasonal produce"* from the restaurant's garden in East Sussex. *"Service is attentive without being cloying"*. And the *"charming"* premises in the tangle of streets near Peter Jones are often tipped for celebrations: *"perfect for romance and decadence"*. / SW3 2SP; www.fivefieldsrestaurant.com; @The5Fields; Tue-Sat 10 pm; closed Tue, Wed L, closed Sun & Mon; Take bookings all week via phone and/or online.

500 N19 £53 **3**4**3**
782 Holloway Rd   020 7272 3406   9–1C

This *"proper neighbourhood gem"* near Archway *"fully deserves its loyal following"* for the *"exceptional Italian food and wonderful service"* it provides. Inspired by the diminutive Fiat Cinquecento, it was founded 15 years ago by Milanese-born chef Mario Magli, who previously worked under Jamie Oliver's mentor, Gennaro Contaldo. / N19 3JH; www.500restaurant.co.uk; @500restaurant; Wed-Sat 10 pm, Sun 9 pm; closed Wed-Sat L, closed Mon & Tue.

500 Degrees SE24 £36 432

153a Dulwich Road 020 7274 8200 11–2D

This "lovely local pizza restaurant" beside Brockwell Park (with branches in Brixton, Crystal Palace and Dulwich) "has an authentic, down-to-earth vibe" and specialises in pizzas with "good chewy crusts and plenty of punchy flavour". / SE24; www.500degrees.co; @500degreesuk; Mon-Sat 11 pm, Sun 10 pm; closed Mon-Thu L.

FKABAM (Black Axe Mangal) N1 £50 433

156 Canonbury Road no tel 9–2D

"Not for the faint-hearted!" – Lee Tiernan's "funky and chilled" feature near Highbury Corner has won fame and acclaim (including from Harden's) over the years for its exotic flatbreads, heavy metal soundtrack and offbeat (in part genital-themed) decor. In September 2021, Lee finally announced its re-opening (it had been closed since the onset of the pandemic). The new name means 'Formerly Known As Black Axe Mangal', and we're guessing it will offer a retread rather than a totally new formula. (Maybe he got bored of listening to KISS over the pandemic and his listening tastes have moved on to Prince?). / N1; www.blackaxemangal.com; @blackaxemangal; Wed-Fri 10.30 pm; closed Wed-Fri L, closed Mon & Tue, Sat & Sun; cards only; Credit card deposit required to book.

The Flask N6 £50 334

77 Highgate West Hill 020 8348 7346 9–1B

This "busy but reliable" Youngs pub, in a backstreet behind Hampstead tube, is "a favourite for Sunday lunch after a walk across the Heath". The cooking is "interesting now they have a new chef", and the Victorian interior helps to ensure a "great atmosphere, even in difficult times". / N6 6BU; www.theflaskhighgate.com; @flaskn6; Mon-Sun 10 pm.

Flat Iron £36 344

17 Beak St, W1 020 3019 2353 4–2B
42-44 James Street, W1 3–1A NEW
17 Henrietta St, WC2 020 3019 4212 5–3C
9 Denmark St, WC2 no tel 5–1A
47-51 Caledonian Rd, N1 9–3D
112-116 Tooley Street, SE1 10–4D
Soho Wharf, Clink Street, SE1 10–3C NEW
88-90 Commercial Street, E1 13–2C
77 Curtain Road, EC2 no tel 13–1B

"If you want a good steak that's half the price you'd pay at Hawksmoor or Gaucho, then this will do nicely!" – so say fans of this "always busy and dependable" chain, which added a Bevis Marks branch in October 2020 and opens a ninth 90-seater venue near Borough Market on Clink Street in late 2021. The success of the formula is its "straightforward" menu ("the simplest I have ever seen in a restaurant: five or six steaks, six sides, no starters, no puddings, but a delicious soft salted caramel in a cornet on the way out"). "Are prices creeping up though...?" – ratings dipped this year with more reports of the "good, but nothing special" variety. (Btw 'Flat Iron', aka 'featherblade', is a cut known for its tenderness, flavour and affordability). / www.flatironsteak.co.uk; @flatironsteak.

Flat Three W11 £67 433

120-122 Holland Park Ave 020 7792 8987 7–2A

Under the radar in a stylish Holland Park basement, Juliana Moustakas's "amazing neighbourhood restaurant" deserves a wider audience. Service is "welcoming, but not 'in yer face'" and there's a variety of "fantastic Japanese/Korean-inspired dishes and exciting foraged ingredients that don't feel gimmicky". "The atmosphere is quiet enough so you can have a conversation and the wine list is sensational". / W11 4UA; www.flatthree.london; @InfoFlat3; Tue-Sat 9.30 pm; closed Tue-Thu L, closed Sun & Mon; Take bookings all week via phone and/or online.

Flat White W1 £12
17 Berwick St   020 7734 0370   4–2D
No feedback this year on this cute indie, NZ-scene café in the middle of Berwick Street Market. We continue to include it on the basis that – in 2005 – it introduced London to the 'Flat White' and is worth remembering in these parts. / W1F 0PT; www.flatwhitesoho.co.uk; @flatwhitesoho; Mon-Sun 6 pm; cash only; No bookings.

Flesh and Buns £60   3 3 3
32 Berners Street, W1   020 3019 3492   3–1D
Bone Daddies, 41 Earlham Street, WC2   020 7632 9500   5–2C
"Delicious steamed bao buns with great fillings" are the star turn at these "loud" and dynamic izakayas (Japanese gastropubs) in Covent Garden and Fitzrovia, backed up by raw fish and hot-stone rice dishes. The newer, bigger Fitzrovia branch, near Oxford Circus, adds a selection of Peruvian-fusion Nikkei plates. They are part of the Bone Daddies group, whose Australian founder, Ross Shonhan, departed in 2020 for pastures new in Dubai. / www.fleshandbuns.com; @FleshandBuns.

Flor SE1 £60   5 4 4
1 Bedale Street   020 3319 8144   10–4C
James Lowe's (he of Lyle's) and JKS Restaurants' all-day bakery and wine bar in Borough Market (mostly) inspires a hymn of praise. Culinary offerings might run from coffee and croissants to calf's brains and a glass of Closeries des Moussis, and there's strong praise for a selection of dishes that's "innovative, but not outré" backed up by a "great wine list". Also, it's "a darling little place and staff are just lovely!". / SE1 9AL; florlondon.com; Wed-Sat 10 pm, Sun 3 pm; closed Wed L closed Sun D, closed Mon & Tue.

Flora Indica SW5 £50   4 3 4
242 Old Brompton Rd   020 7370 4450   6–2A
"Really different" Indian cooking and "quirky decor" – which celebrates the Victorian-era Scottish botanists who collected the subcontinent's flora – combine to good effect at this Earl's Court four-year-old. "After a few wobbles having taken over these premises from Mr Wing (RIP), the kitchen has really found its mojo – and now turns out spot-on flavours every time". One of its many unusual features is the brevity of its menu by comparison with most curry houses. / SW5 0DE; www.flora-indica.com/; @Flora_Indica; Mon-Sun 11 pm.

Florattica,
Canopy by Hilton EC3 NEW
11-15 Minories   020 3988 7480   10–3D
Near Aldgate, a new hotel – a 'with-it' extension of the Hilton brand – opened in April 2021. Later in the year, this large new rooftop terrace and restaurant opens to help it live up to the hotel's name. Attractions will include an all-day menu from breakfast. / EC3N 1AX; www.hilton.com/en/hotels/lonpypy-canopy-london-city; Thu-Sun 5 pm.

FM Mangal SE5 £45   3 3 2
54 Camberwell Church St   020 7701 6677   1–3C
"The grill is clearly in the hands of professionals" at this snug and popular Turk in Camberwell – staffed by "lovely people" who treat their customers to "great food". "The free bread and onion dip to start is divine", and guarantees a good vibe from the get-go. / SE5 8QZ; www.fmmangal.co.uk/; @FM_Mangal; Mon-Sun midnight; no Amex; no booking.

Foley's W1 £51   3 3 2
23 Foley Street   020 3137 1302   2–1B
'A local restaurant that thinks big' – this tightly packed Fitzrovia five-year-old inspires good vibes for its pan-Asian dishes, cocktails and saké. / W1W 6DU; www.foleysrestaurant.co.uk; Mon-Sat 10.30 pm; closed Sun.

Fortnum & Mason, The Diamond Jubilee Tea Salon W1 £86   3 3 4
181 Piccadilly   020 7734 8040   3–3D

This "classy – and very British" location for a refined afternoon tea" on the fourth floor of Fortnum & Mason – once the apartment where the Fortnum family lived 'over the shop' – spells "Treat! Treat! Treat!" (and is "better value than the Savoy or Ritz"). "I don't even like afternoon tea. It was a gift, but who can resist those perfect finger sandwiches, delicious light scones and beautiful cakes…?". / WIA IER; www.fortnumandmason.com; @Fortnums; Mon-Thu 6.30 pm, Fri 7 pm, Sat 7.30 pm, Sun 6 pm; closed Mon-Thu D; No trainers; Take bookings all week via phone and/or online.

The Fortnum's Bar & Restaurant EC3 £77   2 3 3
The Royal Exchange   020 7734 8040   10–2C

Fortnum's hold the catering and bar concession for the spectacular City courtyard of the Royal Exchange, where they provide luxury all-day snacking, sipping and dining (start the day with "the best-ever porridge with whisky and cream!"). It must be the just about the only restaurant in London to provide 'personal shopping advice' to diners, guiding them round the glossy shops that have replaced traders in the surrounding exchange. / EC3 3LR; www.fortnumandmason.com/restaurants/the-bar-and-restaurant-at-the-royal-exchange; @Fortnums; Mon-Fri 11 pm; closed Sat & Sun.

45 Jermyn St. SW1 £80   3 3 3
45 Jermyn Street, St. James's   020 7205 4545   3–3D

The modern update of Fortnums' old Edwardian buttery has become a "go-to eatery in the West End", "much-loved and much-used". "This place is fab and works on many different levels, depending on the occasion you're eating out for" – equally suitable for "a great breakfast (including the healthier stuff)" as for business entertaining, when "you come away pleasantly lighter of wallet, but at least your clients won't think you've gone all hedge-fund on them". / SWIY 6DN; www.45jermynst.com; @45JermynSt; Mon-Fri 11 pm, Sat & Sun 7 pm.

40 Maltby Street SE1 £57   3 3 4
40 Maltby St   020 7237 9247   10–4D

This Victorian railway arch behind London Bridge station has earned a stellar reputation for its stripped-down gastronomy, with "carefully sourced seasonal ingredients transformed into imaginative dishes by Steve Williams and his team". After ten years, there's still no concession to comfort for either cooks or customers, just a chalked-up menu of the day's dishes and some functional furniture. The arch also serves as a warehouse for the Gergovie biodynamic wine import business, so there's an "interesting all-natural wine list" to accompany your meal. / SEI 3PA; www.40maltbystreet.com; @40maltbystreet; Wed-Sat 10 pm; closed Wed-Sat L, closed Mon & Tue & Sun; no Amex; no booking.

Forza Wine SE15 NEW £48   3 4 4
Floor 5, Rye Lane   020 7732 7500   1–4D

Sip your cocktail, nibble on charcuterie and watch the sun fade over the London skyline at this "friendly and accommodating" roof-top bar in Peckham, which fans say has "the best bar view in SE London". On the menu, "interesting cocktails, an array of natural wines, plus small plates of delicious Italian-inspired bites". It's on the fifth-floor of a co-working space, opposite the tube station, and opened in the second half of 2019 – from the same team who ran the now-defunct Forza Win (no 'e') nearby. If you eat inside, not out, it's closely packed. / SE15 4ST; www.forzawine.com; Sun-Thu 11.30 pm, Fri & Sat 12.30 am.

400 Rabbits £30 3|3|3
143 Evelina Road, SE15 020 7732 4115 1–4D
30-32 Westow St, SE19 020 8771 6249 1–4D
Brockwell Lido, Dulwich Road, SE24 020 7737 8183 11–2D NEW
521 Norwood Road, SE27 020 8761 0872 1–4D NEW
This "highly recommended" South London operation gives an original twist
to "sourdough wood-fired pizzas", served with craft beer and "excellent
gelato and desserts". With branches in Crystal Palace, Nunhead, West
Norwood and Elephant & Castle, they have also taken over the Art Deco
café at Brockwell Park Lido, where "cheap and cheerful cocktails and pizza
on the waterside make you feel you're on holiday". Top Tip: "their courgette
chimichurri pizza with added goat's cheese is highly addictive".
/ www.400rabbits.co.uk; @4hundredrabbits.

Four Seasons £54 4|1|1
11 Gerrard Street, W1 020 7287 0900 5–3A
12 Gerrard St, W1 020 7494 0870 5–3A
23 Wardour St, W1 020 7287 9995 5–3A
84 Queensway, W2 020 7229 4320 7–2C
"Cheap 'n' cheerful roast duck and other Cantonese roast meats" have won
a big following for this Chinese quartet, with the "mothership" in Bayswater
hailed as "still the best roast duck in the country". But the "excellent food is
let down by indifferent service" – a steady theme over the years; likewise, the
interiors are unlikely to grace the pages of a design magazine any time
soon. / www.fs-restaurants.co.uk.

14 Hills EC3 NEW £85 3|3|4
120 Fenchurch Street 020 3981 5222 10–3D
A "beautiful location" – and extraordinary foliage – are selling points of this
"relative newcomer to the improving City scene" from D&D London. Opened
in late 2019 on the 14th floor of 120 Fenchurch Street, it is planted with
100 trees and more than 2,000 other plants! The cuisine – billed as British
produce cooked with 'French flair' – is mostly rated as "very good" but
sometimes perhaps predictably dismissed for being "overpriced and
uninspiring – you're paying for the view". / EC3M 5BA; www.danddlondon.com;
@14hillslondon; Mon-Sat 11 pm.

Fox & Grapes SW19 £58 3|2|2
9 Camp Rd 020 8619 1300 11–2A
In attractive, late 18th-century premises on the edge of Wimbledon
Common, this "good local gastropub" is "busy" for good reason – "it does
everything really well" and the food is "definitely a cut above typical pub
fayre". / SW19 4UN; www.foxandgrapeswimbledon.co.uk; Wed-Sat 11 pm, Sun
10 pm; closed Mon & Tue.

The Fox and Pheasant SW10 £50 3|3|4
1 Billing Road 020 7352 2943 6–3B
"A beautiful light and airy dining room with fully opening glass roof for
alfresco style dining, plus a more traditional boozer at the front with darts
board" help make this 'little country pub tucked away in a corner of
Chelsea' a "gem of a find". But it doesn't just look good – its superior menu
is extremely well-realised and excellent value. / SW10 9UJ;
www.thefoxandpheasant.com; Mon-Sat midnight, Sun 11 pm; closed Mon L.

Franco Manca £38 3 3 3

"Seemingly grown very quickly from a small Brixton pizza joint to a national chain" – this 50-plus strong chain has emerged from the pandemic stronger than ever (revenues post-lockdown up since 2019), snapping up recently vacated sites left, right and centre (most of the growth is outside the capital, with about seven new branches planned for the coming year). Their success? "They have still kept the original ethos: simple, authentic sourdough pizzas served quickly with no-label wines", and it's "superb value". Fans feel "it's so reliable, it's taken the PizzaExpress crown!"… which seems reasonable as Fulham Shore, who own Franco Manca, is run by David Page, who was CEO of PizzaExpress in the 1990s. / www.francomanca.co.uk; @francomancapizz.

Franco's SW1 £84 3 3 4
61 Jermyn St 020 7499 2211 3–3C

"A gem on Jermyn Street" – this "swanky St James's Italian classic" has been trading for 75 years but still, paradoxically, "feels a little undiscovered". Generally "reliable" and "a very good place for a business breakfast and lunch", it has to be noted that those not adding the bill to their expenses claim can find it "very expensive". From another perspective, though, "it may be an odd choice for romance, but if you need to show how sophisticated, stylish, discreet and just plain wealthy you are, why go anywhere else?". / SW1Y 6LX; www.francoslondon.com; @francoslondon; Mon-Sat 11 pm, Sun 10 pm; Take bookings all week via phone and/or online.

Frank's SW1 NEW £34
36 Duke Street St James's 3–3D

Below Maison François (see also), this amiable, new, no-bookings wine bar in St James's mixes a nowadays-proven formula of unconventional wines with hearty Gallic small plates: charcuterie, pâté and so forth. Handy to know about in a pricey area. / SW1Y 6DF; www.maisonfrancois.london/home/#franks; Tue-Sat midnight; closed Tue-Sat L, closed Sun & Mon; No bookings.

Frank's Canteen N5 £43 3 4 3
86 Highbury Park 020 7354 4830 9–1D

Originally a catering company, Frank's Canteen has been a Highbury fixture since 2014 and has progressed from weekend-only brunches to supper clubs, and – from late 2019 – to serving simple weeknight dinners (dishes such as hispi cabbage with cashew cheese). It reopened with a few outside tables in April 2021, and opening times look set to grow again over time. Limited initial feedback, but all positive. / N5 2XE; www.frankscanteen.com; @frankscanteen; Sun-Wed 4 pm, Thu-Sat 9.30 pm; closed Sun-Wed D.

Frantoio SW10 £64 3 4 4
397 King's Rd 020 7352 4146 6–3B

This 21-year-old World's End trattoria wins consistent high ratings across the board, and its tone is set by the outspoken owner, Bucci – who insists that mobiles are turned to silent 'because they can affect the cooking process of spaghetti'. The menu also promises that 'red heads get a free drink' – but you can't say 'I was a red-head once'. / SW10 0LR; www.frantoio.co.uk; Mon-Sun 11 pm.

Frederick's N1 £65 3 3 4
106 Camden Passage 020 7359 2888 9–3D

"Celebrating over 50 years in Camden Passage", this cutely located "institution" is "an established Islington staple", and a default choice for business, romance and family celebrations for fans across north London, for whom it's a massive "favourite". The modern European cuisine "continues to innovate" and if results are arguably "unspectacular", they are very "reliable", while the spacious interior and "excellent outdoor seating" create an "impressive environment" that helps imbue a meal with a good sense of occasion. / N1 8EG; www.fredericks.co.uk; @fredericks_n1; Tue-Sat 10.30; closed Sun & Mon.

The French House W1 £72 345
49 Dean Street 020 7437 2477 5–3A

The "intimate" dining room above one of Soho's most historic bars is "the perfect spot for a Soho lunch" ("before a pint at Norman's" for the full media in-crowd experience). Fittingly, it serves "good French food" – "seasonal stuff done deftly" – which you can "eat while admiring the history-laden walls" that tell the tale of General de Gaulle and his Free French, who kept their spirits up here during WWII exile. The kitchen is now run by Neil Borthwick, Angela Hartnett's other half. And it was here, 30 years ago, that Fergus Henderson of St John first made his mark as a chef. / W1D 5BG; www.frenchhousesoho.com; @FrenchHouseSoho; Mon-Sun 11 pm.

Frenchie WC2 £92 332
18 Henrietta Street 020 7836 4422 5–3C

This Gallic Covent Garden five-year-old is the UK outpost of a small, high-quality Paris-based group run by Gregory & Marie Merchand (the former nicknamed 'Frenchie' by Jamie Oliver, when we worked at Fifteen). Its ratings are still not back to the highs when it first opened, but nobody makes any harsh criticisms and reports often refer to "superb and innovative" cuisine and "top-notch wines". (Not to be confused with the street-food business on the Southbank's Belvedere Road – "duck burgers and fat chips to die for"). / WC2E 8QH; www.frenchiecoventgarden.com; @frenchiecoventgarden; Tue-Sat 9.30 pm.

Frog by Adam Handling WC2 £86 543
35 Southampton Street 020 7199 8370 5–3D

The "stunning innovation" of Adam Handling's "clever", but "not crazy" cuisine ("the breads with chicken butter and crispy chicken skin were out of this world!") wins a paean of praise for his Covent Garden HQ. And even some who feel that "not every dish totally works" award the "spectacular" cooking full marks on account of the "degree of talent and creativity on show". The "great front of house staff" also get a big shout-out for their "friendly" style, which adds life to the simple interior with open kitchen (more casual in style than is typically found around such fancy food). A new outside terrace is a recent addition, as is delivery service 'Hame' ("the absolute king of the home delivery options we tried"). / WC2E 7HG; www.frogbyadamhandling.com/; @FrogbyAH; Wed-Sat, Tue 11 pm; closed Tue L, closed Sun & Mon; Take bookings all week via phone and/or online.

La Fromagerie £54 333
2-6 Moxon St, W1 020 7935 0341 3–1A
52 Lamb's Conduit St, WC1 020 7242 1044 2–1D
30 Highbury Park, N5 020 7359 7440 9–2D

You can book any time for the cafés at the Bloomsbury store and for certain sittings in Marylebone if you visit these well-known cheese emporia. Obviously the cheese is an attraction in itself, but there are other high-quality options. / www.lafromagerie.co.uk; @LaFromagerieUK.

The Frontline Club W2 £52 334
13 Norfolk Pl 020 7479 8960 7–1D

The ground-floor restaurant of this 'gathering place for journalists, photographers and other like-minded people' is worth remembering as one of the more civilised dining options right by Paddington Station. The food, though lacking fireworks, "has always been a good, reliable experience", but of greater interest are the striking examples of photo-reportage that decorate the walls. / W2 1QJ; www.frontlineclub.com; @frontlineclub; Mon-Sat 11 pm; closed Sun; booking max 6 may apply.

Fumo WC2 £56 3 3 3
37 St Martin's Lane   020 3778 0430   5–4C
"Handily situated next to the Coliseum, serving tasty cicchetti" – this London outpost of a national chain within the San Carlo group is worth remembering for a light lunch or pre-theatre bite. / WC2N 4JS; www.sancarlofumo.co.uk/fumo-london/; @sancarlo_group; Mon-Thu 11.30 pm, Fri & Sat midnight, Sun 10.30 pm.

Gallipoli £45 2 3 3
102 Upper St, N1   020 7359 0630   9–3D
120 Upper St, N1   020 7226 8099   9–3D
"You genuinely can't go wrong" with the *"good honest Turkish cooking and mezze dishes"* at these two *"great-value"* stalwarts in Islington. *"They've made an effort to Ottomanise the decor, so you feel you are eating in a proper restaurant rather than a café-type mangal grill"*, and it's a great choice for a festive night out on a budget. / www.cafegallipoli.com; @CafeGallipoli.

Galvin at Windows,
Park Lane London Hilton Hotel W1 £124 2 3 4
22 Park Ln   020 7208 4021   3–4A
It's hard not to be wowed by the "wonderful vistas" over Hyde Park and Buckingham Palace at this "beautiful" 28th-floor perch. Under the Galvin Bros' reign here (since 2006), it has generally avoided the culinary complacency typical of rooms with a view, but its cuisine did take some flak this year for "eye-watering prices" and "a loss of sparkle". Still, for "a special romantic celebratory treat" or a "great venue for a business meet-up" it still has much to recommend it. / W1K 1BE; www.galvinatwindows.com; @GalvinatWindows; Wed & Thu 11 pm, Fri & Sat 11.30 pm, Sun 4 pm; closed Wed & Thu L closed Sun D, closed Mon & Tue; No trainers; booking max 5 may apply.

Galvin Bistrot & Bar E1 NEW £60 3 4 4
35 Bishops Square   020 7299 0404   13–2B
"A lovely brasserie-style option at the rear of Galvin La Chapelle" – the Galvins keep reformatting the smallish unit adjacent to their landmark venue (previously Galvin HOP, RIP, and before that Café à Vin). This mid-2020 re-launch pays homage to the formula of their original 'Bistrot de Luxe', which launched their empire 15 years ago. *"Very casual and lots of fun"* – staff are *"very friendly"*; it has *"a lovely outside space on the terrace with a cover"*; and the cooking is *"just what French bistro-style fare should be"*. / E1 6DY; galvinrestaurants.com; @Galvin_brothers; Tue-Sat 9.30 pm; closed Sun & Mon.

Galvin La Chapelle E1 £104 3 4 5
35 Spital Sq   020 7299 0400   13–2B
The *"breathtakingly magnificent"* setting – *"a Grade II listed girls' school built in the late 19th century, with soaringly magnificent high ceilings and a plush fit-out"* – makes the Galvin Brothers' Spitalfields destination *"a great place to celebrate or to take clients"*, and is nowadays the City's No 1 destination for business entertaining. And it helps that the service is *"utterly professional, discreet and attentive"*, too. When it comes to the *"high-end, well-executed"* Gallic cuisine, it has more often seemed a tad more *"unambitious and rather expensive"* of late (*"I adore this restaurant, but they do need to keep the prices in check"*). The winning view, though, is that *"you always feel special when coming here"* for what's *"an exceptional dining experience"*. / E1 6DY; www.galvinlachapelle.com; @galvin_brothers; Sun-Wed 9 pm, Thu-Sat 10 pm; No trainers; booking max 8 may apply.

The Game Bird SW1   £118   3 3 2
16-18 St James's Place   020 7518 1234   3–4C
Hidden away in St James's, this "excellent hotel restaurant" delivers "wonderful" old-school British classics with contemporary aplomb; and is "especially good for a Sunday roast". The Stafford Hotel dates from 1912 and its American Bar has long been famous, but for all its Edwardian trappings, the Game Bird only took flight five years ago. / SW1A 1NJ; thestaffordlondon.com/the-game-bird; @TheGameBirdLON; Mon-Sat 9 pm, Sun 3 pm; Take bookings all week via phone and/or online.

Ganapati SE15   £44   4 3 3
38 Holly Grove   020 7277 2928   1–4D
This "interesting little restaurant" in a residential Peckham street was opened in 2004 by Claire Fisher, to replicate the tastes she had experienced travelling in southern India. "As Peckham's food scene continues to develop, this isn't quite as all-conquering as it once was" – but it still rates highly for the food freshly made in-house. Ganapati is another name for the elephant-headed god, Ganesh. / SE15 5DF; www.ganapatirestaurant.com; Tue-Sat 10.30 pm, Sun 10 pm; closed Mon; no Amex.

Ganymede SW1 NEW   £46
139 Ebury Street   020 3971 0761   2–4B
This posh gastropub from the Lunar Pub Company opened post-pandemic in September 2021. Sibling to South Kensington's Hunter's Moon, it incorporates a 30-cover bar and 46-cover dining room, and inhabits the Belgravia site that was for yonks The Ebury Wine Bar. / SW1W 9QU; ganymedelondon.co.uk.

The Garden Cafe at the Garden Museum SE1   £57   3 2 3
5 Lambeth Palace Rd   020 7401 8865   2–4D
Off a "beautiful open courtyard", the ambitious café of Lambeth's Garden Museum is "well worth a trip". The "fresh, seasonal cooking" – both "well-executed classics and more unusual, interesting dishes" – is prepared by a kitchen headed by chef George Ryle, formerly of Padella. / SE1 7LB; www.gardenmuseum.org.uk; @GardenMuseumLDN; Mon, Wed & Thu, Sat & Sun 5 pm, Tue, Fri 9 pm; closed Mon, Wed & Thu, Sat & Sun D; no Amex; Booking max 12 may apply.

Le Garrick WC2   £58   3 3 4
10-12 Garrick Street   020 7240 7649   5–3C
"A good place for a romantic meal", with its "candlelight and cosy booths", this "welcoming Gallic restaurant" in a "warm basement" near Covent Garden is "perfect for anniversaries, engagements and proposals". A stalwart of 35 years' standing, it also makes "an excellent choice for pre-theatre dining", serving "great classic French food – with a smile". / WC2E 9BH; www.legarrick.co.uk; @le_garrick; Mon-Sat midnight; closed Sun.

The Garrison SE1   £66   3 2 3
99 Bermondsey Street   020 7089 9355   10–4D
"Busy, excellently run pub with a great atmosphere" and "excellent food", that's been a leader of the Bermondsey Street food scene for almost 20 years – and the "revamped menu is testimony of a lockdown well spent". / SE1 3XB; www.thegarrison.co.uk; @TheGarrisonSE1; Mon-Thu 11 pm, Fri & Sat 11 pm, Sun 10.30 pm.

The Gate £59 4️⃣2️⃣2️⃣
22-24 Seymour Place, W1   020 7724 6656   2–2A
51 Queen Caroline St, W6   020 8748 6932   8–2C
87 Allitsen Road, NW8   020 7833 0401.   9–3A
370 St John St, EC1   020 7278 5483   9–3D

"Vegetarian food which will silence a complaining carnivore (i.e. me)" typifies the high enthusiasm for Michael and Adrian Daniel's stalwart veggie chain, particularly the quirkily located original (complete with "lovely courtyard") behind Hammersmith's Eventim Apollo, which fans credibly claim "has probably been the best place in London to go meat-free for ages". Of the other branches, the newest St John's Wood outlet (opened in 2019) inspires most interest, while the Sadler's Wells and Seymour Place branches in particular are often ignored by reporters. In every case, though, the cuisine generally inspires compliments such as "interesting" or "very acceptable". / thegaterestaurants.com; @GateRestaurant.

Gaucho £89 2️⃣2️⃣2️⃣
CEO Martin Williams (who has returned to the business in recent years) still has his work cut out to return this Argentinian steakhouse chain to its former glory. Fans say it's particularly "a winner on business", hailing "top steaks" and the extensive selection of South American wines to complement them. That it's "pricier than competing (better) steak experiences" is a repeat complaint, though, and there are still those who feel the approach smacks of "churn and burn for covers". Top Tips: "beautiful premises on the Thames at Richmond" and a "pretty garden" in NW3. / www.gauchorestaurants.co.uk; @gauchogroup.

Gauthier Soho W1 £77 3️⃣4️⃣3️⃣
21 Romilly St   020 7494 3111   5–3A

"There's an unrivalled emphasis on providing top-quality vegan cuisine" at Alexis Gauthier's "wonderfully quirky" venue: a "charming townhouse", "tucked away in the middle of Soho", where "you ring the bell at the front door to get entry". When he launched it in 2010, the menu was just like any other high temple of French gastronomy ("his foie gras used to be the best"). But gradually he has taken away the meat, going 'proudly 100% vegan' on June 23rd 2021, to offer "serious, considered cooking… that just doesn't happen to have animal products"; and – for London – presents arguably "the best vegan menu for gourmets". In a similar vein, the accompanying wines (also vegan) "are chosen carefully and presented with knowledge and real enthusiasm". The journey has been followed by some reporters all the way from his days at Roussillon in Pimlico, but there's disagreement over its ultimate success, and this has impacted ratings somewhat. Advocates say "the vegan tasting menus will convert even the most red-blooded meat-eater" ("as a confirmed carnivore, I didn't miss the meat here at all"); while sceptics say "I used to give it a 5 all-round and it's still excellent, but as an omnivore I've lost a reason to visit with the new focus". A fair middle summary? "It was actually better before turning vegan, but is still very good". Top Tip: Gauthier at Home, the home delivery business, also gets a big thumbs-up. / W1D 5AF; www.gauthiersoho.co.uk; @GauthierSoho; Tue-Sat 10.30 pm; closed Sun & Mon; booking max 7 may apply.

Le Gavroche W1 £140 4️⃣5️⃣4️⃣
43 Upper Brook St   020 7408 0881   3–2A

"Quite simply, the epitome of what a restaurant should be!" – Michel Roux's "elegant", if old-fashioned Mayfair icon remained a place of ultimate celebration for many reporters before, during the interregna from, and after the lockdowns. Nowhere in London epitomises French gastronomy more than this traditionally decorated basement – the first restaurant in the UK to hold three Michelin stars (and with two since 1993). Its "classic dishes seem more exquisite than ever through enforced absence" and "the welcome you get is second to none". On the downside: bills, as ever, are "stratospheric"; the odd reporter finds the approach "dated"; and its ratings risked slipping this year. Also, "tragically they have had to suspend their prix fixe lunch – the best deal in London! – because of staff shortages caused by beastly Brexit and Covid" (since summer 2021 it has been open for dinner only). While that persists, it's "only a goer if you have deep pockets". In September 2021, Emanuel Landré the GM stepped back, leaving sisters, Sylvia and Ursula Perberschlager, who have been at Le Gavroche for 17 years, as co-managers. (Footnote – Le Gavroche's original founders, Michel Roux's uncle, Michel, and his father, Albert – both passed away since our last survey, in March 2020 and January 2021 respectively. The debt owed by the UK restaurant industry to the Roux Bros is phenomenal.) / W1K 7QR; www.le-gavroche.co.uk/; @michelrouxjr; Tue-Sat 9.15 pm; dinner only, closed Sun & Mon; No shorts.

Gazette £59 2 3 3
79 Sherwood Ct, Chatfield Rd, SW11   020 7223 0999   11–1C
147 Upper Richmond Rd, SW15   020 8789 6996   11–2B
"So VERY French in every way" – this southwest London trio (Clapham, Wandsworth and Putney, plus a Holborn branch) "has worked so hard to keep going with style and panache" over the years, and is recommended unreservedly by many reporters. For quite a few sceptics, though, it's "a great concept", but the execution "needs sharpening up". Top Tip: "the best steak tartare in town". / www.gazettebrasserie.co.uk.

GBR (The Great British Restaurant)
at The Dukes Hotel SW1 £80 3 3 4
35 St James's Pl   020 7491 4840   3–4C
"Remarkably good food that's quite reasonably priced", especially for St James's, won nothing but praise this year for this versatile hotel brasserie whose smart, contemporary decor is very tasteful throughout. Nigel Mendham's all-day menu makes a feature of traditional British dishes, including a selection of pies, and the venue wins particular praise as a "perfect business breakfast setting". / SW1A 1NY; www.dukeshotel.com; @GBR_LONDON; Mon-Fri 9 pm, Sat 9.30 pm, Sun 5 pm.

Gem N1 £45 3 4 2
265 Upper St   020 7359 0405   9–2D
This busy little place near Angel lives up to its name, with friendly staff who look after their customers well, serving them "cheap and cheerful" meals from a menu listing dishes from Greece across Turkey to Kurdistan. / N1 2UQ; www.gemrestaurant.org.uk; @Gem_restaurant; Mon-Sat 11 pm; closed Sun; no Amex.

German Gymnasium N1 £69 2 2 3
1 King's Boulevard   020 7287 8000   9–3C
"A truly lovely building", this huge Victorian former gym from D&D London has "a great buzz" and a "really handy" location, immediately behind King's Cross station. It's generally regarded as "great fun", but although some reporters take a shine to the "delicious schnitzels", most rate the German-themed cooking "unimaginative" – no more than "decent fuel", "which rather lets down an intriguing wine list". / N1C 4BU;
www.germangymnasium.com; @TheGermanGym; Sun-Wed 10 pm, Thu-Sat 10.30 pm; Take bookings all week via phone and/or online.

Giacomo's NW2 £44 3 3 2
428 Finchley Rd   020 7794 3603   1–1B
This family-run Italian in Childs Hill has established itself as "a good local" for more than 20 years – offering "just the right level of sophistication and peace to conduct business". / NW2 2HY; www.giacomos.co.uk; Tue-Sun 10.30 pm; closed Mon.

Giannino Dal 1899 W1 NEW
£112   343

8-10 Blenheim Street   020 8138 1196   3–2B

It took 120 years for the famous Milan original of the same name to spawn this first international spin-off, which opened in Mayfair (on the site of Camillo Benso) in September 2020. They have spent a packet on its very classic looks, which creates a "quiet but not sombre" atmosphere; and for a traditional Italian experience (down to the heart-flutter when the bill arrives) some early reports are high on the "wow!" scale. Initial ratings are tempered, though, by the odd reporter who feels a visit was "fun but not memorable". / W1S 1LJ; www.gianninoristorante.co.uk; Mon-Sat 11.30 pm; closed Sun.

Ginger & White Hampstead NW3
£13   324

4a-5a, Perrins Ct   020 7431 9098   9–2A

For when caffeine withdrawal strikes, this sociable, cutely sited Hampstead haunt – with its heady brews and simple breakfast, eggs and sarnies options – scored impressively this year. Its beans are hand-roasted in small batches by Square Mile Coffee Roasters in East London, its milk comes from cows at Northiam dairy… and its customers come from all over north London! / NW3 1QS; www.gingerandwhite.com; @gingerandwhite; Mon-Fri 5.30 pm, Sat & Sun 6 pm; closed Mon-Sun D; no Amex; no booking.

Ginza Onodera SW1
£100   222

15 Bury St   020 7839 1101   3–3D

After two name changes and a refurb, this upmarket Japanese in a St James's basement is now named after Tokyo's poshest shopping district – and urgently needs to establish a new identity. One or two reporters are wowed, but others have found it "full of middle-aged tourists", with "unexciting food" and "very little input from waiters, who seemed uninterested". "Prefered it under the old name, Matsuri". / SW1Y 6AL; www.ginza-stjames.com; Tue-Sat 10.30 pm; closed Sun & Mon.

The Glasshouse TW9
£90   442

14 Station Pde   020 8940 6777   1–3A

"A superb restaurant close to Kew Gardens station" – this "consistently excellent" neighbourhood spot enjoys a disproportionately large fanclub thanks to its "subtly flavoured" modern cuisine; its "extensive and good-value wine list"; its "sweet and attentive" service; and the "light and airy" style of the relatively "small" dining room. Although ratings are not quite as stellar as they were a few years ago, they remain eminently respectable. Perhaps it's suffering from its fine provenance: "viewed on it's own merits, it's an extremely good restaurant, just not quite as good as its sibling La Trompette (and the slightly further away Chez Bruce)". / TW9 3PZ; www.glasshouserestaurant.co.uk; @The__Glasshouse; Wed & Thu 9 pm, Fri & Sat 9.30 pm, Sun 3.30 pm; closed Sun D, closed Mon & Tue; booking max 8 may apply.

Gloria EC2
£58   335

54-56 Great Eastern Street   13–1B

"A total hoot, especially if it's your birthday" – lunch at this glammed-up 70s-style Italian on two floors in Shoreditch is "like nipping to Sicily for the afternoon". The Big Mamma Group's tone is most definitely tongue-in-cheek rather than po-faced authenticity, with the Insta-friendly decor – "beautiful dining room adorned with flowers" – and cheesy menu items ('pasta alla lamb-orghini', anyone?). Still, the food can be creamily "delicious – with the standout dishes of truffle pasta & lemon meringue pie". / EC2A 3QR; www.bigmammagroup.com; @bigmammagroup; Sun-Wed 10.30 pm, Thu-Sat 11 pm.

La Goccia WC2   £58   3 3 4

Floral Court, off Floral Street   020 7305 7676   5–3C

The courtyard on a summer's day is a "top setting" and adds lustre to this swish Italian in Covent Garden's relatively new Floral Court development. There was more appreciation too this year for Italian cuisine that – while "not cheap" – provides "lovely, fresh, simple dishes with super presentation". / WC2E 9DJ; petershamnurseries.com/dine/la-goccia; @PetershamN; Tue-Sat 10.30 pm, Sun 6 pm; closed Mon.

Goddards At Greenwich SE10   £23   3 4 3

22 King William Walk   020 8305 9612   1–3D

"Pies & liquor, pies & gravy – both are excellent" – this traditional pie 'n' mash house near Greenwich Park was established in 1890, although its menu has moved with the times to incorporate steak, chicken, lamb and vegetarian recipes. "Wonderful counter service" downstairs, or eat with views in the grander first-floor dining room. / SE10 9HU; www.goddardsatgreenwich.co.uk; @GoddardsPieMash; Sun-Thu 7.30 pm, Fri & Sat 8 pm.

Gold W11   £65   2 2 4

95 Portobello Road   020 3146 0747   7–2B

The Notting Hill pub where Bill Clinton famously downed a half and scarpered without paying in the dying days of his presidency is now a vibey sleb-magnet frequented by the likes of Sienna Miller, Ed Sheeran and Princesses Beatrice and Eugenie, following a revamp and name-change (from Portobello Gold, RIP) under Nick House, the founder of nightclubs Mahiki and Whisky Mist. Now featuring an upstairs party room and a garden room with retractable roof, it serves 'modern European' food by former River Café chef Theo Hill. Reports diverge on the new venture's qualities, ranging from enthusiastic – "great atmosphere" – to damning – "a place for posing, not eating". / W11 2QB; goldnottinghill.com; Mon-Thu 12.30 am, Fri & Sat 1 am, Sun 11.30 pm.

Gold Mine W2   £45   3 2 2

102 Queensway   020 7792 8331   7–2C

"Roast duck is the main draw here" – although Queensway could be called "rue du canard roti", such is the concentration of Cantonese roast duck exponents. Still, "the dim sum, roast meats and dishes from the main menu are all brilliant" at a venue that produces "consistently great food in what can be a chaotic environment". / W2 3RR; Mon-Sun 11 pm.

Golden Dragon W1   £49   3 2 2

28-29 Gerrard St   020 7734 1073   5–3A

"Still my favourite" – this "cavernous" Gerrard Street stalwart scores for its "excellent dim sum at a reasonable price", including "some of the best char siu in Chinatown". / W1 6JW; www.gdlondon.co.uk; @goldendragon_uk; Mon-Thu 11.30 pm, Fri & Sat midnight, Sun 11 pm.

Golden Hind W1   £49   3 2 2

73 Marylebone Ln   020 7486 3644   2–1A

"Consistently good traditional fish 'n' chips" make this century-old fixture (est. 1914) a "local favourite" in Marylebone. These days there are Mediterranean touches – fish steamed with olive oil or grilled with olive oil and lemon – as well as such throw-back Anglo treats as spotted dick, treacle syrup sponge or bread-and-butter pudding. But "you go to this lovely place for the well-priced fish and chips, not the ambience" – or the "outdoor tables, which face north!" / W1U 2PN; www.goldenhindrestaurant.com; Mon-Sat 10 pm; closed Sun.

Good Earth £67 3 3 2
233 Brompton Rd, SW3   020 7584 3658   6–2C
143-145 The Broadway, NW7   020 8959 7011   1–1B
11 Bellevue Rd, SW17   020 8682 9230   11–2C
Fans of this "very popular, consistently above-average" family group – with venues in Knightsbridge, Mill Hill, Wandsworth Common and Esher – say it's "on another level to most Chinese restaurants", with "the best cuts of meat and fresh-as-you-like fish and vegetables". Even fans, though, perennially complain about the prices: "still the best Chinese around, still the most expensive". These days, a more affordable option might be the delivery/takeaway-only sites in Swiss Cottage, Battersea, Richmond and Wimbledon. / www.goodearthgroup.co.uk.

The Good Plot W11 NEW
296 Westbourne Grove   020 3887 2211   7–1B
In the heart of Notting Hill – an upmarket, all-day wholefood café, restaurant and deli, where the emphasis is on healthy, ethically sourced dishes, made predominantly from British ingredients. It was opened in December 2020 by deep-pocketed Malaysian model and actress Mandy Lieu, who has also snapped up Ewhurst Park in Hampshire to convert into a farm to help supply the venture. / W11 2PS; thegoodplot.com; Tue, Wed, Sun 5 pm, Thu-Sat 8.30 pm; closed Tue, Wed, Sun D, closed Mon.

Goodman £98 3 3 2
24-26 Maddox St, W1   020 7499 3776   3–2C
3 South Quay, E14   020 7531 0300   12–1C
11 Old Jewry, EC2   020 7600 8220   10–2C
"Portions are similar to what you'd get in any decent steakhouse in the US" at these NYC-style operations (which are in fact Russian-owned), whose comfy styling and "extensive wine list" makes them a natural favourite for red-in-tooth-and-claw business types for wining and dining (particularly in the City, where it vies somewhat with its nearby rival Hawksmoor). "The bill will probably remove all the cobwebs in your wallet, so get ready for that". / www.goodmanrestaurants.com; @goodmanMADDOX.

Goods Way N1 NEW
11 Goods Way   020 7123 4567   9–3C
In March 2020, the team behind Flat Iron Yard in Borough opened a new (if old-school in its theming) street-food hall, bar and live music venue. Stallholders include familiar faces (Breddos Tacos, Temple of Seitan and Duck Truck) and some new ones including New York's respected Sushi On Jones and Pomelo from the Lupins team. / N1C 4PW; www.goodsway.co.uk; Mon-Sat 11 pm, Sun 10.30 pm.

Gordon Ramsay SW3 £174 3 3 2
68-69 Royal Hospital Rd   020 7352 4441   6–3D
For the umpteenth year, Gordon Ramsay's original Chelsea launchpad for TV stardom inspires starkly differing verdicts. To its advocates, "it's obvious why they've retained three Michelin Stars all these years", given modern French cuisine from Matt Abé that's "mind-blowing", service that's "gold star" and an atmosphere – in this intimately sized dining room – that really makes it "a place to savour". (Fans likewise find eating at the 4-seater 'Inspiration Table' – minimum spend £1,000 – as "truly memorable" as one would hope). Its detractors remain very numerous, though! That the experience is "exquisite but too expensive compared with its peers" is, perhaps predictably, the prime accusation: "Nothing made me stop and think 'wow', and at over £600 for two, I expected much more. We had the chef's choice and the kitchen seemed to have gone out of its way to make sure that the food served was sufficiently middle-of-the-road that no-one would dislike it!". / SW3 4HP; www.gordonramsay.com; @GordonRamsay; Tue-Sat 9.45 pm; closed Sun & Mon; No jeans; booking max 9 may apply.

Gordon's Wine Bar WC2 £43 ②②**5**
47 Villiers St   020 7930 1408   5–4D

"Still a great place for a glass of wine, any time of day" – this ancient wine bar near Embankment tube (London's oldest, dating from 1890) has a superb interior, including a cavern where it's hard to stand vertically, and a huge outdoor terrace. Its buffet-style food offering of cold cuts, cheese, salad and dishes of the day is primitive but at least relatively cheap, and in summer there's also a BBQ on the terrace. Just about every London office worker has visited it at some point… in many cases, though, recollections are hazy… / WC2N 6NE; gordonswinebar.com; @GordonsWineBar; Mon-Sat 11 pm, Sun 10 pm; No bookings.

Gourmet Burger Kitchen £36 **3**②
"Many, many times GBK provided me with happiness in the last 12 months" – strong support from regulars and continued high ratings suggest London's original posh burger chain is a brand worth saving, despite its recent travails. In late 2020 it was bought out of administration by Midlands chicken tycoon Ranjit Boparan in a deal that saw the closure of 26 of its 61 branches. Launched 21 years ago in Clapham's Northcote Road by a group of Kiwis including chef Peter Gordon, its *"simple and basic – but perfect – burgers"* were a massive hit, and the chain was valued at £120m by 2016. / www.gbkinfo.com.

Goya SW1 £41 **3**②**3**
34 Lupus St   020 7976 5309   2–4C

This *"old faithful"* tapas local in Pimlico has built a loyal following of regulars over three decades, serving a *"simple but tasty menu"* of Hispanic specialities. *"It was great that it survived the pandemic – and a delight to see the same staff and unchanged menu when we returned for our monthly reunion"*. / SW1V 3EB; www.goyarestaurant.co.uk; Mon-Sat midnight, Sun 11.30 pm.

Granary Square Brasserie N1 £48 ②②**3**
1 Granary Square   020 3940 1000   9–3C

"A superb, airy restaurant – comfortable and relaxed" – is the general view on this three-year-old from Richard Caring's Ivy Collection group, which occupies *"a beautiful setting"* in revamped King's Cross. There is a more downbeat alternative, though, suggesting it's *"rather trading on its name"* with its *"functional"* menu of *"bistro favourites"*. / N1C 4AB; www.granarysquarebrasserie.com; Mon-Thu 10.30 pm, Fri-Sun 11 pm; Booking max 12 may apply.

Grand Trunk Road E18 £62 **4**②**3**
219 High Street   020 8505 1965   1–1D

"A wonderful nugget of culinary excellence" in deepest Woodford, just off London's own 'grand trunk' (the North Circular), this is the first solo venture from Rajesh Suri, a veteran of top-drawer Indian cuisine who managed Tamarind in Mayfair. *"You can feel, sense and taste the passion not only in the extraordinary food, but in the ambience and attention to detail"*. *"It gets better on every visit"* – and offers *"superb vegetarian options"*. / E18 2PB; www.gtrrestaurant.co.uk; @GT_Road; Tue-Sat 10.30 pm, Sun 8.30 pm; closed Tue-Fri L, closed Mon; Take bookings all week via phone and/or online.

Granger & Co £56 ②②②
237-239 Pavilion Rd, SW1   020 3848 1060   6–2D
175 Westbourne Grove, W11   020 7229 9111   7–1B
Stanley Building, St Pancras Sq, N1   020 3058 2567   9–3C
The Buckley Building, 50 Sekforde St, EC1   020 7251 9032   10–1A

The *"great breakfast"* means *"long queues"* at Aussie celeb chef Bill Granger's *"Notting Hill hot spot"* – *"the best brunch place in town"*, say fans – and its spinoffs in Chelsea, Clerkenwell and King's Cross. The *"Asian-Pacific-Antipodean"* fare served later in the day is generally considered *"competent rather than exceptional"* – *"it's never quite as good as the menu suggests"*. / grangerandco.com; @Grangerandco.

Greenberry Café NW1 £47 344
101 Regents Park Road 020 7483 3765 9–2B

"Probably the best brunch, and choices, for miles around" – this cute café on Primrose Hill's main drag *"isn't going to wow"* from a gourmet point of view, but its *"wonderful and fresh-tasting"* brunches and breakfasts win lots of praise, helped by *"good prices"* and *"fabulous staff"*. In recent times it has helped that *"they have made a big effort with their outside eating pods"* (*"I love their shacks with heaters and blankets!"*). / NW1 8UR; greenberrycafe.co.uk; @Greenberry_Cafe; Sun & Mon 3 pm, Tue-Sat 10 pm; closed Sun & Mon D.

The Grill at The Dorchester W1 £100 444
53 Park Lane 020 7629 8888 3–3A

Tom Booton, the 27-year-old head chef, is helping breathe new life into this stately Mayfair chamber, which received nothing but upbeat reviews this year, driven by *"modern British cuisine at its best"*. This is one of the capital's grander traditional dinings rooms and, if he keeps this up, deserves to recapture the destination status that's sometimes eluded it in recent times. In particular, it's a venue that's evidently *"great for business diners"*. But you don't have to be carrying company plastic to appreciate the *"amazing lunch menu"*: *"at £30 it's arguably the best value in London"*. / W1K 1QA; www.dorchestercollection.com/en/london/the-dorchester/; @TheDorchester; Wed-Sat 11 pm, Sun 4 pm; closed Sun D, closed Mon & Tue; No trainers.

Grumbles SW1 £43 333
35 Churton St 020 7834 0149 2–4B

This *"buzzy"* – albeit magnificently dated – *"neighbourhood spot"* in Pimlico remains *"very popular with the locals"* – and proud of the fact that nothing much has changed from the original wooden furnishings since it opened in 1964. The *"good-value"* menu has stood the test of time, too: fish pie, cod in beer batter and steak with Bearnaise, Stilton sauce or an English mustard and brown sugar crust. It claims to be London's first restaurant with a silly name; apparently 'Get Stuffed' was also considered… / SW1V 2LT; www.grumblesrestaurant.co.uk; @grumblesbistro; Mon-Sun 10 pm.

The Guildford Arms SE10 £54 343
55 Guildford Grove 020 8691 6293 1–3D

"Such a well-equipped and attractive outdoor area, warm and well lit" proved a particular boon during the pandemic at this three-storey Georgian tavern in Greenwich. Chef Guy Awford and his team deliver a menu focussed on mezze and grill dishes, including a number of 'feasting' options for the whole table. / SE10 8JY; www.theguildfordarms.co.uk; Tue-Sun 11 pm; closed Mon; Take bookings all week via phone and/or online.

The Guinea Grill W1 £101 344
30 Bruton Pl 020 7409 1728 3–3B

"Superb devilled kidneys" and *"the best steak & kidney pies in London"* take second place to the high-quality British steaks cooked on an open grill that are the headline act at this venerable Mayfair institution, which celebrates its 70th anniversary this year. Business entertaining goes down particularly well here: *"clients love the fact that the Grill is through the pub and hidden at the back"*. / W1J 6NL; www.theguinea.co.uk; @guineagrill; Mon-Sat 11 pm, Sun 5 pm; closed Sun D.

The Gun E14 £57 224
27 Coldharbour 020 7515 5222 12–1C

A *"lovely river view"* is the making of this substantial Grade II listed Georgian Docklands pub from Fullers, directly opposite the 02 Centre. The proximity to Canary Wharf means it is somewhat pitched to a business clientele, with upscale food and smart table dressings. / E14 9NS; www.thegundocklands.com; @thegundocklands; Mon-Sat 9.30 pm, Sun 7 pm; closed Sun D.

Gunmakers W1 NEW £48
33 Aybrook Street   020 7224 0170   2–1A
Winston Churchill was, it is said, once partial to the odd jar at this Marylebone hostelry, reopened in October 2019 by well-known sommelier Xavier Rousset (in charge of the vino) and Anglo-chef Mark Jarvis, who oversees the basement steakhouse. Early social media feedback says results are high quality but can seem pricey. / W1U 4AP; gunmakershouse.co.uk; @GunmakersPub.

Gunpowder £53 4 3 3
One Tower Bridge, 4 Crown Square, SE1   awaiting tel   10–4D
11 Whites Row, E1   020 7426 0542   13–2C
"Brilliant Indian cuisine with an experimental flare" – "glorious morsels of street-style foods" on "tapas-style" small plates – has earned all-but-universal praise for this popular duo, first in Spitalfields and more recently on the South Bank near Tower Bridge ("handy before or after the Bridge Theatre"). Now their signature "tender lamb cutlets" and Kowari soft-shell crab can be sampled at a high-profile new venue in Soho's Greek Street, opened in late 2021. "You always over-order because everything sounds so good!". / www.gunpowderlondon.com; @gunpowder_ldn.

Gustoso Ristorante & Enoteca SW1 £56 3 3 3
33 Willow Pl   020 7834 5778   2–4B
"Still a gem", this "local Italian" near Victoria Station (and behind Westminster Cathedral) pleases its small fan club with freshly made traditional dishes backed up by "excellent service and ambience". / SW1P 1JH; www.ristorantegustoso.co.uk; @GustosoRist; Mon-Sat 9.30 pm; closed Sun.

Gymkhana W1 £82 4 3 3
42 Albemarle St   020 3011 5900   3–3C
"Subtle" yet "exceptional" flavours delivered by the Sethi siblings' famous Mayfair Indian keep it in the Top-40 most-mentioned restaurants in our annual diners' poll, and it's now well established as one of London's foremost dining destinations. Ratings slipped a fraction this year, though – in early 2020 it re-opened after a fire with a remodelled basement and slightly new look and some regulars are "not sure about the redesign", or feel "it's enjoyable but not scaling the highest heights any more post reopening". / W1S 4JH; www.gymkhanalondon.com; @GymkhanaLondon; Tue-Sun 10.15 pm; closed Tue L, closed Mon; cards only.

Haché £46 3 2 2
95-97 High Holborn, WC1   020 7242 4580   2–1D
329-331 Fulham Rd, SW10   020 7823 3515   6–3B
24 Inverness St, NW1   020 7485 9100   9–3B
37 Bedford Hill, SW12   020 8772 9772   11–2C
153 Clapham High St, SW4   020 7738 8760   11–2D
147-149 Curtain Rd, EC2   020 7739 8396   13–1B
A "go-to place for top burgers", this upmarket chain offers a chic Parisian polish that its rivals would struggle to match, and operates seven outlets in Shoreditch, Chelsea, Camden, Clapham, Balham, Holborn and Kingston. Ratings softened this year, however, and one or two reporters feel it's "not as good as it once was". / www.hacheburgers.com.

Hackney Coterie E8 NEW
230 Dalston Lane   020 7254 4101   14–1B
From Anthony Lyon (of Lyon's in Crouch End) – this 'multifaceted dining experience and community hub' (that's what the press release says) opened in August 2021 and comprises a brasserie, wine bar, bottle shop, deli and events space. The eclectic menu is seasonally driven and with zero-waste in mind (from pork cheek and smoked ham hock terrine to stone bass tartare with truffle ponzu). The focus, though, is arguably more on the low-intervention wines, craft beers and good saké selection. / E8 1LA; Mon-Sun 9 pm.

Hakkasan £120 3️⃣2️⃣3️⃣
17 Bruton St, W1   020 7907 1888   3–2C
8 Hanway Pl, W1   020 7927 7000   5–1A
"Still making an impact" – this blingy brand broke the mould when the *"dark"* and nightclubby Hanway Place branch debuted in 2001, and, for its army of fans, it *"still sets the standard for modern Chinese cuisine"*, enhanced by the *"extremely lively"* atmosphere, which is buoyed along by *"ordering one of their many delicious cocktails that leave you in a blissful haze"*. Nowadays the cornerstone of an international group with 18 branches across the globe, it's evidently no longer as cutting-edge as once it was, and ratings slipped a little further this year on gripes that it can seem *"so overpriced"*. All things considered, though, it retains an impressive level of support. / www.hakkasan.com; @HakkasanMayfair; no trainers, no sportswear.

The Halal Restaurant E1 £15
2 St Mark Street   020 7481 1700   10–2D
East London's oldest Indian (established 1939 in Whitechapel) briefly found fame in late August 2020, when it was reviewed by Marina O'Loughlin for The Sunday Times. Run by four generations of the same family – and with somewhat antediluvian decor – it's not the place to uncover the latest in food fads; or as Marina eloquently put it: "it tastes like the past, deliciously". Reports please! / E1 8DJ; www.halalrest.co.uk; Mon-Sun 10.30 pm; closed Sat & Sun L.

Halo Burger EC2 NEW £19 3️⃣3️⃣2️⃣
105 Great Eastern Street   020 7490 0444   13–1B
YOM! So say vegan types about the Beyond Meat patties at this expanding meat-free burger chain. Having been based in Pop Brixton, its horizons have now expanded to a permanent outlet near Silicon Roundabout (and also a residency in Brighton and delivery in Bristol). / EC2A 3JD; haloburger.co.uk; Sun-Thu 10.30 pm, Fri & Sat 11 pm.

Ham NW6 £63 3️⃣3️⃣2️⃣
238 West End Lane   020 7813 0168   1–1B
"Very good modern British food" from a *"fresh, inventive menu"* has made Aussie chef and Ledbury alumnus Matt Osborne's West Hampstead four-year-old a *"beloved local"* – it really earned its spurs as a *"lockdown life-saver"* with delicious delivery boxes. / NW6 1LG; www.hamwesthampstead.com/ham; @hamwhampstead/; Tue-Sat 11 pm, Sun 4.30 pm; closed Sun D, closed Mon; Take bookings all week via phone and/or online.

Ham Yard Restaurant, Ham Yard Hotel W1 £66 2️⃣2️⃣4️⃣
1 Ham Yd   020 3642 1007   4–3D
"What a delightful spot", just off Piccadilly Circus (*"my favourite place at the moment, both inside and in the courtyard, love the overall vibe"*). The food is *"simple but well cooked"* and comes at a *"fair price"*, making it *"great for pre-theatre"* and *"an absolute bargain for lunch"*, while the classic hotel afternoon tea is served with some style and *"always reliable"*. / W1D 7DT; www.firmdalehotels.com/hotels/london/ham-yard-hotel/ham-yard-bar-restaurant/; @Firmdale_Hotels; Mon-Sat 11.30 pm, Sun 10.30 pm.

The Hampshire Hog W6 £57 3️⃣3️⃣3️⃣
227 King Street   020 8748 3391   8–2B
Near the building site also known as Hammersmith Town Hall, this large pub was given a very attractive re-fit several years ago. In recent times, the food has 'gone Indian' and initial reports say it's a step up on its former typical gastropub offering. There's a "lovely garden" too, which now has a shisha menu if that's your bag. / W6 9JT; www.thehampshirehog.com; @TheHampshireHog; Mon-Fri midnight, Sat & Sun 11 pm.

Hankies £35 4️⃣2️⃣2️⃣

4 Suffolk Place, SW1   020 7112 4894   2–2C NEW
61 Upper Berkeley Street, W1   020 7958 3222   2–2A
67 Shaftesbury Avenue, W1   020 7871 6021   5–3A
55 Westbourne Terrace, W2   020 7723 3434   7–1C NEW

Named for the Roomali roti bread that's one of its menu mainstays, Anirudh Arora's small group aims to bring Delhi-style 'tapas' to Theatreland, Marble Arch (in a smart, if slightly "sterile" hotel dining room) and – most recently – Paddington. Feedback is more limited than we'd like, but once again speaks of "superb food".

Hannah SE1 NEW £122 4️⃣3️⃣2️⃣

Southbank Riverside, Belvedere Road   020 3802 0402   2–3D

"A great addition to the area" – the reason to re-evaluate this hotel Japanese at County Hall includes the CV of chef patron Daisuke Shimoyama, who joined in early 2020. Daisuke spent six years as head chef at UMU under the immensely talented Yoshinori Ishii. At lunch you can eat for as little as £17 from the bento box selection, but aficionados of Japanese cuisine will go for the evening omakase tasting menu. Staff are "very pleasant and efficient" and the "zingy" cuisine is "really imaginative and delicious". More reports please! / SE1 7PB; www.hannahrestaurant.london; Tue-Sun 10 pm; closed Mon; No trainers; Credit card deposit required to book.

Hans' Bar & Grill SW1 £79 3️⃣3️⃣3️⃣

164 Pavilion Road   020 7730 7000   6–2D

Only upbeat feedback this year on this "excellent spot behind Sloane Square in made-over Hans Mews" – a food operation that's part of nearby luxury boutique hotel, 11 Cadogan Gardens, recommended by fans "for a casual lunch from its eclectic menu" of salads, sharing plates and meat or fish 'bowls'. / SW1X 0AW; www.hansbarandgrill.com; @HansBarGrill; Mon-Sat 10.30 pm, Sun 7 pm; Take bookings all week via phone and/or online.

Hare & Tortoise £43 3️⃣3️⃣2️⃣

11-13 The Brunswick, WC1   020 7278 9799   2–1D
373 Kensington High St, W14   020 7603 8887   8–1D
156 Chiswick High Rd, W4   020 8747 5966   8–2A
38 Haven Grn, W5   020 8810 7066   1–2A
296-298 Upper Richmond Rd, SW15   020 8394 7666   11–2B
90 New Bridge St, EC4   020 7651 0266   10–2A

These pan-Asian pitstops can knock up anything from "reliable Japanese" dishes to "amazing curry laksa" with great speed and efficiency. Launched in Bloomsbury, the chain has expanded slowly over 25 years and now has branches in Ealing, Putney, Kensington and Chiswick. / www.hareandtortoise-restaurants.co.uk.

Harrods Dining Hall SW1 £70 3️⃣4️⃣4️⃣

Harrods, 87-135 Brompton Road   6–1D

Incredibly beautiful tiled chamber that once housed the Harrods meat counters and nowadays hosts London's poshest food court. A silver lining of the pandemic is that evening opening is now available here. There are six outlets, of which the most mentioned offers "exceptional" Indian dishes at Kama by Vineet (Bhatia). Other options include Kerridge's Fish & Chips; Pasta Evangelists' first pasta bar; Caviar House & Prunier; as well as a grill and a sushi bar. / SW1X 7XL; www.harrods.com/en-gb/restaurants; Mon-Wed 7 pm, Thu-Sat 10.30 pm, Sun 6 pm.

Harrods Social SW1 NEW   £110   3 4 4
87-135 Brompton Road   020 7225 6800   6–1D
Jason Atherton has installed himself in this bold conversion by Harrods of
2,000 sq ft of its lower ground floor (formerly men's shoes!) into a
"spectacular" new 114-seat brasserie. Fleetingly opened in March 2020 as
an in-store operation, it was transformed post-pandemic with Atherton at
the helm and a menu showcasing the best of British ingredients, such as
Wye Valley asparagus salad, roasted Cumbrian lamb and shepherd's pie,
Devon crab and Cumbrian beef tartar. On early feedback, one diner was
"underwhelmed", especially given the Knightsbridge prices, while others have
been won over the "outstanding" cuisine. Harrods has lacked a destination
restaurant in its own right in recent times: maybe they have finally cracked it!
/ SW1X 7XL; www.harrods.com/en-gb/restaurants/harrods-social-by-jason-atherton;
Mon-Thu 7 pm, Fri & Sat 8 pm, Sun 6 pm; closed Sun D.

Harry's Bar W1   £63   2 2 3
30-34 James Street   020 3971 9444   3–1A
"It's lovely to be able to sit outside" at this carefully styled Italian, not far
from Selfridges – Richard Caring's second spin-off carrying the brand of
Mayfair's famous Harry's Bar (which is still resolutely members only).
Feedback otherwise is fairly thin on the ground and a little up-and-down.
/ W1U 1EU; www.harrys-bar.co.uk; @harrysldn; Mon-Sun 11 pm.

Harwood Arms SW6   £74   4 3 3
Walham Grove   020 7386 1847   6–3A
"Unbeatable in the gastropub category" – this characterful Fulham
backstreet boozer is "still exceptional even though Sally Abé has left" and,
yet again, was voted London's No. 1 pub in our annual diners' survey.
Specialising in game, its "traditional" menu is "more elevated than is usual
for pub fayre" and "cooked with flair and enthusiasm". The place still looks
like a pub though, and they do a mean Scotch egg – it's the "gastropub
experience at its best!". (In September 2021, Jake Leach was inaugurated as
the new head chef). / SW6 1QP; www.harwoodarms.com; @HarwoodArms;
Mon-Thu, Sat 9.15 pm, Fri 9.15pm, Sun 8.15 pm; closed Mon-Thu L; credit card
required to book.

Hashi SW20   £49   3 4 2
54 Durham Rd   020 8944 1888   11–2A
This "very good neighbourhood Japanese" in Raynes Park wins consistently
solid ratings from a happy band of regulars in the area. "Food and service
are always excellent" – with the sushi winning particular praise.
/ SW20 0TW; Tue-Sat 10.30 pm, Sun 10 pm; closed Tue-Fri L, closed Mon; no Amex.

Hatay SW20   3 3 2
94-96 Coombe Lane   020 8947 9758   11–2A
You don't have to eat Korean food to eat well in Raynes Park! This "very
friendly Turkish restaurant" serves "some original dishes alongside Turkish
favourites and some excellent Turkish vintages". "It's a bonus to be able to
see into the kitchen". / SW20 0AY; hatayrestaurant.co.uk; Tue-Thu midnight, Fri &
Sat 1 am.

Hatched SW11   £73   5 3 3
189 Saint John's Hill   020 7738 0735   11–2C
Ambitious young chef Shane Marshall conjures up a short menu of
"exquisite" modern sharing plates at his minimalist three-year-old venue in
Battersea. Each dish is refined down to a maximum of four 'movements' to
be made for service from the open kitchen – although the preparation of
individual elements may already have taken several hours. / SW11 1TH;
www.hatchedsw11.com; @HatchedSW11; Take bookings all week via phone and/or
online.

Haugen E20 NEW
5 Westfield Avenue   020 4568 1444   14–1D

Part of Stratford's coming of age as a restaurant destination – and part of East London's International Quarter development: this D&D Group launch occupies a new, sustainably constructed three-floor landmark – The Pavilion – within the Olympic Park. It has a sizeable 550 covers in all and comprises a ground-floor deli plus large restaurant and 'winter garden' (sounds a bit like Bluebird); plus a first-floor dining room, also with terrace; and a rooftop bar with views of Stratford and the Olympic stadium. Foodwise, it's akin to The German Gymnasium – an Alpine theme with references to France, Germany, Switzerland and Austria. / E20 1HZ; www.haugen-restaurant.com; Wed-Sat 9.30 pm, Sun 2.30 pm.

The Havelock Tavern W14   £57   3 2 3
57 Masbro Rd   020 7603 5374   8–1C

"What a great pub!" – this classic blue-tiled late-Victorian tavern in an Olympia backstreet has been well-known for its "excellent food" for 25 years. "Back with a vengeance after lockdown 2" it "retains its high standards". / W14 0LS; www.havelocktavern.com; @havelocktavern; Mon-Sat 11 pm, Sun 10 pm.

The Hawk's Nest W12 NEW   £31   3 3 4
Goldhawk Rd, Shepherd's Bush Market   020 3620 6528   8–1C

With its foliage, fairy lights and heaters, this September 2020 newcomer – where tables are predominantly outside – injects a festive spark into a quirky space, next to Shepherd's Bush market and the Goldhawk Road tube bridge (opposite the station). Founders Will Fuller of Soho House Group and Frazer Timmerman of Incipio Group aimed, apparently, to import a bit of East London groove to this converted railway arch and adjoining large yard, and judging by it being permanently packed they've succeeded! Pizza is the menu mainstay and staff try hard. A 120-seater, it's also available for events. / W12 8DF; the-hawks-nest.co.uk; Mon-Sun 10.30 pm; closed Mon-Thu L.

Hawksmoor   £94   3 3 2
5a Air St, W1   020 7406 3980   4–4C
11 Langley St, WC2   020 7420 9390   5–2C
3 Yeoman's Row, SW3   020 7590 9290   6–2C
16 Winchester Walk, SE1   020 7234 9940   10–4C
157 Commercial St, E1   020 7426 4850   13–2B
10-12 Basinghall St, EC2   020 7397 8120   10–2C

"Perfectly aged, hung and cooked – this place is steak-heaven". Huw Gott and Will Beckett absolutely nailed it with this zeitgeisty 15-year-old chain of steakhouses, which they still part-own (and which – in July 2021 – announced the possibility, later cancelled, of floating on the London Stock Exchange to fuel future growth). For a generation of London restaurant-goers, "Hawksmoor hits it every single time" and the increasing introduction of fish from a dedicated buyer at Brixham market is a popular (and wise) innovation. Is it finally becoming a victim of its own success though? Ratings slipped notably this year due to an assortment of non-pandemic-related gripes ("beginning to feel formulaic…"; "just not tasty enough for such high prices…"; "still knocks out a succulent ribeye, but not what it was…"). Still, in late 2021 they're gearing up for the biggest and most ambitious space yet, and their first branch amidst the scrapers of Canary Wharf. Spread over three levels, it will be housed in an eco-friendly floating pavilion made from sustainably sourced timber decking, aluminium extracted from hydro sources, and with a green roof planted with wildflowers and grasses! [Instead of the wildflowers and grasses and aluminium extracted from hydro sources, should we all maybe just eat less meat!? Ed] / www.thehawksmoor.com.

Haya W11
333

184a Kensington Park Road   0203 995 4777   7–1B

In the heart of Notting Hill, this East-Mediterranean café opened a couple of years ago and offers a range of Tel Aviv-inspired bites and sharing plates, as well as a brunch menu. Feedback so far is limited, but a couple of locals say it's "always a great experience". / W11 2ES; haya.london; Mon-Fri 11.30 pm, Sat & Sun 4.30 am.

Haz
£59
232

9 Cutler St, E1   020 7929 7923   10–2D
14 Finsbury Square, EC2   020 7920 9944   13–2A
34 Foster Ln, EC2   020 7600 4172   10–2B
64 Bishopsgate, EC2   020 7628 4522   10–2D
112 Houndsditch, EC3   020 7623 8180   10–2D
6 Mincing Ln, EC3   020 7929 3173   10–2D

"Exceedingly large portions of simple, fresh and tasty Turkish food" draw a busy lunchtime crowd to this group of six restaurants within a mile or two of each other in the City. "The meat especially is good quality", while social distancing has had its compensations: "tables were further apart, which made for easier conversation". / www.hazrestaurant.co.uk.

Heddon Yokocho W1 NEW
£27
423

8 Heddon Street   4–3B

Just off Regent Street – in the pedestrianised enclave surrounding Heddon Street – this late winter 2020 newcomer is the brainchild of the Japan Centre Team. Inspired by the yokocho 'alleyways' of Japan and 1970s Tokyo, you eat ramen and other Japanese bites washed down with well-priced drinks options amidst "authentically fake kitsch" decor. Most reporters are very enthusiastic about the "full-flavoured, thick broths – occasionally you can tell this is all pre-prepared food, but the prices are very reasonable and it's not supposed to be a temple". See also, Panton Yokocho. / W1B 4BU; www.heddonyokocho.com; @japancentre; Mon-Thu 10.30 pm, Fri & Sat 11 pm, Sun 10 pm.

Hélène Darroze,
The Connaught Hotel W1
£173
332

Carlos Pl   020 3147 7200   3–3B

"Absolutely iconic, with superb everything!" or "not up to the hype" ("how she was awarded three Michelin Stars, goodness knows!!!") – Hélène Darroze's 12-year tenure at the most blueblooded of Mayfair hotels continues to split reporters, as it always has. With its "exceptional, amazing presentation and exotic flavours", the cuisine's overall scores in our survey do, undoubtedly, rank it amongst London's best; but equally they suggest that the Tyre Men's January 2021 promotion to its top billing is over-egging things a bit (perhaps because she's French?). Also divisive is the "somewhat under-the-radar, modern-luxe refurb" of this famous dining room in late 2019. To fans, the new guise is "warm" and "well-spaced", but to detractors it seems "funny peculiar" ("if only the surroundings had preserved a little of the elegance of the old Connaught dining room"). The excruciating final bill is also an issue, even to its most ardent fans: "words cannot do the food justice. I could have cried eating every dish… But I did actually cry when the bill arrived!". / W1K 2AL; www.the-connaught.co.uk; @TheConnaught; Tue-Sat 9.30 pm; closed Sun & Mon; No trainers.

Heliot Steak House WC2
£66
333

Cranbourn Street   020 7769 8844   5–3B

"My go-to comfort venue" – it's worth knowing about this surprisingly good steak restaurant overlooking the floor of London's biggest casino, on Leicester Square. It serves a wide range of dishes, but undoubtedly the biggest culinary draw is the selection of USDA steaks, which is something of a point of pride for casino owner Simon Thomas (as is the superior wine selection). It's all super-handy and "very reasonably priced". / WC2H 7AJ; www.hippodromecasino.com; @HippodromeLDN; Mon-Sat 1 am, Sun 11 pm; closed Mon-Fri L.

Helix (Searcys at The Gherkin) EC3 £80 3 3 5
30 St Mary Axe   0330 1070816   10–2D

"Amazing views from the top of the Gherkin" are the most prominent highpoint at this 40th-floor dining room. Nowadays run by well-known caterers, Searcys, it won solid ratings all round this year. / EC3A 8EP; searcysatthegherkin.co.uk/helix-restaurant; @SearcysGherkin; Mon-Wed 10 pm, Fri & Sat 11 pm, Sun 6 pm; closed Sat L closed Sun D, closed Thu.

Hereford Road W2 £54 4 4 3
3 Hereford Rd   020 7727 1144   7–1B

"Inventive food and solid service" make chef Tom Pemberton's 15-year-old Bayswater venture a particularly strong *"favourite local"*. Housed in an artfully converted Victorian butcher's shop, it majors on seasonal British produce. Water damage from a leak in an upstairs flat delayed the reopening after lockdown, but as of September 2021 the restaurant's Twitter feed was advertising for a new front of house, implying reopening some time soon thereafter. Top Tip: *"amazing value set lunch"*. / W2 4AB; www.herefordroad.org; @3HerefordRoad; Thu-Sun-Wed 10 pm; closed Mon-Wed L.

Heritage W1 £71
18 Rupert Street   020 3995 7500   4–3D

Woody decor and a vaguely Swiss theme to the menu underpin the Alpine atmosphere of this stylish-looking Soho two-year-old, although – in other respects – its mix of seafood, steaks and typical brasserie fare wouldn't look out of place under many other national flags. Feedback was too limited for a rating, but fans say it's *"always a good time"* here, with *"excellent food and service"*. / W1D 6DF; www.heritagerestaurant.co.uk; Wed & Thu, Sun midnight, Fri & Sat 1 am; closed Wed-Sun D, closed Mon & Tue.

Heritage SE21 NEW £50 4 3 3
101 Rosendale Road   020 8761 4665   1–4D

"Inspired modern Indian cuisine from chef Dayashankar Sharma, formerly of the Grand Trunk Road" wins strong praise for this brave, January 2021 opening in West Dulwich. The regional small plates are hailed as *"top-quality"* – *"the whole menu was inventive and it was difficult to pick what to eat"* – as are the Indian-inspired cocktails. *"Service is friendly and lovely, too"* (*"the GM and the chef came to say hi"*) and *"it has a really buzzy atmosphere"*. *"So happy that it has landed on my doorstep"*. / SE21 8EZ; www.heritagedulwich.co.uk; Tue-Sat 10.30 pm, Sun 9 pm; closed Tue-Fri L, closed Mon.

The Hero of Maida W9 £63 3 3 3
55 Shirland Rd   020 7266 9198   7–1C

This *"great local pub (doggy-friendly too)"* in Maida Vale has found some equilibrium after an up-and-down performance since an acclaimed opening under Harcourt Inns in 2018. Highly rated chef-director Harry Harris left the group last summer, so the menu has become less exciting – but our latest survey indicates that it is winning over its (now smaller) following in our survey. / W9 2JD; theheromaidavale.co.uk; @The Hero of Maida; Mon-Thu 11 pm, Fri & Sat midnight, Sun 10 pm; closed Mon-Thu L.

Hicce N1 £66 2 2 3
Coal Drops Yard   020 3869 8200   9–3C

"Great sharing Mediterranean dishes", many of them cooked over wood, is the USP at this Coal Drops Yard, King's Cross, venue – the first solo outing from Pip Lacey, former head chef at Angela Hartnett's Murano. Most reporters enjoyed the food, and ratings would almost certainly have been higher had one or two reporters not continued to gripe at the portion size (*"plates were so tiny the staff asked us to double our order"*). / N1C 4AB; www.hicce.co.uk; @hiccelondon; Tue-Sat 10.30 pm, Sun 4 pm; closed Sun D, closed Mon.

Above at Hide W1 £160 343
85 Piccadilly 020 3146 8666 3–4C

"A wonderful situation opposite Green Park" with "marvellous views" adds to the high lustre of this luxuriously spacious first-floor venue, found up a beautifully carved wooden staircase from the cheaper 'Hide Ground' below. As you might expect of somewhere under common ownership with the well-known Hedonism Wines, it boasts an "incredible wine selection", which is set off to good effect by Ollie Dabbous's "exceptional and innovative" cuisine, boasting "unique dishes and combinations that you won't find elsewhere". And "the great care and professionalism of the warm and welcoming staff" is mentioned in numerous reports, too. You can guess the catch! – if you are counting the pennies, cross the street to avoid the place (and its harshest critics find it "so overpriced"). By most accounts, though, "the whole experience is absolutely phenomenal!". / W1J 8JB; www.hide.co.uk; @hide_restaurant; Mon-Thu 9.30 pm, Fri & Sat 10 pm, Sun 9.15 pm.

Hide Ground W1 £122 444
85 Piccadilly 020 3146 8666 3–4C

The "wallet-friendly lunch" in the ground-floor dining room constitutes a welcome invitation to this otherwise eye-wateringly expensive venture opposite Green Park from chef Ollie Dabbous and Russian tycoon Evgeny Chichvarkin (owner of Hedonism Wines). "Once inside, it feels as though you've stepped onto the set of an ultra-chic modern-day remake of Alice in Wonderland", with "fantastic food and ambience". Top Tip: "Since lockdown, they've reduced the wine prices by £20 a bottle so it's now perhaps the most exciting wine list in London AND at a very reasonable price – long may that last". / W1J; www.hide.co.uk; @hide_restaurant; Tue-Sun 9 pm; closed Tue L, closed Mon.

High Road Brasserie W4 £65 122
162-166 Chiswick High Rd 020 8742 7474 8–2A

Soho House seem to have forgotten about their all-day brasserie in a prominent spot on the Chiswick High Road – the most generous critic in our latest survey says it's "unfortunately not as good as it was". Others are much harsher: "pretentious and not worth the money"; "grabby on pricing"; "lazy, careless and very popular – go figure". / W4 1PR; highroadbrasserie.co.uk; @HRBrasserie; Sun-Wed 11 pm, Fri & Sat 1 am, Thu midnight; booking max 8 may apply.

High Timber EC4 £63 443
8 High Timber Street 020 7248 1777 10–3B

Hidden away by the Wobbly Bridge directly opposite Tate Modern, this 12-year-old venture is "the place to go if you want to explore South African wine alongside some of the best steaks in the City". It's also a place were "lunchtimes can – and often do – stretch into dinner", under the expert guidance of "host and owner Neleen Strauss, who's bonkers, in a great way" (she personally presented Boris Johnson as mayor of London with a bill for £80,000 to cover her losses during the London Olympics!). / EC4V 3PA; www.hightimber.com; @HTimber; Mon-Fri 10 pm; closed Sat & Sun.

Hispania EC3 £72 344
72-74 Lombard Street 020 7621 0338 10–2C

This "smart City restaurant", close to the Bank of England, serves "excellent Spanish food backed by attentive but discreet service" and "an educative wine list", in "great surroundings" set over two floors. "The emphasis seems to be on meat, and they also do the tapas classics to near-perfection – I love their take on a Russian salad and also the garlic prawns". / EC3V 9AY; www.hispanialondon.com; @hispanialondon; Mon-Fri 10 pm; closed Sat & Sun; Take bookings all week via phone and/or online.

Holborn Dining Room WC1 £78 3 2 2
252 High Holborn 020 3747 8633 2–1D
The "great pies" from chef Calum Franklin – from classic hand-raised pork pie to curried mutton or dauphinoise, black truffle and aged Comté – are "justifiably well known" at this "very well-situated" and very business-friendly dining room on the edge of the City, which also specialises in grills and British charcuterie. The imposing interior is certainly "grand", although some find it "a bit cavernous". / WC1V 7EN; www.holborndiningroom.com; @HolbornDining; Mon-Fri 10 pm, Sat 10.30 pm, Sun 9.45 pm.

Holly Bush NW3 £71 2 2 3
22 Holly Mount 020 7435 2892 9–1A
The rare treat of a relatively unmodernised Grade II listed Georgian tavern in Hampstead, visited by everybody from Dr Johnson to Liam Gallagher (although only the latter was barred, after an altercation with staff). "The quality of the food has improved". / NW3 6SG; www.hollybushhampstead.co.uk; @TheHollyBushPub; Mon-Sat 11 pm, Sun 10.30 pm.

Homeslice £42 3 2 3
50 James Street, W1 020 3034 0621 3–1A
13 Neal's Yd, WC2 020 7836 4604 5–2C
101 Wood Lane White City, W12 020 3034 0381 1–2B
374-378 Old St, EC1 020 3151 1121 13–1B
69-71 Queen Street, EC4 020 3034 0381 10–3C
These "trendy pizza joints with a modern twist and clean, industrial interiors" serve "generously portioned and always-fresh" thin-crust pizza, attracting a good fan club for this 10-year-old group run by the late Terry Wogan's sons, Mark and Alan. They make no claim to authenticity and are more influenced by New York than Naples – but the "bizarre combinations on the blackboard always turn out to be unexpectedly delicious. Believe in them!". / www.homeslicepizza.co.uk; @homesliceLDN.

Homestead E14 NEW £41
45 Hope Street 020 4519 1951 12–1D
'A welcoming hub for the local island community' is the aim of this new all-day neighbourhood dining spot – the first to open on the developing London City Island, opposite The O2 and a short stroll via pedestrian bridge from Canning Town Tube & DLR. Launched at the worst of times – in late 2020 – it started as a deli/take-away but opened its bar and restaurant as lockdown eased. / E14 0QG; homestead-lci.com; @homesteadldn; Tue-Sun 11 pm, Mon 5.30 pm; closed Mon D.

Honest Burgers £32 2 3 2
"Rosemary fries to die for" are still a mainstay of this "gourmet burger" chain: now with around 40 branches in the UK (and which raised money in early 2021 to allow it to take up opportunities as they present themselves post-pandemic). "Although they have been around for some time, the burgers are arguably among the best in London, and they have maintained standards despite expanding to become a sizable chain". Well, that was our view till now anyway, and it remains the majority verdict. Is the brand finally becoming a victim of its success, though? Ratings were dragged into chain territory for the first time this year by a few reporters who felt "the old flair and fun were missing…", or that it's "sometimes interesting but overall so-so". On the whole, though, it still gets a big thumbs-up: "had to eat and run but worth almost missing the last train for!". / www.honestburgers.co.uk; @honestburgers.

Honey & Co W1 £64 4️⃣2️⃣2️⃣

25a Warren St   020 7388 6175   2–1B

"Fascinating Levantine cooking, of exceptional tastiness" established Sarit Packer and Itamar Srulovich's little café near Warren Street tube as a leader on the capital's Middle Eastern food scene when it opened 10 years ago. Marks have slipped as the excitement of the new has dissipated, but comments are still overwhelmingly positive, whether for *"delightful vegetarian dishes (and I'm a meat-eater)"* or *"out-of-this-world cheesecake"*. Home-delivery food boxes have also been a hit in the last year. The Honey and Spice deli and Honey and Smoke grillhouse (see also) are both a short walk away. / W1T 5LZ; www.honeyandco.co.uk; @Honeyandco; Mon-Sat 10 pm; closed Sun.

Honey & Smoke W1 £69 5️⃣4️⃣2️⃣

216 Great Portland Street   020 7388 6175   2–1B

"Outstanding and memorable food, full of flavour" makes this Middle Eastern grillhouse near Great Portland Street tube station a worthy follow-up to Honey & Co. Many diners reckon it's *"better than many of the West End's most expensive and celebrated venues"* – and it certainly has overtaken its older siblings in terms of ratings in our survey. *"The ambiance is a bit basic, but that is part of the charm"*. / W1W 5QW; honeyandco.co.uk/places/honey-smoke/; @Honeyandco; Mon-Sat 10.30 pm; closed Sun.

Hood SW2 £53 4️⃣3️⃣3️⃣

67 Streatham Hill   020 3601 3320   11–2D

The name says it all about this cute, casual Streatham Hill fixture. It's most recommended for breakfast, but provides a wide array of options including steak suppers and a prix fixe evening menu (two courses for £26). / SW2 4TX; www.hoodrestaurants.com; @HoodStreatham; Wed-Sat 11 pm, Sun 2.30 pm; closed Sun D, closed Mon & Tue; booking online only.

Hoppers £53 3️⃣2️⃣3️⃣

49 Frith St, W1   no tel   5–2A

77 Wigmore Street, W1   020 3319 8110   3–1A

Unit 3, Building 4, Pancras Square, N1   020 3319 8125   9–3C **NEW**

"Eating here is like being back in Sri Lanka", say fans of this superbly *"authentic"* South Asian concept from JKS Restaurants, which now has branches in Soho, Marylebone and King's Cross. But is the shine beginning to wear off a bit? – most reporters do still talk of *"amazing spicing"*, *"Sri Lankan street food at its best"* and *"probably the tastiest food in London"*, but, for a minority this year, the cooking *"did not live up to the hype"*. / www.hopperslondon.com; @HoppersLondon.

Hot May Pot Pot SW3 **NEW** £84

30 Beauchamp Place   020 3637 6666   6–1C

Amidst the glossy boutiques of Beauchamp Place, this beautiful, luxuriously decorated Chinese opened at the end of 2019, and – aside from a favourable review by Fay Maschler – has never really had the chance to make waves. It specialises in hot pots, and the menu features much in the way of seafood and wagyu beef to accompany or incorporate. It's listed (without a star) by Michelin, who typically list only extremely expensive, culinarily 'safe' Chinese restaurants: you can view that as either a positive or negative. / SW3 1NJ; www.hotmay.co.uk; Mon-Sun 11.30 pm.

Hot Stone £130 4️⃣4️⃣4️⃣

3 Windmill Street, W1   020 7419 0305   2–1C **NEW**

9 Chapel Market, N1   020 3302 8226   9–3D **NEW**

"Exceptional food every time" and *"high-quality and attentive service"* inspire early reporters who have visited both of Padam Raj Rai's duo of ambitious ishiyaki (hence the name), where the serving of certified Kobe beef is a highlight (only eight restaurants in the UK offer it). Also on the menu: top-quality sushi and sashimi and 48-hours marinated black cod. Islington's Chapel Market branch launched first in August 2020, with a 14-course omakase chef's table experience (for up to 4 people). Later in 2020, the branch closed and rebranded itself 'Omakase at Hot Stone', opening for

just 2-3 days per week for 6 people at a time for an 'Omakase' (chef's choice) experience. Despite the travails of the pandemic, in May 2021 Padam opened a second 50-cover sibling in Fitzrovia. The interior of the new branch boasts traditional wooden panelling, accent tiling and artwork by Japanese Edo-period ukiyo-e painter Katsushika Hokusai. / hotstonelondon.com.

House Restaurant, National Theatre SE1 £62 2️⃣2️⃣2️⃣

National Theatre, South Bank   020 7452 3600   2–3D

"The set menu is good value" at the National Theatre's most salubrious in-house dining option, so it's "always reliable" as a pre-show pit-stop. But critics would welcome a bit more ambition, saying the current effort is "a wasted opportunity" given the site and its captive audience. Top Tip: "the waiters are always a good source of play reviews". / SE1 9PX; house.nationaltheatre.org.uk; @NT_House.

Humble Chicken W1 NEW £35 5️⃣3️⃣3️⃣

54 Frith Street   020 7434 2782   5–2A

On the original site of Barrafina, this Soho newcomer has been three years in the making, serving yakitori made from every bit of the bird. Will it do for yakitori what Barrafina did for tapas? Chef patron Angelo Sato has a fine CV – including as head chef at Restaurant Story – and is looking to build on the success of his grab-and-go outlet Omoide in Bermondsey (which he opened in early 2019). In a July 2021 review, Jay Rayner branded it "superb... I feel the heart-fluttering joy that comes with the insufferably smug knowledge that I am in exactly the right place". Our early reporters similarly award it full marks – "it's been long overdue for another nose-to-tail yakitori restaurant to reopen in London. And while the skewers are outstanding, the non-skewer dishes have some highlights too". / W1D 4SJ; www.humblechickenuk.com; Tue-Thu 10 pm, Fri & Sat 11 pm; closed Tue-Thu L, closed Sun & Mon.

Humble Grape £60 3️⃣4️⃣3️⃣

11-13 Theberton Street, N1   020 3887 9287   9–3D
2 Battersea Rise, SW11   020 3620 2202   11–2C
18-20 Mackenzie Walk, E14   020 3985 1330   12–1C
8 Devonshire Row, EC2   020 3887 9287   10–2D
1 Saint Bride's Passage, EC4   020 7583 0688   10–2A

James Dawson's 12-year-old wine shop/bar/kitchen operation has gathered momentum in recent years, expanding from its Battersea base to branches in a Fleet Street crypt, Islington, Liverpool Street and Canary Wharf. The "great wine list" from sustainable, small-scale producers is the focus, with "lots by the glass" and at "good value". It's backed up by "consistently good" small plates, cheese and charcuterie. / www.humblegrape.co.uk; @humblegrape.

Hunan SW1 £110 5️⃣3️⃣1️⃣

51 Pimlico Rd   020 7730 5712   6–2D

"Tell Mr Peng what you don't eat or like, and the courses will continue to come until you say 'no thank you'", at this family-run Pimlico veteran (founded in 1982), which has long been one of the best Chinese restaurants in London and continues to "nail it every time". "There's no menu" – they will just ask what kind of food you like, then "bring you a string of delicious little courses"; and "if you are into adventurous Chinese cuisine then it's a magical experience, with superb dishes such as the spicy venison". Service is discreet and the wine list is "exceptionally good and should cover any palate." / SW1W 8NE; www.hunanlondon.com; Mon-Sat 11 pm; closed Sun.

The Hunter's Moon SW3 NEW   £58   3 4 4
86 Fulham Road   07497 425819   6–2C

"Classy, with a nice grown-up atmosphere" – this 'traditional countryside pub and dining room in southwest London' (the first from the Lunar Pub Company) opened in late 2019, and is successfully living up to its 'rus-in-urbe' aspirations. There are lots of warm vibes for its well-realised food and cosy style (even if the prices are those of SW3, not the shires). They are already onto their second project (opening in late 2021) – The Ganymede in SW1 (see also). / SW3 6HR; huntersmoonlondon.co.uk; Mon & Tue, Thu 11 pm, Fri & Sat midnight, Sun 8.30 pm; closed Wed.

Huo SW10 NEW   £67   2 3 4
9 Park Walk   020 3696 9090   6–3B

Opened at the start of June 2021: this Chelsea newcomer – on the former site of Farm Girl – is aiming to replicate the success of its long-standing sibling, Uli in Notting Hill. Michael Lim's easy sense of hospitality twinned with attractive casual decor plus well-priced Southeast Asian food and a separate bar are a promising formula in this neck of the woods. Early reports are very mixed, though. Everyone wishes the place well and thinks it's potentially *"a great neighbourhood addition with a wide range of Asian food"*. But for a couple of *"so disappointed"* reporters, *"the menu is appealing, ambience very good"*, but results were *"no better than OK"*. / SW10 0AJ; huo.london; Mon-Sat midnight, Sun 11 pm.

Hush W1   £95   2 2 3
8 Lancashire Ct   020 7659 1500   3–2B

"Buzzy but relaxed", this 1920s-themed bar/bistro for the Mayfair crowd is known for *"lovely courtyard dining in the summer months"* – *"it's right in the middle of town but feels away from it all"*. It is also well connected: co-owners include Evgeny Lebedev, the Evening Standard owner elevated to the House of Lords by Boris Johnson. / W1S 1EY; www.hush.co.uk; @HushMayfair; Mon-Sat midnight, Sun 6 pm; closed Sun D; booking max 12 may apply.

Hutong, The Shard SE1   £109   2 2 5
31 St Thomas St   020 3011 1257   10–4C

"Stunning views… but overpriced" is the predictable trade-off at this elevated – in both senses – Chinese perch on the 33rd floor of the Shard. *"The food is good but not great"* while *"the location and views are truly amazing"* – so a visit can represent *"good value for a special occasion"*. Perhaps the best tactic is to *"stick to the set menus – it gets very expensive beyond them"* – and the *"fantastic cocktails"*. / SE1 9RY; www.hutong.co.uk; @HutongShard; Mon-Sun 10.30 pm; No shorts.

Ibérica   £65   3 2 2
Zig Zag Building, 70 Victoria St, SW1   020 7636 8650   2–4B
195 Great Portland St, W1   020 7636 8650   2–1B
12 Cabot Sq, E14   020 7636 8650   12–1C
89 Turnmill St, EC1   020 7636 8650   10–1A

"High quality, reasonably priced tapas" – *"as traditionally Spanish as ever and properly prepared"* – alongside an *"interesting selection of Spanish wines (many from less usual wine areas)"* – is the hallmark of this group that originated in Great Portland Street 15 years ago; now joined by branches in Victoria, Canary Wharf, Marylebone, Farringdon and Leeds. *"The paella had just the right degree of socarrat"* (the caramelised crust on the bottom). / www.ibericarestaurants.com; @Iberica_UK.

Icco Pizza £20 4 3 2
46 Goodge St, W1   020 7580 9688   2–1C
21a Camden High Street, NW1   020 7380 0020   9–3B
"Not just cheap and cheerful but good, cheap and cheerful" – "you can't
fault the pizza, thin-crust, well made to order, and tasty" at this veteran
Goodge Street pizzeria, est. 1999, where a basic marinara costs just £3.95.
There's now a branch in Camden, as well as delivery-only outlets in Wood
Green, Wandsworth and Croydon. / www.icco.co.uk; @ICCO_pizza.

Ikoyi SW1 £212 4 3 2
1 St James's Market   020 3583 4660   4–4D
"Truly surprising African ingredients and flavour combinations, showcased
with stunning presentation" have rightly won culinary renown for Iré Hassan-
Odukale and Jeremy Chan's "serene and calm" venture in the swish but
slightly soulless St James's development, near Piccadilly Circus. "You will not
find anywhere else a West African contemporary fusion tasting menu quite
like this, with flavour combinations to die for: superb and exciting in every
way". "Excellent wine pairings, too". / SW1Y 4AH; www.ikoyilondon.com; Mon-Sat
10.30 pm; closed Sun.

Il Guscio N5 £56 3 3 3
231 Blackstock Road   020 7354 1400   9–1D
"Delighted to see this has survived the pandemic!" – this little Sardinian
local, not far from the Arsenal ground, delights its Highbury fanclub. They say
it serves "Islington's top pizza". / N5 2LL; www.ilgusciohighbury.co.uk; Sun-Thu
10.30 pm, Fri 10 pm, Sat 11 pm; closed Mon-Fri L; Take bookings all week via phone
and/or online.

Il Teatro della Carne W1 NEW
39-45 Shaftesbury Avenue   020 3727 6161   5–3A
On the prominent Theatreland site that was Café Monico (RIP) – next to
the Gielgud Theatre – Roberto Costa opened his own spectacle dedicated to
meat in July 2021. It's based on his successful Macellaio chain, where you
choose your own cut and have it cooked to order. Can he succeed on this site
where Soho House failed? / W1; www.macellaiorc.com; Mon-Fri 4 pm, Sat 6 pm,
Sun 5 pm.

Imad's Syrian Kitchen W1 NEW £16 4 4 3
Kingly Court, Kingly Street   07473 333631   4–2B
Since fleeing Damascus in 2015 after his restaurant businesses were
destroyed, chef Imad Alarnab has cooked for refugees in Calais and provided
free falafel for those in need during lockdown. This crowdfunded Soho
newcomer is his first permanent London venture and occupies the Kingly
Court site vacated by Asma Khan after she moved Darjeeling Express to her
new, bigger Covent Garden site. Due to open in December 2020, it finally
launched properly in May 2021 and early reports say it's "a real gem" –
"attentive, homely, considered" – and providing "great, tasty food, a simple
menu, and an enjoyable time". / W1B 5PW; imadssyriankitchen.co.uk;
@ImadsKitchen; Tue-Sat 11 pm; closed Sun & Mon.

Imperial Treasure SW1 £124 3 2 2
9-10 Waterloo Place   020 3011 1328   4–4D
This "ultra-high-end Chinese" two-year-old – set in an "extremely hushed"
former banking hall off Pall Mall "with sumptuous interiors by Christian
Liaigre" – is the first London branch of a Singapore-based group with
offshoots across mainland China. Its menu is led by a signature Peking duck
that must be ordered in advance and is "delicious – if outrageously priced"
at £100 a pop. Other choices get much the same verdict: "the quality of the
dishes is exceptional", but "most are very pricey for what they are".
/ SW1Y 4BE; www.imperialtreasure.com; Mon-Fri 10.30 pm, Sat & Sun 10 pm.

India Club,
Strand Continental Hotel WC2   £29   3 3 2
143 Strand   020 7836 4880   2–2D
"So special and deserving to be saved" – this truly "iconic venue for a meal",
up a flight of stairs in the Strand, has barely changed since its foundation in
1951, when Prime Minister Nehru and Lady Mountabatten were among the
members. Fans say the "food is reliably amazing", but it's as a "cheap"
venue for a meal in a distinctively grungy setting that it wins such loyalty. For
several years now it has been under threat of closure from a landlord who
wants to develop the site as a new hotel, and in 2021 a crowdfunding
campaign raised £50,000 towards legal fees to fight against eviction. The
club and its bar have been run by three generations of the same family since
launch. BYO from the hotel bar. / WC2R 1JA; www.theindiaclub.co.uk;
@saveindiaclub; Mon-Sun 10.50pm; booking max 6 may apply.

Indian Moment SW11   £35   3 3 2
44 Battersea Rise   020 7223 6575 / 020 7223 1818   11–2C
This "brilliant local Indian" off Clapham's foodie Northcote Road knocks out
"wonderfully flavoured dishes at a good price point" – and is "definitely not
your generic curry house". Now approaching two decades in the
neighbourhood, although "it moved round the corner to Battersea Rise a
couple of years ago". Top Tip: unusually, it has a children's menu – perhaps a
concession to the area's reputation as 'Nappy Valley'. / SW11 1EE;
www.indianmoment.co.uk; @indianmoment.

Indian Ocean SW17   £29   3 3 3
214 Trinity Rd   020 8672 7740   11–2C
"Great food" and some unusual flavours give this long-established curry
house next to Wandsworth Common the edge over its rivals. A large local
fanbase bears witness to its qualities. / SW17 7HP;
www.indianoceanrestaurant.com; Sun-Thu 11 pm, Fri & Sat 11.45 pm; closed
Sun-Thu-Sat L; Take bookings all week via phone and/or online.

Indian Rasoi N2   £35   3 2 2
7 Denmark Terrace   020 8883 9093   1–1B
This tiny and deceptively modest-looking Muswell Hill curry house has
established a good track record for its Mughal-inspired cuisine over more
than a decade. / N2 9HG; www.indian-rasoi.co.uk; @indianrasoi; Tue-Sun 10.30 pm;
closed Mon; no Amex.

Indian Room SW12   £17   4 3 3
59 Bedford Hill   020 8675 8611   11–2D
Regularly ranking in the top 10 of TripAdvisor does no harm to the custom
of this Balham High Street Indian of about ten years standing. Our reporters
are not quite as mega-enthusiastic, but rate it consistently highly. / SW12 9EZ;
www.indianroom.co.uk; @indianroom; Sun-Thu 11 pm, Fri & Sat 11.30 pm; closed
Mon-Fri L.

Indian Zing W6   £55   4 3 2
236 King St   020 8748 5959   8–2B
"If you want top-class Indian food, look no further" than Manoj Vasaikar's
"unremarkable-looking" and cramped neighbourhood spot near Ravenscourt
Park tube. Open since 2005, it was touted, back in the day, as the late
Michael Winner's favourite curry house and all reports recommend its
"interesting" dishes with "wonderful flavours". / W6 0RS; www.indian-zing.co.uk;
@IndianZing; Mon-Sun 10 pm.

Inko Nito W1   £56   3 3 4
55 Broadwick Street   020 3959 2650   4–2B
"Our daughters love this restaurant – especially the cubed steak and iceberg
lettuce!". This manifestly cool Soho three-year-old offers sushi and sashimi as
well as a wide range of fish and meat from the robata grill. / W1F 9QS;
www.inkonitorestaurant.com/london-soho/; Mon-Sat 10.30 pm, Sun 8 pm; closed
Mon & Tue L.

INO W1 NEW
4 Newburgh Street   020 3701 6618   4–2B

From the team behind the well-rated Opso (and in Athens, Michelin two-star Funky Gourmet), this tiny, new (May 2021) Greek 'gastrobar' in Soho aims to combine modern Greek small plates – many of them cooked over the 'psistaria' (charcoal grill) – with Hellenic wines and cocktails. Seating incorporates a counter looking onto the narrow open kitchen. It opened too late for survey feedback, but Felicity Capon of The Week declared it "noisy, hot, full of life and vitality, offering superb and generous small plates designed to share" and showing "real pride and passion" in their preparation. / W1F; www.inogastrobar.com; Mon-Sun 10.30 pm.

Ishtar W1   £69   3 3 3
10-12 Crawford St   020 7224 2446   2–1A

"Imaginative Turkish food with beautifully prepared, high-quality ingredients" make this a "very good Marylebone local". Lunch and early-evening menus are good value. / W1U 6AZ; www.ishtarrestaurant.com; Mon-Thu 11 pm, Fri & Sat 12.30 am, Sun 11.30 pm.

Isola by San Carlo W1 NEW   £45
3-5 Barratt Street, St Christopher's Place   3–1A

Open in Autumn 2021 – a smart and traditional flagship for the San Carlo group on the prominent former St Christopher's Place site of Carluccio's. It's big, with 220 seats and a 50-cover al fresco terrace. Managing director Carlo Distefano describes it as the group's "most exciting project in years". / W1U 1BF; sancarlo.co.uk; @sancarlo_group.

Issho-Ni E2   4 4 3
185 Bethnal Green Road   020 7366 0314   13–1D

"Fantastic, very fresh sushi, and top hot dishes too" (from chef Eduardo Agauiar) win praise for this "local gem" – an izakaya-style Japanese restaurant in Bethnal Green, whose owner Claire Su converted it from the premises previously run by her parents as a noodle bar (Noodle King). It's more vibey than more traditional Japanese locals, and does a handy line in bottomless brunches. / E2 6AB; issho-ni.com; Wed-Sat 9.30 pm; closed Mon & Tue & Sun.

Italian Greyhound W1 NEW   £55
62 Seymour Street   020 3826 7940   7–1D

On the Marylebone site, just off Edgware Road, that was formerly Bernardi's, this new Italian 80-seater bar/restaurant (with 20-seat outside terrace) opened in early June. It is an evolution under the continued ownership of restaurateurs Marcello and Gabriel Bernardi and Barry Hirst (Cubitt House, Open House, Pantechnicon). Head chef Yohei Furuhashi spent nine years at The River Café, then went on to work at Dinings SW3 as head chef, from which he moved to Petersham Nurseries. His menu is based around small plates: handmade pasta, pizza, grilled dishes, salads and desserts. / W1; theitaliangreyhound.co.uk; Wed-Sat 11 pm, Sun 5 pm; closed Sun D, closed Mon & Tue.

The Ivy WC2   £87   2 3 3
1-5 West St   020 7836 4751   5–3B

"Nowhere near as exclusive as it once was, but still a formidable competitor" is perhaps a fair summary of the disparate views on the original Theatreland icon that Richard Caring used to inspire his national brasserie chain. That it's "now no better than the lookalikes across the country" certainly carries a lot of weight when it comes to its middling comfort food: "there was plenty of sparkle and fun amongst our fellow diners but none on the plate: I've had better pub food!". Still, it continues to inspire an impressive amount of feedback, especially amongst romantics who feel "its seductive interior is still great for dates" ("not the glamour spot it was, but can still impress!"). / WC2H 9NQ; www.the-ivy.co.uk; @TheIvyWestSt; Mon-Sat 11 pm, Sun 10.30 pm; No shorts; booking max 6 may apply.

The Ivy Asia £66 ②④③
8-10 North Audley Street, W1   3–2A **NEW**
201-203a King's Road, SW3   020 7486 6154   6–3C **NEW**
20 New Change Passage, EC4   020 3971 2600   10–2B **NEW**

Richard Caring continues to pimp the Ivy brand to the max: since this Asian-themed sub-brand first debuted in Manchester in 2018, it has expanded with a 200-seat venue in the City's One New Change mall ("great view of St Paul's") and – in August 2021 – a second branch opened in SW3 near The Ivy, Chelsea Garden; (and there's a third coming soon on the Mayfair site that was once Princess Garden). True to Caring's restaurant DNA, the decor in all locations is wildly maximalist, with fluorescent onyx floors, replica samurai armour and (cringey?) pagoda-style roofs over the bars. Some reporters do find the effect "very cool, in a see-and-be-seen kind of way". To say the least, though, the Asian-theme-park styling doesn't send the message that authenticity is on the agenda – a concern which the Chelsea branch's risibly off-message launch video did nothing to allay ('naive… totally inappropriate and culturally insensitive'… and that was just what they said about it themselves!). As to the sushi and wide menu of other Asian-inspired scoff: some diners find it "surprisingly good" but, all things considered, it's kinda beside the point. / www.theivyasia.com.

The Ivy Café £62 ①②③
96 Marylebone Ln, W1   020 3301 0400   2–1A
120 St John's Wood High St, NW8   020 3096 9444   9–3A
75 High St, SW19   020 3096 9333   11–2B
9 Hill Street, TW9   020 3146 7733   1–4A

"A bit clichéd, but never lets us down", say fans of the sub-sub brand of this famous brasserie chain, who "have no idea why its reviews are so bad". For too many reporters, though, these outlets represent "a failing imitation of a classic that is itself rather variable", with a "disappointing. expensive, mundane menu and inattentive service". The best bet? "Stick to breakfast and enjoy the surroundings".

The Ivy Grills & Brasseries £66 ②③④
66 Victoria Street, SW1   020 3971 2404   2–4B **NEW**
26-28 Broadwick St, W1   020 3301 1166   4–1C
1 Henrietta St, WC2   020 3301 0200   5–3D
197 King's Rd, SW3   020 3301 0300   6–3C
96 Kensington High St, W8   020 3301 0500   6–1A
One Tower Bridge, 1 Tower Bridge, SE1   020 3146 7722   10–4D
Dashwood House, 69 Old Broad St, EC2   020 3146 7744   10–2D

"Always ambient and fun" – Richard Caring's stretching (twisting?) of the Ivy brand is easy to snipe at but has so far avoided degenerating into farce. For sure, "the food is certainly nothing superior": fans may claim it's "more than adequate", but its overall ratings nowadays are only just the right side of poor. That said, even critics of the cooking often feel that the "lovely" interiors and "welcoming service" provide compensation, and fit the bill for making an occasion of a meal. In the capital, the most mentioned outlets are The Ivy Chelsea Garden ("delightful garden tables and ideal for a noisy girls' night out"); and The Ivy Kensington Brasserie ("huge fun, loads of buzz" and "always a treat"). The Ivy City Garden and Canary Wharf's Ivy in the Park follow along in terms of volume of feedback. The newest member of the spin-off family is The Ivy Victoria – a vast space with 300 guests over two floors. / ivycollection.com.

Jaffna House SW17 £24 ④②②
90 Tooting High St   020 8672 7786   11–2C

"A must-visit on Tooting High Street" – this modest and "amazing-value" family-run café was one of the first in London to serve "authentic and delicious hoppers and other Sri Lankan specialities" when it opened 31 years ago. "The lunch menu is really good for a cheap 'n' cheerful meal, but for the best experience go in the evening and eat in the back dining room". / SW17 0RN; www.jaffnahouse.uk; Mon-Sun midnight.

Jamavar W1 £81 **5 4 4**
8 Mount Street   020 7499 1800   3–3B
"Cracking and very consistent cuisine", full of "subtle and innovative flavours", wins nothing but the highest praise for this Mayfair Indian – the highest rated in town this year – which occupies a "beautiful", colonial-themed dining room. Naturally it's not cheap, but by general agreement the experience is definitely "worthy of the prices". Founder Samyukta Nair is the London-educated scion of the dynasty behind India's ultra-luxe Leela Palace group. / W1K 3NF; www.jamavarrestaurants.com; Mon-Sat 10.30 pm, Sun 9.30 pm; No shorts.

Jashan N8 £39 **3 4 2**
19 Turnpike Ln   020 8340 9880   1–1C
Regulars swear by this classic curry house of 30 years' standing in Turnpike Lane, as a "local Indian that always delivers". It also hits the target as a "cheap and cheerful" destination. / N8 0EP; www.jashan.co.uk; @indian_jashan; Mon-Sat 10.30 pm, Sun 10 pm; closed Mon-Sun L; no Amex; May need 6+ to book.

Jean-Georges at The Connaught W1 £109 **3 3 3**
The Connaught, Carlos Place   020 7107 8861   3–3B
French-born, NYC-based mega-chef Jean-Georges Vongerichten is playing the British at their own game with a "most delightful and luxurious afternoon tea" – "perfect, memorable cucumber sandwiches" – served at his all-day conservatory brasserie in Mayfair's Connaught hotel. The room itself, as plush as you might imagine, is "very impressive, very romantic, with impeccable service". For more substantial meals, though, his diverse menu inspires a range of reactions – mostly positive but including the odd disappointment. / W1K 2AL; www.the-connaught.co.uk/mayfair-restaurants/jean-georges; @TheConnaught; Mon-Sun midnight.

Jiji N1 NEW £31
6g Esther Anne Place   020 7486 3929   9–3D
This Israeli-Japanese (it's OK, you read that right!) sits at the foot of the swanky new Islington Square development (main entrance on Upper Street). It's a mega £435m joint venture creating over 4.5acres of space on the site of north London's former main sorting office (London Mail Centre built in 1904). Opened in July 2021, it features an outside terrace and stylish interior, serving the likes of roast cauliflower with jalapeno sauce; egg with truffle polenta; flamed aubergine with tahini jalapeno and a selection of sushi dishes – blow-torched scallop nigiri with crème fraiche and ikura, anyone? / N1 1WL; jijirestaurants.com; Tue-Sun 11 pm; closed Tue-Thu L, closed Mon.

Jikoni W1 £76 **4 3 4**
21 Blandford Street   020 7034 1988   2–1A
"Chef Ravinder Bhogal maintains very high standards with the delicious and inventive dishes" served at her "welcoming" Marylebone venue. She conjures up a "lovely mixture of East African and Indian cuisine" that "celebrates food memories – abundant with poetry, romance and nostalgia". On a more earth-bound level, the restaurant is also certified as Climate Neutral. / W1U 3DJ; www.jikonilondon.com; @JikoniLondon; Tue-Sat, Mon 10.30 pm, Sun 4 pm; closed Mon L closed Sun D.

Jin Kichi NW3 £54 **5 4 3**
73 Heath St   020 7794 6158   9–1A
"Simply the best for authentic yakitori and Japanese grills", this small-but-perfect Hampstead veteran inspires an ardent fan club, having provided food of the very highest quality for four decades now. It's no one-trick pony, either, complementing its yakitori grills with wonderful sushi, sashimi and hotpots, along with a good range of wine, beer and saké. / NW3 6UG; www.jinkichi.com; Tue-Sat 10.30 pm, Sun 10 pm; closed Mon; cards only.

Jinjuu W1 £69 4 3 3
16 Kingly St 020 8181 8887 4–2B
"Everything is delicious, from small snack plates to mains" at this modern Korean bar and basement off Carnaby Street. The classics are all there, from bibimbap and bulgogi to double-fried chicken, but there "always seems to be something pleasantly surprising on the menu" – and "great cocktails too!". The outfit has clearly survived the 2019 departure of its high-profile founder, the Korean-American TV chef Judy Joo, without missing a beat. She now fronts the Seoul Bird fried-chicken outlets in Westfield Shepherd's Bush and Canary Wharf. / W1B 5PS; www.jinjuu.com; @JinjuuSoho; Mon-Thu 10 pm, Fri & Sat 11 pm, Sun 7 pm; Take bookings all week via phone and/or online.

Joan E1 NEW £43
19-23 Bethnal Green Road 020 3848 0512 13–1C
In the big site opposite Shoreditch station that was formerly Beach Blanket Babylon (RIP), this mid-lockdowns, autumn 2020 newcomer retains a large central bar but the emphasis is now much more on dining than during its BBB days. Greek chef Niko Kontogiannatos was previously former head chef at Caravan Fitzrovia and the menu here is also an eclectic mashup mixing Med-inspired creations (pizzettas, braised octopus, burrata) with some international fave-raves (tandoori chicken thighs… burger… cheesecake). / E1 6LA; www.joanshoreditch.co.uk; Mon-Sun midnight.

Joanna's SE19 £55 3 4 4
56 Westow Hill 020 8670 4052 1–4D
"Local lively bistro in the heart of Crystal Palace, where if you get the right table you have gorgeous views north over the London skyline". "It's been around since 1978 but there is a reason it's stayed for so long" – it's "always an excellent experience, be it for brunch, lunch or dinner". / SE19 1RX; www.joannas.uk.com; @Joannas_1978; Mon-Sun 11 pm.

Joe Allen WC2 £56 3 3 3
2 Burleigh St 020 7836 0651 5–3D
"Still great fun" – this easy-going American-style all-day restaurant sealed its long-running status as a key Theatreland venue a couple of years ago when it moved – lock, stock and resident piano-player – to a new Covent Garden address, after Robert de Niro requisitioned its former basement for his new hotel. "Excellent brunch" is the best bet food-wise – "dinner not so much" – although for a bite post-show it remains something of an institution. From late 2021, another option is a visit to Joe's Bar, overseen by Russell Norman (who started his restaurant career here as a waiter in the 1990s). Top Tip: the off-menu burger is always available – this is, after all, a 1970s spin-off from the original NYC Joe Allen. (Note, founder Joe Allen passed away in February 2021, aged 87. His advice to would-be restaurateurs? "Think twice!"). / WC2E 7PX; www.joeallen.co.uk; @JoeAllenWC2; Wed-Fri 11 pm, Sat midnight, Sun 7 pm; closed Mon & Tue.

Joe Public SW4 £15 3 3 2
4 The Pavement 020 7622 4676 11–2D
This convenient spot next to Clapham Common tube station serves Californian-style pizzas (with the "brilliant option" of buying by the slice) and own-label lager from a converted public convenience. (If you are not 'au fait' with the distinction between Ca and NYC pizza, it's all about the toppings, apparently). / SW4 7AA; www.joepublicpizza.com; @JOEPUBLICSW4; Mon-Sat midnight, Sun 11 pm; No bookings.

Jolene N16 £67 3 2 3
21 Newington Green   020 3887 2309   1–1C
This hipster Newington Green bakery and restaurant from the founders of Primeur and Westerns Laundry is every bit the archetypal, achingly on-trend East End operation. As well as coffee, bread and bakes it provides a short and simple blackboard menu of bistro-esque dishes: for example, grilled sardines, pasta with tomato and mussels, baked custard. Sceptics, though, find the whole scene just too right-on: "there are queues around the block, so taking yourself too seriously is clearly popular!". Its undisputed success has spawned a new flagship brand 'Big Jo Bakery' (see also) and later in 2021 there are three other satellites promised in Islington, Shoreditch and Crouch End. / N16 9PU; www.jolenen16.com; Tue-Sun 10 pm; closed Mon.

Jolie SW10 NEW £52
Chelsea Funhouse, 459 King's Road   020 3488 1678   6–3B
The World's End – a huge Grade II listed late-Victorian gin palace that's long been a landmark of the more distant stretches of Chelsea's King's Road – offers an 'immersive' experience nowadays, comprising basement 'Bletchley' Bar (1940s vibe), top-floor Chelsea Black Martini bar and a ground-floor restaurant. Initially branding as 'Journey' was replaced with 'Jolie' mid-lockdowns in autumn 2020 – a 'salon' serving French-inspired sharing plates and with bottomless brunch a big feature. / SW10 0LR; www.joliechelsea.com; Mon-Sun midnight.

Jones & Sons N16 £61 3 3 4
Stamford Works, 3 Gillett Street   020 7241 1211   14–1A
"A menu that's interesting without being pretentious, plus friendly staff and fun cocktails" underpins the appeal of this airy, industrial-ish venue, near Dalston station. Nice outside terrace, too. / N16 8JH; www.jonesandsonsdalston.com; @JonesSons; Tue-Sat 10 pm, Sun 6 pm; closed Tue-Fri L, closed Mon; booking max 7 may apply.

The Jones Family Kitchen SW1 £52 4 3 4
7-8 Eccleston Yard   020 7739 1740   2–4B
"Superb steak from the Josper grill, a brilliant wine list and a gorgeous, secluded terrace" make this successor to Shoreditch's Jones Family Project – part of the stylish-looking Eccleston Yards courtyard development – "an oasis of calm, and a great place for a meal out, in bustling Victoria". / SW1W 9AZ; www.jonesfamilyproject.co.uk; @JonesBelgravia; Mon-Sat midnight, Sun 6 pm.

José SE1 £56 5 3 5
104 Bermondsey St   020 7403 4902   10–4D
"A couple of glasses of sherry in hand, perched at the bar, eating super-tasty tapas: wonderful!" – José Pizarro's tiny Bermondsey haunt is "the absolute exemplar of a Spanish tapas bar in London" ("better than Barrafina!"). "The classics are spot-on: just order a pan con tomate, then marvel at how something so simple can be done so well" It helps that it's such a "friendly and bustling" place too, winning it some recommendations as a good venue for a date. / SE1 3UB; www.josepizarro.com; @JosePizarroRest; Mon-Sat 10.30 pm; closed Sun; no booking.

José Pizarro EC2 £62 3 3 2
Broadgate Circle   020 7256 5333   13–2B
Viewed in its own terms, José Pizarro's outpost in Broadgate Circle offers fair value for the City: "despite not being a huge fan of tapas, I decided to give it a go and was not disappointed – the dishes were really good". But, for such a prominent Hispanic chef, "the ambience is very 'chainy'" and "it's hard to believe it's from the same stable as the Bermondsey restaurant, given the amazing reviews the other place gets". / EC2M 2QS; www.josepizarro.com/jose-pizarro-broadgate; @JosePizarroRest; Mon-Fri 10.30 pm, Sat 9.45 pm; closed Sun.

José Pizarro at the RA W1 NEW
Royal Academy, Burlington Gardens, Piccadilly   3–3D
*One of two new eateries arriving in late summer 2021 at the Royal
Academy from the star Spaniard – see also Poster Bar by José. This one
takes over the Dorfman Senate Room and is a formal fine-dining affair.
/ W1J 0BD; Wed-Sat 10.30 pm, Sun 5 pm.*

The Jugged Hare EC1   £61   3 2 3
49 Chiswell Street   020 7614 0134   13–2A
*"Amazing" British game in season is the USP at this City boozer next to the
Barbican, which makes for some "great gastro evenings". This is
supplemented in the off-season (so March to July) by spit-roasted whole
suckling pig, rare-breed meat and wild fish and seafood. It's also a useful pre-
and post-show dining option for concert- and theatre-goers at the Barbican
Centre, five minutes' walk away. / EC1Y 4SA; www.thejuggedhare.com;
@thejuggedhare; Mon-Sun 11 pm.*

Julie's W11   £92   2 2 4
135 Portland Rd   020 7229 8331   7–2A
*"We're so happy to have Julie's back – the atmosphere is brilliant", say long-
time fans of this Holland Park veteran – a hugely characterful subterranean
warren that's a throwback to the louche 1970s and still under long-time
owners Tim and Cathy Herring. Its reopening in late 2019 after four years of
closure soon turned into a rebaptism of fire with the onset of the pandemic
in early 2020, and eventual departure of launch chef Shay Cooper on
reopening in May 2021. Overall, however, the impression this romantic
destination gives is that it has been successfully resurrected much as before:
"with a brilliant atmosphere, and food that's a bit overpriced". / W11 4LW;
www.juliesrestaurant.com; @JuliesW11; Thu-Sun 9 pm.*

Junsei W1 NEW
132 Seymour Place   020 7723 4058   7–1D
*Eight skewers and sides for £48 is the blow-out omakase option at this
Japanese June 2021 newcomer in Marylebone. But you can also order
individually and there are sharing plates available, too. The PR tells us that
the name means 'pure' – apparently a reference to the white wood used to
fuel the robata. / W1H 1NS; junsei.co.uk; Thu-Sun 5 pm.*

Kaffeine   £16   3 5 4
15 Eastcastle St, W1   020 7580 6755   3–1D
66 Great Titchfield St, W1   020 7580 6755   3–1C
*"Superb coffee" is backed up by "great breakfast & brunch" at the two
Fitzrovia sites of this independent outfit. One of the pioneers of Antipodean
coffee culture when it launched a dozen years ago, it is still "as good as
ever". / kaffeine.co.uk; @kaffeinelondon.*

Kahani SW1   £75   4 4 3
1 Wilbraham Place   020 7730 7634   6–2D
*An "excellent overall" experience can be had at this "stylish (both food and
decor)" Indian three-year-old near Sloane Square, behind Cadogan Hall. The
owner is ex-Tamarind executive chef Peter Joseph, who was raised in Tamil
Nadu, and whose variety of offerings includes a "very good tasting menu" as
well as a bottomless brunch, and menus dedicated to vegans, pre-theatre
and Sunday roast. / SW1X 9AE; www.kahanilondon.com/; @kahanilondon; Tue-Sat
10.30 pm, Sun 8 pm; closed Tue-Fri L, closed Mon; Take bookings all week via phone
and/or online.*

Kai Mayfair W1 £114 3 4 3
65 South Audley St 020 7493 8988 3–3A

A stylish Mayfair fixture that pulls out all the stops to provide the best possible Chinese cuisine, with "amazing food" and a "very good, albeit expensive, wine list" (featuring some of the world's most acclaimed vintages). Proprietor Bernard Yeoh, who represented Malaysia as a trap shooter in the 2004 Athens Olympics, describes it as "liberated Nanyang cuisine" – his take on the cooking of the overseas Chinese throughout southeast Asia. / W1K 2QU; www.kaimayfair.co.uk; @kaimayfair; Mon-Sun 11 pm.

Kaifeng NW4 £74 3 3 2
51 Church Road 020 8203 7888 1–1B

Named after a Chinese city with an ancient Jewish enclave, this smart kosher restaurant in Hendon serves "really excellent Chinese food – every course, without exception". But, while there is general agreement on the "high culinary standards" (including "excellent crispy duck"), it's also felt that being kosher makes it "more expensive than it should be". / NW4 4DU; www.kaifeng.co.uk; @KaifengKosher.

Kaki N1 £46 3 2 2
125 Caledonian Road 020 7278 6848 9–3D

"Lovely Sichuan food is served in an airy space on the Regent's Canal" at this converted pub in the nomansland between King's Cross and Islington. There's "a good range of meat and vegetarian options, and more unusual options for the adventurous including the delicious dry pot pig intestines". "Great views from the small outside deck", too. / N1 9RG; www.thekaki.co.uk; Mon-Sat 11 pm, Sun 10.30 pm.

Kalimera N8 NEW
43 Topsfield Road 07446 981139 1–1C

This 40-cover, mid-2021 newcomer in Crouch End is the work of Télémaque Argyriou, who first launched his gourmet Greek street food truck in 2015. The olives and olive oil come from his family's 200-year old farm in Greece. At lunch there's a simpler menu, including wraps, while the concise drinks list includes numerous vintages from small Greek producers. / N8 8PT; www.kalimera-streetfood.co.uk; Wed-Sat 11.30 pm.

Kanada-Ya £43 5 2 2
3 Panton St, SW1 020 7930 3511 5–4A
64 St Giles High St, WC2 020 7240 0232 5–1B
3B Filmworks Walk, W5 1–3A NEW
35 Upper Street, N1 020 7288 2787 9–3D

"Truly outstanding ramen" – possibly "the finest in town" – have won a major reputation among the noodle cognoscenti for his small Japan-based chain, which has branches in Covent Garden, Piccadilly and Angel. "The tasty bowls are always more filling than they seem", and fans put up with "so-so service and a hot, cramped venue" to secure their fix. The all-important 18-hour pork bone broth was developed to a secret recipe by former racing cyclist Kazuhiro Kanada, who opened his first noodle shop in his native Kyushu in 2009. A new branch in Ealing and a delivery-only kitchen for South London were scheduled to open in late 2021. / www.kanada-ya.com; @KanadaYa_LDN.

Kanishka W1 £95 3 3 2
17-19 Maddox Street 020 3978 0978 4–2A

"Love Atul Kochhar's cooking" (focused on dishes from India's northeastern 'Sister States') say fans of his three-year-old, who award "five stars all the way" for "incredible meals, with levels of spice and heat like nothing else I've experienced". The interior design is not everyone's idea of a "posh Indian", however, and – more significantly – ratings are undercut by those who feel culinary results are "below expectations for such a talented chef", or alternatively feel that "it's very nice, but my word, the prices…". / W1S 2QH; kanishkarestaurant.co.uk; @kanishkamayfair; Mon-Sun 11 pm.

Kaosarn £28 **4****3****3**
110 St Johns Hill, SW11   020 7223 7888   11–2C
181 Tooting High Street, SW17   020 8672 8811   11–2C
Brixton Village, Coldharbour Ln, SW9   020 7095 8922   11–2D
This "cracking Thai" trio in Battersea, Brixton and Tooting are highly
recommended for their delicious and authentic dishes. Run by a large
extended family, they have a "great atmosphere" – and the BYO policy
keeps prices down.

Kappacasein SE16 £10 **4****3****3**
1 Voyager Industrial Estate   07837 756852   12–2A
"You will literally not get a better toasted cheese and onion sandwich in this
world!" – so say fans of Bill Oglethorpe's market stall, which is a mainstay of
Borough Market. On Saturday mornings and lunchtime, you can also eat-in
at their dairy in nearby Bermondsey. / SE16 4RP; www.kappacasein.com;
@kappacasein; Sat 2 pm; closed Sat D, closed Mon-Fri & Sun; No bookings.

Kashmir SW15 £47 **3****3****2**
18-20 Lacy Road   07477 533888   11–2B
A "unique menu" – billed as the first specialist Kashmiri in Britain – and
"always delicious" food have established Rohit and Shweta Razdan's five-
year-old as a local favourite in Putney. The couple developed their skills in
New Delhi and Singapore before alighting in southwest London. / SW15 1NL;
www.kashmirrestaurants.co.uk; @KashmirRestUK; Mon, Wed & Thu 10.30 pm, Fri-Sun
11 pm; closed Mon, Wed-Fri L, closed Tue.

The Kati Roll Company W1 £24 **3****2****2**
24 Poland Street   020 7287 4787   4–1C
"Authentic, fast Indian food" is on the menu at this Soho outpost of a
Manhattan chain, whose founder, Payal Saha, missed the street food of her
native Kolkata – kati rolls, buttery parathas filled with grilled meat, cheese or
vegetables. / W1F 8QL; www.thekatirollcompany.com; @KatiRollCompany; Mon-Sun
3 pm.

Kazan £57 **3****3****2**
77 Wilton Rd, SW1   020 7233 8298   2–4B
93-94 Wilton Rd, SW1   020 7233 7100   2–4B
"Blown away by the flavours and excellent service – our friends are regulars
and say it's been consistently great!" – this straightforward Pimlico duo,
opposite each other near Victoria station, are worth remembering as a
welcoming haven of affordable Turkish mezze and other fare.
/ www.kazan-restaurant.com.

Kebab Queen WC2 £113 **4****4****3**
4 Mercer Walk   020 7439 9222   5–2C
"The not-very-well-kept-secret kitchen counter in the basement of Kingly
Court's Le Bab is gimmicky" – "you eat kebabs elevated to haute cuisine
with no implements, directly from the specially-made heated counter" – but
it's "a strange but exhilarating experience" that, on practically all accounts, is
rated as "sensational". "Manu (formerly of Le Gavroche) has created a truly
exceptional, creative-yet-always-delicious menu that is far better than it
needs to be" and "the execution leaves no stone unturned". "Some of the
best value and most innovative fine dining in London. If you can get a table,
GO!" / WC2; www.eatlebab.com; @eatlebab; Mon-Thu 10 pm, Fri & Sat 10.30 pm,
Sun 9 pm.

Ken Lo's Memories SW1 £66 **2****2****2**
65-69 Ebury St   020 7730 7734   2–4B
A pioneer of Chinese haute cuisine for more than 30 years, the late Ken Lo's
elegant Belgravia venue soldiers on and is still mostly credited with serving
"satisfying" meals, even if "its prices reflect the fact that the locals are
loaded". / SW1W 0NZ; www.memoriesofchina.co.uk; Wed-Sat, Tue, Sun 10.30 pm;
closed Tue L, closed Mon.

Kennington Tandoori SE11 £56 343
313 Kennington Rd 020 7735 9247 1–3C

This high-profile but "reliable" Kennington curry house has become a local institution under owner Kowsar Hoque, an entrepreneurial vascular surgeon whose father founded it 37 years ago. "It's a bit of a club but anyone can join and will feel welcome among the politicians and media people" (former PMs Gordon Brown and David Cameron have both dined here). "Prices are a little above average but this is not your standard curry house". / SE11 4QE; www.kenningtontandoori.com; @TheKTLondon; Mon-Sun 10.30 pm; closed Mon-Sun L; no Amex.

Kerridge's Bar & Grill SW1 £119 223
Whitehall Place 020 7321 3244 2–3C

TV-star Tom's first London outpost – a wonderfully impressive-looking brasserie in a happening five-star near Embankment – wows many reporters thanks to the "lovely dining room", "delightful and varied menu" and "an appeal that extends to all ages, from 15 to 75". (It also incorporates in the same space "a good bar for a quick meet-up pre-theatre"). Ratings came under pressure this year, with a number of reporters finding the experience "massively overpriced" for "high-quality gastropub-level fare at eye-watering prices". For an equal number, though, it's an investment well made and "a firm favourite". / SW1A 2BD; www.kerridgesbarandgrill.co.uk; @kerridgesbandg; Sun-Wed 9 pm, Fri, Thu, Sat 10 pm.

Kibou London SW11 NEW £60 343
175-177 Northcote Road 020 7223 8551 11–2C

"It's worth trekking to the far end of Northcote Road for this fresh and energetic newcomer" – the "vibrant and fun" outpost of a popular Cheltenham Japanese, which landed in Battersea in August 2020. "For something a little different, it's an excellent destination". "The menu is split in two: one half is sushi, sashimi etc whilst the other half includes hot-plate staples like ramen and katsu curry". "Staff are friendly" and "the sushi is tops for the neighbourhood". / SW11 6QF; kibou.co.uk.

Kiln W1 £47 544
58 Brewer Street no tel 4–3C

"The best Thai food in London?"… "The most authentic Thai food outside Bangkok?" – after five years, Ben Chapman's charcoal-fired Soho haunt and its legion of fans show no sign of slackening standards or waning enthusiasm. Better still, it offers "ridiculous value for some of the best food ever", along with a "buzzy atmosphere". The inevitable drawback in such a small and central hit venue is "horrendous queues". Top Tip: "the pot-cooked noodles are as good as everyone says". / W1F 9TL; www.kilnsoho.com; Mon-Sat 10 pm, Sun 8 pm.

Kipferl N1 £50 333
20 Camden Passage 020 77041 555 9–3D

This "impressive Austrian café" in Islington's "atmospheric Camden Passage" has established itself as a "lovely local gem" over almost 20 years. It serves "traditional Austrian classics" – from "delicious and very reasonable soup" and schnitzel to Sachertorte, Linzertorte and cheesecake, along with "excellent coffee". Kipferl means croissant – the French pastry reputedly invented in Vienna. / N1 8ED; www.kipferl.co.uk; @KipferlCafe; Tue-Thu 10 pm, Fri & Sat 11 pm, Mon 5 pm, Sun 7 pm; closed Mon D; Take bookings all week via phone and/or online.

Kiraku W5 £50 433
8 Station Pde 020 8992 2848 1–3A

"The food is very good" at this "typically impersonal" – but actually, by the standards of the genre, pretty "convivial" – Japanese joint near Ealing Common tube, which serves a variety of set meals at lunchtime and izakaya-style dining in the evening. / W5 3LD; www.kiraku.co.uk; @kirakulondon; Tue-Sun 11 pm; closed Mon; no Amex.

Kiss the Hippo £25 3 3 3
51 Margaret Street, W1   3–1C
50 George Street, TW9   020 3887 2028   1–4A
"Simply top for coffee" ("not cheap but the best I've had in a while") say fans of this "stylish" Scandi-vibe Fitzrovia outlet, which opened in 2019, a year after the original set up shop in Richmond. As well as the sustainably sourced brews, workshops (and all the kit available by mail), there is a small selection of light snacks (eggs, cinnamon rolls, cakes). / kissthehippo.com.

Kitchen Table W1 £329 4 5 4
70 Charlotte Street   020 7637 7770   2–1C
"Truly extraordinary" — James Knappett and Sandia Chang's gastronomic vision continues to blossom at their Fitzrovia 18-seater, which reopened in July 2021 after a major refurbishment. The reformatting included ditching the adjacent Bubbledogs concept, which they led with in 2012, and converting that space into a lounge and bar for diners at the main event: the chef's table. It also included a not-insignificant price hike to £250 for up to 20 courses, which on opening included dishes such as Glazed Cornish Blue Lobster, Tahitian Vanilla Brown Butter, and Pickled Beach Roses. Sandia's wine list now features some of the rarest grower champagnes (which she also sells online). The ratings are something of a guesstimate based on past performance and — the restaurant being closed leading up to the survey — rave meal kit reports. / W1T 4QG; www.kitchentablelondon.co.uk; Wed-Sat 11.30pm; closed Wed-Sat L, closed Mon & Tue & Sun; booking online only.

Kitchen W8 W8 £88 4 3 2
11-13 Abingdon Road   020 7937 0120   6–1A
"The cuisine's always delicious, seasonal and inventive" at this smart venue in a sidestreet off Kensington High Street – a "top local" more akin to "West End quality" due to the input of stellar chef Phil Howard (of Elystan Street and formerly the Square), who is a part owner, alongside Rebecca Mascarenhas, who has a long history in running excellent establishments. Not everyone agrees about the low-key interior, though – what is "a little souless" to some folks, is, to others, "lovely". / W8 6AH; www.kitchenw8.com; @KitchenW8; Tue-Thu, Sun 9.30 pm, Fri & Sat 10 pm; closed Mon; Take bookings all week via phone and/or online.

Kitty Fisher's W1 £76 3 3 4
10 Shepherd's Market   020 3302 1661   3–4B
This "romantic destination restaurant" – named after an 18th-century courtesan remembered in a nursery rhyme – makes the most of its location in Mayfair's cute-but-seedy Shepherd Market. "Cramped, yes; too noisy, yes; too close to the Bunch of Grapes, yes; sometimes hard to get into, yes; but very fine food, the most charming front of house team, and an atmosphere that is intimate but animated". Top Tip: "how they get their crispy potatoes to taste like that is beyond me – one portion is never enough". / W1J 7QF; www.kittyfishers.com; @kittyfishers; Mon-Sat 10.30 pm; closed Sun; Take bookings all week via phone and/or online.

Knife SW4 £73 4 4 3
160 Clapham Park Road   020 7627 6505   11–2D
"A real carnivore's delight" – this small brick-walled steakhouse on the Clapham/Brixton borders is a local favourite, including for Sunday roast. "The small menu is always special, plus an extra mention for the amazing staff!". / SW4 7DE; kniferestaurant.co.uk; @KnifeLondon; Wed-Sat 10 pm, Sun 4.30 pm; closed Wed-Sat L closed Sun D, closed Mon & Tue.

Koji SW6 £83 **3** **3** **4**
58 New King's Rd   020 7731 2520   11–1B
"More fusion than Asian, but with clearly Eastern flavours" – the menu at this long-established pan-Asian haunt near Parsons Green is a "diverse and interesting one". The decor is very "sophisticated for a local restaurant" and "innovative cocktails at the bar" help fuel its "wonderful ambience".
/ SW6 4LS; www.koji.restaurant; @koji_restaurant; Tue, Wed 11 pm, Thu-Sat 11.30 pm; closed Tue-Sat L, closed Sun & Mon; cards only.

Kol W1 £123 **3** **3** **4**
9 Seymour Street   020 3829 6888   2–2A
"Eye-opening…", "inspired…", "every course genius…" – this long-awaited Mexican from Santiago Lastra finally debuted amidst the lockdowns of 2020, just off Portman Square (opposite Locanda Locatelli), and has been "hailed as one of the most exciting openings of recent times", not least by Giles Coren of The Times for whom it is "world-class, genre-defying [and] entirely new". "There aren't many top-level Mexicans in London" and here "clever combinations use British ingredients for Mexican dishes" ("so you get seed guacamole instead of avocado, and sea buckthorn instead of limes – sounds contrived, but works brilliantly"). It helps that the "impeccable service sets the perfect context for the procession of fascinating dishes, all served up in a glamorous but unpretentious space" around a "vibrant open kitchen"; and there are "excellent sommelier recommendations" too, which are engagingly "left-field and fun". But, while fans say it's "good value for such quality and novelty", its ratings are dragged down by those who feel it ultimately falls short: "hailed as one of the most exciting openings recently, I think this may have been oversold. The food, as innovative as it was, did not feel like it lived up to the hype and was pretty pricey for what it was".
/ W1H 7BA; kolrestaurant.com; Tue-Sat midnight, Sun 6.30 pm; closed Tue L closed Sun D, closed Mon; cards only.

Kolamba W1 NEW £35 **4** **3** **3**
21 Kingly Street   020 3815 4201   4–2B
"Interesting" and "reasonably priced" Sri Lankan dishes are presented by "friendly and knowledgeable waiting staff" at this Soho two-year-old just off Regent Street – part of the new wave of Sri Lankan restaurants following in the footsteps of the Sethi family's pioneering Hoppers. Naturally, there are "egg hoppers to die for", plus a "good range of vegetarian options" and a "nice array of Sri Lankan drinks". Kolamba is Sinhalese for Colombo.
/ W1B 5QA; kolamba.co.uk; Mon-Wed 11 pm, Thu-Sat midnight, Sun 9 pm.

Koya £40 **4** **4** **4**
50 Frith St, W1   020 7434 4463   5–2A
Bloomberg Arcade, Queen Victoria Street, EC2   no tel   10–3C
"Excellent, fresh udon" – the original Japanese noodles – are to be found at the Soho mothership of this small multiple and its offshoot in the City's foodie Bloomberg Arcade. Other specialities include tempura and kara-age fried chicken. (Udon are more difficult to find in London than the highly popular Chinese-influenced ramen, and are generally considered subtler, lighter and more refined.) / www.koyabar.co.uk.

Kricket W1 £52 **5** **4** **4**
12 Denman St   020 7734 5612   4–3C
"The most flavourful Indian food (adapted from seasonal British ingredients)", served in a "fun tapas-style by friendly staff", is a formula that has come up trumps for Rik Campbell and Will Bowlby, who opened their first subcontinental-inspired street-food operation in a shipping container in 2015. They now have permanent sites in Soho, Brixton and White City, where the small plates are served in "modern and cool" interiors with a "convivial atmosphere". Top Tip: "Iberico ham vindaloo is stunning".
/ W1D 7HH; www.kricket.co.uk; @kricketlondon; Tue-Sat 10.30 pm; closed Sun & Mon.

Kudu SE15 £55 5 4 4
119 Queen's Rd 020 3950 0226 1–4D
"Worth travelling to Peckham for" (and "an absolute gem to have on one's doorstep") – Patrick Williams and Amy Corbin's "fun, buzzy and cramped-in-a-good way" venture enjoys an ever-increasing reputation. The South African-influenced food is "knockout with all sorts of wonderful flavour combinations, and service is especially warm and friendly – really on the ball, but also relaxed". There's a back garden for dining on warmer days. (See also Kudu Grill). / SE15 2EZ; www.kudu-restaurant.com; @KuduRestaurant; Wed-Sat 10 pm, Sun 9 pm; closed Wed & Thu L, closed Mon & Tue.

Kudu Grill SE15 NEW £45
57 Nunhead Lane 020 3172 2450 1–4D
On the Nunhead site of Babette (RIP): this latest part of Amy Corbin (yes, her father) and Patrick Williams's Kudu empire is – as befits Patrick's South African roots – centred on the braai – so expect lots of open-fire dishes. It opened in September 2021, too late for survey feedback. / SE15; www.kuducollective.com; Wed-Sat 10 pm, Sun 2.30 pm; closed Wed-Fri L closed Sun D, closed Mon & Tue.

Kutir SW3 £63 4 4 4
10 Lincoln Street 020 7581 1144 6–2D
"Brilliantly vivid and fresh flavours" from Rohit Ghai's "wonderful" Indian three-year-old make it a worthy successor to the previous incumbent on this Chelsea site (Vineet Bhatia's Rasoi, RIP). Adding to its appeal, "it feels like dining in a private house" ("a great setting for a proper catch-up with friends") with "charming staff". And – on the first floor – "a small rooftop space lends further appeal". / SW3 2TS; kutir.co.uk; @kutirchelsea; Tue-Sun 10 pm; closed Mon; No shorts; booking online only.

L'Antica Pizzeria da Michele £52 5 3 4
44 Old Compton Street, W1 020 7434 4563 5–2A NEW
199 Baker Street, NW1 020 7935 6458 2–1A
"Amazing, authentic pizzas" – "straight out of Naples" – are the USP at these Soho and Baker Street outposts of a Neapolitan business that traces its origins back to 1870 and which featured in Elizabeth Gilbert's global hit 'Eat Pray Love'. The newer Soho venue, on the former site of Patisserie Valerie, is a "wonderful dining space". Top Tip: "the two Naples original pizzas (Marinara and Margherita) are the best". / www.anticapizzeriadamichele.co.uk.

L'Artigiano SW10 NEW £40
343 Fulham Road 020 3972 9848 6–3B
This Fulham Road newcomer on 'The Beach' opened mid-lockdowns with a contemporary Italian offering. It's the brainchild of Leandro Longo (La Caricatura) and chef Ignacio Fuggiero (The Met). You can opt for an eight-course tasting menu (as well as two-course, three-course and à la carte options) but the approach has strong, traditional Italian roots. / SW10 9TW; lartigianorestaurant.co.uk; Mon, Wed 10 pm, Thu-Sat 10.30 pm, Sun 9 pm; closed Mon, Wed L, closed Tue.

L'Oscar Restaurant WC1 NEW £71
L'Oscar Hotel, 2-6 Southampton Row 020 7405 5555 2–1D
The former HQ of the Baptist Church provides the gracious quarters for this swish Holborn hotel, converted by design guru Jacques Garcia. Since Tony Fleming left in December 2019, the main food operation (formerly known as The Baptist at L'Oscar hotel) has shifted to this all-day dining-room operation offering a more accessible, Parisian-café-style menu from breakfast through to dinner. Allan Pickett (former head chef at Orrery, and briefly chef-patron of Piquet) is the new head chef. / WC1B 4AA; www.loscarlondon.com; @loscar_london; Mon-Sun 9.30 pm; Take bookings all week via phone and/or online.

The Ladbroke Arms W11 £64 322

54 Ladbroke Road   020 7727 6648   7–2B

This upscale, flower-bedecked gastropub, off the smarter end of Ladbroke Grove, is one of London's more genteel-looking gastropubs (although it still draws a lively crowd). The food is "always good" and it's an "enjoyable place for Sunday lunches" – it's dog-friendly, too, so the perfect culmination of a walk in nearby Holland Park. / W11 3NW; www.ladbrokearms.com; @LadbrokeArms; Mon-Sat 9.30 pm, Sun 9 pm; no booking after x pm.

Lahore Kebab House E1 £32 422

2-10 Umberston St   020 7481 9737   12–1A

The legendary lamb chops are "great – but all the food is delicious" – at this teeming Whitechapel landmark, which notches up its half-century this year. "The atmosphere is an experience – cricket on big screens, and the weirdest mix of Indian and Pakistani families, East End geezers, hipsters and City boys". "You don't come for the indifferent service". / E1 1PY; www.lahore-kebabhouse.com; @lahorekebabhous; Mon-Sat 10 pm.

Lahpet £56 333

21 Slingsby Place, WC2   020 3883 5629   5–3C **NEW**
58 Bethnal Green Road, E1   020 3883 5629   13–1C

Named for the Burmese salad of pickled tea leaves, Dan Anton and Zaw Mahesh's Shoreditch three-year-old delivers "a good experience and tasty food". Slated for late 2021, they have announced a new Covent Garden sibling will open this year – a 2,500 sq ft unit in the flashy new 'The Yards' development (near the recently relaunched Dishoom). / lahpet.co.uk; @lahpet.

Laksamania W1 £51 322

92 Newman Street   020 7637 9888   3–1D

"The best laksa ever" (spicy noodle soup) might be overdoing it, but this well-appointed two-year-old, just off Oxford Street, wins consistent praise for its Malaysian cooking. / W1T 3EZ; www.laksamania.co.uk; Mon, Wed & Thu 10 pm, Fri & Sat 10.30 pm, Sun 9 pm; closed Tue.

The Landmark, Winter Garden NW1 £95 235

222 Marylebone Rd   020 7631 8000   9–4A

The stunning, glass-roofed, eight-storey atrium, complete with mature palm trees, makes a "fantastic setting" for daytime meals at this Marylebone hotel – particularly the "exquisite" afternoon tea. Breakfast is highly rated, too – "so much choice, and hot dishes made to order". / NW1 6JQ; www.landmarklondon.co.uk; @landmarklondon; Mon-Sun 10 pm; No trainers; booking max 12 may apply.

Langan's Brasserie W1 £70

Stratton Street   020 7491 8822   3–3C

A new era beckons for this once-legendary brasserie. Created in 1976 out of a partnership between actor Michael Caine and the late Peter Langan, it was the A-lister magnet of its days (and the cradle for the careers of some of London's leading restaurateurs, including Christopher Corbin & Jeremy King). In recent years, it risked sinking into self-parody as an old-school haunt for senior business suits loyal since its glory days. Now – from mid-October 2021 – it's to relaunch with each of its three floors having a completely new identity from designer and 'master of metamorphosis' Peter Mikic. The new owners are Graziano Arricale and James Hitchen – the former includes a stint as operations director of Birley Clubs on his CV, while the latter is a former chief executive of East Coast Concepts. / W1J 8LB; www.langansrestaurants.co.uk; @langanslondon; Mon-Thu 11 pm, Fri & Sat 11.30 pm; closed Sun.

Palm Court,
The Langham W1 £88 **3**|**3**|**4**
1c Portland Place 020 7636 1000 2–1B

"A wonderful afternoon tea, more personal than some big hotels where you're conscious of being in a time-slot" – the gracious space at the heart of this luxurious five-star claims to have invented afternoon tea back in the day. Nowadays run in collaboration with Michel Roux, it was highly recommended this year. / W1B 1JA; www.palm-court.co.uk; @Langham_London; Mon-Wed, Fri & Sat 11 pm, Thu 5 pm, Sun 12.30 pm; closed Thu & Sun D; No trainers.

Lao Cafe WC2 £36 **3**|2|2
60 Chandos Place 020 3740 4748 5–4C

"Excellent Laotian food" wins praise for this handily located small fixture, off Trafalgar Square (near ENO). "I've never had this cuisine before but it was excellent!" / WC2N 4HG; laocafe.co.uk; Mon-Sun 10 pm; May need 8+ to book.

Larry's SE15 NEW £32 **3**|**3**|**3**
Unit 5, 12-16 Blenheim Grove 020 3795 7385 1–4D

"Levan's sister restaurant is a useful addition to the Peckham dining experience, and also revolves around sharing plates". Originally due to open on the first week of the first 2020 lockdown, this all-day Peckham diner (in the same stable as Levan and Salon) is named after groundbreaking NYC DJ Larry Levan and is a homage to Jewish and Italian NYC diners, circa 1975. You are served at retro orange tables, with diner-style sarnies at lunch, or more substantial dishes like schnitzel and cheesecake, all dolled up a bit for 21st-century sensibilities (I don't remember any gochujang mayo served back in the day…). / SE15 4QL; larryspeckham.co.uk; Tue-Thu 11.30 pm, Fri & Sat 12.30 am, Sun & Mon 4.30 pm; closed Sun & Mon D; cards only.

The Laughing Heart E2 £78 **3**|**4**|**3**
277 Hackney Road 020 7686 9535 14–2A

Charlie Mellor's (ex-Brawn and Elliot's) cute Hackney wine bar and merchant provides a high- quality fixed-price modern European menu, accompanied by artisan wines from small producers. There's also 'The Cave', for evening DJ sets, behind the off licence. / E2 8NA; thelaughingheartlondon.com; Thu-Sun 2 am; closed Thu-Sun L, closed Mon & Tue & Wed.

Launceston Place W8 £94 **4**|**4**|**4**
1a Launceston Pl 020 7937 6912 6–1B

"Discreet and off the beaten track" – this supremely "cosy and classy neighbourhood restaurant" is "tucked away in an attractive street in Kensington and well worth a visit". "Ben Murphy's cuisine is fun and playful", providing "absolutely sensational" dishes that are "packed with flavour". In the last year he has rightly been elevated to being chef/patron here and – in terms of quality, if not perhaps fame – this is "definitely the jewel in the crown of the D&D empire". / W8 5RL; www.launcestonplace-restaurant.co.uk; @LauncestonPlace; Wed-Sat 10 pm, Sun 9 pm; closed Mon & Tue.

The Laundry SW9 **3**|**3**|**3**
374 Coldharbour Lane 020 8103 9384 11–2D

This two-year-old all-day restaurant and wine shop occupies a "lovely conversion of an Edwardian laundry" in Brixton. "The terrace is fantastic" and "the food is good – bavette steak & chips for £17 is pretty good value these days". It's the first restaurant from Melanie Brown, a former chef and wine buyer for Kiwi star Peter Gordon who went on to found the New Zealand and Australian Cellar wine businesses. / SW9 8PL; thelaundrybrixton.com; Mon-Wed 11 pm, Thu-Sat midnight, Sun 9 pm.

Le Bab £52 4|2|3
Top Floor, Kingly Court, W1   020 7439 9222   4–2B
4 Mercer Walk, WC2   020 7240 9781   5–2C
130 Kingsland High St, E8   020 3877 0865   14–1A **NEW**
231 Old Street, EC1   020 3456 7890   13–1A **NEW**
"Wow!! Tasty or what?" This upscale kebab group has expanded from its well-known Kingly Court base, and been busy during the pandemic with a couple of new openings. In May 2021 they opened both a new café in a funky Dalston coworking space (part of a new aparthotel from Locke) and a retro, old-school kebab shop in the heart of Old Street, open till the wee hours. "You can't really fault the food and it's at a very good price. It's a nice place too, relaxed but well managed". See also Kebab Queen.

The Ledbury W11 £170
127 Ledbury Rd   020 7792 9090   7–1B
Brett's back!! Having closed his superb Notting Hill legend in June 2020, Brett Graham announced in August 2021 that its reopening is imminent. Pundits bent over backwards to be amazed, but a less surprising announcement is difficult to imagine. As always appeared possible/likely, Aussie Brett and team clearly made the smart move of shutting up shop, merely in order to sit out the pandemic (at the pub he co-owns, the Harwood Arms). There will be changes on its return, we are told, but these are still somewhat shrouded in mystery as we go to press. Whatever changes, it is still likely to be pitched at the very pinnacle of London dining. The press never mention Brett's low-profile but high-impact backer, Nigel Platts-Martin OBE, who owns a very significant stake in the restaurant (as he does at the tremendous Chez Bruce, Trompette and Glasshouse). / W11 2AQ; www.theledbury.com; @theledbury; Mon-Sun 9.45 pm; closed Mon & Tue L; Take bookings all week via phone and/or online.

Legare SE1 £45 4|4|3
Cardamom Building, 31g Shad Thames   020 8063 7667   10–4D
"Very good Italian food made from the freshest of ingredients, prepared simply but with imagination and great care, and nicely served" wins good all-round ratings for this small Bermondsey Italian, a short walk down the South Bank from Tower Bridge. / SE1 2YB; legarelondon.com; Wed-Sat, Tue 10 pm; closed Tue L, closed Sun & Mon.

Lemonia NW1 £57 1|3|3
89 Regent's Park Rd   020 7586 7454   9–3B
This "fun" Greek taverna in Primrose Hill has become a major north London institution in its 40-plus years, loved for its "friendly staff", "great service" and "homely comfort cooking". Complaints about "very average" meals – particularly "so disappointing" food – get louder every year though, with a chorus of critics saying it's "living on memories" – "not sure why it's still so popular". / NW1 8UY; www.lemonia.co.uk; @Lemonia_Greek; Mon-Thu 10 pm, Fri & Sat 10.30 pm, Sun 4.30 pm; closed Sun D; no Amex.

Leroy EC2 £69 3|4|3
18 Phipp Street   020 7739 4443   13–1B
"A favourite spot in Shoreditch" – this sassy little haunt offers fab small plates "with an affordable price-tag" alongside well-chosen wines, to provide a very "pleasurable experience". And it's certainly a good all-rounder. But "a Michelin star? Simply put, why?". The team has also spun out a lockdown project into something more permanent in the form of Royale at Bow Wharf (see also). / EC2A 4NP; www.leroyshoreditch.com; Mon-Sat 10.30 pm; closed Mon L, closed Sun; Credit card deposit required to book.

Levan SE15 £59 [5][3][3]
3-4 Blenheim Grove   020 7732 2256   1–4D
"Sublime" and *"innovative contemporary cuisine"* makes this Peckham two-year-old the sort of place you *"happily return to again and again"* – and you won't get bored because *"the menu constantly changes, reflecting seasonal fare"*. *"Our group literally tried everything and there wasn't one disappointing dish"*. The *"enjoyable"* atmosphere is *"nice and buzzy"* but *"are they as cool as they think they are!?"*. (The team behind Levan cut their teeth with Salon in Brixton, see also.) / SE15 4QL; levanlondon.co.uk; Tue-Sat 11.30 pm, Sun 3 pm; closed Sun D, closed Mon.

The Light Bar E1 NEW £75
233 Shoreditch High Street   020 8194 1685   13–2B
We have Tracey Emin and Madness front-man Suggs to thank, along with the rest of the OPEN campaign, for saving this iconic (for once the word is merited) Shoreditch landmark north of Liverpool Street, which – after its original launch in 2000 – became a seminal venue for emerging hipster East London. It closed in 2014 when it was about to be flattened for a skyscraper, but this 5,000 sq ft former rail power station (built in 1893) reopened in April 2021, initially with its terrace in operation. This was followed in May and June by its ground-floor 'Engine Hall' bar and restaurant and first-floor 'Timber Loft'. Survey feedback was too limited for a rating, but all-round extremely positive. / E1 6PJ; www.lightbarlondon.com; Mon-Sun 10 pm; closed Mon L; cards only.

The Light House SW19 £51 [3][3][3]
75-77 Ridgway   020 8944 6338   11–2B
"Just how a local should be", say fans of this indie near Wimbledon Village, as it approaches its 24th year. The kitchen has sometimes stood accused of *"trying too hard"* – *"the style of food has not changed much over the years and the quality can be a bit hit 'n' miss, but it remains very popular nevertheless"*. *"Service is excellent"*, and *"the venue has just the right level of buzz"*. / SW19 4ST; www.lighthousewimbledon.com; Mon-Sat 10 pm, Sun 3.30 pm; closed Mon-Thu L closed Sun D.

Light of India SW7
67/69 Gloucester Road   0207 584 7654   6–2B
Worth knowing about near Gloucester Road tube – this large hotel dining room has been serving Indian cuisine since 1984. Too few reports for a rating, but promising feedback and worth bearing in mind if you are in the vicinity. / SW7 4PG; www.lightofindia.co.uk; Mon-Sat 11 pm, Sun 22.30; Take bookings all week via phone and/or online.

The Lighterman N1 £56 [2][2][3]
3 Granary Square   020 3846 3400   9–3C
Due to its *"great location on the canal at King's Cross"*, this *"large and popular"* modern three-storey restaurant at the Granary Square development is *"always busy"* and *"so successful that, strictly speaking, it doesn't need to try"*. Accounts differ slightly on what that means for its food offering. The majority of reporters feel that *"the traditional menu may have few thrills or surprises but everything is nicely done"*. There is, though, a minority to whom the food feels *"fairly bland"*, or that the *"pleasant buzz"* can slip into feeling *"really far too busy and noisy"*. / N1C 4BH; www.thelighterman.co.uk; @TheLightermanKX; Mon-Thu 11.30 pm, Fri & Sat midnight, Sun 10.30 pm.

Lighthaus Café E10
11 Argall Avenue   1–1D
East London community café and brunch venue in a reimagined lighting factory in Leyton. Too few reports for a rating, but we hear good things about both its all-day dining possibilities and its evening menu (served at weekends). / E10 7QE; www.lighthauscafe.co.uk; Wed-Sat 11.30 pm.

Lina Stores £43 4|3|3
51 Greek Street, W1   020 3929 0068   5–2A
20 Stable Street, N1   awaiting tel   9–3C
"Small plates but big flavours" from "a lovely short menu of top-quality antipasti and pasta dishes" win numerous "cheap 'n' cheerful" nominations for this small chain, which consists of the "busy, lovely but very crammed" Soho original (for 75 years a deli, but since 2018 and its relaunch by Private Equity firm White Rabbit, in this new guise) and a newer, bigger but less commented-on King's Cross spin-off. "We need more branches of this great restaurant" plead fans… whose prayers are soon to be answered with a 90-seater outlet in Marylebone (in Wigmore Street, on the former Sourced Market site) plus in Bloomberg Arcade and Clapham, as well as one in Tokyo! / www.linastores.co.uk; @linastores.

Little Social W1 £73 3|3|3
5 Pollen Street   020 7870 3730   3–2C
Briefly branded 'No 5 Social', Jason Atherton's "fun" bistro sits on the other side of the street from his original 'Social' mothership. Chef Frankie van Loo's relatively straightforward menu is well-priced (three courses for £35) and wins solid support. / W1S 1NE; www.littlesocial.co.uk; @_littlesocial; Tue-Sat 9.45 pm; closed Sun & Mon.

Little Taperia SW17 £49 3|3|3
143 Tooting High St   020 8682 3303   11–2C
This "busy little local" in Tooting is "always buzzing", with a crowd drawn by a "brilliant range of tasty tapas, with new ones added recently". "A local favourite but worth a longer trip if you're in SW London". / SW17; www.thelittletaperia.co.uk; @littletaperia; Sun-Thu 10 pm, Fri & Sat 11 pm; May need 6+ to book.

Llewelyn's SE24 £68 3|3|2
293-295 Railton Rd   020 7733 6676   11–2D
"The menu hugely understates the deliciousness that will soon follow" and "service is lovely and easygoing", say southeast London fans of their "dream neighbourhood restaurant", opposite Herne Hill station, which they acclaim for "very good", if rather understated, "modern European, primarily Italian food". The interior is the weakest link – it's an "oddly shaped space" and "lacks character" – meaning that for some fans it's "not quite as much fun as it could be". / SE24 0JP; www.llewelyns-restaurant.co.uk; @llewelynslondon; Tue-Thu 9 pm, Fri & Sat 9.30 pm, Sun 3.15 pm; closed Tue-Thu L closed Sun D, closed Mon; Booking max 8 may apply.

LOBOS Meat & Tapas SE1 £56 3|2|2
14 Borough High St   020 7407 5361   10–4C
This "great little tapas bar with simple service" at the edge of Borough Market is "a place where the food speaks for itself" – which may be a good thing, since its "cramped" accommodation inside a Victorian railway arch is "decidedly grotty". There's a definite meat bias to the menu, although the "squid with black rice is particularly good". / SE1 9QG; lobostapas.co.uk; @LobosTapas; Mon-Thu 10.30 pm, Fri & Sat 11 pm; closed Mon-Sat L, closed Sun; booking max 8 may apply.

Locanda Locatelli W1 £97 3|4|3
Hyatt Regency, 8 Seymour St   020 7935 9088   2–2A
Giorgio Locatelli's "elegant and sophisticated" Italian off Portman Square (run, with wife Plaxy, since 2002) is "a favourite of many years' standing" for many reporters. The modern Italian cuisine delivers "flavours second to none", "service is personal and attentive" and it's "an unusual combination of the informal (making everyone feel welcome) and the impeccable". (Though slightly less high-profile in UK media in recent times, Giorgio's big in Italy now as a new judge on Italian MasterChef). / W1H 7JZ; www.locandalocatelli.com; Wed-Sat 11 pm, Sun 10 pm; closed Wed L, closed Mon & Tue; booking max 8 may apply.

London Shell Co. W2 £79 **3** **3** **4**
The Prince Regent, Sheldon Square 07818 666005 7–1C
"What a wonderful way to spend an afternoon!" – dining on "excellent seafood" aboard a barge, either cruising along the Regent's Canal on the Prince Regent, or static but floating on the Grand Duchess, docked by Paddington station. It's a "good-quality fish experience", with supplies fresh from Cornwall and "very amiable service". / W2 6EP; www.londonshellco.com; @LondonShellCo; Tue-Sat 9.30 pm, Sun 3 pm; closed Tue-Fri L closed Sun D, closed Mon.

London Stock SW18 NEW £48
2 Bubbling Well Square, Ram Quarter 020 8075 3877 11–2B
In Wandsworth's 'Ram Quarter' – the shiny new development on the site that was for 500 years Young's Brewery – this ambitious venture opened in January 2020. Chefs Assem Abdel Hady and Andres Bernal offer multi-course tasting menus (typically about £65 for 8 courses) of a level that you would not expect, given the unpretentious modern decor and a hard-to-shake memory of what Wandsworth town centre used to look like! There's outdoor seating too, and a cut-down version of the offering at lunch. / SW18 1UQ; londonstockrestaurant.co.uk; @london_stock; Wed-Sat 8.30 pm, Sun 8 pm; closed Mon & Tue.

The Lore of the Land W1 £60 **3** **3** **4**
4 Conway Street 020 3927 4480 2–1B
"Our local and by far the best pub in Fitzrovia" – Guy Ritchie and David Beckham seem to have hit the target with the 'country pub' they opened three years ago, serving beer from the former's Gritchie brewery and venison from his Wiltshire estate – "their own Angel Lore lager is fantastic". The site has housed a pub since 1829, known as the Adams Arms and the Lukin within living memory, while "Alan McGee's Creation Records started its infamous club the Living Room here in the 1980s". A fire in June 2021 has temporarily closed the pub, which hopes to be open again by Christmas. / W1T 6BB; gritchiepubs.com; @LoreoftheLandpb; Tue-Sat 11 pm, Sun 10 pm; closed Tue-Sat L, closed Mon.

Lorne SW1 £71 **5** **5** **3**
76 Wilton Road 020 3327 0210 2–4B
"Having survived the lockdowns which were preceded by a major flood", this "modest" but "delightful and comfortable small restaurant", a short walk from Victoria, "is back and on top form". "Katie Exton is now sole owner, with a new head chef (previously the number two in the kitchen) and the food remains superb". "Katie is not only one of London's slickest hostesses but also one of its best sommeliers", and has assembled a "focused, somewhat classical list" which she introduces with "knowledge and enthusiasm". "Bang for buck, given the size of the restaurant and its prices? Lorne can't be beaten!". / SW1V 1DE; www.lornerestaurant.co.uk; Mon-Sat 9.30 pm, Sun 3 pm; closed Mon L closed Sun D.

Louie WC2 NEW £95 **3** **3** **4**
13-15 West Street 020 8057 6500 5–2B
Glorious New Orleans-inspired decor is just one of the attractions of this September 2020 newcomer, which inherited the Covent Garden site of L'Atelier de Joël Robuchon (RIP), just by The Ivy. The first London venture of successful restaurant group Paris Society – with 'boots on the ground' in the form of restaurateurs Guillaume Glipa and Laurent de Gourcuff and American chef Slade Rushing – it's somewhat a case of 'plus ça change'. The setting – in a different vein – is still luxurious and captivating (including the upstairs bar); the culinary influences are still Gallic (only here with a Creole spin); prices are still vertigo-inducing, but – if you have dosh to burn – our early reports say it's worth it. / WC2H 9NE; www.louie-london.com; Mon-Sat 10.30 pm; closed Sun.

Louie Louie SE17 £54 3 3 3
347 Walworth Rd 020 7450 3223 1–3C
This "good breakfast spot" in Walworth morphs into an evening hang-out with DJs, biodynamic and natural wines, cocktails and "top-class" chef residencies to keep the crowd fed and entertained. / SE17 2AL; louielouie.london; @LouieLouie_Ldn; Mon & Tue, Sun 3 pm, Wed-Sat midnight; closed Mon & Tue, Sun D; Take bookings all week via phone and/or online.

LPM W1 £114 4 3 4
54 Brook's Mews 020 7495 4774 3–2B
"Every dish is a winner" – "the freshest-tasting ingredients, served simply, Mediterranean-style" – at this slice of the French Riviera transposed to a Mayfair mews. Much of its personality derives from the "expensive and very international crowd" that it attracts ("the noise level can make conversation difficult"), but while it's "not cheap, great care is taken". Now known by its acronym, it is modelled on the original La Petite Maison in Nice, and chef Raphael Duntoye has spun the concept out to the Middle East, Miami and Hong Kong in recent years. The London flagship was extended in 2020, with the addition of a seafood and cocktail bar. / W1K 4EG; www.lpmlondon.co.uk; @lpmlondon; Wed-Sat 10.30 pm, Sun 3.30 pm; closed Wed L closed Sun D, closed Mon & Tue.

Luca EC1 £90 4 3 4
88 St John St 020 3859 3000 10–1A
"Love it every time", agree fans of this Clove Club spin-off in Clerkenwell that uses prime British ingredients to create "elegant Italian dishes". "The menu is always original, and whether you sit in the cosy booths at the front or amid the light and glass at the back", where there is a gorgeous conservatory, "the ambience is great – fun, but serious about the food". It's also "excellent for business" – "smooth, polished and reliable". / EC1M 4EH; luca.restaurant; @LucaRestaurant; Wed-Sat 11 pm; closed Mon & Tue & Sun.

Luce e Limoni WC1 £61 4 4 3
91-93 Gray's Inn Rd 020 7242 3382 10–1A
"Excellent" Sicilian cooking and a "terrific atmosphere", orchestrated by charismatic host Fabrizio Zafarana – who is "simply meraviglioso!" – are to be found in this 10-year-old venture at an "awkward location on the unlovely Grays Inn Road". It also has an impressive list of Sicilian wines. / WC1X 8TX; www.luceelimoni.com; @Luce_e_Limoni; Mon-Thu 10 pm, Fri & Sat 11 pm; closed Sat L, closed Sun.

Luciano's SE12 £57 4 4 3
131 Burnt Ash Road 020 8852 3186 1–4D
It's "always a treat" to visit this "perfect local neighbourhood eatery" in Horn Park – a family-run Italian that's "a favourite for drop-in lunches or dinners" among the residents of Lee and beyond. Owner Enzo Masiello named it after his father, who played football for Charlton Athletic before transfering into restaurants. / SE12; lucianoslondon.co.uk; @lucianoslondon; Tue-Sat 9 pm, Sun 3 pm; closed Sun D, closed Mon.

Lucio SW3 £93 3 2 2
257 Fulham Rd 020 7823 3007 6–3B
This family-run Italian in the Fulham Road has built a solid fan-base over almost two decades for its seasonal cooking – including "particularly good fish" – and offers "spectacular value" for lunch. It is not hugely known, but regulars will travel from across town for a meal. / SW3 6HY; Mon-Sat 10.45 pm, Sun 9.45 pm.

Lucky & Joy E5 NEW £46 433
95 Lower Clapton Road 07488 965966 14–1B
"A terrific take on Chinese food" with *"interesting and 'different' flavours"* wins a warm early reception for this funky Clapton canteen. Opened at the start of 2020 – after a series of pop-ups – it serves a short menu of excellent Chinese dishes as filtered by the sensibilities and chef's travels of (non-Chinese) owners Ellen Parr (ex-Rochelle Canteen and Moro) and Pete Kelly (ex-Morito). Spicy cocktails also abound as does retro '80s-tastic decor. Jay Rayner drooled and all our initial survey feedback rates it very good or excellent. / E5 0NP; luckyandjoy.co.uk.

Lucky Cat W1 £81 222
10-13 Grosvenor Square 020 7107 0000 3–2A
On the site that was Maze (RIP), the f-word chef launched this Mayfair pan-Asian fixture in summer 2019 with the aim of emulating 'the drinking dens of Thirties Tokyo and the Far East'… only to unleash a social media storm about cultural appropriation. Our initial diner reports are quite mixed, and skewed to the negative: *"basically anything by Gordon Ramsey is overpriced and only funds his narcissism"*. / W1K 6JP; www.gordonramsayrestaurants.com/lucky-cat; @LuckyCatGR; Mon-Wed midnight, Thu-Sat 1 am, Sun 10 pm.

Lume NW3 £82 343
38 Primrose Hill Road 020 7449 9556 9–2A
A small, well-chosen array of Sardinian wine – including many *"small growers"* – is a highpoint (one of the backers is a wine distributor) at this informal Italian deli/wine shop, which opened in spring 2019. *"The menu likewise is small, simple and well-executed"*, including *"good, fresh pasta as you'd expect"*. Made more desirable by its cute neighbourhood location in ultra-desirable Primrose Hill – it received a big early thumbs-up for its cucina from someone with strong family ties to the area: Evening Standard (now Tatler) critic, Fay Maschler. *"It's a little pricey, but you pay for the postcode plus they only have about a dozen covers"*. / NW3 3AD; www.lume.london; Tue-Sun 10 pm; closed Tue-Thu L, closed Mon.

Lupins SE1 £51 422
66 Union St 020 3908 5888 10–4B
The *"fabulous Anglicised tapas"* at this *"hidden gem next to the Omeara music venue"* have made a hit of Lucy Pedder and Natasha Cooke's four-year-old venture. It's *"tiny and unpromising on the outside, but has a really lovely menu of superb small plates, generally modern British with an Iberian inflection"*. There's now a spinoff, Pomelo, at the new Goods Way food market in King's Cross. / SE1 1TD; www.lupinslondon.com; Sat, Wed-Fri 10 pm; closed Wed-Fri L, closed Mon & Tue & Sun; cards only.

Lure NW5 £48 332
56 Chetwynd Rd 020 7267 0163 9–1B
A modern Dartmouth Park chippy, which draws fans from beyond its 'hood for *"really fresh fish imaginatively cooked"*, plus *"enormous portions of chips – skinny or chunky – very crisp and very salty!"*. Top Tip – *"worth ordering the interesting tenderstem side"*. / NW5 1DJ; www.lurefishkitchen.co.uk; @Lurefishkitchen; Wed-Sat 10 pm, Sun 9.30 pm; closed Wed-Fri L, closed Mon & Tue; booking weekends only.

Lurra W1 £67 433
9 Seymour Place 020 7724 4545 2–2A
This *"outstanding restaurant with a concise but impressive menu"* brings the spirit of Basque dining to Seymour Village, near Marble Arch. The twin specialities are whole turbot and large ribs of retired Galician Blond dairy cows, grilled over charcoal to share. *"The great croquetas, amazing steak and sublime cheesecake bring back fond memories of San Sebastian"*. Its nearby stablemate, Donostia, serves equally authentic Basque tapas. / W1H 5BA; www.lurra.co.uk; @LurraW1; Mon-Sat 10.30 pm, Sun 3.30 pm; closed Mon L closed Sun D.

Lusitania SW8 £64 3|3|2
353 Wandsworth Road   020 7787 0600   11–1D
Near the shiny new Vauxhall riverside developments, this Stockwell two-year-old (with hidden 'Olive Tree Garden') aims for a festive experience, aiming higher than is often associated with Portuguese cuisine. One early report captures it well: "If you're a Portuguese ex-pat then I suspect the menu at Lusitania will be a comforting reminder of home. With its well-cooked classic dishes and big portions, nothing really stands out as excellent, but it's all good. The dining room is large, can get noisy, and there's a big-screen TV". / SW8 2JH; www.restaurantelusitania.co.uk; Mon-Sun 10 pm.

Lutyens Grill,
The Ned EC2 £106 3|2|4
27 Poultry   020 3828 2000   10–2C
All red leather and wood panelling – this plush steakhouse is the centrepiece dining option at the Ned: Soho House's vast transformation of the former Midland Bank HQ in the heart of the City. It's the sort of place where plutocrats meet to carve up international corporations over lunch while waiters carve beef Wellington from the trolley. The steaks, both British and imported, are top quality. / EC2R 8AJ; www.thened.com/restaurants/lutyens-grill; @TheNedLondon; Tue-Sat midnight; closed Sat L, closed Sun & Mon.

Lyle's E1 £97 5|3|2
The Tea Building, 56 Shoreditch High Street   020 3011 5911   13–1B
"Led by fantastic British ingredients, the cooking seems simple but it's not" at James Lowe's acclaimed canteen, at the foot of Shoreditch's well-known landmark, the Tea Building. His "superb combinations" deliver "amazing and unexpected flavours" – "it's easy to see why this restaurant is so highly rated" and fans still consider the cuisine "some of the best in London". (In February 2020, co-founder John Ogier stepped away from the business). / E1 6JJ; www.lyleslondon.com; @lyleslondon; Tue-Sat 11 pm; closed Tue L, closed Sun & Mon.

Lyon's N8 NEW £53 4|4|3
1 Park Road   020 8350 8983   1–1C
"Top-notch small plates, oysters and superb fishy delights" – plus an interesting selection of wine and "lovely service" – inspire nothing but rave reviews for this family-run two-year-old, which didn't get the memo that good restaurants aren't allowed in Crouch End. It's well decked out too, with green banquette seating and a white marble bar. They must be doing something right, as they have already opened a second place in Hackney (see Hackney Coterie). / N8 8TE; lyons-restaurant.com; Tue-Sat 10 pm; closed Tue L, closed Sun & Mon.

M Restaurants £87 3|2|3
Zig Zag Building, Victoria St, SW1   020 3327 7776   2–4B
Brewery Wharf, Brewery Lane, TW1   020 3327 7776   1–4A
60 Threadneedle Street, EC2   020 3327 7770   10–2C
Martin Williams's duo of glossy 'gastro-playgrounds' (that's what they call themselves) in the City and Victoria combine no-expense-spared, Miami-esque design with a top-of-the-range assortment of grills which incorporate non-beef options but go large on luxurious steaks, including top USDA, Kobe, and Wagyu cuts and with meat sourced from Somerset to Argentina. Feedback was limited this survey (both branches are in office-dependent locations) but all of it was very enthusiastic. The Twickenham 'bar and grill' is a more casual outlet, and in late 2021/early 2022, a further branch will open in Canary Wharf, occupying the ground floor of the 58-storey Diamond Building, serving a menu of surf 'n' turf, split into four distinct areas; 'Smoke', 'Coal', 'Wood' and 'Ice'. / www.mrestaurants.co.uk; @mrestaurants_.

Ma Goa SW15 £43 **3 3 3**
242-244 Upper Richmond Rd   020 8780 1767   11–2B
"Consistently good home-style Goan cuisine" has paid off handsomely for the Kapoor family, whose "Putney stalwart" celebrates its 30th anniversary next year. A well-known sight on the South Circular, the facade changed dramatically a few years ago to reflect a relaunch in a stripped-back street food style, complete with a wall of craft beers. / SW15 6TG; www.magoaputney.co.uk; @MaGoaLondon; Tue-Thu 10 pm, Fri & Sat 10.30 pm; closed Tue-Sat L, closed Sun & Mon.

Macellaio RC £53 **4 3 3**
6 Store Street, WC1   020 3848 7230   2–1C
84 Old Brompton Rd, SW7   020 7589 5834   6–2B
Arch 24, 229 Union St, SE1   07467 307682   10–4B
124 Northcote Rd, SW11   020 3848 4800   11–2C
38-40 Exmouth Market, EC1   020 3696 8220   10–1A
"Exceptionally fine beef" from the Italian Fassone breed in the valleys north of Genoa is theatrically presented – as if in a butcher's shop – at Roberto Costa's growing group of steakhouses, where the "superb cuts are butchered in front of you". "I finally went to try out what looked like magnificent beef, from the haunches in the window. I wasn't disappointed – it delivered magnificently." The South Ken branch in Old Brompton Road remains the most popular. There are others in Fitzrovia, Exmouth Market, Union Street and Battersea. (The latest to open in summer 2021, in the West End's Theatreland, is called Il Teatro del Carne – see also). / www.macellaiorc.com; @macellaiorc.

Madame Pigg E8 £61 **4 4 4**
480 Kingsland Road   07956 925695   14–1A
For a "really satisfying Sunday lunch (all you would wish for: crispy roast potatoes; HUGELY risen Yorkshire; delicious gravy; roast pork that's typically on every day, plus beef)" – Haggerston hipsters recommend Adam Hardiman's converted burger bar, with its "lovely service". On top of Covid, he lost a finger in late August 2021, and soon after launched a crowdfunded appeal to help keep going. As we go to press in early September 2021, the restaurant is still closed. / E8 4AE; www.madamepigg.com; @madamepigg; Tue-Sun 11 pm; closed Tue-Fri L, closed Mon.

Made in Italy £51 **3 2 2**
249 King's Rd, SW3   020 7352 1880   6–3C
141 The Broadway, SW19   020 8540 4330   11–2B
The nice roof terrace at the 30-year-old Chelsea branch is the main reason to mention this small pizza chain, which also has siblings in Battersea and Wimbledon (the latter has yet to re-open as of September 2021). / www.madeinitalygroup.co.uk; @MADEINITALYgrp.

Madera W1 **NEW** £53
Treehouse Hotel, Langham Place   020 3988 4273   3–1C
On the 15th floor of a two-year-old hotel next to the Beeb – this large (160 seat) and expensively designed perch is little sister to Los Angeles-based Toca Madera. Alongside its (not inexpensive) cocktails, it serves a Mexican menu (lots of tortillas) which early reviewers were not especially impressed by. (On the floor above there's the rooftop NEST bar which is open for weekend brunch.) / W1B 2QS; www.treehousehotels.com/london/eat-drink/madera; @maderalondon; Sun-Fri 10.45 pm, Sat midnight.

Maggie Jones's W8 £57 2 2 **4**
6 Old Court Pl   020 7937 6462   6–1A

Named for Princess Margaret – who used to slip away from Kensington Palace and eat here under this pseudonym – this romantic, golden oldie bistro provides a dated but very cosy and comforting combination of solid Anglo/French cuisine, country kitchen decor and wine sold out of a magnum bottle with a measuring stick (although finer vintages are available). It's not dis-similar from its much better known sibling, La Poule Au Pot. / W8 4PL; www.maggie-jones.co.uk; Mon-Fri 9.15pm, Sat & Sun 9.15 pm.

Maguro W9 £56 **4 4** 2
5 Lanark Pl   020 7289 4353   9–4A

"Lovely food" – including "wonderful sushi" – and "efficient service" have made this tiny Japanese near Little Venice extremely popular – deservedly so, for cuisine of this freshness at very reasonable prices. Set meals represent the best value, and the "well-presented bento boxes were a top delivery experience during lockdown". / W9 1BT; www.maguro-restaurant.com; Mon-Sat 11 pm, Sun 10.30 pm; closed Mon-Sun L; no Amex.

The Maine Mayfair W1 NEW
6 Medici Court, 20 Hanover Square   09714 4576719   3–2C

Opening in October 2021, an enormous, American-style, 350-cover brasserie, split over three levels, residing in one of Mayfair's only surviving Georgian Grade II listed buildings (which dates back to 1720, and is the former home of the Duke of Montrose). Its backer is Joey Ghazal, who has blown in from Dubai, where he has three venues, and aims to bring some life to slightly dead Hanover Square. The PR announcement said it will be a 'blend of old-world British elegance, New England extravagance, and subterranean decadence'. Can't wait! / W1S 1JY; www.themainemayfair.com; Tue-Thu midnight, Fri & Sat 1 am.

Maison Bertaux W1 £8 **4 4 5**
28 Greek St   020 7437 6007   5–2A

"A piece of old Soho that outshines all newcomers", this "eccentric and delightful" pâtisserie has just celebrated its 150th anniversary – in premises opened by a Parisian exile in 1871. The "delicious cakes and pastries" are still made on site, and it's a "perfect spot to watch the world go by". Generations of bohos, artists and revolutionaries have passed through the door – including Karl Marx – and Bastille Day, 14 July, is always celebrated here. / W1D 5DQ; www.maisonbertaux.com; @Maison_Bertaux; Mon-Sat 11 pm, Sun 9.30 pm.

Maison Francois SW1 NEW £87 **4 4 4**
36 Duke Street St James's   020 3988 5777   3–3D

"A modern, London take on a classic French format" – this high-ceilinged, "super-cool looking" newcomer opened in September 2020 and sits inside a "beautifully fitted out" new St James's building ('The Marq' – on the site that once was Green's, long RIP). The longish menu of "classic" small plates and more 'haute' brasserie dishes (with desserts from a posh trolley) is a witting homage to the grand brasseries of Paris, Lyon and Alsace – but the more substantial options are not served at prices we associate with the term 'brasserie'. There's also a basement wine bar, Frank's (see also). Top Tip – as well as the expected wine list, there's also a "fun cocktail selection, which is unusually comprehensive for a restaurant of this high level of cooking". / SW1Y 6DF; maisonfrancois.london; Tue-Sat midnight; closed Sun & Mon.

Malabar W8 £53
27 Uxbridge St   020 7727 8800   7–2B

We're hoping against hope that this age-old Indian stalwart, tucked away near Notting Hill, reopens post-pandemic (it's still 'temporarily closed' as of September 2021, although its website says: 'we hope to reopen'). Still decorated like the Italian premises it inherited over 30 years ago, it pioneered a new look for sub-continental restaurants, its menu was consistently excellent and few eateries of any type can match its performance over the decades. / W8 7TQ; www.malabar-restaurant.co.uk; @kitchen_malabar; Mon-Sun 11 pm; closed Mon-Fri L.

Malabar Junction WC1 £40   3 3 2
107 Gt Russell St   020 7580 5230   2–1C

A "low-key South Indian with welcoming, gracious staff", this Bloomsbury Keralan serves "great meals full of good flavours", from a "well-composed menu" with "a lot of vegetarian choices". / WC1B 3NA; malabarjunctionbloomsbury.co.uk; Mon-Sat 10.30 pm; closed Sun.

Mallow SE1 NEW
1 Cathedral Street   10–4C

Opposite Southwark Cathedral, this autumn 2021 opening from the Mildreds team looks set to be a new flagship for that meat-free group, gearing up on its proximity to Borough Market 'bringing to life the history of the market and the produce that it sells'. The restaurant will open from early morning with a plant-based breakfast, operating all day and with a list of vegan wines, beers and handcrafted cocktails. / SE1 1TL; www.mallowlondon.com; Wed-Sat 9 pm, Sun 4 pm.

Mama Shelter Restaurant E2 NEW £70
437 Hackney Road   020 7613 6500   14–2B

The wild and wacky French chain opened this eclectically designed 194-room hotel in late 2019, complete with clashing fabrics, retro gaming machines, füsball and karaoke rooms. The loungy restaurant offers an easy-grazing selection of dishes to suit the tastes of globe-trotting hipsters: initial feedback suggests it's better than you might expect (given all the competing attractions). / E2 8PP; www.mamashelter.com/en/contact-us/london; @MamaShelter_LDN; Sun-Thu 11 pm, Fri & Sat midnight.

Mama's Jerk SE8 £20   4 3 2
Arch 10, Deptford Market Yard   020 7998 9200   1–3D

Jerk BBQ sauce, passed down through the generations (from great grandmother, Mama Charlotte's secret recipe) is part of the backstory at this "friendly, local Jamaican place" in Deptford's Market Yard, serving 'new-style Caribbean street food'. (There are other stalls, in Pop Brixton and Canary Wharf, but this is the one generating most feedback). "Jerk chicken is the main attraction (but 'biriyardi' and plantain are well worth a go, too)." / SE8 4NS; www.mamasjerk.com; @mamasjerk; Tue-Thu midnight, Fri & Sat 1 am.

Mamma Dough £47   4 3 2
40 Ladywell Road, SE13   020 8690 7550   1–4D
179 Queen's Rd, SE15   020 7635 3470   1–4D
76-78 Honor Oak Pk, SE23   020 8699 5196   1–4D
1 Station Road, SE25   020 8653 2537
299 Kirkdale, SE26   020 8778 1234
303-307 Balham High Road, SW17   020 3409 4671
354 Coldharbour Ln, SW9   020 7095 1491   11–2D

"The kids are always delighted by their 'bunny' pizzas, and we think you can't go wrong with the sourdough offerings" at this highly rated South London group, with seven venues from Brixton and Peckham to Tooting and Sydenham. The stripped-down interiors are matched by home-made desserts, local craft beers and small-batch coffee. / www.mammadough.co.uk.

Mandarin Kitchen W2 £59 4 3 2
14-16 Queensway   020 7727 9012   7–2C

"This stalwart of Queensway's mini-Chinatown is back and better than ever", thrilling diners with its signature lobster noodles (a dish invented on the premises) as well as superlative "steamed scallops, razor clams and all-round seafood". "The best meal we've had for a long time." Founded in 1978, MK is "always crammed", but a makeover a couple of years ago, and improved service, are signs that more effort is now going into the ambience. / W2 3RX; www.mandarin.kitchen/; Mon-Sat 11.15 pm, Sun 23.

Mangal 1 E8 £37 5 2 2
10 Arcola St   020 7275 8981   14–1A

"Often imitated, never beaten!" – Dalston's original Mangal grill is still "the long-running undisputed champion" of "sublime Turkish/Kurdish barbecues". And it's not just for carnivores: "they also serve top, authentic homemade mezze – including a good range of veggie choices". Regularly name-checked by celeb chefs (Ottolenghi, Oliver et al), it's also "great value – a meal for two for the price of a single course elsewhere". Top Tip: "BYO policy means you can bring along the best bottle from your own cellar!" (Mangal 2, two minutes' walk away, has been taken over by Ali Dirik's sons, and is now a place of some ambition; The Observer's Jay Rayner called it "serious and inventive... properly delicious".) / E8 2DJ; www.mangal1.com; @Mangalone; Sun-Thu midnight, Fri & Sat 1 am; cash only; No bookings.

Manicomio £84 2 2 3
85 Duke of York Square, SW3   020 7730 3366   6–2D
6 Gutter Lane, EC2   020 7726 5010   10–2B

The Chelsea branch of this modern Italian duo (the other is in The City) "was a real godsend during the Covid restrictions" for its "special terrace" – "one of the best in London" – "well away from the King's Road traffic" and with "lots of flowers and heaters when needed". "The food is very good but rather pricey" – perhaps as expected at these locations. / www.manicomio.co.uk; @ManicomioSW3.

Manteca EC2 NEW
49-51 Curtain Road   13–1B

Hand-rolled pasta has been a highlight at Chris Leach and Smokestak's David Carter's year-old concept – a follow-up to their hit residency at 10 Heddon Street – which, in October 2021, is set to shift from Soho to Shoreditch, re-opening in a former PizzaExpress at the address given above. As well as the trademark pasta (which you can watch being made), expect a range of small and sharing plates – featuring nose-to-tail offal dishes and meat from selected farms – cooked in the open central kitchen and wood-fired oven. The basement, glass-walled hanging room showcases their in-house butchery and the making of their in-house salumi. / EC2A 3PT; Mon-Sun 4 pm.

Manthan W1 NEW £60
49 Maddox Street   020 7491 9191   4–2A

Rohit Ghai (of Kutir) returns to Mayfair with this September 2021 opening on the former site of Lucknow 49 (RIP) with his eyes on the Michelin star he won in his Jamavar days. The offer incorporates traditional-with-a-twist dishes (such as 'goat shami kebab in bone marrow sauce', and 'Burford brown egg curry') and lots of cocktails (including of the non-alcoholic variety). / W1S; manthanmayfair.co.uk; @manthanmayfair; Thu-Sat 9 pm, Sun 3 pm.

Manuka Kitchen SW6 £58 3 2 3
510 Fulham Rd   020 7736 7588   6–4A

A favoured Fulham option for weekend brunch, helped by its outside seating: the eclectic, New Zealand-inspired menu is big on wagyu mince – on sourdough toast with poached eggs, or in a spaghetti Bolognaise. / SW6 5NJ; manukakitchen.co.uk; @manukakitchen; Tue-Sat 11 pm, Mon 10 pm; closed Mon L, closed Sun; booking max 8 may apply.

Manzi's W1
1 Bateman's Buildings   5–2A

Remember the original Manzi's on a corner south of Chinatown? You're definitely dating yourself. Nearby (if not quite on exactly the same site) the great Corbin & King are launching this homage to the original. The aim is to be 'fun and affordable' like Brasserie Zédel with something of a 1940s vibe. That hits the rose-tinted remembrances of the original, which – for ages – was one of London's great post-theatre rendezvous. / W1D 3EN; @corbinandking; Tue-Sat 11 pm.

Mãos E2   £203   5 5 4
41 Redchurch Street   02070336788   13–1C

Within Shoreditch's Blue Mountain School ('dedicated to nurturing engagements and interactions between diverse practices'… most of them expensive!), this hipster dining room is nowadays on version 2.0. Nuno Mendes is no longer involved, and diners no longer all share a communal table: parties of up to four are served in the main dining room; a larger group might be served in the adjacent 'R&D library'; or there's a chef's table for up to six diners. In any case, you are in for £170 per person (with wine pairing at £125 per person) to sample Edoardo Pellicano's innovative menus – an investment all our reporters who made it say was worth it on account of the outstanding results. / E2 7DJ; bluemountain.school/maos; Wed-Sat 11.30 pm; closed Wed-Sat L, closed Mon & Tue & Sun.

Mar I Terra SE1   £49   3 4 3
14 Gambia St   020 7928 7628   10–4A

This old Southwark pub "is not the smartest venue" but it's a favourite near the South Bank and Young Vic. The unexpected find of good value, contemporary Spanish tapas is key to its popularity, but its highest rated asset is its "wonderful staff". / SE1 0XH; www.mariterra.net; Mon-Sat 11 pm; closed Sat L, closed Sun.

Marcella SE8   £44   3 4 3
165a Deptford High Street   020 3903 6561   1–3D

This hip local (named after the great Italian food writer Marcella Hazan) brings "great authentic Italian food" to Deptford High Street. Sibling to Peckham's Artusi, it keeps its regulars happy with a short seasonal menu and Italian-only wine list. / SE8 3NU; www.marcella.london/; @MarcellaDeptfrd; Wed & Thu 10 pm, Fri & Sat 10.30 pm, Sun 4 pm; closed Sun D, closed Mon & Tue; May need 6+ to book.

Marcus,
The Berkeley SW1   £155   3 3 3
Wilton Pl   020 7235 1200   6–1D

"Exceptional attention to detail" – not least the "very refined", "classical" cuisine – helps win very solid support this year for Marcus Wareing's illustrious, flagship Belgravia dining room, where chef patrons Mark and Shauna Froydenlund provide the day-to-day hands on the tiller. There is the odd measured report – "everything was lovely enough, but didn't really take flight" – but on most accounts a trip here provides an experience that's "not cheap… but amazing!" / SW1X 7RL; www.marcusrestaurant.com; @marcusbelgravia; Tue-Sat 10 pm; closed Sun & Mon; No trainers; Take bookings all week via phone and/or online.

Mare Street Market E8   £50   3 2 5
117 Mare Street   020 3745 2470   14–2B

The "vibrant dining space" is a "very cool setting" with oodles of "laid back" street cred at this remarkable 10,000 square foot market (vintage design pieces, flowers, artisan coffee…) inside a groovily transformed Hackney office block. Strike lucky and you get "great pizza and burgers" too, but some dishes are "a bit less successful than others and the service can go a little MIA at times". / E8 4RU; www.marestreetmarket.com; Mon-Sun 10 pm.

Maremma SW2 £59 444

36 Brixton Water Lane   020 3186 4011   11–2D

"Incredibly good, inventive food" – *"delightfully light, with loads of flavour"* – has put this Brixton two-year-old on the map with its focus on the cuisine and wine of the Tuscany marshland it's named after. It's a *"lovely local"*, run by *"friendly and knowledgeable people"*, and the unusual wine list includes some *"good choices at a reasonable price"*. / SW2 1PE; www.maremmarestaurant.com; Tue-Sat 10 pm, Sun 4 pm; closed Tue-Thu L closed Sun D, closed Mon.

Margot WC2 £86 244

45 Great Queen Street   020 3409 4777   5–2D

Near the Freemasons' Hall, this "classy" and "traditional"-looking Italian brasserie in Covent Garden is a "perfect business lunch place", thanks to its classic cuisine and "well-paced" service (which is fitting for a place founded by two front-of-house specialists). Co-founder Paulo de Tarso has left, leaving Nicolas Jaouën (ex-La Petite Maison and Rivea) in charge. A small minority of reporters complained this year that, for all its qualities, the offering "lacks personality". / WC2B 5AA; www.margotrestaurant.com; @MargotLDN; Tue-Sat 9.30 pm; closed Sun & Mon.

The Marksman E2 £69 323

254 Hackney Road   020 7739 7393   14–2A

Good, if slightly up-and-down reports this year on Tom Harris and Jon Rotheram's well-regarded pub near Columbia Road Market, known for its superior gastropub menu and terrific Sunday roasts. / E2 7SJ; www.marksmanpublichouse.com; @marksman_pub; Wed & Thu midnight, Fri & Sat 1 am, Sun 11 pm; closed Wed & Thu L, closed Mon & Tue.

Maroush £61 322

5 McNicol Drive, NW10   020 3941 3221   1–2A NEW
38 Beauchamp Pl, SW3   020 7581 5434   6–1C
68 Edgware Rd, W2   020 7224 9339   7–1D

"The garlic sauce is a symphony on your tongue when you have shish taouk or a mixed shawarma at 3am on the way home" from the café sections of this *"long-standing favourite Lebanese chain"* (you may need to ask for the wrap menu at the posh Beauchamp Place branch). When it comes to the main menu, *"expect the usual staples"* of Lebanese cuisine. Opened 40 years ago by Marouf and Houda Abouzaki, sites have come and gone over the years, especially over the pandemic. The original 'Maroush I' at 21 Edgware Road is closed as of September 2021, and its return seems very uncertain at this point, so we've marked it as closed, RIP. That leaves four in the stable currently open – the well-known Knightsbridge branch, a smaller Earl's Court Café, and a very dramatic, vast new-build restaurant, wine bar and market that opened in the boonies of Park Royal in summer 2021 (a bold opening that deserves support); and finally the (not listed here) Maroush Express on Edgware Road. (Under the same ownership: the eccentric but excellent Crockers Folly in St John's Wood – see also – plus the more grab-and-go Ranoush chain). / www.maroush.com.

Maru W1 NEW £170 544

18 Shepherd Market   020 3637 7677   3–4B

On the former Shepherd Market site of Taka Mayfair (whose closure was announced at the end of 2020, RIP), and under the same ownership: this ambitious newcomer opened in late Spring 2021, post-lockdown. Adding to London's growing stable of ritzy Japanese countertop options, it offers a 20-course omakase tasting menu, priced at £160 with the speciality dry-aged fish features prominently on the daily changing menu. It's led by chef Taiji Maruyama, a former sushi chef at Nobu London and head chef at Surrey hotel Beaverbrook. (See also Taka Marylebone). Limited early feedback on which the rating is based, but all very enthusiastic: "the smallest restaurant I have been to and the absolutely best fish ever tried. All food is prepared in front of you, explained by the chefs and the combination of flavours is mind blowing". Fay Maschler in Tatler also raved. / W1J 7QH; www.marulondon.com; Tue-Sat 11 pm; closed Tue-Sat L, closed Sun & Mon.

Masala Zone £49 444

"Fabulous Indian street food and thalis" make the seven sites in this "exceptional" central London chain real crowd-pleasers, and they show no sign of running out of steam two decades after their launch in Soho. Far from it, by all accounts they have "really improved over the past year or so – the quality of the dishes is now far beyond where it used to be" – and "they are not expensive". Ranjit Mathrani, veteran chair of the family company behind the group, plans to open more branches; they also own high-end restaurants Amaya, Veeraswamy and Chutney Mary. / www.masalazone.com; @masalazone.

Master Wei WC1 £32 332
13 Cosmo Place 020 7209 6888 2–1D

"Exceptional, hand-pulled biang biang noodles" are the star turn at this "no-frills diner" near Russell Square, where an "unprepossessing" exterior gains access to a menu of "subtle, interesting and authentic regional Xi'an cuisine". "The prices are very reasonable for the West End." Proprietor Wei Guirong also runs Xi'an Impression near Arsenal's Emirates Stadium. / WC1N 3AP; master-wei.com; @MasterWei5; Sun-Thu 10 pm, Fri & Sat 10.30 pm.

Masters Super Fish SE1 £35 322
191 Waterloo Rd 020 7928 6924 10–4A

For a "cheap 'n' cheerful" fish 'n' chips hit, fans still recommend a meal at the Formica tables of this long-standing Waterloo chippy. / SE1 8UX; masterssuperfish.has.restaurant/; Mon-Thu 10.30 pm, Fri 11 pm; closed Sat & Sun; no Amex; no booking, Fri D.

Mathura SW1
4 Greycoat Place 2–4C

Is this a rival for the nearby Cinnamon Club? Celeb Indian chef Atul Kochhar is in collaboration with the former commercial director of The Cinnamon Collection, Tina English, for this bold new opening. Transforming a big (5000 square feet), old fire station building in Victoria, it will have 200 covers and will focus on the cuisine of India's north eastern states (the Seven Sister States). First announced in 2019, it was confirmed in April 2021 as coming 'later in the year'. / SW1P 1SB; mathura.co.uk; @mathurawfs.

Matsuba TW9 £46 432
10 Red Lion St 020 8605 3513 1–4A

This "lovely little Japanese restaurant with a very decent range" is a "very welcome option in Richmond". Run by a Korean family, it has provided "sterling service" for 17 years. / TW9 1RW; www.matsuba-restaurant.com; @matsuba; Tue-Sat 10.30 pm; closed Sun & Mon.

Maya EC2 NEW £51
The Hoxton Shoreditch, 1 Willow Street 020 7550 1000 13–1B

Breezing in from West Hollywood, Soho House's latest opening is a groovy-looking 80-seater plus loungey terrace, which sits on the glam rooftop (lots of steel, glass and greenery) of the Hoxton Hotel, with interesting views over The City. Exec chef Giacomo Pettinari has created a menu of Baja-Mexican dishes and a roving guacamole cart is all part of the fun (plus cocktails a-go-go too, of course). It opened too late for any survey feedback, but Fay Maschler, nowadays of Tatler, gave it a thumbs-up: "urbanista East London… meets leafy, bohemian Mexico" with food that's "wonderfully light", "delightfully more-ish" and "gone in a mouthful". / EC2A 4BH; thehoxton.com/london/shoreditch/maya-restaurant/; Mon-Sun 11 pm.

Mazi W8 £75 3|3|4
12-14 Hillgate St   020 7229 3794   7–2B

With its fresh angle on "genuine Greek food", this popular local in Hillgate Village, near Notting Hill Gate, provides something still rare in London – "a modern gastro take on the traditional taverna". Top Tip – "the tarama is fantastic, as the courgette cakes". / W8 7SR; www.mazi.co.uk; @mazinottinghill; Mon-Sun midnight.

MEATliquor £42 4|2|3
37-38 Margaret Street, W1   020 7224 4239   3–1C
17 Queensway, W2   020 7229 0172   7–2C
133b Upper St, N1   020 3711 0104   9–3D
37 Lordship Lane, SE22   020 3066 0008   1–4D
7 Dartmouth Rd, SE23   020 3026 1331   1–4D
74 Northcote Road, SW11   020 7228 4777   11–2C

"Glorious burgers and great music in grungy surroundings" – this punk-inspired dirty burger operation "has many imitators now – but it's still the best" for its diehard devotees. A decade after making the transition from a food van to a permanent site, the chain now has nine venues in the capital. If the excitement of its early years has dimmed a little, its food ratings continue to shine: "Dead Hippie burger, deep-fried mac'n'cheese, salted caramel brownie – is that not a perfect (heart-stopping) indulgent meal?" / meatliquor.com; @MEATliquor.

Mediterraneo W11 £67 3|2|3
37 Kensington Park Rd   020 7792 3131   7–1A

This "enjoyable and reasonably priced" Italian in Notting Hill is "always full and busy" – perhaps because it delivers exactly "the sort of food one thinks one would have on holiday in Italy". The same team is also behind two other Italian venues in the same street, Osteria Basilico and Essenza – so clearly they know what locals like. / W11 2EU; www.mediterraneo-restaurant.co.uk; Mon-Sun 10.30 pm; booking max 10 may apply.

Medlar SW10 £99 3|4|3
438 King's Rd   020 7349 1900   6–3B

"Consistency and total professionalism" have won a major following (in the Top 40 most-mentioned names this year) for Joe Mercer Nairne and David O'Connor's "first class" and "always welcoming" destination in a nondescript corner of Chelsea, which transcends its neighbourhood character ("it's a bit of a cheek-by-jowl affair") by attracting a far-flung fan club. Reporters have often cited Joe's cuisine as worthy of a Michelin star (which it briefly held) and he continues to win praise for well-judged cooking that's "good value, too, considering the quality" (even if its ratings slipped a smidgeon this year on some reports that were "good but not outstanding"). The "fabulous wine list" is also a major attraction in its own right. "Sommelier Melania has put together a stellar selection from across the world, at fair mark-ups, and with plenty of variety". And "the £10 corkage deal at lunch is an added incentive to regular visits". "It's filled with people who love great food, and not just another trendy 'place to be seen." / SW10 0LJ; www.medlarrestaurant.co.uk; @MedlarChelsea; Tue-Sat 10.30 pm, Sun 9.30 pm; closed Mon.

Megan's £50 2|3|3
571 King's Road, SW6   020 7348 7139   6–4A
Unit B, 57-69 Parsons Green Lane, SW6   020 7348 7139   11–1B
214 Chiswick High Road, W4   020 3468 0224   8–2A
204 Kensington High Street, W8   020 3468 0219   8–1D NEW
6 Esther Anne Place, N1   020 3468 0221   9–3D NEW
27 Circus West Village, SW11   020 3468 0218   11–1C
43 Bedford Hill, SW12   020 3468 0216   11–2D
86 High Street Wimbledon, SW19   020 3411 5550   11–2B
55-57 The Pavement, SW4   020 3468 0215   11–2D

With their very "pretty interiors" and "great brunch" – this "reliable chain" of "cheerful" all-day hang-outs has emerged completely undaunted from the pandemic, expanding beyond its south west London heartlands as far as Islington, Marlow and St Albans. With new openings scheduled for late 2021 in Dulwich and Richmond, the roll-out shows no sign of slowing down. They're very "dog friendly" too. / megans.co.uk; @MegansCafes.

Mei Mei SE1 NEW £70 5 3 2
Unit 52 Borough Market Kitchen, Jubilee Place   10–4C

"The chicken rice takes me back to holidays in Singapore, it's just so good." Ex-Pidgin chef, Elizabeth Haigh, was one of the first arrivals in Borough Market's new 'Market Kitchen' showcasing street food, and her tiny stall (with 14 seats, mostly at the counter although there is one table) is one of the zone's biggest PR coups. She won a Michelin star for Pidgin, but here she returns to her Singaporean roots. Amidst the clatter of the market and railway arches, it's not a choice for comfort merchants, but does have its own lively charm. You can grab a very superior snack by day, hawker style, or – Friday and Saturday nights – book for an eight-course tasting experience. "You get enough garlic to kill a vampire but beautiful flavours throughout" and fans say a meal here is "London's best value". / SE1 9AG; www.meimei.uk; @meimeilondon; Thu & Fri 10.30 pm, Wed 4 pm, Sat 11.30 pm; closed Wed D, closed Mon & Tue & Sun; No bookings at lunch.

Mele e Pere W1 £51 2 2 3
46 Brewer Street   020 7096 2096   4–3C

This Italian indie in Soho is entering its tenth year, and hides a large basement bar (boasting a wide range of vermouths) behind a small exterior. Feedback was a bit up-and-down this year – some former fans found blips in service and a poor ambience, while others continue to laud its "very good" Italian food and say a visit is "always fun". / W1F 9TF; www.meleepere.co.uk; @meleEpere; Tue-Sat 10 pm; closed Tue-Thu L, closed Sun & Mon.

The Melusine E1 NEW £83 4 3 3
Unit K, Ivory House, St. Katherine Dock   02077022976   10–3D

Theodore Kyriakou – who, back in the day, built both Livebait and The Real Greek – is part of the team behind this simply decorated, early 2020 newcomer in lovely St Katherine Dock (which comes complete with outside tables): "a confident gem of a fish restaurant" with "an unusual wine list which pairs exceptionally well with the well-prepared and presented dishes" (sourced from around the British Isles). It won a recent 10/10 from The Guardian's Grace Dent. / E1W 1AT; www.themelusine.co.uk; @themelusine_skd; Tue-Sat 10.30 pm, Sun 9.30 pm; closed Mon; Take bookings all week via phone and/or online.

Meraki W1 £75 3 3 4
80-82 Gt Titchfield St   020 7305 7686   3–1C

"Slick and stylish modern Greek" in Fitzrovia, whose "buzzing atmosphere" indicates that this bid to give Hellenic cuisine a glossy makeover is on track to succeed with its good looks and "tasty and imaginative" cuisine – a formula that has worked before for investors Peter and Arjun Waney, the brothers behind the phenomenal global success of Japanese restaurant brands Zuma and Roka. / W1W 7QT; www.meraki-restaurant.com; @meraki_lon; Tue-Thu 10.30 pm, Fri & Sat 11 pm; closed Sun & Mon.

Mercato Metropolitano SE1 £27 **3 3 4**
42 Newington Causeway   020 7403 0930   1–3C
"Fabulous atmosphere" and "so many choices": this 45,000 sqare foot
former paper factory near Elephant & Castle hosts 40-odd operators at any
time, offering anything from Argentinian grilled meat to Uzbeck rice dishes
along with London's biggest beer garden. "We love it: everyone can please
themselves and meet again in the middle", while "it's great for kids because
they can make as much noise as they like". "You just have to avoid the really
crowded times as it's pretty popular now". Founder Andrea Rasca also runs
markets in Milan and Turin – and across London in deconsecrated Grade-1-
listed St Mark's church, Mayfair. / SE1 6DR; www.mercatometropolitano.com/;
@mercatometropol; Mon-Thu 11 pm, Fri & Sat midnight, Sun 10 pm; Take bookings all
week via phone and/or online.

The Mercer EC2 £61 **3 2 3**
34 Threadneedle St   020 7628 0001   10–2C
Moments from the Bank of England, this converted banking hall is nowadays
a well-established City amenity, known for its "consistently good food", which
is served from breakfast on. / EC2R 8AY; www.themercer.co.uk;
@TheMercerLondon; Mon-Fri 9.30 pm; closed Sat & Sun.

Le Mercury N1 £35 **2 2 3**
140a Upper St   020 7354 4088   9–2D
Jolly, old-school Islington bistro of over 30 years' standing, known for its low
prices and "good value". Not so many places in town now where you can
have Soup, Beef Bourguignon and Apple Cake with Vanilla Ice Cream for
£14.50. / N1 1QY; www.lemercury.co.uk; @le_mercury; Mon-Thu midnight, Fri & Sat
1 am, Sun 11 pm.

Mere W1 £101 **4 5 4**
74 Charlotte Street   020 7268 6565   2–1B
"Monica and David have nailed it here" – their Fitzrovia basement "ticks
every box for a truly special night out in London", starting with "the personal
greeting in the beautiful, ground level bar area" before descending into the
"lovely", "bright" yet "romantic" dining room. Monica's cuisine is "a dream"
with "hints of the exotic that subtly differentiate the menu"; and is further
bolstered by some "superb and unusual wine pairings", not to mention
"fantastic service". As ever, "it seems inexplicable that it hasn't been
awarded a Michelin star, as it is way above the quality of many others that
have been". / W1T 4QH; www.mere-restaurant.com; @MereRestaurant; Tue-Thu
9 pm, Fri & Sat 9.30 pm; closed Sun & Mon; Jacket & tie required; Take bookings all
week via phone and/or online.

Meson don Felipe SE1 £46 **3 3 3**
53 The Cut   020 7928 3237   10–4A
This "long-lived favourite" in Waterloo is packed early most evenings before
shows at the nearby Young and Old Vic theatres. "Love the atmosphere" and
the "fabulous tapas and wines" – although "the menu hasn't changed since
it opened". Not everything stays the same, though – "now there are good
tables outside and you can book". / SE1 8LF; www.mesondonfelipe.com; Mon-Sat
11 pm; closed Sun; Take bookings all week via phone and/or online.

Meza Trinity Road SW17 £36 **3 2 3**
34 Trinity Rd   07722 111299   11–2C
"The original on Trinity Road is still going strong" – an inviting little Lebanese
café that's of a high standard for a local restaurant. "Sad to see the
Mitcham Road branch has closed". / SW17 7RE; www.mezarestaurant.co.uk;
Mon-Fri 5 pm.

Michael Nadra £70 442
6-8 Elliott Rd, W4   020 8742 0766   8–2A
42 Gloucester Ave, NW1   020 7722 2800   9–3B

"Top-quality cooking" at "very reasonable prices" is a consistent refrain from aficionados of Michael Nadra's neighbourhood duo, in Chiswick and Camden Town. They are a slightly odd couple – the former tightly packed off the high street; the latter out-of-the-way, near the Regent's Canal, and with a "nice little courtyard for warm evenings". In both locales, the modern European menu uses "high-quality ingredients" and is "pleasantly served by charming staff who meet all demands". Recent changes have been generally welcomed: "it's more of a brasserie-style offering now (I preferred the old cooking, but I'm in a minority of people I know)". Note – Chiswick remains 'temporarily closed' as of September 2021, but a relaunch is promised 'as soon as possible'. / www.restaurant-michaelnadra.co.uk; @michaelnadra.

Mien Tay £43 333
45 Fulham High St, SW6   020 7731 0670   11–1B
433 Lordship Lane, N22   020 3302 9530   1–1C
180 Lavender Hill, SW11   020 7350 0721   11–1C
122 Kingsland Rd, E2   020 7729 3074   14–2A

This family-run Vietnamese quartet has won popular acclaim for 15 years or so on Shoreditch's 'Pho Mile' as well as more recently in Battersea, Fulham and Wood Green. Hardly stylish but very "good value", they're "often rammed" with diners attracted by the first-class pho and dishes such as goat with galangal – one of the late critic AA Gill's all-time favourites. / mientay.co.uk; @Mien_Tay.

Mike's Peckham SE15 NEW £45 433
Unit 4.1, 133 Copeland Rd   020 7732 9012   1–4D

"A lovely, cheap 'n' cheerful pizza joint, with interesting and delicious brunch options and very friendly staff." This Peckham debutante, which opened in April 2021 – in the funky site that used to house Forza Win (RIP, but looking for a new home) – has an 80-seater outdoor space, in addition to the indoor 40 covers. Michael 'Mike' Davies is the chef director of the Camberwell Arms and Frank's Café. On the menu: Roman-style pizza (and other small plates). / SE15; mikespeckham.co.uk; @mikespeckham; Mon-Fri 10 pm, Sat & Sun 10.30 pm.

Mildreds £52 333
45 Lexington St, W1   020 7494 1634   4–2C
200 Pentonville Rd, N1   020 7278 9422   9–3D
9 Jamestown Rd, NW1   020 7482 4200   9–3B
Thomas Tower, Upper Dalston Sq, E8   020 8017 1815   14–1A

"A Soho institution" after 34 years – and in very recent years with spin-offs in Dalston, Camden Town and King's Cross – this slice of "veggie heaven (with great cocktails!)" is "just the best, even for a carnivore" and has done an impressive job of keeping up quality across the new group. The interiors of the new branches are clean cut and well-designed, and the food is "non-fussy and non-fake"; and will "stretch your mind but not your wallet". / @mildredslondon.

Milk SW12 £18 323
20 Bedford Hill   020 8772 9085   11–2C

"Get in early to avoid long weekend queues" at this well-known Antipodean artisan café – a star of the Balham scene for the past 10 years. You'll "always find good coffee and delicious food", and "their brunches are great value for money". / SW12 9RG; milklondonshop.uk/info; Mon-Fri 3.30 pm, Sat & Sun 4 pm; closed Mon-Sun D; No bookings.

MiMi Mei Fair W1 NEW £71
55 Curzon Street   020 3989 7777   3–3B
From Jamavar and Bombay Bustle creator Samyukta Nair (who studied in China), this September 2021 replacement to Matsya (RIP) is inspired by 1920s Shanghai and the three-floor restaurant is, apparently, inspired by a reimagination of the building as the secret London residence of Empress Mimi, which means 'secret' in Mandarin. Former Hakkasan chef Peter Ho oversees a high-end, modern Chinese menu, including wood-roasted Peking duck. For cocktails, head to The Moon Bar. / W1J 8PG; mimimeifair.com/; Mon-Sat 10.30 pm, Sun 10 pm.

Min Jiang,
The Royal Garden Hotel W8 £91 ４３５
2-24 Kensington High St   020 7361 1988   6–1A
The "excellent Chinese cuisine" – led by "exceptional and authentic Beijing duck" and "high-level dim sum" – makes nonsense of the usual rule that restaurants with spectacular views must be a rip off. On the 8th floor of the Royal Garden Hotel, with "fantastic vistas over Kensington Gardens and Hyde Park", this consistent performer has bounced back in our food ratings this year. Even its most ardent fans concede it's "not cheap", mind, but their overall estimation? – "wonderful!" / W8 4PT; www.minjiang.co.uk; @minjianglondon; Mon-Sun 10.30 pm.

Mint Leaf Lounge EC2 £66 ３３４
Angel Court, Lothbury   020 7600 0992   10–2C
Striking design and high-quality cuisine make it worth knowing about this nouvelle Indian cocktail lounge and restaurant, hidden away behind the Bank of England. / EC2R 7HB; www.mintleaflondon.com; @MintLeafLondon; Tue-Sat 11 pm; closed Sat L, closed Sun & Mon.

Mio Yatai E2 NEW £33
129a Pritchard's Road   020 7739 2540   14–2B
In Hackney's Broadway Market and next to the Regent's Canal, this Japanese street food and ramen bar opened in December 2019. It's smallish – 45 seats – mixing communal seating and some individual tables. Early reports suggest it's an OK standby – not enough feedback for a more hearty endorsement at this stage. / E2 9AP; mioyatai.co.uk; @mioyatai; Mon-Sun 10 pm.

Mirch Masala SW17 £26 ４２２
213 Upper Tooting Rd   020 8767 8638   11–2D
"Still one of the best curries on the high street" – this basic Pakistani canteen is one of the better bets on Tooting's curry corridor: in particular, "the grill items are delicious". / SW17 7TG; mirchmasala-takeaway.co.uk; Mon-Sun 10 pm; closed Mon-Thu L; cash only; No bookings.

Los Mochis W8 NEW £40
2 Farmer St   020 7727 5528   7–2B
On the site just off Notting Hill that was for over half a century Geales (RIP) – this new urban-grunge taqueria and tequileria hangout is the antithesis of the traditional English fish 'n' chips restaurant that preceded it, and opened post-lockdown in late Spring 2021. No survey feedback as yet on its funky sounding Mexican/Japanese menu, but in August 2021 The Daily Mail's Tom Parker Bowles was grudgingly impressed: "far better than expected…[for] good tacos and sashimi, cracking cocktails and a merry night out, you're very much in luck. Los Mochis is a blast". / W8; www.losmochis.co.uk; Sat, Tue-Fri midnight, Sun 10.30 pm; closed Mon.

Molly's Café E2 NEW
Museum of the Home, 1 Geffrye Street   020 8161 0501   14–2A
Although it's from the Anchor and Hope stable, this all-day operation near Hoxton tube is not a pub: it's a new café (opened May 2021) within the rebranded Geffrye Museum (which features exhibits on domestic living since 1600). On offer – breakfast, lunch and buns, and – in the fullness of time – a dinner service. / E2 8JH; www.mollys.cafe; Tue-Sun 5 pm; closed Tue-Sun D, closed Mon.

Momo W1   £84
25 Heddon Street   020 7434 4040   4–3B
Despite its über-glam past, Mourad Mazouz's party-Moroccan (which opened in 1997) is off-grid for most Londoners nowadays, attracted little feedback this year, and is still 'temporarily closed' as of September 2021, presumably due to the high proportion of out-of-towners amongst its customer-base. We've continued to include it, though, on the basis that we think it will return and – on a good night – it's a fab party scene with decent (if sometimes expensive) food. / W1B 4BH; www.momoresto.com; @momoresto; Mon-Sat 1 am, Sun midnight; credit card required to book.

Mon Plaisir Restaurant WC2   £58   3 3 4
19-21 Monmouth Street   020 7836 7243   5–2B
"London's oldest family-run French bistro never fails", and still offers a "quirkily traditional experience" 75 years after its launch in Covent Garden in the post-war era. It's "a bit dated", of course, but that's part of the appeal: "the cooking is good rather than exceptional – more Gallic comfort food than gastronomic", so "go for the classics, onion soup and steak frites". Top Tip: "great for pre- or post-theatre". / WC2H 9DD; www.monplaisir.co.uk; @MonPlaisir4; Tue-Sat 9.30 pm, Sun 4 pm; closed Sun D, closed Mon.

Mona Lisa SW10   £43   2 3 2
417 King's Rd   020 7376 5447   6–3B
"Excellent value, especially set meals" (at what feels like 1980s prices) mean this age old Italian greasy spoon in Chelsea has a wider constituency than you might imagine. / SW10 0LR; www.mona-lisa.business.site; Mon-Sat 4 pm, Sun 3 pm; closed Mon-Sun D; no Amex; Take bookings all week via phone and/or online.

Monmouth Coffee Company   £7   3 4 4
27 Monmouth St, WC2   020 7232 3010   5–2B
2 Park St, SE1   020 7232 3010   10–4C
"You can't beat the coffee from Monmouth", which is "still the best in town", agree the caffeine hounds who flock to the capital's most famous artisan coffee specialists. They rave about "top beans turned into wonderful coffee by talented baristas", who "seem to extract an extra level of flavour – I can only put it down to alchemy!" "Super-friendly staff and good pastries" complete the deal. Any downsides? – "shame about the queues" which are a permanent feature of both the long-established Soho and Borough Market venues and the newer Wednesday-Saturday Spa Terminus branch in Bermondsey. Top Tip: "don't miss the Sally Clarke truffles (great after an espresso)!" / www.monmouthcoffee.co.uk.

Morena SW1 NEW   £49
10-11 Eccleston Yards   020 3488 6490   2–4B
Caffeine aficionados should truffle out this all-day dining spot and coffee house from sisters Juliana and Valentina Beleno, who import green beans from their native Colombia and roast 'em themselves. It's a pleasant spot, too – for a snack or brunch on the likes of poke bowls and Latino-inspired salads – located in the attractive Eccleston Yards development. / SW1W 9AZ; morenalondon.com; Tue, Wed, Sun 5 pm, Thu-Sat 10 pm; closed Tue, Wed, Sun D, closed Mon.

Morito £50 3️⃣3️⃣4️⃣

195 Hackney Road, E2 020 7613 0754 14–2A
32 Exmouth Mkt, EC1 020 7278 7007 10–1A

"Keep the tapas coming" – *"top Spanish food"*, with North African inflections – say fans of this little bar in Exmouth Market, which *"still holds its own against its larger siblings"* – the original Moro a few doors away, and the Hackney Morito. Some punters rate it even higher: *"why go to Moro when Morito is just as good and cheaper?"*. *"The new extension at the back makes it easier to get a table"*, and *"they take young kids in their stride"*.

Moro EC1 £73 4️⃣3️⃣3️⃣

34-36 Exmouth Mkt 020 7833 8336 10–1A

"A firm favourite for years" – Sam & Sam Clark's Exmouth Market stalwart helped put the area on London's foodie map and maintains a huge fan club with its *"vibrant"* and *"deliciously spiced"* Spanish and Moroccan influenced dishes, *"alongside an excellent list of Spanish wines and sherries!"* That there's *"nothing poncy about the place"* is much of its enduring appeal, although *"what with all those hard surfaces, it's always a bit noisy"* (sometimes deafeningly so). There is a small minority who feel the experience here is *"not quite what it was"* in days gone by. Even they can feel it's *"still worth patronising"*, though, and most reporters would go much further – *"Every time I go, I vow to go more often!"* / EC1R 4QE; www.moro.co.uk; @RestaurantMoro; Mon-Sat midnight, Sun 2.15 pm; closed Sun D.

Morso £66 3️⃣3️⃣3️⃣

43 Chamberlayne Rd, NW10 020 8964 3939 1–2B NEW
130 Boundary Road, NW8 020 7624 7412 9–3A

"Useful neighbourhood restaurants" in St John's Wood and now Kensal Rise (since March 2020), consistently praised for *"very tasty Italian tapas"*. Both sites have seating outside.

Motcombs SW1 £65 2️⃣2️⃣4️⃣

26 Motcomb St 020 7235 6382 6–1D

As a *"fun and buzzy"* haunt, this long-established (since 1982) Belgravia bar/brasserie (ground floor) and dining room (basement) has a fair few fans. Some enjoy its *"low-lit and relaxing"* interior, whereas others feel it's *"best to sit outside"*. There's a wide ranging menu (from shepherd's pie to chicken gyozas via vodka penne) which no-one pretends is hugely foodie but which is generally well-reviewed. Breakfast is the meal most often tipped here. / SW1X 8JU; www.motcombs.co.uk; @Motcombs; Wed-Sun 9 pm.

Mr Bao SE15 £32 4️⃣3️⃣3️⃣

293 Rye Ln 020 7635 0325 1–4D

This *"lovely little Taiwanese local"* is the place to go in Peckham *"for delicious bao buns and dumplings"*. It is the six-year-old original from which founder Frank Yeung has spun out a small group, with offshoots in Tooting and Westfield Shepherd's Bush. / SE15 4UA; www.mrbao.co.uk; @MrBaoUK; Mon-Sun 10.30 pm; closed Mon-Wed L.

Mr Ji W1 NEW £15 3️⃣3️⃣2️⃣

72 Old Compton Street 020 7052 5770 4–2D

"A Taiwanese take on the fried chicken phenomenon, which comes with a punchy Sichuan kick" at Samuel Haim's heart-of-Soho haunt. After years in Camden selling street food, this bricks -and-mortar branch opened in late 2019, and has morphed into a more full-service offering (with a little help from the team behind cult favourite Ta Ta Eatery). The menu centres around the chicken, alongside a fun selection of trendy Asian snacks and small eats: chicken gizzards with cream cheese and Doritos anyone? It worked for Jay Rayner anyway: *"reasonably priced and well-executed"*. Reporters similarly feel it's *"fun"*, with *"so many things to choose"* and delivering *"excellent"* results. / W1D 4UN; mrji.co.uk; Tue-Sat 10.30 pm; closed Tue-Thu L, closed Sun & Mon; cards only; Credit card deposit required to book.

Munal Tandoori SW15 £31 4 4 2
393 Upper Richmond Road, Putney 020 8876 3083 11–2A
This "great-value local" Nepalese/Indian on the South Circular has performed sterling service for more than 30 years with its "generous" servings of excellent curry. Family-run, it has a strong following in the Putney-Barnes-Roehampton area. / SW15 5QL; www.munaltandoori.co.uk; Sun-Thu 10 pm, Fri & Sat 11 pm; closed Sun-Thu-Sat L.

Murano W1 £111 4 4 3
20-22 Queen St 020 7495 1127 3–3B
Angela Hartnett's popular Mayfair HQ put in an impressively steady performance in this year's survey, thanks to its "beautifully prepared and presented" cuisine – which comes at "relatively reasonable prices" for such a swanky address. Other pluspoints include very well-pitched service, and surroundings that, if low key, are very "calm and attractive". (Note – although the website says the menu 'is a reflection of Angela's upbringing cooking alongside her Italian grandmother and aunts', the actual dishes – though they do often nod to Italy – are actually in a fairly mainstream modern European mould). / W1J 5PP; www.muranolondon.com; @muranolondon; Mon-Sat 11 pm; closed Sun; Take bookings all week via phone and/or online.

Muse SW1 NEW £171 5 4 4
38 Groom Place 020 3301 2903 6–1D
"A welcome return by Tom Aikens" – his "bijou" new Belgravia HQ debuted in January 2020 and was the best high-end opening of the year. Occupying a slightly wackily converted Belgravia townhouse, it's very "cosy" with just 25 seats over two floors: six are at a counter on the ground floor overlooking the open kitchen and part of the entry lounge. As the name hints, culinary themes are inspired by musings on Tom's life and upbringing ("don't expect to recognise the dishes: eg 'Conquering the Beech Tree'"). In the evening, choose from a seven-course (£95) or 10-course (£145) tasting menu: at lunch there's also a three-course (£50) option. Results are "exceptional" ("even if the long background to each course is a bit OTT and risks being self-indulgent") delivering "genius", "light, fresh flavours" ("those looking for rich sauces and luxury ingredients will be disappointed"). And the experience is further enhanced by "an excellent sommelier, with a flair for wine pairings that enhance each course without a push for trophy wines that dominate the food". / SW1X 7BA; www.musebytomaikens.co.uk; @musebytomaikens; Tue-Sat 11 pm; closed Tue, Wed L, closed Sun & Mon; booking online only.

My Neighbours the Dumplings £32 3 2 2
165 Lower Clapton Road, E5 020 3327 1556 14–1B
179-180 Victoria Park Road, E9 020 3327 0447 14–2C NEW
In a good week, these East London dumpling haunts dispense upwards of 14,000 Asian pastry parcels to a hipster crowd. The original was in Clapton, with a second more grown-up branch near Victoria Park opening in late 2019. / www.myneighboursthedumplings.com; @my_neighbours.

Myrtle SW10 £75 5 4 3
1a Langton Street 020 7352 2411 6–3B
Dublin-born chef Anna Haugh is making waves with her "sophisticated" take on Irish cuisine at her two-year-old debut venture, in a "cosy" Chelsea townhouse near World's End. "This is truly a local restaurant with charm", and the Irish-inflected cooking displays some "distinctively original flair". It's named after Myrtle Allen, who launched modern Irish cuisine at Ballymaloe House in Co. Cork, and many key ingredients are sourced from Ireland. Top Tip: "try the warm marinated oyster". / SW10 0JL; www.myrtlerestaurant.com; @https://twitter.com/myrtlerest?lang=en-gb; Tue-Sat 10 pm; closed Sun & Mon.

Naifs SE15 NEW £41
56 Goldsmith Road   020 3490 2422   1–3D
Vegan and vegetarian neighbourhood bistro, set in a quiet street near Peckham Rye station. It was opened in autumn 2019 by ex-Vanilla Black chef Tom Heale (plus his two brothers and a business partner) and – though it's a simple, cosy venue – it quickly attracted favourable press from The Torygraph and Marina O'Loughlin in The Sunday Times. Sharing is encouraged and drinks include biodynamic, organic and vegan, and numerous fancy teas. / SE15 5TF; www.naifs.co.uk; Thu-Sat 11.30 pm; closed Thu-Sat L, closed Mon-Wed & Sun.

Nakanojo SW3 NEW
358 King's Rd   020 7349 5488   6–3C
This large (4,500 square feet) two-floor, summer 2021 newcomer occupies the site that used to be Busaba Chelsea (RIP). The Nikkei cuisine (Peruvian meets Japanese) is aiming for 'casual fine dining'. / SW3; Mon-Sat 12.30 am.

Nanban SW9 £40 4 2 2
426 Coldharbour Ln   020 7346 0098   11–2D
"Sink your teeth in and savour!" the "bold flavours" of former MasterChef winner Tim Anderson's take on Japanese cooking using foreign or 'barbarian' (Nanban) ingredients, showcased in his "fast and furious" 10-year-old pop-up-gone-permanent on the edge of Brixton Market. "Their noodle dishes became a lockdown delivery staple, packed with flavour, a wonderful smoky depth to the tea eggs, heart-warming broths". A new Covent Garden offshoot opened in September 2021 at Kerb's Seven Dials Market, focused on ramen dishes. / SW9 8LF; www.nanban.co.uk; @NanbanLondon; Tue-Fri, Mon, Sat 11 pm, Sun 10 pm; closed Mon L.

Nandine SE5 3 4 3
45 Camberwell Church Street   020 7703 3221   1–3C
"Worth trying for the interesting selection of Kurdish dishes", this "good-value" café in Camberwell shines a different light on Middle Eastern cuisine. Founder Pary Baban was forced from her home as a teenager by Saddam Hussein's forces in 1989, collecting recipes as she fled across Kurdistan. Nandine means kitchen in Kurdish; there's also Peckham Levels sibling. / SE5 8TR; @NandineUK; Sun-Thu 10.30 pm, Fri & Sat 11 pm; closed Mon-Fri L.

The Narrow E14 £62 2 2 3
44 Narrow St   020 7592 7950   12–1B
Inspiring views from a "wonderful location", perched on a bend of the Thames, justify an outing to Gordo's Limehouse pub – but why has such a prominent chef never managed to deliver consistently good cooking here? Granted, some reporters mention "lovely dining", but others rate it "average" or even "terrible (after OK meals in the past)". / E14 8DP; www.gordonramsayrestaurants.com/the-narrow; @thenarrow; Mon-Sat 11.30 pm, Sun 10.30 pm.

Native at Browns W1 NEW £75 5 4 3
Browns, 39 Brook Street   3–2B
"An absolute find in the middle of Mayfair!" Having just escaped Borough for Osea Island last year, Imogen Davis and Ivan Tisdall-Downes returned to London in April 2021 to set up this newcomer in the fashionable Browns store on Brook Street. Good move, as it's had utter raves from all and sundry for its "really brilliant food, with original food combinations" upholding the couple's zero-waste, ethical ethos featuring hyper-seasonal, freshly foraged dishes ("Ivan must spend every waking moment conjuring up new creations"). It helps that "Imogen is a terrific front of house" and that it has the benefit of a 40-seater courtyard (lovely for this bit of town and "a gift during semi-lockdown"). / W1K 4JE; www.brownsfashion.com/uk/services/native-at-browns; @eatnativeUK; Tue-Sun 10.30 pm.

Naughty Piglets SW2 — £50 — 4 4 4
28 Brixton Water Ln   020 7274 7796   11–2D

"A Brixton gem" – Joe Sharratt and Margaux Aubry's French-inspired small-plates venue "is a wonder", and wins plaudits across the board for "food, wine, service and vibe that are just unbeatable!" "What I love is that the menu doesn't constantly change – they're creating modern classics that will endure, especially the pork belly and the crab salad". "Margaux is a miracle of grace, enthusiasm and good taste" – "she keeps some of the most interesting drinks in town and she's got the gift of knowing how to translate one's vague ideas into actual glasses of loveliness and surprise". "Book well ahead as it is always crammed." (As at September 2021, the offshoot at Andrew Lloyd Webber's The Other Palace theatre in Victoria remains closed due to the pandemic.) / SW2 1PE; www.naughtypiglets.co.uk; @naughtypiglets; Tue-Sun 9 pm; closed Mon.

Nautilus NW6 — £42 — 3 3 2
27-29 Fortune Green Rd   020 7435 2532   1–1B

Known for its "beautiful fresh fish fried in matzo meal" – much lighter than traditional batter – this veteran West Hampstead chippy is "always full of regulars", many of whom suggest that "the fish 'n' chips are the best ever" here. "The dining room has been revamped during lockdown – much needed!" / NW6 1DU; Mon-Sat 10 pm, Sun 9 pm; no Amex.

Nebula Pizza E2 NEW — £26
455 Hackney Road   07950 380135   13–1D

A late 2020 arrival in Hackney – this new haunt bills itself as 'a neighbourhood oasis in east london'. It's a large space (200 covers), complete with bar made out of recycled materials and garden courtyard. Everything is 'curated' including the craft pizza. No survey feedback as yet, but the general social buzz about the place is a good one. / E2 9DY; nebulabar.com; Mon-Sun 11 pm.

NEST E9 NEW — £48 — 4 4 3
177 Morning Lane   020 8986 0065   14–1B

This intimate (just 7 tables) Hackney gem opened in 2018 and was inexplicably left out of our last edition. It certainly rates mention – chef and co-owner Johnnie Crowe (ex Harwood Arms and Anglo) delivers some delectable, small plates from a seasonal tasting menu. The endearing no-waste ethos incorporates a focus on a single meat for six weeks at a time. / E9 6LH; www.nestfood.co.uk; @nestfooduk; Tue-Sun 8.30 pm; closed Tue-Fri L, closed Mon.

Ngon W4 — £20 — 4 2 2
195 Chiswick High Road   020 8994 9630   8–2A

"Cheap 'n' cheerful but absolutely delicious Vietnamese street food" – "zinging bahn mi" and other "great, simple, freshly made" food, particularly the rice dishes – win lots of fans for this "basic" canteen: a "small, unassuming shop" that's easily missed in the middle of Chiswick's busy high street (opposite Waterstones). / W4 2DR; www.ngondeli.com; @ngondeli; Wed-Sat 11.30 pm.

1947 London W1 NEW — £80
33 Charlotte Street   020 7693 6290   2–1C

Chef Krishna Negi (who first made his name when he launched Tangawizi in Richmond in 2004) opened this Fitzrovian basement spot in October 2019, with a menu featuring 'nano plates' (small plates and sharing bowls) inspired by 1947's partition of India. Some initial reviews on its cuisine have been very upbeat. / W1T 1RR; www.1947london.com; Thu-Sun 11 pm; closed Thu-Sun L, closed Mon & Tue & Wed; Jacket required.

The Ninth London W1   £80   5 4 3
22 Charlotte Street   020 3019 0880   2–1C

Jun Tanaka's brilliant Mediterranean-inspired cooking is showcased at its best at his casual six-year-old HQ in Fitzrovia. It's "notably good value" for cooking of this "excellence" and "variety of flavours" – the sort of place you'll "definitely go back to again". Tanaka has done some TV but is relatively unsung – if he was a little better known, this place would be a household name. / W1T 2NB; www.theninthlondon.com; @theninthlondon; Mon-Sat 10 pm; closed Sun; No shorts; Take bookings all week via phone and/or online.

No 35 Mackenzie Walk E14 NEW   £54
29-35 Mackenzie Walk   020 8059 8881   12–1C

A marvellous waterside location, plus large terrace – in the heart of Canary Wharf overlooking Middle Dock – is a key strong point of this early 2020 newcomer. It's not a foodie hotspot, but a good-looking after-work rendezvous or somewhere to head to at weekends for a bottomless brunch. / E14 4AP; no35mackenziewalk.co.uk; Mon-Wed midnight, Thu-Sat 12.30 am, Sun 7 pm.

No. Fifty Cheyne SW3   £106   3 3 4
50 Cheyne Walk   020 7376 8787   6–3C

Chef Iain Smith oversees the open grill at this gorgeous Chelsea restaurant, by the river near Albert Bridge (which in recent times has become licensed as a wedding venue). Central to the casual British menu are simple. high-quality surf 'n' turf grills, but there are also more complex dishes: results are "very good, but a bit pricey". Don't miss the cute first floor 'Ruby' cocktail bar. / SW3 5LR; www.fiftycheyne.com; @50Cheyne; Wed-Sat 11 pm, Sun 4 pm; closed Wed & Thu L closed Sun D, closed Mon & Tue.

Noble Rot WC1   £75   3 5 5
51 Lamb's Conduit St   020 7242 8963   2–1D

"Such a special place" – Mark Andrew and Daniel Keeling's Bloomsbury five-year-old entered diners' Top 20 most-mentioned restaurants in our survey for the first time this year. "You come here more for the wine than food (although we love both)" – "a visit allows you to meander through one of the most adventurous and imaginative lists" in town: "a real wonder, with some extraordinary wines by the glass, and passionate and knowledgeable staff who heighten the experience". (Not coincidentally, Mark is an MW, and they publish a wine mag of the same name). By comparison, "the excellent ingredient-focused cooking" can almost become "a sideshow". Further anchoring the experience is the "delightful location on Lamb's Conduit Street", and the "very atmospheric" site they inherited from the ancient 1970s wine bar Vats (long RIP). Thus, "it feels like a 'real' restaurant, untouched by an expensive corporate interior designer". "The bill adds up but meals at this place are always a pleasure" – "a perfect combination of warmth and style". See also Noble Rot Soho. / WC1N 3NB; www.noblerot.co.uk; @noblerotbar; Mon-Sat 9.30 pm; closed Sun; Take bookings all week via phone and/or online.

Noble Rot Soho W1 NEW   £59   4 4 5
2 Greek Street   020 7183 8190   5–2A

"An admirable replacement for the Gay Hussar and a great sibling to the original Noble Rot" – this legendary Soho site (founded as the Gay Hussar in 1953, and closed in 2018) has been rejuvenated by Dan Keeling and Mark Andrew and re-opened in September 2020. Even in its heyday, the point of a meal here was to polish off a conspiratorial bottle of wine or two, rather than critiquing its stodgy Hungarian scoff. So its resurrection by a wine-focussed group feels like a true continuation of its former spirit and "there is no end to exploring the wine list" which recreates the excellence of the first Noble Rot; as does its "warm, knowledgeable and impressively passionate service". The interior was always "really lovely" and retains its still old-fashioned looks, with dark wood-panelling and cartoons from Martin Rowson. Meanwhile "the food quality has been transformed for the better" (thank heavens!) with chef Paul Weaver (aided by input from The

Sportsman's Stephen Harris) "maintaining a more-than-respectful nod to the past" by including the odd Mitteleuropean note in what's essentially a hearty, modern European menu. "Love it!" / W1D 4NB; noblerot.co.uk; @noblerotbar; Mon-Sat 9.30 pm; closed Sun.

Nobu,
Metropolitan Hotel W1 £99 4 3 3
19 Old Park Ln   020 7447 4747   3–4A
"It's been a rockstar forever!!!!", according to dedicated fans of this still-famous haunt (where Boris Becker became a father in a broom cupboard back in the day). London's original Nikkei venture sits on a stylishly minimal first floor overlooking Park Lane and is the best-rated member of the group nowadays. Perhaps, when the going gets tough, the tough get going, as its ratings strengthened notably this year, winning praise for "very delicate and finely balanced" Japanese-Peruvian dishes of a quality and value closer to when it first opened. The environment is "very noisy, not helped by the loud music and hard surfaces"… but, for diehards, that's the whole point. / W1K 1LB; www.noburestaurants.com; @NobuOldParkLane; Sun-Wed 10 pm, Thu-Sat 10.30 pm.

Nobu Portman Square W1 NEW £99 3 2 2
22 Portman Square   020 3988 5888   2–1A
Almost as soon as the Berkeley Street branch of Nobu shut, the luxury brand opened its second London hotel (with 249 rooms) in December 2020: this time on the corner of Portman Square (in a swankily refurbished former Radisson Blu). Selling points include a soaring entrance hall, its bar with outside terrace, and one of its famous restaurants. Early reports ("still brilliant", "stylish, overpriced, but lovely") cast it in the same good-but-pricey mould as its stablemates, for wizard Japanese-fusion delicacies (black cod, yada yada). Initial support for the ambience and service, though, is lukewarm. / W1H 7BG; london-portman.nobuhotels.com; @NobuRestaurants; Sun-Thu 10 pm, Fri & Sat 10.30 pm.

Nobu Shoreditch EC2 £99
10-50 Willow St   020 3818 3790   13–1B
Still establishing itself pre-pandemic, this svelte Shoreditch Hotel – whose big, high-ceilinged Japanese-inspired dining room is in the basement, looking out onto a stylish, sunken garden – has never fully reached its stride, although it did inspire the odd "brilliant" report. As of September 2021, the hotel has yet to re-open post lockdown and its website reads: "we expect to reopen in late 2021. Please continue to visit our site for updates". / EC2A 4BH; www.nobuhotelshoreditch.com; @NobuShoreditch; Sun & Mon 10.45 pm, Tue-Sat midnight.

Noizé W1 £92 4 5 3
39 Whitfield St   020 7323 1310   2–1C
"This corner of Fitzrovia is a must-visit if you enjoy fine and very well-priced wine", also accompanied by "superb French cooking". Owner Mathieu Germond (former manager of Pied à Terre) is "a great host", who provides "absolutely stellar service". He named the venture after his grandparents' village in the Loire Valley, and makes it "feel like a local restaurant even though it's in central London". / W1T 2SF; www.noize-restaurant.co.uk; @NoizeRestaurant; Wed-Fri, Tue, Sat 10 pm; closed Tue, Sat L, closed Sun & Mon; Take bookings all week via phone and/or online.

NoMad London WC2 NEW £77 3 3 5
4 Bow Street   020 3906 1600   5–2D
"Shot to the top of my romantic list!" – the Grade-II-listed former home of
Bow Street Magistrates' Court and Police Station provides a magisterial –
very London – background to this outpost of a hip NYC hotel. It was
originally scheduled to open in 2020, but finally opened its doors in May
2021. Its main restaurant sits inside a stunning three-storey, glass-ceilinged
atrium complete with "hanging lanterns and lush greenery" – a "beautiful"
space that creates an "exciting and very intimate" ambience. NYC chef
Daniel Humm was originally linked with the project but is no longer
mentioned on the website. The food somewhat plays second fiddle to all the
electricity of the backdrop, but early feedback suggests it's more than an
afterthought. (Another option here is 'Side Hustle' – NoMad's take on a
British pub serving Mexican sharing plates – plus a cocktail bar and a
guests-only library bar.) / WC2E 7AH; www.thenomadhotel.com/london/;
@NomadLondon; Mon-Sat 10.30 pm, Sun 5 pm; closed Mon-Fri L closed Sun D.

The Nook N1 NEW £62
220 St Paul's Road   020 7288 2929   9–2D
*It's a bit less nook-like than it looks, if you head to the larger basement of
this summer 2020 Highbury newcomer: a deli by day and neighbourhood
café in the evenings. With a vague connection to Linden Stores (RIP), which it
replaced in 2020, there's a Turkish twist to the contemporary European
small dishes and sharing plates. Limited early feedback, but very positive all-
round.* / N1; thenooklondon.co.uk; Wed-Sat 11 pm, Sun 6 pm; closed Sun D, closed
Mon & Tue; cards only.

Noor Jahan £52 3 3 2
2a Bina Gdns, SW5   020 7373 6522   6–2B
26 Sussex Pl, W2   020 7402 2332   7–1D
"Been a dedicated customer of the Noor for 40 years" – this "classic, old-
style" curry house has served "very tasty Indian food" to a loyal clientele on
the Earl's Court-South Ken border since 1964. To regulars (and the
occasional sleb, from Eric Clapton to Gwyneth Paltrow), it makes "the perfect
Sunday evening meal, for comfort food". It has a younger offshoot in
Bayswater. Top Tip: "the food can come very fast, so best to stagger the
order".

Nopi W1 £77 4 4 3
21-22 Warwick St   020 7494 9584   4–3B
The "delicious and unusual food combinations" – an "outstanding and very
different" interpretation of Middle Eastern/Asian cuisines – win general
applause for Israeli chef and food writer Yotam Ottolenghi's Soho restaurant,
the flagship of the self-named group he launched exactly 20 years ago. The
wine list is equally unusual, and the staff notably "charming". / W1B 5NE;
ottolenghi.co.uk/restaurants; @ottolenghi; Mon-Sat 10.30 pm; closed Sun.

Nordic Bakery W1 £14 3 3 2
14a Golden Sq   020 3230 1077   4–3C
"Still turning out wonderful cinnamon buns and coffee" along with some
"excellent Scandi sandwiches", this Nordic fixture in Soho remains "well
worth a visit". / W1F 9JG; www.nordicbakery.com; Sun-Fri 7 pm, Sat 8 pm; no Amex;
no booking.

The Norfolk Arms WC1 £48 3 3 3
28 Leigh St   020 7388 3937   9–4C
*In a sidestreet near King's Cross, this very regular-looking pub is known for its
surprisingly wide selection of tapas from around the Med. Fans say, "they've
tightened the menu in recent times, but some of the dishes are out of this
world!"* / WC1H 9EP; www.norfolkarms.co.uk; Mon-Sat 11 pm; closed Sun; no Amex.

Norma W1   £74   3 4 4
8 Charlotte Street   0203 995 6224   2–1C
"A beautiful restaurant with equally beautiful food!" – the Stafford Hotel's
first 'extra-curricular' venture in late 2019 has created an impressive all-
rounder. In the *"intimate"* setting of a Fitzrovia townhouse, *"delightful"* staff
provide dishes either from *"an attractive seafood array"* or from a menu of
Italian small plates, focused on Sicily. One or two reporters feel results are
"nice but nothing amazing", but more numerous are those who say the food
is *"super tasty"* and *"absolutely fabulous"*. / W1T 2LS; www.normalondon.com/;
@Norma_ldn; Mon-Sat 10.30 pm; closed Sun.

Normah's W2   £15   4 3 2
23-25 Queensway Market   07771 630828   7–2C
A superb cheap eat, unexpectedly tucked away in a (slightly downbeat) small
Bayswater shopping mall – Normah Abd Hamid's friendly small café offers
superior quality Malaysian home cooking at bargain basement prices. We all
owe the website Eater a favour for putting the place on the map! / W2 4QP;
www.normahs.co.uk; @Norma_ldn; Tue-Sat 9 pm; closed Tue-Sat L, closed Sun & Mon.

North China W3   £48   4 3 3
305 Uxbridge Rd   020 8992 9183   8–1A
"Authentic Hong Kong grub" makes the Lou family's 45-year veteran
possibly the *"best Chinese in west London"* – certainly the best this far out,
in the suburbs of Acton. Current owner Lawrence Lou has been involved
since he was a child, and his father Heng Sun, known as 'Chef Lou', still
makes his presence felt in his 80s – all of which shows in the care with
which they present their northern Chinese cuisine. / W3 9QU;
www.northchina.co.uk; @NorthChinaRest; Tue-Sun 10.30 pm; closed Mon.

North Sea Fish WC1   £51   3 3 2
7-8 Leigh St   020 7387 5892   9–4C
This Bloomsbury chippy with *"very high standards"* has been run by the
Beauchamp family for 45 years, and is listed on the 'Knowledge' test
required to be a London black cab driver. Ten varieties of fresh fish are
delivered every morning, and there's a good choice of traditional English
puddings. *"The ambience is a bit dated and it can be a tourist trap – but on
a Friday lunchtime you can't beat this place"*. / WC1H 9EW;
www.northseafishrestaurant.co.uk; @TheNorthSeaFish; Tue-Sat 9.30 pm; closed
Sun & Mon.

Novikov (Asian restaurant) W1   £116   3 3 4
50a Berkeley Street   020 7399 4330   3–3C
"Top buzz and people watching" are undoubtedly the highlight of a visit to
this oligarch playground in Mayfair, run by Russian restaurateur, Arkady
Novikov. If you are budget conscious, a visit is madness, but – particularly if
you like the scene – it offers a *"very expensive but very good Russian take
on Japanese cuisine"*, plus other pan-Asian bites, grills and noodles.
/ W1J 8HA; www.novikovrestaurant.co.uk; @NovikovLondon; Mon-Sun midnight; No
trainers; Take bookings all week via phone and/or online.

Novikov (Italian restaurant) W1   £125   2 2 2
50a Berkeley St   020 7399 4330   3–3C
Navigate through the pan-Asian section of Russian restaurateur Arkady
Novikov's ultra-luxe Mayfair scene, and you find an elegant if slightly
incongruous classic Italian dining room at the rear. Key themes that emerge
in survey feedback: it's notably *"overpriced"*; the food's not bad; and for a
business encounter, it's worth considering. / W1J 8HA;
www.novikovrestaurant.co.uk; @NovikovLondon; Mon-Wed midnight, Thu-Sat
12.30 am, Sun 11 pm.

Nue Ground SW4 NEW £30
32 Abbeville Road   020 7525 9030   11–2D
"Super neighbourhood spot that balances being cool with being welcoming" – this all-day café bar in Clapham (same owners as WC), promotes an ethos promising 'a conscious effort towards quality coffee, healthy food, lifestyle and environment'. Early reports suggest it lives up to its aims, with excellent brews and "interesting and varied food options with an Australian twist, in a friendly, bright setting with a lovely courtyard". / SW4 9NG; www.nueground.co.uk; Tue-Sat 11.30 pm, Sun & Mon 4 pm; closed Sun & Mon D; cards only.

Numero Uno SW11 £45   3️⃣2️⃣3️⃣
139 Northcote Rd   020 7978 5837   11–2C
Providing sterling service to the families of Battersea's 'Nappy Valley' for the best part of 30 years, this "good local Italian" remains "very busy". Don't expect culinary pyrotechnics, but the cooking "has maintained a steady quality". / SW11 6PX; Wed-Fri 11 pm, Sat midnight, Sun 7 pm; no Amex.

Nusr-Et Steakhouse SW1 £175
The Park Tower, 101 Knightsbridge   01821 687738   6–1D
Istanbul, Dubai, Doha, New York, Miami… finally – having been first announced in 2017 – London now has its very own outpost for the globe-trotting brand of Nusret Gökçe's (aka Salt Bae's) social media sensation. He is The Park Tower hotel's answer to breathing life into the formerly deathly dull-looking space that was for many years the accomplished but un-Instagram-friendly One-O-One (RIP). A butcher-turned-chef, this is not first choice for vegans, with a menu extending to every variety of chop, burger and steak (some gold-plated for maximum conspicuous consumption). Early press feedback has not been kind. Despite eating a 'shockingly good' steak, Jimi Famurewa for The Standard branded it as 'wasteful masochism' to visit a 'vibeless business lounge' that's 'really quite boring' given the 'gleeful robbery of the prices' – not least the menu's 'pointlessly gilded items (not just an £830 version of the notorious tomahawk but a £50 cappuccino).' / SW1X 7RN; www.nusr-et.com.tr/en/home.aspx.

Nutbourne SW11 £68   2️⃣2️⃣2️⃣
29 Ransomes Dock, 35-37 Parkgate Rd   020 7350 0555   6–4C
A lovely canalside location near the Thames adds to the appeal of this Battersea fixture, nowadays run as part of the Gladwin brothers' farm-to-fork empire, and named for the family's Sussex vineyard. Limited and disappointing feedback this year, though – including on its modern British dishes – hopefully, post pandemic, things will be on the up. / SW11 4NP; www.nutbourne-restaurant.com; @NutbourneSW11; Wed & Thu 10.30 pm, Fri & Sat 10 pm, Sun 8 pm; closed Wed & Thu L, closed Mon & Tue.

Nutshell WC2 £65   3️⃣2️⃣2️⃣
30 Saint Martin's Lane   020 3409 7926   5–4C
"Precisely made and imaginative" new-wave Iranian cuisine at "reasonable prices" makes Mohammad and Marwa Paknejad's two-year-old an intriguing option for diners in the heart of the West End's theatreland. The name is a reference to Tehran-born Mohammad's family pistachio orchards, and the site is split over two floors and features an open kitchen with some counter-style seating. "It was good to see Armenian wine on the list – it went well with the food." / WC2N 4ER; nutshelllondon.co.uk; @NutshellLondon; Tue-Sun 9.30 pm; closed Mon.

O'ver £57   3️⃣3️⃣3️⃣
1 Norris Street, St James's Market, SW1   020 7930 9664   4–4D
44-46 Southwark Street, SE1   020 7378 9933   10–4B
"Some really delicious Italian food using very good ingredients and a stylish, if low key, venue" – that's the deal at this Neapolitan duo in Borough and the St James's Market development. Pizza – using seawater in the dough – is a staple of the menu which also extends to pasta and other fare. / www.overuk.com.

Oak £66 323

243 Goldhawk Rd, W12   020 8741 7700   8–1B
137 Westbourne Park Rd, W2   020 7221 3355   7–1B
39 Parkgate Road, SW11   020 7924 3999   6–4C

"Delicious pizzas" backed up by a starter-heavy Mediterranean menu ensure things stay "busy" at west London's Oak trio – stylish pub conversions in Notting Hill and Shepherd's Bush, with a modern bistro on the river at Battersea (plus the same group's Bird in Hand gastroboozer at Brook Green). There's generally a "good atmosphere", too.

Oblix SE1 £123 213

Level 32, The Shard, 31 St. Thomas Street   020 7268 6700   10–4C

"It should be excellent", but there were too many ropey reviews this year of this spectacularly located 32nd floor eatery, owned by Rainer Becker (of Zuma and Roka fame). Gripes are not that its luxurious grills, steaks, raw dishes and seafood are poor – it's that they are "much too expensive" and that "service makes you feel like a number" rather than an individual. / SE1 9RY; www.oblixrestaurant.com; @OblixRestaurant; Mon-Fri 11 pm; closed Mon-Fri L, closed Sat & Sun; booking max 6 may apply.

Odette's NW1 £77 333

130 Regents Park Road   020 7586 8569   9–3B

This Primrose Hill veteran of 40-plus years may not be "revolutionary", but it is much more than a "reliable and friendly neighbourhood local" under acclaimed chef-patron Bryn Williams, the owner for almost 15 years. Strengths include the "reinstated tasting menu", a list full of "intriguing wines", and excellent ingredients that include produce from the Williams family farm in Wales. Service is "friendly and attentive", and it offers "excellent value for money". / NW1 8XL; www.odettesprimrosehill.com; @Odettes_rest; Wed-Sun 9.30 pm; closed Mon & Tue.

Ognisko Restaurant SW7 £59 335

55 Prince's Gate, Exhibition Road   020 7589 0101   6–1C

"Stylish, high-ceilinged and opulent" – the marvellous period dining room of the Polish Hearth Club (an émigré haunt in South Kensington) serves "well-cooked Polish specialities" alongside a selection of "extraordinary vodka", all overseen by Jan Woroniecki. It's just "a stone's throw from the Royal Albert Hall" and the museums, "so perfect for a relaxing meal in sumptuous surroundings" during cultural outings, all at a very surprisingly reasonable price. The "peaceful terrace" is particularly recommended in this bit of town – and is now covered and heated in chilly weather. / SW7 2PG; www.ogniskorestaurant.co.uk; @OgniskoRest; Mon-Sat 11.15 pm, Sun 10.30 pm; No trainers.

Oka £53 322

Kingly Court, 1 Kingly Court, W1   020 7734 3556   4–2B
19 New Cavendish Street, W1   020 7486 4388   2–1B
251 King's Road, SW3   020 7349 8725   6–3C
71 Regents Park Rd, NW1   020 7483 2072   9–3B
88 Church Road, SW13   020 8741 8577   11–1A

"Consistently good food from an appealing menu" has earned a solid following for this Asian-fusion chain with branches in Soho, Marylebone, Primrose Hill, Chelsea and Barnes. Opinion is split on the relative merits of its two main offerings – all agree on the "terrific sushi" but others register both pros and cons for the hot dishes. / www.okarestaurant.co.uk.

Oklava EC2 £74 443

74 Luke St   020 7729 3032   13–1B

Selin Kiazim's "incredible" Turkish-Cypriot cooking "delivers every time" at her six-year-old Shoreditch venture, and is "paired with a great list of Turkish wines" by Laura Christie, who runs the front of house. The pair's spin-off in Fitzrovia, first called Kyseri and later Oklava Bakery & Wine, closed down in 2020. / EC2A 4PY; www.oklava.co.uk; @OKLAVA_LDN; Fri & Sat, Tue-Thu 10 pm; closed Tue-Thu L, closed Sun & Mon; cards only; booking max 6 may apply.

Oliveto SW1 £70 4️⃣3️⃣2️⃣
49 Elizabeth Street   020 7730 0074   2–4A
This long-standing Belgravia Sardinian keeps its many regulars happy with some of the "best pizzas in London", and other dishes made with "fantastic, simple, fresh ingredients". There's also an interesting selection of Sardinian wines, including magnums. Top Tip: "always have the special of the day. They're delicious". / SW1W 9PP; www.olivorestaurants.com/oliveto; @OlivoGroup; Mon-Sun 10.30 pm; Take bookings all week via phone and/or online.

Olivo SW1 £79 3️⃣3️⃣2️⃣
21 Eccleston Street   020 7730 2505   2–4B
"Rustic Sardinian food comes to moneyed Belgravia" at the original of Mauro Sanna's four nearby ventures in the area, which serves "a perfect choice of excellent seafood, regional dishes and pasta". Charming service helps overcome his penchant for slightly "soulless" interiors. And if the bill might shock a Sardinian, it is not outrageous by local standards. / SW1W 9LX; www.olivorestaurants.com; @OlivoGroup; Mon-Sun 10.30 pm; closed Sat & Sun L.

Olivocarne SW1 £86 3️⃣3️⃣2️⃣
61 Elizabeth St   020 7730 7997   2–4A
The meat specialist in Mauro Sanna's upscale (read "pricey") Sardinian group scattered across Belgravia celebrates its tenth anniversary this year. Its steaks and Sardinian-style slow-roast suckling pig are "excellent", while its red-blooded clientele have access to Joe's, the in-house members' bar, and to a heated terrace to enjoy a post-prandial cigar. / SW1W 9PP; www.olivorestaurants.com; Sun-Fri 10.30 pm, Sat 11 pm.

Olivomare SW1 £83 3️⃣3️⃣2️⃣
10 Lower Belgrave St   020 7730 9022   2–4B
This smart modern Sardinian seafood specialist in Belgravia is "always busy", thanks to its "good fresh fish" and "bright service". Part of the Olivo group, it was opened in 2007 by Mauro Sanno, who arrived in London 30 years earlier with the aim of studying architecture – which might explain the restaurant's decidedly non-rustic interior. / SW1W 0LJ; www.olivorestaurants.com; @OlivoGroup; Tue-Sun 10.30 pm; closed Mon; booking max 10 may apply.

Olley's SE24 £37 3️⃣4️⃣3️⃣
65-69 Norwood Rd   020 8671 8259   11–2D
This "relaxed" chippy in a "lovely location by Brockwell Park" provides a "great range of fish and a variety of ways to cook it" – fried, grilled or steamed with various garnishes. Harry Niazi has run it for 35 years, garnering a strong reputation in Herne Hill and beyond. / SE24 9AA; www.olleys.info; @olleysfishexp; Tue-Sun 9.30 pm; closed Mon; no Amex.

**Olympic,
Olympic Studios SW13** £54 2️⃣2️⃣3️⃣
117-123 Church Road   020 8912 5170   11–1A
"Brunch takes some beating" at this casual all-day brasserie, which is attached to the legendary recording studios-turned-indie cinema that has become a favoured hangout amongst well-heeled Barnes residents. It has a "great terraced outdoor area" and the "members-only bar is uber-cool". "Afternoon tea with all the trimmings looks very good and tastes ... almost as good as it looks" – while the main menu "almost never changes, and is a bit boring". / SW13 9HL; www.olympiccinema.co.uk; Sun-Thu 10 pm, Fri & Sat midnight; cards only.

Olympus Fish N3 £38 **3** **4** **2**
140-144 Ballards Ln 020 8371 8666 1–1B
"Very fresh fish with crispy batter and great chips" is just what you want
from a *"good local chippy"* – and just what you get at this Turkish-run outfit
in Finchley, which has just celebrated its 21st anniversary. *"We've been
patrons since it first opened, and the service is attentive and friendly"* – and
certainly exceeds chippy norms in the restaurant, where there's a range of
mezze and other starters, the option of charcoal-grilled fish, and even
tablecloths. / N3 2PA; www.olympusrestaurant.co.uk; @Olympus_London; Mon-Sun
10 pm.

On The Bab £40 **3** **2** **2**
305 Old St, EC1 020 7683 0361 13–1B
9 Ludgate Broadway, EC4 020 7248 8777 10–2A
"Top Korean street/junk food", say fans of Linda Lee's K-pop-styled pit stops,
known for their funky fried chicken and other luridly flavoured bites. In the
second half of 2021, she closed her Covent Garden branch, leaving just
Shoreditch and St Pauls open, but north London and Nine Elms branches
are coming soon apparently. / onthebab.co.uk; @onthebab.

108 Brasserie W1 £67 **3** **2** **3**
108 Marylebone Ln 020 7969 3900 2–1A
This *"chic casual brasserie"* – *"in a very convenient Marylebone location"* –
rates well for its *"fresh and seriously tasty food"*. *"Dining on the terrace on a
sunny evening evokes a European brasserie where everything is done well"*
(although *"prices are distinctly W1"*). / W1U 2QE; www.108brasserie.com;
@108Marylebone; Mon-Sat 9.45 pm, Sun 4.45 pm; closed Sun D; Take bookings all
week via phone and/or online.

104 Restaurant W2 £93 **4** **4** **3**
104a Chepstow Road 020 3417 4744 7–1B
Less feedback than we'd like on this tiny, 14-seat venture on the fringes of
Notting Hill, perhaps reflecting its small size and the disrupted nature of the
last year. Such as we have, though, is uniformly highly complimentary about
its ambitious cuisine from chef-patron Richard Wilkins with luxury
ingredients such as Wagyu beef and truffle typical features of a menu.
Service led by front-of-house Matt Hough also gets a thumbs-up.
Heavyweight wine list, too, reflecting its gastronomic aims – it starts
inexpensively, but go for the top vintages and you could spend over £1,000!
/ W2 5QS; www.104restaurant.com; Wed-Sun 9.30 pm; closed Wed-Fri L, closed
Mon & Tue.

101 Thai Kitchen W6 £42 **3** **1** **2**
352 King St 020 8746 6888 8–2B
*"Uncompromising and authentic northern Thai cooking that pulls no
punches in terms of chilli heat and flavour"* is the draw to this *"basic, no-
frills"* family canteen near Stamford Brook Tube that has attracted a cult
following. The Isaan dishes from northwest Thailand are complemented by
southern Thai seafood by 'Auntie Bee', offering a remarkably wide range of
cuisines. *"Very tasty but a bit limited with its portions, which partly accounts
for its very reasonable prices"*. / W6 0RX; Sun-Thu 10.30 pm, Fri & Sat 11 pm;
no Amex.

116 at the Athenaeum W1 **NEW** £64 **2** **4** **2**
Athenaeum Hotel, 116 Piccadilly 020 7499 3464 3–4B
FKA Galvin at the Athenaeum, this gracious Piccadilly hotel dining room was
formatted and rebranded over the pandemic period. Few reports on the new
regime as yet, but it's not as pricey as many top London hotels despite its
prime location – perhaps try it out for its fine selection of afternoon teas,
with vegan, gluten-free, savoury and 'free flowing Prosecco' options. / W1;
www.athenaeumhotel.com; @theathenaeum; Mon-Sun 10.30 pm.

One Hundred Shoreditch E1 NEW
100 Shoreditch High Street   020 7613 9800   13–1B

Hipster haunt, Ace Hotel Shoreditch – and its restaurant Hoi Polloi (RIP) – have gone, but this new Lore Group (Sea Containers et al) opening in autumn 2021 is stepping into its boots and aiming to boost appeal with an expanded rooftop bar and terrace (panoramic views of East London), and a restaurant and wine bar specialising in sustainably sourced seafood. It being EC2, there's even going to be a take-out hatch (that's a sign of groovy sophistication these days, apparently…) / E1; www.onehundredshoreditch.com; Mon-Sat 1 am, Sun 11 pm.

1 Lombard Street EC3   £67   222
1 Lombard St   020 7929 6611   10–3C

"Very useful for City business lunches" – former financier, Soren Jessen's "buzzy, well-spaced" converted banking hall, near Bank station, has been a well-known linchpin of expense accounter life in the Square Mile for the last two decades ("you see everyone if you lunch here"), with the option of eating in the less formal brasserie or more formal restaurant, depending on how overtly you are wooing the client. The "reliable" menu "is a mix of classics, holding something for everyone. They understand that business is business and staff know how to handle service to accommodate that". / EC3V 9AA; www.1lombardstreet.com; @1LombardStreet; Mon-Sat midnight; closed Sun; booking max 10 may apply.

123V W1 NEW   £57   442
Fenwick, 63 New Bond Street   020 8132 9088   3–2B

"Outstanding fast-casual vegan food" has won instant acclaim for star Gallic chef and vegan pioneer, Alexis Gauthier's latest venture – a "super-friendly" vegan cafeteria that's part of Fenwick in Mayfair – which opened in April 2021, first on their pavement terrace, and then also in the basement. It serves simple staples (salads, burgers) alongside a slightly more ambitious prix-fixe menu and sushi from a dedicated counter: "although it's entirely vegan, frankly, you would not realise it: the flavours he gets from vegetables are amazing!" / W1S 1RQ; 123vegan.co.uk; @123vegan_w1; Mon-Sun 8 pm; cards only.

Only Food and Courses SW9 NEW   £72
Pop Brixton, 49 Brixton Station Road   11–1D

'You've never seen fine dining like this!' is the claim at this new 28-seater amidst Pop Brixton's containers, which first opened in December 2020 and which has its sights on a London high-street opening (originally earmarked for summer 2021). It's a novel formula for sure, with decor modelled on a classic greasy spoon. But former Shard and Chelsea FC chef, Robbie Lorraine's 'brilliantly cheeky twist on classic British food' (their words) is certainly an upscale one (crab Scotch eggs, duck éclairs, lobster doughnuts) and comes complete with 'cocktails raided from your mum's drinks cabinet'. In the evening, there's a six-course tasting menu format. / SW9 8PQ; www.onlyfoodandcourses.co.uk; @Foodandcourses; Fri & Sat, Thu 11 pm, Sun 5 pm; closed Thu L closed Sun D, closed Mon & Tue & Wed; booking online only.

Les 110 de Taillevent W1   £88   333
16 Cavendish Square   020 3141 6016   3–1B

"The clue is in the name – they really do offer 110 wines by the glass (au homage to the Coravin wine storage system) with a menu designed to pair with this vast selection", at this spin-off from Paris's famous Taillevent group, which occupies a smartly appointed dining room on Cavendish Square. The vintages themselves are carefully selected and this is one of the most interesting destinations for taking a wine-lover in town. Perhaps inevitably, it sometimes feels like the seasonal French cuisine "is playing catch-up with the wines", but most reporters this year felt it "was rather good too!" / W1G 9DD; www.les-110-taillevent-london.com; @110London; Tue-Sat 10.30 pm; closed Tue-Sat L, closed Sun & Mon; Credit card deposit required to book.

F S A

Opera Tavern WC2   £53   3|3|3
23 Catherine Street   020 7836 3680   5–3D
"Excellent tapas" – "served in a refurbished traditional pub", "with a relaxed atmosphere" – makes this Spanish-Italian, small-plates venue on two storeys a useful address in Covent Garden. Part of the Salt Yard chain, it was revamped to good effect following a change of ownership three years ago. / WC2B 5JS; www.saltyardgroup.co.uk/opera-tavern; @saltyardgroup; Mon-Sat 11 pm; closed Sun.

Opso W1   £77   3|2|2
10 Paddington St   020 7487 5088   2–1A
"Modern versions of moussaka and other Greek classics", backed up by a "wide range of Greek wines", are the attraction at this Marylebone venture from the Modern Greek Food Group, who also run the Funky Gourmet restaurant in Athens and have an Opso franchise in Dubai. The food is by all accounts "very tasty" – but decidedly "pricey". / W1U 5QL; www.opso.co.uk; @OPSO_london; Mon-Sat 11.30 pm, Sun 11 pm.

The Orange SW1   £59   2|2|3
37 Pimlico Rd   020 7881 9844   6–2D
Useful to know about in a pretty square on the Chelsea-Pimlico border, this rustic-chic gastropub serves up "reliable" wood-fired pizzas as well as a decent range of standard pub classics. / SW1W 8NE; www.theorange.co.uk; @theorangesw1; Mon-Thu 11.30 pm, Fri & Sat midnight, Sun 10.30 pm; closed Mon & Tue L.

Orange Pekoe SW13   £37   3|3|4
3 White Hart Ln   020 8876 6070   11–1A
This "friendly neighbourhood coffee shop" in riverside Barnes attracts visitors from across London for its popular afternoon teas (booking recommended), "with an outstanding selection of brews and freshly made sandwiches and cakes". "Their lunches are great, too". Top Tip: "the Oreo brownie is a standout". / SW13 0PX; www.orangepekoeteas.com; @OrangePekoeTeas; Mon-Sun 5 pm; closed Mon-Sun D.

Orasay W11   £59   5|4|4
31 Kensington Park Road   020 7043 1400   7–1A
"Outstanding fish and seafood" form the backbone of the menu at this Notting Hill two-year-old that celebrates the Hebridean island that supplies the name – where chef Jackson Boxer (of Brunswick House in Vauxhall) spent his childhood summers. The food is "delivered with great consistency" and there's a "short but interesting wine list, too". There's a danger of the place being "over-hyped" – but Boxer brings it off and provides "a nice change from the surrounding Italianesque and fusion hangouts". Top Tip: "Béarnaise sauce worth eating on its own" (but you may have to order one of the "fab steaks" to get a taste). / W11 2EU; orasay.london; @Jackson_Boxer; Tue-Sat 11 pm; closed Tue-Thu L, closed Sun & Mon.

Oren E8 NEW   £64   4|2|2
89 Shacklewell Lane   020 7916 6114   14–1A
Tel Aviv comes to Dalston at Oden Oren's autumn 2019 venture, which he opened – just off Kingsland High Street – after a series of well-reviewed pop-ups and residencies. It's simple and small (about 30 seats), serving modern Israeli and east Mediterranean small plates, alongside wine recommendations from Zeren Wilson. Our diners' early reports go from upbeat ("a wide range of good, if salty, dishes") to ecstatic ("the best Middle Eastern food in London, hands down!"). The latter view was echoed by The Sunday Times's Marina O'Loughlin in August 2021 ("the fierce intensity... the immediacy... the shimmering beauty... exhilarating!") [Wow, can I have what she's having? Ed] / E8 2EB; www.orenlondon.com; Tue-Sat 10 pm.

Ormer Mayfair by Sofian, Flemings Mayfair Hotel W1 £104 4 4 3
7-12 Half Moon Street 020 7016 5601 3–4B

Sofian Msetfi took over the stoves at this "beautiful restaurant situated within one of Mayfair's best hotels" in May 2021: the interior is inspired by the 1930s, and lined with aged oak panelling. Initial reports applaud cuisine that has "interesting twists without trying too hard". There are three tasting menus – five-courses (£50 lunch only) plus seven (£70) and nine-courses (£90), including vegetarian options, all delivered by staff who are "warm, welcoming and charming". / W1J 7BH; www.flemings-mayfair.co.uk/fine-dining-london/ormer-mayfair-restaurant; @ormermayfair; Thu-Sat, Wed 9 pm; closed Wed L, closed Mon & Tue & Sun; No shorts; Take bookings all week via phone and/or online.

Oro Di Napoli W5 £40 3 4 2
6 The Quadrant, Little Ealing Lane 020 3632 5580 1–3A

"Evenly cooked, crispy and fluffy in just the right places, with toppings that aren't trying too hard – this South Ealing kitchen knocks out "top Neapolitan pizza". "The only downside is the horde of Deliveroo riders hanging around outside." Top Tip: "try the pizza fritta (fried pizza) if you're feeling particularly self-destructive". / W5 4EE; www.lorodinapoli.co.uk; @oronapoli; Mon-Sun 10 pm.

Orrery W1 £88 2 2 2
55 Marylebone High St 020 7616 8000 2–1A

"Cool, calm and elegant" – this D&D Group operation usually rates as one of the late Sir Terence Conran's better creations, but suffered uneven reports this year. On the first floor, above the eponymous Conran Shop – it's a "smart" (slightly "clinical") space with agreeable views over the neighbouring churchard, and, up above, "a very nice terrace on the upper floor, which makes this a very suitable summer venue". But even fans who reported "lovely" modern French cuisine felt "the bill can really mount up, even after a very modest meal"; and critics thought that "though dishes were well-prepared and presented, for verve and flavour they didn't really punch up to their (high) price point". Similarly, "service sometimes isn't as good as it should be, but they are doing their best in difficult times". / W1U 5RB; www.orrery-restaurant.co.uk; @the_Orrery; Mon-Sat 10 pm, Sun 9 pm; booking max 8 may apply.

Oscar Wilde Lounge at Cafe Royal W1 £97 3 3 5
68 Regent St 020 7406 3333 4–4C

A "beautiful venue with impeccable service", the rococo riot of the Café Royal's former Grill Room, designed in 1865, is "worth a visit just to see the over-the-top decorations" – and its "afternoon tea does not disappoint". "Care is taken to serve cakes with a London theme and the savoury course includes more than just sandwiches. Second helpings were offered… and accepted!" / W1B; www.hotelcaferoyal.com/oscarwildebar; @HotelCafeRoyal; Wed-Sun 5 pm; closed Wed-Sun D, closed Mon & Tue.

Oslo Court NW8 £71 3 4 4
Charlbert Street 020 7722 8795 9–3A

"It's always a joy to hear 'Happy Birthday' being sung again and again" at this buoyant family-run "relic", "tucked away at the foot of a Regent's Park apartment block". "From the salmon pink tablecloths, 'Kings'-style cutlery, candles, roses, toast melba and crudités with garlicky mayonnaise" to the resolutely dated, but "well executed" menu ("my potatoes were sautéed as they would have been c1972"), it's a "unique, old skool dining experience" whose fundamentals "haven't changed in over forty years". For sure, "you won't leave hungry" and you will eat "at very reasonable prices". The very characterful service is "second to none" and ultimately what seals its appeal: "you cannot refer to this restaurant without mentioning the lovely Maria & Tony and never-to-be-forgotten Neil the dessert supremo". / NW8 7EN; www.oslocourtrestaurant.co.uk; Mon-Sat 11 pm; closed Sun; No jeans.

Osteria Antica Bologna SW11 £63 4 3 3
23 Northcote Rd   020 7978 4771   11–2C
"Traditional Bologna fodder at excellent prices" is the secret to 31 years of busy trade for this Clapham trattoria. "It's always strived to serve authentic and interesting Italian food – and succeeded". What's more, ratings are up this year: "everything from the food to the service to the ambience was more switched on – seems to have had a kick up the backside due to Covid". Whatever the reason, eating here is "a very agreeable experience". / SW11 1NG; www.osteria.co.uk; @OsteriaAntica; Mon-Fri 21.45 pm, Sat 10 pm, Sun 8.45 pm.

Osteria Basilico W11 £70 3 3 3
29 Kensington Park Rd   020 7727 9957   7–1A
"A good package of food and buzz", this "classic Italian trattoria" has served Notting Hill for three decades – "and delivers the goods reliably and with panache". It has two younger stablemates in the same street – Essenza and Mediterraneo. / W11 2EU; www.osteriabasilico.co.uk; Mon-Sun 10.30 pm; no booking, Sat L.

Osteria Tufo N4 £57 4 4 2
67 Fonthill Rd   020 7272 2911   9–1D
This "friendly" Finsbury Park local is "just what a neighbourhood Italian should be" – "an (occasionally) opera-singing waiter delivers a menu that's limited but all good, with vegetarian options", and there's "a pleasant outside terrace". Strong points noted in its Neapolitan-based repertoire include home-made pasta, and also branzino (European bass). / N4 3HZ; www.osteriatufo.co.uk; @osteriatufo; Mon-Fri 10.30 pm, Sat 22.30 pm, Sun 9 pm; closed Mon-Fri L closed Sat D; no Amex.

Other Side Fried SW9 NEW £16
3 Atlantic Road   020 7501 8347   11–2D
Fried chicken junkies beat a path to this first permanent site – in Brixton's Atlantic Road arches – of a team who also have street food stalls in Leicester Square, Pop Brixton and elsewhere around town. / SW9 8HX; www.othersidefried.com; @othersidefried; Mon-Sun 11 pm.

Otto's WC1 £91 4 5 3
182 Gray's Inn Road   020 7713 0107   2–1D
"A wonderful throwback to those halcyon days when you didn't think of what you were eating and just tucked in with reckless abandon!" – Otto Tepasse's "quirky" dining room, near Gray's Inn, offers a masterclass in "unashamedly old-school French gastronomy" (most famously duck or lobster 'à la presse'). Not only is his personal, eccentric approach welcome in an ever-more homogenous world, but it's "also a wonderful reminder of what traditional, classic French cuisine is like and why it has led the world for as long as it has as the gold standard in culinary skill". The famed 'canard à la presse' itself is "staggeringly good – a wonderful experience with plenty of theatre". "A unique experience in London" and "very memorable", but "not to be repeated often if you care about your waistline or artery linings!" / WC1X 8EW; www.ottos-restaurant.com; @ottosrestaurant; Wed-Sat 10 pm; closed Sat L, closed Mon & Tue & Sun.

Ottolenghi £64 **4**|**3**|**3**

13 Motcomb St, SW1   020 7823 2707   6–1D
63 Marylebone Lane, W1   020 3148 1040   2–1A **NEW**
63 Ledbury Rd, W11   020 7727 1121   7–1B
287 Upper St, N1   020 7288 1454   9–2D
50 Artillery Pas, E1   020 7247 1999   10–2D
"Mouthwatering salads" which look as dazzlingly good as they taste set the tone at Yotam Ottolenghi's deli-restaurants, where "the food is always outstanding" and "you always discover new ingredients and different takes on traditional dishes". It's now 20 years since the Israeli-born writer and TV chef opened his original Notting Hill venue, sparking a new interest in Levantine cuisine; in summer 2021 he opened a fifth branch, near the Wallace Collection in Marylebone. / www.ottolenghi.co.uk.

The OWO SW1 NEW
The Old War Office, 57 Whitehall Place   2–3C
The Old War Office – the Grade II listed building in which Winston Churchill made many of the most important decisions of World War II – was sold in 2014 to the Hinduja Group and will open in 2022 as a luxury, 125-bedroom hotel (and apartments). The hotel will be run in partnership with Raffles (their first venture in Europe) and it is fair to assume a pretty ambitious level will be set for the nine restaurants and bars it will house. / SW1A 2HB; www.theowo.london; Sun-Thu 11 pm, Fri & Sat 11.30 pm.

Oxeye SW11 NEW
14 New Union Square   11–1D
After six years of planning, chef Sven-Hanson Britt opens his debut restaurant in Embassy Gardens in October 2021. The MasterChef: The Professionals winner is planning a fine-dining restaurant based on tasting menus, plus a bar and British wine shop, too. It's all to be an artisanal bonanza – Sven's partner Kae is a chocolatier, his uncle a ceramicist and the wool and skins used for the decor will be bespoke from their own farm animals. The bottle shop will feature 300 wines, alongside simple dishes, cheese and chocolate. / SW11 7AX; oxeyerestaurant.co.uk; Mon-Sat 10.30 pm, Sun 10 pm.

Oxo Tower, Restaurant SE1 £96 **1**|**1**|**1**
Barge House St   020 7803 3888   10–3A
"A bit of a let-down…", "still not worth it…", "so disappointing…", "far too expensive for the view" – few restaurants are as consistent as this South Bank rooftop, which has topped our list of London disappointments for as long as we can remember. / SE1 9PH; www.harveynichols.com/restaurant/the-oxo-tower; @OXO_Tower; Tue-Sun 10 pm; closed Mon; booking max 10 may apply.

Oxo Tower, Brasserie SE1 £83 **1**|**1**|**3**
Barge House St   020 7803 3888   10–3A
"Splendid views, especially from the balcony" are the saving grace of this brasserie, in the well-known Art Deco landmark building on the South Bank. Food and service have been so-so more or less since day one, but that hardly seems to matter – it still gets "very busy". / SE1 9PH; www.harveynichols.com/restaurants/oxo-tower-london; @oxo_tower; Mon-Sun 10 pm; Take bookings all week via phone and/or online.

The Oystermen Seafood Kitchen & Bar WC2 £63 **4**|**3**|**3**
32 Henrietta St   020 7240 4417   5–3D
"Superb oysters" are the star attraction at this "casual and relaxed" venue just a few steps from bustling Covent Garden – but there's "plenty of superb fresh seafood to choose from, if oysters aren't your thing". Ceviche and crab are highly recommended, while "the staff are absolutely lovely and very accommodating". / WC2E 8NA; oystermen.co.uk; Tue-Sun 11 pm; closed Mon.

Ozone Coffee Roasters £49 | 3 4 4

Emma Street, E2   020 7490 1039   14–2B **NEW**
11 Leonard Street, EC2   020 7490 1039   13–1A

"The smell of the coffee being ground in the basement is intoxicating!" at this large, "hipster vibe" Shoreditch coffee shop, whose origins are down-under in New Zealand. "It has the perfect vibe for brunch and coffee", with exposed brickwork and central island coffee bar – "the hot brunch dishes are decent, but the coffee is outstanding!" In late 2019, they opened a second branch (not counting Auckland and New Plymouth) in London Fields. / ozonecoffee.co.uk.

P Franco E5 £53 | 4 3 3

107 Lower Clapton Road   020 8533 4660   14–1B

A darling of the online fooderati – Clapton's small bar and bottle shop enjoys a media reputation out of all proportion to its modest size. If you want to run with the East End hip crowd – or just enjoy the excellent natural wines – it's worth a visit (but is walk-in only). Small, simple plates (choose from about 10 costing £5-£10) are prepared by an ever-changing roster of chefs. / E5 0NP; www.pfranco.co.uk; Thu, Sun 9 pm, Fri & Sat 10 pm; closed Thu-Sun L, closed Mon & Tue & Wed; no Amex; No bookings.

Pachamama £80 | 2 2 3

18 Thayer Street, W1   020 7935 9393   3–1A
73 Great Eastern Street, EC2   020 7846 9595   13–1B

This "sassy Peruvian" duo in Marylebone and Shoreditch are "spaciously set out, very atmospheric and pleasing to the eye". But while the vibey locations are a big draw, they also offer "a multiplicity of delicious options", making them "perfect for a mixed party of meat/fish eaters, vegetarians and vegans".

Padella £31 | 5 4 3

6 Southwark St, SE1   no tel   10–4C
1 Phipp Street, EC2   13–2B **NEW**

"Every time we go to Padella, we're just bowled over by the splendid simplicity of their dishes, packed with flavour, and at the most ridiculous value prices!" – Tim Siadatan and Jordan Frieda's Borough Market staple added a stylish Shoreditch sibling, in early 2020 (just before Covid-19 struck) and in EC2 in particular they are absolutely crushing it as one of the capital's best options on a budget. Indeed, "it's hard to comprehend how they can serve such a quality meal at the price". The formula is deceptively simple: "no reservations, no frills": just "superlative, freshly made pasta" ("it is lovely to see the dough being rolled by hand every morning on my way to the office") from a "compact menu". "Arrive ultra-early to dodge the worst of the perma-queues", although "the line moves relatively quickly, and their beeper system means you can go for a drink and come back to get your table". "Portion sizes are definitely not large, but it's definitely worth the wait". "Knock back a perfectly great Negroni, tuck away three dishes and a glass of wine, and walk out less than £30 lighter!"

Paladar SE1 £56 | 4 4 4

4-5 London Road   020 7186 5555   10–4A

"The most incredible South American food" combined with "the atmosphere of a very sexy permanent street party" make this Elephant & Castle bar/restaurant (with walled garden) a stand-out local attraction. "It's fun, fun, fun, and it never disappoints." Food and wine come from "a variety of Latin American sources, not what Londoners are generally used to", and include "plenty of vegan and veggie options". Top Tip: "I'd go back for the plantain crisps". / SE1 6JZ; www.paladarlondon.com; @paladarlondon; Mon-Thu 9.30 pm, Fri & Sat 10 pm, Sun 8 pm; closed Mon L; Take bookings all week via phone and/or online.

Palatino EC1 £66 **4** **3** **2**
71 Central Street 020 3481 5300 10–1B
On a Clerkenwell corner – part of a Scandi-style workspace called Fora – chef Stevie Parle's four-year-old has carved a reputation as a good-value pasta stop, specialising in Roman-inspired dishes. Marked 'temporarily closed' as we go to press (and with no social activity since spring 2020), we have rated it on the hope and expectation that it will reopen as before. / EC1V 8AB; palatino.london; @PalatinoLondon.

Pali Hill W1 NEW £55 **3** **3** **2**
79-81 Mortimer Street 020 8130 0101 3–1C
Adopting the site near Selfridges of Indian veteran Gaylord (RIP), this October 2020 newcomer is the first London venture of Rahul Khanna and Kabir Suri: the duo behind New Delhi-based Azure Hospitality, one of India's more successful hospitality businesses. It's named for one of Mumbai's poshest suburbs, whose foodie heritage is a mash-up based on communal living. Here that translates to swish, contemporary decor and an eclectic menu which early survey (and newspaper) reports consider "well spiced, interesting Indian food". Below is Bandra Bhai, a basement cocktail bar inspired by an illicit smuggling den. / W1W 7SJ; palihill.co.uk; Tue-Sat 11 pm, Sun 4 pm; closed Sun D, closed Mon.

The Palomar W1 £60 **4** **4** **3**
34 Rupert Street 020 7439 8777 4–3D
"A little hidden treasure" on the edge of Chinatown, this Tel Aviv-inspired grill produces "wonderful", "genuinely imaginative Middle Eastern cooking" – much of it served in "tapas-style portions". It's best enjoyed from a perch at the bar, so you can watch the chefs in action. "If you're sat opposite the oven it's like being in a furnace, but they always do a great job". / W1D 6DN; www.thepalomar.co.uk; @palomarsoho; Wed-Sat 11 pm, Sun 9 pm; closed Wed L, closed Mon & Tue; Take bookings all week via phone and/or online.

Il Pampero SW1
20 Chesham Place 020 3189 4850 6–1D
A short walk from Sloane Street, this elegantly panelled Belgravia dining room is part of a luxurious five-star hotel. Perhaps because it's tucked away in such an expensive 'hood, it doesn't generate a huge volume of survey feedback, but such as there is says it successfully sets a superior standard of Italian cuisine. / SW1X 8HQ; www.ilpampero.com; @ilPamperoLondon; Sun & Mon 11, Tue, Wed 11, Thu-Sat 10.30 pm; closed Sun-Wed D; Take bookings all week via phone and/or online.

Panton Yokocho SW1 NEW
35 Panton Street 5–4A
A Japan Centre venture along the same lines as Heddon Yokocho, this large (5,800 sq feet) just off Leicester Square is also to feature ramen and retro '70s decor. It opens in autumn 2021. / SW1Y 4EA; ramenyokocho.com; Mon-Sat 4.30 pm.

Paradise W1 £45 **4** **3** **3**
61 Rupert Street 4–2D
"Classic Sri Lankan flavours, with a perfect balance of spices and some really deft twists" win a thumbs-up for this contemporary Soho two-year-old – on the site of Spuntino (RIP) and with an interior by the designer behind Thai star Kiln. "I'm not one for drinking top wines with spicy foods, but if you wanted to, this is the place to go, with an excellent list of high-quality wines". "The restaurant is run by ex-Wasps rugby player Sam Jones – an added bonus if you're a rugby nut". / W1D 7PW; www.paradisesoho.com; Tue-Sat 11 pm; closed Tue-Fri L, closed Sun & Mon.

Paradise Hampstead NW3 £39 **3 5 3**
49 South End Rd   020 7794 6314   9–2A
"A Hampstead gem", this traditional, family-run curry house, est. 1969, serves "great, freshly cooked and well-spiced food" – and "the owner and his staff really put themselves out". "We've been going for over 40 years, and always look forward to the most charming hospitality from this neighbourhood favourite". / NW3 2QB; www.paradisehampstead.co.uk; Mon-Sun 11.30 pm.

Paranhodu SE14 £25 **3 3 3**
125 Lewisham Way   020 3573 8175   1–4D
"A good local Korean, with all the usual suspects present and correct on the menu". An unassuming place, not far from Goldsmiths. / SE14 6QJ; Tue-Thu, Sun 10.30 pm, Sat 11 pm; closed Tue L, closed Mon & Fri.

Park Chinois W1 £146 **2 2 3**
17 Berkeley St   020 3327 8888   3–3C
The aim is to evoke 1920s Shanghai decadence at this opulent Mayfair Chinese, founded by Alan Yau in 2015 and now in the hands of a family of Turkish restaurant owners. Limited feedback this year, but we've maintained its rather middling ratings on the basis of repeat feedback that a meal here can seem "ridiculously overpriced". / W1S 4NF; www.parkchinois.com; @ParkChinois; Mon-Sat 2 am, Sun midnight; closed Mon-Fri L; No jeans.

Park Row W1 NEW £118
77 Brewer Street   02037 453 431   4–3C
Holy Guacamole, Batman! The basement near Piccadilly Circus that was Mash Steakhouse (RIP) has been taken over by Wonderland Restaurant group, in association with Warner Bros and DC. With their evil master plan it's been relaunched. But not just as a themed diner. Oh no! But a 'Gastronomic Amusement Park' with five restaurants, three bars and 330 covers in total. For the 20-seat Monarch Theatre experience, enjoy 11-courses for... £195 per person. Great Scott!! There are some serious folks in the kitchen here, though. Executive chef at The Monarch, Karl O'Dell, was formerly head chef of the sadly now defunct, but superb, Texture (RIP). / W1F 9ZN; www.parkrowlondon.co.uk; @W1dathome; Tue-Sat 1 am, Sun 4.45 pm; closed Sun D, closed Mon.

Parlour Kensal NW10 £55 **4 3 4**
5 Regent St   020 8969 2184   1–2B
"An absolute pleasure every time we visit" – this "innovative and buzzy, local gastropub" on Kensal Rise features "colourful, delicious cooking" from Jesse Dunford Wood (a well-travelled chef with a fine-dining background) and service is delivered by "a team that really care". "There's a great outdoor seating area", and what regulars say is "probably the best Sunday roast in London". / NW10 5LG; www.parlourkensal.com; @ParlourUK; Mon-Sun 10 pm.

The Parlour,
Great Scotland Yard SW1 NEW £82
Great Scotland Yard   020 7925 4744   2–3C
On the site of the original Metropolitan Police HQ, this 100-seater hotel (owned by an Indian entrepreneur and operated by Hyatt) opened in December 2019. The comfortable, ground-floor lounge – with Raj-inspired decor – serves a contemporary take on afternoon tea, with added spice; there are spicy chai options and tea-based cocktails too. / SW1A 2HN; www.hyatt.com/en-US/hotel/england-united-kingdom/great-scotland-yard/lhrub/dining; Wed-Sat 5 pm; closed Wed-Sat D, closed Mon & Tue & Sun.

Parlour,
The Ned EC2 NEW £70
27 Poultry 020 3828 2000 10–2C

Yet another option for eating at The Ned! This time, the colossal hipster hotel near Bank has added a new basement bar and entertainment space, complete with regular live music. The food is more than just bar bites though – Lobster Thermidor anyone? / EC2R 8AJ; www.thened.com/restaurants/the-parlour; Wed-Sat midnight; closed Wed-Sat L, closed Mon & Tue & Sun.

Parrillan N1 £72 334
Coal Drops Yard 020 7018 3339 9–3C

"A smokey, fun, tasty and companionable way to enjoy an outdoor lunch or dinner" – the Hart Bros' "great terrace" (all outside) overlooking the Regent's Canal in Coal Drops Yard provides a form of DIY mini-grill, whereby you BBQ your selection to your liking. Even the odd reporter who is "not too convinced by the cook-for-yourself format" thinks it's "good for a change". / N1C 4AB; barrafina.co.uk; @ParrillanLondon; Tue-Sat 11 pm, Sun 10 pm; closed Tue, Wed L, closed Mon.

Parsons WC2 £64 432
39 Endell Street 020 3422 0221 5–2C

"A tiny, buzzing space which serves delicious fish and other seafood delights in a friendly and efficient manner", this tiled Covent Garden four-year-old has been a welcome addition to the new wave of fish specialists in the West End. "The interesting wine list comes from 10 Cases over the road", which is under the same ownership. "We hardly ever go beyond the starters/small plates here – smoked cod's roe, potted shrimp croquettes, brown crab pissaladière, tartare of sea trout with spicy bloody Mary jelly – all hit the spot". / WC2H 9BA; www.parsonslondon.co.uk; Tue-Sat 10 pm; closed Sun & Mon.

Party Store Pizza SW4 NEW £21
15-16 Lendal Terrace 11–1D

'Shocked' (that's what the PR says anyway) that Detroit-style deep-pan pizzas weren't properly represented on the London pizza scene', Matt Wells (co-founder of The Dairy and Dandy) and music promoter Fred Letts launched this pizza stop at Brixton's Market House in summer 2020. Rectangular in format, the pizzas have a thick, focaccia base and there are plenty of vegan options on the menu. / SW4 7UX; www.partystorepizza.co.uk; Wed-Sat 11 pm, Sun 6 pm; closed Wed-Fri L closed Sun D, closed Mon & Tue; No bookings.

Pascor W8 NEW £51
221 Kensington High Street 020 7937 3003 8–1D

On the site of Melabes (RIP), the new occupant since December 2020 of this mezzanine site, with large windows overlooking Kensington High Street, offers an eastern Mediterranean menu (inspirations from Bulgaria, Serbia, Greece and Turkey) with many of the main dishes from the mangal (BBQ). / W8 6SG; www.pascor.co.uk; Mon-Sun 11 pm.

Passyunk Avenue £52 224
80 Cleveland Street, W1 020 3960 2251 2–1B
Westfield Stratford, Level 1, E20 020 8519 0092 14–1D NEW

This 'Philadelphia dive bar' in Cleveland Street, Fitzrovia, has certainly "got the American vibe", with "US-style beer and bar food" giving a real taste of the City of Brotherly Love. Philly street food classics such as the hoagie and cheesesteak are on the menu – and "it's not health food, that's for sure". Reporters are divided on the results – "defining the category" for fans, "pretty underwhelming" for sceptics. There's now a second site at Westfield Stratford, complete with baseball batting cages, but a 2021 crowdfunding bid to raise £150,000 for a massive bar under the railway arches in Leake Street, Waterloo, struck out. / passyunkavenue.com; @passyunkavenue.

Pastaio £50 3|3|3
19 Ganton Street, W1 020 3019 8680 4–2B
South Ter..., Westfield White City, W12 020 8629 2268 1–3B **NEW**
"Delicious freshly made pasta" at "good value" prices helps win solid ratings for Stevie Parle's duo of pasta pit stops in Soho and on Westfield White City's Southern Terrace. Even a reporter complaining that it's "a bit of a 2020s Instagram trap with more style than substance" rates it a good all-rounder. / www.pastaio.london; @PastaioLondon.

Patara £69 3|3|2
15 Greek St, W1 020 7437 1071 5–2A
7 Maddox St, W1 020 7499 6008 4–2A
181 Fulham Rd, SW3 020 7351 5692 6–2C
9 Beauchamp Pl, SW3 020 7581 8820 6–1C
82 Hampstead High St, NW3 020 7431 5902 9–2A
18 High St, SW19 020 3931 6157 11–2B
"Thai food with a modern twist that's miles away from the standard Siamese" is the hallmark of this long-established group whose half-dozen venues are "just the kind of local reliable Thai that everyone needs". Having launched in South Ken in 1990, more recent expansion has seen branches opening in the affluent suburbs of Hampstead and Wimbledon. / www.pataralondon.com; @PataraLondon.

Paternoster Chop House EC4 £65 2|2|2
1 Warwick Court 020 7029 9400 10–2B
This City-based grill overlooking St Paul's Cathedral, from D&D London, is pitched firmly at the location's business diners – but it does have a romantic side, as the location for seven years of 'reality' TV show First Dates, starring maître d' extraordinaire Fred Sirieix, with actors playing the parts of waiting and bar staff. / EC4M 7DX; www.paternosterchophouse.co.uk; @paternosterchop; Mon-Sat 10.30 pm; closed Sun; booking max 12 may apply.

Patri £45 3|4|3
139 Northfield Avenue, W13 020 3981 3388 1–3A
29 Bond Street, W5 020 8579 9999 1–3A **NEW**
103 Hammersmith Grove, W6 020 8741 1088 8–1C
"Some really interesting menu options that are a bit different from the average Indian", help distinguish these colourful street-food cantinas, which added a third Ealing branch in January 2020. "The owners and waiting staff are very friendly and helpful" and "although conditions are a little cramped", dishes are "delicious" and "good value-for-money".

Patty and Bun £32 4|3|3
18 Old Compton St, W1 020 7287 1818 5–2A
26 Kingly Street, W1 020 7287 9632 4–2A **NEW**
54 James St, W1 020 7487 3188 3–1A
14 Pembridge Rd, W11 020 7229 2228 7–2B
19 Borough High Street, SE1 020 7407 7994 10–4C
36 Redchurch Street, E2 020 7613 3335 13–1C
2 Arthaus Building, 205 Richmond Road, E8 020 8525 8250 14–1B
22-23 Liverpool St, EC2 020 7621 1331 10–2D
8 Brown's Buildings, Saint Mary Axe, EC3 020 3846 3222 10–2D
The "succulent, juicy burgers" at Joe Grossman's indie burger chain are "a sloppy-ish mess... and all the better for it" – "and the food can be washed down with a decent glass of wine or a good margarita". Having started out with pub-based pop-ups, Grossman opened his first branch in James Street, Fitzrovia, 10 years ago, and now has a further eight in London and one in Brighton. / www.pattyandbun.co.uk; @pattyandbunjoe.

Peachy Goat SE24 NEW £42 3|3|3
16 Half Moon Lane 1–4D

Opened in February 2020, a plant-based café with cute outside terrace in Herne Hill from brothers Oliver and Luca, who used to run the Bean & Bowl stall in Herne Hill Market. During the day, there's a menu of brunch plates and plant-based burgers – by night, pasta and one or two more substantial dishes complete the offering. "We actually didn't realise it was a vegan restaurant until we sat down but all our food was so delicious we'll definitely be back!" / SE24 9HU; www.peachygoat.com; Tue-Sat 10.30 pm, Sun 4 pm; closed Tue-Fri L closed Sun D, closed Mon.

Pearl Liang W2 £52 3|3|2
8 Sheldon Square 020 7289 7000 7–1C

This modern basement in Paddington Basin is an excellent destination for "upmarket Chinese dining" – a "favourite for dim sum" (evenings included) and "traditional Cantonese cuisine cooked to a high standard". "For this price range, it's all well prepared, fresh – and better than the Chinatown options." Top Tip: "the lobster noodles are not to be missed". / W2 6EZ; www.pearlliang.co.uk; @PearlLiangUK; Mon-Sun 11 pm.

Peckham Bazaar SE15 £59 4|3|3
119 Consort Rd 020 7732 2525 1–4D

"Delicious pan-Balkan cuisine is served, including on the newly spruced-up terrace" at this "outstanding" charcoal grill specialist, off the beaten track in Peckham. The culinary territory of the old Ottoman empire, "traversing Balkan, Greek and Anatolian cuisines", makes for an "interesting" dining experience, accompanied by some "wonderful Greek and Croatian wines", and served by "friendly and attentive staff". Top Tips: "you have to try the octopus", and the "fabulous and addictive flatbread!". / SE15 3RU; www.peckhambazaar.com; @PeckhamBazaar; Tue-Sat 10 pm, Sun 8 pm; closed Tue-Thu L, closed Mon.

Peckham Cellars SE15 NEW £79 4|5|3
125 Queens Road 020 7207 0124 1–4D

"The guys here are obsessed with wine and it shows!" – This modern 'neighbourhood kitchen, wine bar and shop' is part of the ongoing foodie gentrification of Peckham and a relatively 'grown up' arrival to the 'hood in late 2019. It offers "imaginative" Mediterranean-esque small plates from a list that's "varied, but crucially also very delicious. Love that you can buy bottles of what you had to take home (though they do operate a delivery service if it's too much to carry!)" / SE15 2ND; peckhamcellars.co.uk; @peckhamcellars; Credit card deposit required to book.

Peg E9 4|3|3
120 Morning Lane 020 3441 8765 14–1B

From the backers of fooderati favourites, P Franco and Bright, this hipster natural wine bar in Hackney opened in summer 2019, but then closed for an extended period, finally to open again post-pandemic in September 2021. The small space – with its cool, minimal vibe – remains, but the Japanese-influenced modern British food offering has morphed a little: now they offer a £45 set menu of four or five courses, driven by the best produce coming into the kitchen at the time. (We have reinstated its historical ratings, taking a wild guess that the fundamentals haven't altered much.) / E9 6LH; www.peglondon.co.uk; Wed-Sat 11 pm, Sun 4 pm; closed Wed L closed Sun D, closed Mon & Tue; cards only; Take bookings all week via phone and/or online.

E Pellicci E2 £20 3|5|5
332 Bethnal Green Rd 020 7739 4873 13–1D

"Great food and even better banter" is why so many regulars "just have to keep going back" to this Bethnal Green greasy spoon, run by four generations of the Pellicci family since 1900. The unique wood-panelled Art Deco interior narrowly escaped destruction in a fire 20 years ago, and is now Grade II listed. / E2 0AG; epellicci.has.restaurant; Mon-Sat 4 pm; closed Mon-Sat D, closed Sun; cash only; No bookings.

The Pem SW1 NEW
Conrad London St. James, 22-28 Broadway   020 3301 8080   2–3C
Named for a pioneering suffragette, this July 2021 arrival marks a new determination by the Conrad St James's Hotel to put itself on the map. At the stoves – Sally Abé – who recently arrived from the Harwood Arms to oversee the hotel's kitchen generally, with this her showcase. It offers an ambitious menu with classic British overtones. Did no-one tell Sally the unwritten rule that good British restaurants are just not allowed in Westminster? Early social feedback suggests she may – at last – break the mould! (See also The Blue Boar.) / SW1H 0BH; thepemrestaurant.com; @pemrestaurant; Mon-Sat 8 pm, Sun 4 pm.

Pentolina W14   £60   4 4 4
71 Blythe Rd   020 3010 0091   8–1C
"The perfect local for those intimate meals", this very attractive, family-owned and run Italian near Brook Green has built a loyal following in recent years for "innovative cooking which varies with the seasons". It's also "affordable on a regular basis". / W14 0HP; www.pentolinarestaurant.co.uk; Tue-Sat 9.30 pm; closed Sun & Mon; no Amex.

Pergola on the Wharf E14 NEW   £31
Crossrail Place Roof Garden, Crossrail Place   020 8176 6105   12–1C
A 'botanical, waterside Garden of Eden' – according to the Canary Wharf PR team – this foliage-filled street food market (with siblings including Pergola Padington, The Prince Earl's Court and Lost in Brixton) opened on the Crossrail Place roof garden in May 2021 (on a site that was formerly E14's Giant Robot). A roster of street-food stars inhabit a space that's a little slicker than its siblings, but there's also an in-house food offering and three bars. / E14 5AB; www.pergolacanarywharf.co.uk; @IncipioGroup; Mon-Sun midnight.

Perilla N16   £71   4 4 3
1-3 Green Lanes   020 7359 0779   1–1C
"More than the sum of its parts", this stripped-down modern venue with picture windows overlooking Newington Green showcases the skills of chef Ben Marks, who wins impressively high ratings for his "short menu" of skillful dishes (including a tasting four-course option with bread for £59). Marks began working at the age of 13 and is a veteran of some of Europe's leading restaurants, including Noma and Phil Howard's late, lamented The Square in Mayfair. / N16 9BS; www.perilladining.co.uk; @perilladining; Fri & Sat, Tue-Thu 11 pm, Sun 9 pm; closed Tue-Thu L, closed Mon.

The Perry Hill SE6 NEW   £27   3 2 4
78-80 Perry Hill   020 8699 3334   1–4D
"What a treat to discover the suntrap garden" behind a "reinvented boozer on the South Circular" that was previously closed for many years – "a huge (250 seat) outdoor eating area, some of it undercover". This April 2021 newcomer in Perry Vale (between Catford and Sydenham) has a characterful interior too, and a "good menu" overseen by Jamie Young, who used to own Dulwich's excellent Palmerston pub (and who still runs Peckham's Begging Bowl). / SE6 4EY; www.perryhillpub.co.uk; @theperryhillpub; Mon-Sun midnight.

The Petersham WC2   £99   2 2 4
Floral Court, off Floral St   020 7305 7676   5–3C
A classic 'rus in urbe' venue – this lavish, flower-filled destination in a still-new-feeling Covent Garden development channels the charms of the well-known Richmond Park plant nursery in its two restaurants, interiors shop and florist. A "nice place", undoubtedly, but one too often accused of serving "tiny, overpriced portions" of modern Italian food. / WC2E 9DJ; petershamnurseries.com; @PetershamN; Thu-Sat, Tue, Wed 9.30 pm; closed Sun & Mon; No trainers.

Petersham Nurseries Cafe TW10 £89 225
Church Lane (signposted 'St Peter's Church'), off Petersham Road
020 8940 5230 1–4A
"Quirky and delightful", "stylish and charming" – it's the "lovely garden setting" of a plant nursery bordering Richmond Park that underpins such major support for this shabby chic greenhouse (which owes its culinary fame to long-departed chef Skye Gyngell). These days, reporters continue to enthuse about some "original and beautifully presented food" (and "scrumptious cakes"), but can also sometimes judge the cuisine "second rate"... and "expensive". Still, there's no let-up in its popularity, so it's often packed – despite the extensions installed by the current owners, who have also invested in a large sister venue in Covent Garden. / TW10 7AB; www.petershamnurseries.com; Tue, Wed, Sun 5 pm; Thu-Sat 11 pm; closed Tue, Wed, Sun D, closed Mon; SRA-Food Made Good – 3 stars.

Le Petit Citron W6 £55 344
98-100 Shepherds Bush Road 020 3019 1175 8–1C
On a slightly tatty stretch of the Shepherd's Bush Road, this well-appointed French brasserie (with the same owners as Covent Garden's Joe Allen) is something of a surprise. The formula is a classic Gallic one and it's "very good value". / W6 7PD; lepetitcitron.co.uk; @lepetitcitronw6; Tue-Sat 10 pm, Sun 4 pm; closed Sun D, closed Mon.

Petit Ma Cuisine TW9 £57 333
8 Station Approach 020 8332 1923 1–3A
Modelled on the classic, Gallic mid-century bistro, this "friendly and popular neighbourhood restaurant" in Kew Village is "just so authentically French". Feedback is remarkably consistent and free of gripes. The "exceptional prix-fixe lunch" makes it a favourite refuelling spot for visitors to nearby Kew Gardens. / TW9 3QB; www.macuisinebistrot.co.uk; Tue-Sun 11.30 pm; closed Mon; no Amex.

Pétrus SW1 £115 332
1 Kinnerton St 020 7592 1609 6–1D
"So delicate, so refined and so delicious" – the "elegant" cuisine at Gordon Ramsay's luxurious Belgravian has proved commendably consistent over the years, and its "wine offering has something to tempt even those most well-trained palates". Thus, it remains one of the brighter spots in GR's ever-more middling restaurant empire. On the downside, although the room itself is "swanky – with a huge wine cage in the centre of the space" – its atmosphere can fail to ignite. And then of course there's the "ridiculous bill". For most folks, though? "First class!" / SW1X 8EA; www.gordonramsayrestaurants.com; @petrus; Wed-Sat 11 pm, Sun 6 pm; closed Sun D, closed Mon & Tue; No trainers.

Pham Sushi EC1 £52 433
159 Whitecross St 020 7251 6336 13–2A
This modest Japanese venue near the Barbican scores consistently high ratings for its "very very good" sushi and other specialities, at what are "quite reasonable" prices for the central location. / EC1Y 8JL; www.phamsushi.com; @phamsushi; Mon-Sat 9 pm; closed Sat L, closed Sun.

Phat Phuc SW3 £38 322
Chelsea Courtyard, 151 Sydney Street 020 7351 3843 6–3C
"Large portions of cheap, tasty food" gives this street-food operation rarity value in pricey Chelsea. "Nothing fancy, just really tasty Vietnamese noodles and soup, located below street level with an eating area under tents". The name translates as "happy Buddha" – but that's not why they sell branded T-shirts... / SW3 6NT; www.phatphucnoodlebar.co.uk; @Phat_PhucNoodle; Mon-Sun 7 pm.

Philippe Conticini NW1 NEW £36
732-736 North Yard, Chalk Farm Road   9–2B

Just a few years after leaving London (and his two Pâtisserie des Rêves stores) behind, Philippe Conticini is back, with this huge new Camden Market patisserie, traditionally tiled and where much of the seating is outside on a large sunny days terrace. (There's also a smaller, less characterful outlet now nearby (since November 2020) in Buck Street Market). / NW1 8AH; www.camdenmarket.com/food-drink/philippe-conticini; Mon-Sun 6 pm; closed Mon-Sun D.

The Phoenix W12 NEW £33
1078 Ariel Way   8–1C

Promising to be Westfield Shepherd's Bush's largest eating operation – this 650-seat capacity operation is a new venture from Bird House, who run the nearby Hawk's Nest by Goldhawk Road Tube. On the prominent site at the top of the escalators to the South Terrace that was formerly Jamie's Italian (RIP), it will offer sourdough pizza and steak frites, with DJs providing the ambience. Most of the seating – 400 covers – will be on a huge outside terrace. / W12 7GB; thephoenixlondon.com; Mon-Sat midnight, Sun 10.30 pm.

Phoenix Palace NW1 £64   3 2 2
5-9 Glentworth St   020 7486 3515   2–1A

"Exceptional and authentic Hong-Kong-style cuisine" can be enjoyed at this huge, old-style banqueting hall near Baker Street tube, with more than 300 dishes on eight different menus, including top-class dim sum served until 5pm. / NW1 5PG; www.phoenixpalace.co.uk; Mon-Sat 11.30 pm, Sun 10.30 pm.

Piazza Italiana EC2 NEW £65
38 Threadneedle Street   020 7256 7223   10–2C

This traditional Italian newcomer (with siblings in Moscow and Riga) opened briefly in late 2020 with a second debut in May 2021. It occupies an impressive Edwardian (1902) banking hall in the heart of the Square Mile – the former telling room of the British Linen Bank (later Bank of Scotland). The dramatic columns and ceiling of the space remain and chef Aleksandr Sarujev is at the stoves. Early reports are very enthusiastic (but too limited in number for a rating). / EC2R 8AY; www.piazzaitaliana.co.uk; Tue, Wed 10 pm; Thu-Sat 11 pm; closed Sat L, closed Sun & Mon; Take bookings all week via phone and/or online.

Pidgin E8 £79   5 3 3
52 Wilton Way   020 7254 8311   14–1B

"A beautiful little spot in a tucked away part of Hackney" – this 'unassuming neighbourhood restaurant' won particular renown a couple of years after its opening in 2015 when it won a Michelin star. The tyre men removed it again the next year, but – whatever the changes of mind in Clermont-Ferrand – our reporters consistently acclaim its "fresh, thoughtful and well-executed tasting menu, which, with the pairing wines, are a real treat". Also, it was a godsend for many during lockdown thanks to its "consistently high-quality At Home service". / E8 1BG; www.pidginlondon.com; @PidginLondon; Wed-Sun 11 pm; closed Wed-Fri L, closed Mon & Tue.

Pied à Terre W1 £113   5 4 4
34 Charlotte St   020 7636 1178   2–1C

"David Moore is an absolutely charming host" and – having kept his foodie temple in a Fitzrovia townhouse at the pinnacle of London's dining scene for the last 30 years (he launched at roughly the same time as Harden's) – "he certainly knows how to keep up with the times with his constantly evolving menu and restaurant offerings", most notably of late, one of London's most ambitious vegan menus. Head chef, Asimakis Chaniotis delivers "fascinating dishes with fabulous ingredients" – "sheer class" – and there's a heavyweight wine list "with some really interesting suggestions". "The truly

personal service seems unfazed by the stresses and shenanigans of recent times" and creates a "first class ambience" in the compact space.
/ W1T 2NH; www.pied-a-terre.co.uk; @PiedaTerreUK; Tue-Sat 10 pm; closed Tue-Sat L, closed Sun & Mon; May need 12+ to book.

Pig & Butcher N1 £64 333
80 Liverpool Road   020 7226 8304   9–3D
"Never had a duff meal" – this ten-year-old Islington gastroboozer is "consistently great", and regulars reckon themselves "very lucky to have it as our local gastropub". As the name suggests, they specialise in butchering their own meat for the kitchen. / N1 0QD; www.thepigandbutcher.co.uk; @pigandbutcher; Mon-Sat 10 pm, Sun 9 pm.

Pino W8 NEW £61 443
267 Kensington High Street   020 7602 6777   8–1D
Formerly Pizzicotto (RIP) – the Chiavarini family (who have run nearby Il Portico since the '60's) have revamped their six-year-old spin-off and in June 2021 took in a slightly more serious culinary direction. The wood-burning pizza oven is still in operation, but there's more of an emphasis on trattoria-style dishes, cured meats and pasta. We've rated this on the basis that it's more of a retread than a full re-launch. / W8; www.famigliaportico.co.uk; Mon-Sat 8 pm, Sun 4 pm.

Pique Nique SE1 £69 433
32 Tanner Street   020 7403 9549   10–4D
"Just love the sheer over-Frenchness of Pique-Nique!" – "quirky" sister restaurant of Bermondsey's Casse-Croûte nearby. "They make the best out of their odd converted park pavilion building" – a "random Alpine chalet-looking thing next to a kids' playground and overlooking tennis courts" – and the terrace by Tanner Street Park can be "lovely on a summer's evening". "Very tasty and generous" sharing plates are par for the course, including "Chateaubriand that's an absolutely monster – plenty for three people" and "offal tart just stuffed with rich flavour". / SE1 3LD; pique-nique.co.uk; @piquenique32; Mon-Sat 11 pm, Sun 10 pm.

El Pirata W1 £54 233
5-6 Down St   020 7491 3810   3–4B
"Service is super-helpful and friendly" at this blast-from-the-past in Mayfair – an old-fashioned tapas haunt that's very modestly priced for this luxurious 'hood. Don't expect culinary fireworks – "it's good, wholesome scoff". "The space is basic, but the vibe is awesome." / W1J 7AQ; www.elpirata.co.uk; @elpiratiw1; Mon-Sun 10.30 pm.

Pivot WC2 NEW
3 Henrietta Street   5–3D
Opening in September 2021, on the first floor of a new Covent Garden restaurant development (see also El Ta'koy), this new venture is named for its monthly changing menu from accoladed Scottish chef Mark Greenaway. From the website, we are told to expect spectacular views of the piazza, an open kitchen, and a choice of four- or eight-course menus. / WC2E 8LU; 3henrietta.com.

Pizarro SE1 £66 333
194 Bermondsey St   020 7256 5333   10–4D
José P's larger restaurant sibling to his nearby Bermondsey tapas bar continues to be outrated by its nearby stablemate and can be viewed as being "quite expensive". On the plus side, though, the food is "fabulous" – at times "exquisite" – service is "really friendly", "attentive and quick", and "it's a great room". / SE1 3TQ; josepizarro.com/pizarro-restaurant-bermondsey; @josepizarrorestaurants; Mon-Sat 10.45 pm, Sun 5 pm; closed Sun D.

Pizza da Valter SW17 £45 333

7 Bellevue Road   020 8355 7032   11–2C

This "consistently good" pizzeria overlooking Wandsworth Common from foodie-haven Bellevue Parade "goes from strength to strength", and has built a strong local following in the past five years. It also serves "good lasagne and seafood pasta (when it's on)". / SW17 7EG; www.pizzadavalter.co.uk; @pizzadavalteruk; Mon-Sun 11 pm; Take bookings all week via phone and/or online.

Pizza East £64 434

310 Portobello Rd, W10   020 8969 4500   7–1A
56 Shoreditch High St, E1   020 7729 1888   13–1B

The "excellent Italian/American menu" means these "very buzzy", industrial-style venues in Shoreditch (a former tea factory) and Portobello offer "much more than their consistently great pizzas". They "can get busy, so book – especially on Fridays" and note: this is "not the place for a quiet romantic date". A third site in Kentish Town closed a couple of years ago, and the owners, Soho House, seem to be focused elsewhere, but the ratings are very strong in our latest survey. / www.pizzaeast.com; @PizzaEast.

Pizza Metro SW11 £53 333

64 Battersea Rise   020 7228 3812   11–2C

"Still delivering top pizza in a crowded market", this Battersea Neapolitan has served pizza by the metre for 28 years – if it has managed five metres a day in that time, its total output would easily stretch around the world. / SW11 1EQ; www.pizzametropizza.com; @pizzametropizza; Mon-Thu 10.30 pm, Fri & Sat 11 pm, Sun 10 pm; closed Mon-Thu L; no Amex.

Pizza Pilgrims £45 333

32-34 Buckingham Palace Road, SW1   020 3963 5800   2–4B NEW
102 Berwick St, W1   07780 667258   4–2D
11-12 Dean St, W1   020 7287 8964   4–1D
Kingly Ct, Carnaby St, W1   020 7287 2200   4–2B
23 Garrick Street, WC2   020 3019 1881   5–3C
The Balcony, Westfield, W12   020 3019 1888   1–3B NEW
40-42 Parkway, NW1   020 8167 8366   9–3B NEW
12 Hertsmere Rd, E14   020 3019 8020   12–1C
136 Shoreditch High St, E1   020 3019 7620   13–1B
15 Exmouth Mkt, EC1   020 7287 8964   10–1A
22 Old Broad Street, EC2   020 3974 9820   10–2C NEW
8 Brown's Buildings, Saint Mary Axe, EC3   no tel   10–2D

"Quality pizzas served by nice people in a bustling, energetic atmosphere. What's not to like?" It's a formula that's winning massive, post-pandemic expansion for the Elliot brothers' chain, which is adding eight London sites this year. Perhaps inevitably with such fast growth, it no longer enjoys the stellar ratings of yesteryear, but to an impressive degree also evades criticism: "always decent…", "I can't speak for the authenticity, but they're tasty as hell". Top Tip: "their pizza home delivery kit is great fun". / pizzapilgrims.co.uk; @pizzapilgrims.

PizzaExpress £55 122

"Probably gradually getting worse, but you know what you are going to get… if you can work out the discount codes…" – this 56-year-old, high-street pizza chain still enjoys a high amount of lingering support from reporters, who haven't quite given up on it yet. Once the UK's 'gold standard' for chain dining, its performance in recent years has nose-dived, especially the ambience rating. Hony Capital ("the former Chinese private equity owners, who were ruining this once-great business") have recently "exited with their tails between their legs" and it's now in the hands of its debtors, who – during the pandemic – closed 73 restaurants with the loss of over 1,100 jobs. "Hopefully the new owners will return the chain to what it once was: first step should be to remove the extra tables which were crammed in

*making it an almost communal dining experience… always going to be
disastrous given the number of kids ever present".* There's hope, as in
September 2021 the new team announced the refurb of 300 sites.
/ www.pizzaexpress.co.uk.

Pizzeria Mozza W1 NEW £46
Treehouse Hotel, 14-15 Langham Place   020 3988 4273   3–1C
*The involvement of a Netflix star ('Chef's Table') – LA chef, Nancy Silverton
– is the justification for including this new, July 2021 pizzeria (with 'wild
Mediterranean garden' interior), just across the road from Broadcasting
House. Her pizzas are, apparently, 'famed for their unique dough recipe and
well-structured crusts' and you can round off with her own-brand ice cream:
Nancy's Fancy. It opened too late for survey feedback, but an early review
from The Standard's David Ellis was cautiously upbeat on the quality of the
pizza: "I'll need to wait and see but there might just be enough here to
make Silverton a star this side of the pond, too".* / W1B 2QS;
www.treehousehotels.com/london/eat-drink/pizzeria-mozza; Tue-Sat 11 pm; closed
Tue-Sat L, closed Sun & Mon.

Pizzeria Pappagone N4 £35   3 4 3
131 Stroud Green Rd   020 7263 2114   9–1D
*This "great local restaurant" has been a Finsbury Park fixture for nearly 25
years, serving a full range of "cheap and cheerful" Italian fare as well as
pizza. A significant following from North London's Italian community is a
testament to its authenticity – and, naturally, it is bambino-friendly.* / N4 3PX;
www.pizzeriapappagone.co.uk; @pizza_pappagone; Mon-Sun midnight.

Planque E8 NEW
322 Acton Mews   020 7254 3414   14–2A
*Two Haggerston railway arches will host this September 2021 newcomer –
a wine bar, restaurant, club and shop for hipsters keen on a glass of vino. At
the stoves, Aussie-born Seb Myers, who made a name for himself at the not-
dissimilar P Franco.* / E8 4EA; www.planque.co.uk; cards only; booking online only.

Plaquemine Lock N1 £47   3 3 3
139 Graham St   020 7688 1488   9–3D
*Perfect "when you want a quick po'boy or gumbo" – Jacob Kenedy (of Bocca
di Lupo) pays tribute to his Louisiana ancestry, with this labour-of-love
project: a colourfully decorated, converted boozer on the side of an Islington
canal. Its "nice Cajun food" is well-rated: "still a little too much fried stuff for
my liking, but the taste is good".* / N1 8LB; plaqlock.com; @plaqueminelock; Sun &
Mon 10 pm, Tue-Fri 11 pm, Sat midnight; cards only.

Plateau E14 £80   2 2 3
4th Floor, Canada Sq   020 7715 7100   12–1C
*Stunning views over Canary Wharf are the most reliable attraction at D&D
London's expense-accounter haven, atop Canada Place. Perhaps due to the
Covid-inspired closure of the money-factories for much of the previous
period, it has inspired limited feedback in recent times, of a solid but
unspectacular nature.* / E14 5ER; www.plateau-restaurant.co.uk; @plateaulondon;
Mon-Sat 11.30 pm; closed Sun.

The Plimsoll N4 NEW
52 Saint Thomas's Road   9–2B
*Ever-changing and fantastic small plates served by an ambitious chef duo
won praise for Jamie Allan and Ed McIlroy in their two years at The
Compton Arms in Islington. With the aid of a Kickstarter campaign, they
have converted a clapped-out old boozer (The Auld Triangle) in Finsbury
Park to be this new forever home, set to open in Autumn 2021.* / N4 2QW;
Thu-Sun 6 pm.

The Plough SW14 £56 ②②④
42 Christ Church Rd   020 8876 7833   11–2A

"More a pub with food than a gastropub" – it's worth knowing about this large hostelry in the backstreets of Sheen, "close to Richmond Park", thanks to its characterful interior and lovely outside terrace. / SW14; www.theplough.com; Mon-Thu 9.30 pm, Fri & Sat 10 pm, Sun 9 pm.

PLU NW8 NEW £160 ⑤④④
12 Blenheim Terrace   020 7624 7663   9–3A

"One of the most creative and delicious meals I've ever had" – Elliot Moss inspires rapturous reviews from a small but very enthusiastic fan club, who acclaim his "luxurious" and "intimate" St John's Wood two-year-old as one of London's unsung gastronomic adventures. The restaurant recommends three hours to enjoy its £125, twelve-course tasting menu: "a feast that will amaze and delight any gourmand, providing sensory overload of the sights, smells and tastes". ("My husband let the restaurant know in advance that it was my birthday, I think in the hope of scoring me a little extra cake or some such but what happened was phenomenal. At the end of the meal my dessert arrived with my portrait, in chocolate, on the plate!!! The chef, who works alone in the kitchen, is an artist with some of the best cooking skills either of us have ever experienced.") / NW8 0EB; www.plurestaurant.co.uk; Wed-Sun 8 pm.

Plum Valley W1 ③②②
20 Gerrard St   020 7494 4366   5–3A

"Delicious dim-sum" is the menu highlight at this favourite, family-run Cantonese stalwart on Gerrard Street. "Their terrace was a real find during the pandemic" – one reason why it generated more reports than some in Chinatown this year. / W1D 6JQ; www.plumvalleylondon.com; Sun-Thu 11.30 pm, Fri & Sat 12.30 am.

Pollen Street Social W1 £127 ④④④
8-10 Pollen St   020 7290 7600   3–2C

"More relaxed than some other more pompous establishments" – Jason Atherton's renowned Mayfair HQ maintained strong ratings this year. "So slick and so professional" – "you can't help but smile when you eat his food", which is "reliably superb, as is the warm welcome". "It's definitely the kind of place men take their girlfriends to propose – fabulously glamorous." / W1S 1NQ; www.pollenstreetsocial.com; @PollenStSocial; Tue-Sat 9.30 pm; closed Sun & Mon; booking max 6 may apply.

Le Pont de la Tour SE1 £95 ②②②
36d Shad Thames   020 7403 8403   10–4D

"You can't beat the amazing views" over the Thames at this D&D stalwart near Tower Bridge, although the golden glow that made it famous, when it was launched at the heart of the late Sir Terence Conran's 1990s 'gastrodome' – has somewhat dissipated nowadays. It still has real attractions – a large outside terrace, "outstanding wine", and Gallic cuisine that's fair-to-good – and, given its convenience to the City – it's "especially good for entertaining overseas clients" (as Tony and Cherie Blair did Bill and Hillary Clinton back in the day). / SE1 2YE; www.lepontdelatour.co.uk; @lepontdelatour; Mon-Sat 10 pm, Sun 9 pm; No trainers; Take bookings all week via phone and/or online.

Popolo EC2 £55 ⑤④③
26 Rivington Street   020 7729 4299   13–1B

"Exceptional food" – in a Spanish/Moorish vein – combined with a friendly buzz and "great staff, too" again all win a major thumbs-up for Jonathan Lawson's small and casual Shoreditch fixture, with counter seating on the ground floor and a compact upstairs dining room. / EC2A 3DU; popoloshoreditch.com; @popolo_EC2; no booking.

Poppies £53 [3][3][2]

59 Old Compton St, W1 020 7482 2977 4–2D
30 Hawley Cr, NW1 020 7267 0440 9–2B
6-8 Hanbury St, E1 020 7247 0892 13–2C

"Proper fish 'n' chips" is the order of the day at this self-consciously old-school trio from Pat 'Pops' Newland, an 81-year-old East Ender with a lifetime in the trade behind him. The fish arrives daily from Peterhead in Aberdeenshire, and 1950s memorabilia adorns the walls. Sceptics say it's "not bad, but expensive for what it is".

Poppy's £25 [3][2][4]

129-131 Brackenbury Road, W6 020 8741 4928 8–1C
30 Greyhound Road, W6 020 7385 9264 8–2C
78 Glenthorne Road, W6 020 8748 2351 8–2C

"Eclectic decor" (foliage, stuffed animals, antiques…) – "so quirky, I always love it!" – adds va-va-voom to these "cheap 'n' cheerful" Thai cafés in W6. They make a great choice for a budget get-together, as "BYOB means a trip is excellent value".

Il Portico W8 £73 [3][4][3]

277 Kensington High St 020 7602 6262 8–1D

This "lovely neighbourhood restaurant" opposite the Design Museum on Kensington High Street has welcomed customers with "delicious family cooking" from Emilia-Romagna for 55 years. Current owner James Chiavarini has driven its modernisation since the retirement of his father, Pino, who now runs the family farm in Kent. "It's not cheap", but "there's a reason it's packed every day without having done a marketing drive". / W8 6NA; www.ilportico.co.uk; @ilporticolondon; Tue-Sun 11 pm; closed Mon.

Portland W1 £92 [5][5][3]

113 Great Portland Street 020 7436 3261 2–1B

"Very serious cooking that's totally unpretentious", with "exciting seasonal flavour combinations" and "sensational tastes", won adulatory reviews this year for Will Lander and Daniel Morgenthau's well-known Fitzrovian. It's not a flash place – "a simple interior with open kitchen" – but "friendly, highly professional service" and access to "a good selection of sensible-price wines" further add to its appeal. / W1W 6QQ; www.portlandrestaurant.co.uk; @portland113; Tue-Sat 10 pm; closed Sun & Mon; Take bookings all week via phone and/or online.

Portobello Ristorante Pizzeria W11 £73 [3][3][5]

7 Ladbroke Road 020 7221 1373 7–2B

A "friendly Italian serving great fresh fish" (dramatically displayed in a chiller cabinet) – this Notting Hill local has a "real buzz" – and is "always reassuringly full of Italians". It also serves "top pizza – among a lot of competition", and a decent range of pasta dishes. There's a "great year-round terrace with a roof which opens in the summer". / W11 3PA; www.portobellolondon.co.uk.

Poster Bar at the RA W1 NEW

Royal Academy, Burlington Gardens, Piccadilly 3–3D

Joining José Pizarro at the RA is this less-formal tapas bar from the star Spaniard. The RA's food operations in recent years have always conformed to the low expectations of gallery catering generally, but our hunch is that José didn't get the memo telling him that no great shakes are expected, and that actually it may be rather good… / W1J 0BD; Wed-Sat 10.30 pm, Sun 5 pm.

Potli W6 £46 **3 4 3**
319-321 King St 020 8741 4328 8–2B

"Imaginative food" at *"good prices"* has won a big local reputation for this zesty Indian on Hammersmith's *'restaurant row'* near Ravenscourt Park. Its ratings slipped a tad this year though, on account of those who thought it *"still impressive but arguably finding it harder to stay ahead of the strong local competition"*. / W6 9NH; www.potli.co.uk; @Potlirestaurant; Mon-Thu 10 pm, Fri & Sat 10.30 pm, Sun 9 pm.

La Poule au Pot SW1 £66 **2 2 5**
231 Ebury St 020 7730 7763 6–2D

"Forty years old, with great character and personality, and never, ever changing" – this *"most romantic and cosy"*, candle-lit Pimlico charmer has long been in contention as London's top tip for seduction, thanks not least to its numerous secluded tables in dark niches (or, *"you can sit outside on a sunny lunchtime and transport yourself to the South of France"*). For a *"French hit"*, the *"typical bistro fare"* (circa 1975) is *"enjoyable"* if resolutely un-foodie and delivered with variable efficiency, but lots of characterful *"Gallic charm"*. *"The magnum bottles of unlabelled wine are fun"* too (*"they dip it with a stick at the end to measure how much you have had...."*) / SW1W 8UT; www.pouleaupot.co.uk; @PouleAuPot; Mon-Sun 9 pm; No trainers; Take bookings all week via phone and/or online.

Prairie Fire W12 NEW £35
Arch 88-89 Wood Lane Arches 020 8740 5349 1–2B

This late 2019 newcomer was the first opening in the glossy-looking row of redeveloped railway arches by Wood Lane tube (near the Westfield John Lewis). It is the first permanent site for Kansas-born chef and pitmaster Michael Gratz, who – since 2013 – has been earning street-food cred for his proper Kansas smoked brisket (lots of sauce) plus other US-style meaty treats (dogs, pulled pork...). Limited survey feedback as yet, but all of it very enthusiastic and we've had good vibes from everything we've heard of the place. / W12 7LH; www.prairiefirebbq.com; @Prairiefire_bbq; Sun-Thu 11 pm, Fri & Sat midnight.

Prawn on the Lawn N1 £65 **5 3 2**
292-294 St Paul's Rd 020 3302 8668 9–2D

It's *"hard to beat PoTL"* for *"fantastic, fresh and tasty fish and seafood"* – a restaurant/fishmonger on Highbury Corner which is supplied daily from Devon and Cornwall (it has a sister venue in Padstow). Staff are *"knowledgeable and friendly"*, and there's *"a great matching wine list"*. The only – but frequent – complaint is that it's *"teeny-tiny"*, so you *"have to book ahead, and can't always get a table when you want one"*. / N1 2LY; prawnonthelawn.com; @PrawnOnTheLawn; Wed-Sat 10 pm, Sun 5 pm; closed Sun D, closed Mon & Tue; no Amex.

Primeur N5 £56 **3 4 3**
116 Petherton Rd 020 7226 5271 1–1C

High quality 'bistronomy' wins praise for this communal-table and low-intervention-wine venue, set inside a 1920s car garage between Highbury and Stoke Newington. *"I love the fact that the menu is small and things occasionally run out towards the end of the night"* – a clear indication that the produce is fresh and not stored for long. / N5 2RT; www.primeurN5.co.uk; Tue-Sat 11 pm, Sun 8.30 pm; closed Tue-Fri L, closed Mon; booking max 7 may apply.

The Prince of Wales W6 NEW £41
73 Dalling Road 020 8563 1713 8–2B

In November 2020, this gastropub-with-rooms newcomer (from the Big Smoke Brew Company) opened on a Hammersmith site formerly known as The Rook's Nest, following extensive refurbishment. Eats are hearty, including smoked meats from the pub's wood-fired Bertha oven, while at weekends, there's bottomless brunch and Sunday roasts. / W6 0JD; www.princeofwales-townhouse.co.uk; @PrinceofwalesW6; Mon-Sun 11 pm.

Princess of Shoreditch EC2 £70 443
76 Paul St 020 7729 9270 13–1B

You're dating yourself if you remember when this busy, characterful pub was part of the first colonisation of Shoreditch as hipster central. Cuisine-wise, it has had highs and lows in recent years. But in early 2021 came news that 25-year-old Ruth Hansom – Great British Menu finalist and the youngest woman to win Young Chef of the Year – is now at the stoves. "Creative without reinventing anything, her emphasis is on fresh seasonal produce and the end result is mighty fine!" It's served alongside "a small, decent but reasonably priced wine list". / EC2A 4NE; www.theprincessofshoreditch.com; @princessofs; Mon-Sun 11 pm; no Amex; booking D only.

The Princess Victoria W12 £49 334
217 Uxbridge Road 020 8749 4466 8–1B

Set a little back from the busy Uxbridge Road, this large Victorian gin palace (est. 1829) retains much of its period grandeur and celebrates its history nowadays by offering over 100 artisan and big-name gins at the bar. Part of the Three Cheers Pub Co, it wins all-round solid ratings, including for its gastropub menu and pizzas (also available to take away). / W12 9DH; www.princessvictoria.co.uk/; @threecheerspubs; Mon-Thu 11 pm, Fri & Sat midnight, Sun 10.30 pm; Take bookings all week via phone and/or online.

Prix Fixe W1 £48 322
39 Dean St 020 7734 5976 5–2A

"A decent French option in Soho", with a "good varied menu" – this brasserie (sibling to nearby Pierre Victoire) provides "excellent value for the West End". It's especially "handy for the early fixed-priced menus"; after 6pm, despite the name, it moves to an à la carte format – which "isn't as much to shout about". / W1D 4PU; www.prixfixe.net; @rixfixesoho; Mon-Sun 11.30 pm.

The Promenade at The Dorchester W1 £148 244
The Dorchester Hotel, 53 Park Lane 020 7629 8888 3–3A

A "quintessentially British afternoon tea" is served in the Promenade, the heart of this grand hotel – ideal for idly people-watching as you gossip over finger sandwiches, scones and Earl Grey. Needless to say, it comes with "impeccable service". / W1K 1QA; www.dorchestercollection.com; @TheDorchester; Mon-Wed 8 pm, Thu-Sun 10.30 pm; No shorts.

Provender E11 £41 443
17 High St 020 8530 3050 1–1D

This neighbourhood café-brasserie in Wanstead "can be relied on to please and delight", as it has for a decade under veteran restaurateur Max Renzland and his team – "lovely people, consistently professional and kind". The dishes are "beautifully prepared" and range from such French bistro classics as "onion soup and celeriac remoulade – to the gourmet Christmas dinner they do some years". / E11 2AA; www.provenderlondon.co.uk; @ProvenderBistro; Tue-Sun 10 pm; closed Mon; booking max 10 may apply.

Prufrock Coffee EC1 £14 333
23-25 Leather Ln 020 7242 0467 10–2A

This established and well-known Leather Lane caffeine hub may well be equal to the boast: "best coffee shop and baristas in the UK" – it's certainly "much better than the nearby chains", and serves "very good, proper coffee" from a selection of leading independent roasters. The breakfasts and light meals are also tasty renditions of carefully sourced ingredients. / EC1N 7TE; www.prufrockcoffee.com; @PrufrockCoffee; Mon-Fri 4.30 pm, Sat & Sun 5 pm; closed Mon-Sun D; no Amex.

Punjab WC2 £43 3 2 3
80 Neal St 020 7836 9787 5–2C

This Covent Garden institution lays claim to being the oldest north Indian restaurant in London, est. 1946, and is now run by the great-grandson of the founder. It owes its staying power to the "great Punjabi regional dishes" on the menu – "a friend was so impressed, he said it was nearly as good as his grandmother's cooking" – and these days there are also "interesting vegan and vegetarian options". / WC2H 9PA; www.punjab.co.uk; Mon-Sat 11 pm, Sun 10 pm; booking max 8 may apply.

Pure Indian Cooking SW6 £49 3 4 3
67 Fulham High Street 020 7736 2521 11–1B

This "underrated", modern curry house, just north of Putney Bridge, showcases "Indian cooking on another level" – "the room may be simple but the food is complex, delicious and varied". Chef-patron Shilpa Dandekar trained in both Eastern and Western culinary traditions, under Raymond Blanc and India's smart Taj Group, while her husband and co-owner Faheem Vanoo runs the front of house. / SW6 3JJ; www.pureindiancooking.com; @PureCooking; Thu-Sat 11 pm, Sun 10.30 pm; closed Sat L, closed Mon & Tue & Wed.

Quaglino's SW1 £88 2 2 5
16 Bury St 020 7930 6767 3–3D

Big, "stylish and atmospheric space" in St James's – a 1920s ballroom rescued and revamped by the late Sir Terence Conran in 1993, and now run by D&D London – that's one of the few places in London where you can make a splashy occasion of a meal with live music. Its modern British cuisine steers a middle ground nowadays – avoiding the brickbats of a number of years ago, but seldom igniting passionate praise. / SW1Y 6AJ; www.quaglinos-restaurant.co.uk; @quaglinos; Mon-Wed 10.30 pm, Thu 12.30 am, Fri 2 am, Sat 3 am, Sun 4 pm; closed Sun D; No trainers.

The Quality Chop House EC1 £86 3 5 4
94 Farringdon Rd 020 7278 1452 10–1A

"The service is always excellent – really warm and welcoming", at this "nostalgic" and loveable Victorian relic in Clerkenwell: a 'Progressive Working Class' institution, established in 1869 and lovingly restored from the 1990s onwards by a succession of owners, of which the latest are Will Lander and Daniel Morgenthau. In line with the subtle updating of its ancient and boothed interior, the "classic" cuisine has been "modernised and amped-up a notch" and it offers an attractive combination of "tradition and sheer flavour". Top Tip – "mince on dripping toast cannot be beaten!" / EC1R 3EA; thequalitychophouse.com; @QualityChop.

Quartieri NW6 £46 4 3 3
300 Kilburn High Road 020 7625 8822 1–2B

Full marks for tasty Neapolitan pizza, pasta, arancini and other tasty bites, say fans of this Kilburn independent, started by a group of friends who met in Naples back in the day. / NW6 2DB; www.quartieri.co.uk; @quartierilondon; Mon-Sun 11 pm; Take bookings all week via phone and/or online.

Queens of Mayfair W1 NEW £37
17 Queen Street 020 7459 4617 3–3B

For a posh coffee (caffeine aficionados Difference coffee supply the rare beans), a civilised bun, breakfast, lunchtime sarnie or simple supper (complete with cocktails), this August 2020 newcomer is worth remembering. It's the passion project of sisters Victoria and Grace Sheppard, whose successful careers elsewhere finally led here. / W1J 5PH; www.queensofmayfair.com; @mayfairqueens; Mon-Wed, Fri 6 pm, Thu 10 pm; closed Mon-Wed, Fri D, closed Sat & Sun.

Le Querce SE23 £53 5 4 3
66-68 Brockley Rise   020 8690 3761   1–4D

"Wonderful Italian food, cooked and served by the family" is the hallmark of this Brockley Rise trattoria from Sardinian chef Antonello Serra, his wife Rosanna and her brother Roberto. "We're lucky to live nearby – love it", is the locals' chorus. "The seafood is always superb, and the home-made ice creams are not to be missed – once I'd tried their banana, cardamom and ginger gelato, I was ever after confused why all ice cream isn't made in that flavour". Other off-the-track gelato options include chilli, garlic and aubergine! / SE23 1LN; www.lequerce.co.uk; @lequercerest; Wed-Sat 8 pm, Sun 4 pm; closed Wed-Sat L closed Sun D, closed Mon & Tue; Take bookings all week via phone and/or online.

Quilon SW1 £79 5 4 2
41 Buckingham Gate   020 7821 1899   2–4B

"South Indian cuisine at its best" – with "coastal influences and high-quality ingredients" – and notably "great seafood dishes" – has established this Westminster venue from the luxury Taj Group at the top of the capital's dining scene for more than two decades. Founding chef Sriram Aylur is still at the helm, and champions Keralan cuisine for its lightness and multidimensional flavours. A few minutes' walk from Parliament, it's a known haunt of politicos. Top Tip: "the restaurant is more dark and gloomy at the back, so ask for a table at the front". / SW1E 6AF; www.quilon.co.uk; @thequilon; SRA-Food Made Good – 2 stars.

Quo Vadis W1 £83 3 3 5
26-29 Dean St   020 7437 9585   4–1D

Dining in the "grande dame of Soho restaurants", now edging towards her centenary year, is "always a treat", with "wonderful ambience", "small but perfectly formed menu" and "fine cuisine" from Jeremy Lee. There is also a slightly more cautious school of thought on the place, which says: "the food doesn't knock your socks off, but overall it's a great place for a meal". These days it shares the premises – formerly a brothel and home to Karl Marx – with a private members' club and the Hart Brothers' Barrafina. / W1D 3LL; www.quovadissoho.co.uk; @QuoVadisSoho; Tue-Sat 10 pm; closed Sun & Mon.

Rabbit SW3 £68 3 2 3
172 King's Rd   020 3750 0172   6–3C

"Tasty sharing plates" – sourced from the family farm and vineyard in Sussex – earn general praise for this "charming" but "cramped" and oddly proportioned faux-rustic dining room in Chelsea. Rabbit was the second of the Gladwin brothers' 'farm-to-fork' small plates London venues, following The Shed in Notting Hill and preceding Nutbourne in Battersea and Sussex in Soho. The fifth, The Fat Badger in Richmond, is due to open in late 2021. / SW3 4UP; www.rabbit-restaurant.com; @RabbitResto.

Rabot 1745 SE1 £64 2 2 3
2-4 Bedale St   020 7378 8226   10–4C

"Out-of-this-world hot chocolate" is the star turn at this choc-themed bar-restaurant in Borough Market, "decorated in the style of a West Indian chocolate plantation, which gives it a great vibe". "Coffee is good", the "breakfasts are also decent", and there's a "great terrace overlooking Borough Market". "It turns from coffee shop by day to bar by night, serving cocktails inspired by chocolate". / SE1 9AL; www.rabot1745.com; @rabot1745; Mon & Tue 4.30 pm, Wed-Sat 11 pm, Sun 5 pm; closed Mon & Tue, Sun D.

Radici N1 £75 222
30 Almeida St 020 7354 4777 9–3D

This modern Italian from D&D London and chef Francesco Mazzei – on the Islington site that once housed Almeida (RIP) – wins OK feedback, but inspires nothing approaching the excitement that might be expected from such a team of backers. Local fans hail its "generous" Calabrian cuisine and "good quality pizza" – sceptics feel its "saving grace is the location opposite the Almeida Theatre…" / N1 1AD; www.radici.uk; @radici_n1; Tue-Sat 10 pm, Sun 3.45 pm; closed Tue, Wed L closed Sun D, closed Mon.

Ragam W1 £37 432
57 Cleveland St 020 7636 9098 2–1B

"Superb", "authentic Keralan food and old-fashioned Indian service" are the hallmarks of this veteran, close to the Telecom Tower – and "the value is unbelievable, especially for central London". "The food went through a down patch but has improved again" – "despite the somewhat odd recent renovation and updated menu". / W1T 4JN; www.ragamindian.co.uk; Mon-Sun 11 pm.

Randall & Aubin W1 £68 445
14-16 Brewer St 020 7287 4447 4–2D

"Freshest seafood"… "buzzy vibe"… "excellent staff"… "fabulous location and decor" (inherited from an Edwardian butchers, est. 1911) – "you can't possibly go wrong" at this Soho landmark, converted nowadays into a "fun" Champagne and seafood bar. "Not a place for a peaceful dinner but then not everyone has a glitter ball. Despite all they've been through in the last 18 months, staff are still welcoming and cheerful" – while "the new outside tables are a bonus". Top Tip: "go for the specials, you'll never be disappointed". / W1F OSG; www.randallandaubin.com; @randallandaubin; Mon-Sat midnight, Sun 11 pm; booking L only.

Rasa N16 £41 433
55 Stoke Newington Church St 020 7249 0344 1–1C

The "dosas are absolutely delicious" at the Stoke Newington original – and now sole remaining – restaurant from Kerala's Das Sreedharan, who opened it 28 years ago. The bright-pink outfit has long been in contention as the "best veggie curry house in north London" – and its high food ratings this year show standards have held up well over the years. It has spawned seven offshoots since it first opened, of which the last two (opposite and off Oxford Street), closed down recently. / N16 0AR; www.rasarestaurants.com; Thu-Sat 9.30 pm, Wed 2.30 pm.

Ravi Shankar NW1 £35 322
132-135 Drummond St 020 7388 6458 9–4C

"Amazing Indian veg food at bargain prices", not least the "tasty thali", makes this well-established fixture one of the most popular in the Little India block behind Euston station, long-time home to "excellent value" South Asian scoff. / NW1 2HL; www.ravishankarbhelpoori.com; Mon-Sun 10 pm.

RAW – Fish & Cocktails W1 NEW £57 432
110 Great Portland Street 07958 051896 3–1C

"Incredibly fresh fish" (oysters, ceviche, prawns with truffle…) "and sea-themed cocktails" help win a strong thumbs-up for Ivan Simeoli's "friendly" new Fitzrovia seafood bar… and you can buy seafood to take home for your supper, too. He launched it in May 2021, and it's inherited the (sometimes "noisy") premises, furniture and decor of what was formerly his venture, Laboratorio Pizza (RIP). / W1W; www.rawfishlondon.com; @rawfishlondon; Fri & Sat, Tue-Thu 10 pm, Sun 5 pm; closed Tue-Thu L closed Sun D, closed Mon; Take bookings all week via phone and/or online.

The Red Lion & Sun N6 £55 **3** **3** **4**
25 North Road   020 8340 1780   9–1B

This "excellent local" freehouse in Highgate Village offers "really good pub food at reasonable prices for the area", a "strong wine list" and "often interesting cooking" that references cuisines as far flung as Basque, Korean and Sri Lankan. / N6; www.theredlionandsun.com; @redlionandsun; Mon-Sun 11 pm.

Regency Cafe SW1 £15 **3** **3** **5**
17-19 Regency Street   020 7821 6596   2–4C

"It feels like you're stepping back in time" at this "traditional greasy spoon", down a Westminster side street, where nothing much has changed with the decor since it first opened in 1946 (it's much in demand for films set in the post-war era). "The best bargain in town", with a "buzzing atmosphere", it receives top billing as "everything you could want for the perfect breakfast" (indeed, it won the Harden's breakfast award a few years back). / SW1P 4BY; regencycafe.co.uk; Mon-Fri 7.15 pm, Sat 12 pm; closed Sat D, closed Sun.

Le Relais de Venise L'Entrecôte £53 **3** **2** **2**
120 Marylebone Ln, W1   020 7486 0878   2–1A
50 Dean St, W1   020 3475 4202   5–3A
5 Throgmorton St, EC2   020 7638 6325   10–2C

"If you like steak-frites, Relais de Venise can't be beaten", say fans of this vieille école French steakhouse chain, where a set menu (including second helpings) of walnut salad, frites, and sliced entrecôte beef with a 'secret' sauce has been served in Paris since 1959. "Still a good place to eat, and I've been going to their restaurants for over 40 years." A London branch opened in Marylebone 15 years ago, followed by Soho and the City. There's a choice of desserts, with sticky toffee pudding added as a concession to les Rosbifs. / www.relaisdevenise.com.

Republic W4 NEW £49
301-303 Chiswick High Road   020 8154 2712   8–2A

Chef Kuldeep Mattegunta and Mustaq Tappewale, both formerly of Kricket, joined forces to open this permanent location in Chiswick (on the former site of Hedone, RIP) in late 2020, just at the moment Tier 3 came into operation (and had coverage on the Beeb as a result). It's the product of a series of pop-ups serving adventurous Indian food – little initial feedback so far, but such as we have says the Indian tapas cuisine is "outstanding". / W4 4HH; republicw4.com; @Republic - An Indian Eatery; Mon-Sat 10 pm; closed Sun.

Restaurant at The Capital SW3 £85
22-24 Basil St   020 7591 1202   6–1D

After a succession of different chefs (including Nathan Outlaw and Adam Simmonds), Chris Prow has presided over the stoves since May 2021 at this small, luxurious hotel, a short walk from Harrods. A new, all-day dining menu is a recent introduction, as well as an outdoor seating area which opened for the first time this summer, boosting the capacity of what is a bijou dining space. / SW3 1AT; www.warwickhotels.com/the-capital; @hotelcapital; Mon-Sun 10 pm; Take bookings all week via phone and/or online.

Reubens W1 £50 **3** **2** **2**
79 Baker St   020 7486 0035   2–1A

"Terrific salt beef on rye in a great location" – this classic Jewish deli in Marylebone can claim to be the only kosher restaurant in the West End, and celebrates its half-century next year. Two years ago it was rescued from closure by Golders Green restaurateur Lee Landau, who had eaten here as a boy. He has renovated the basement to add fine dining to the deli counter and tables on the ground floor. / W1U 6RG; www.reubensrestaurant.co.uk; Sun-Thu 10 pm, Fri 3 pm; closed Fri D, closed Sat; no Amex.

Rhythm & Brews W4 £25 3 4 5
22 Walpole Gardens 020 7998 3873 8–2A

Select sounds from the in-house vinyl collection to listen to while you sip excellent coffee at this "wonderful local café" near Turnham Green. There's also "surprisingly great food (the chicken salad is a delight to the eye and the palate)". / W4 4HA; rhythmandbrews.co.uk; @InfoBrews; Mon-Sat 6 pm, Sun 5 pm; closed Sun D.

The Rib Man E1 £14 5 3 -
Brick Lane, Brick Lane Market no tel 13–2C

'Holy Fuck' hot sauce is just one of Mark Gevaux's unique contributions to the London street food scene. His Sunday stall – selling ribs from outdoor-reared pigs sourced from Norfolk and Suffolk farms – has only just, as of September 2021, returned to Brick Lane post-lockdown, but fans know that he also pops up at his beloved West Ham's home games, and items are available to buy online. / E1 6HR; www.theribman.co.uk; @theribman; Sun 2 pm; closed Sun D, closed Mon-Fri & Sat; No bookings.

Riccardo's SW3 £55 3 2 3
126 Fulham Rd 020 7370 6656 6–3B

It's "nice to sit under the canopy on a summer's evening", even if it "can be crowded and noisy", at this "well-established neighbourhood Italian", on a prominent Chelsea corner site. An early exponent of serving Italian food tapas-style, it still wins praise for its "reasonable prices" and dependable standards. / SW3 6HU; www.riccardos.it; @ricardoslondon; Mon-Sun 11.30 pm.

Rick Stein SW14 £83 2 2 4
Tideway Yard, 125 Mortlake High St 020 8878 9462 11–1A

A "wonderful setting on the banks of the Thames" near Barnes Bridge means it's often hard to secure a booking at this famous Cornish brand's London outpost. But even those who find the trip "an enjoyable experience", can note that "it's a bit overpriced for not-awe-inspiring seafood", and less enthusiastic reports are "quite disappointed" by both "flavourless" food and the odd incident of "'off' service". "Our conclusion was that the Stein magic had been stretched a little too far… but the view is nice!" / SW14 8SN; www.rickstein.com/eat-with-us/barnes; @SteinBarnes; Mon-Sun 10 pm.

Riding House Café W1 £63 2 3 3
43-51 Great Titchfield St 020 7927 0840 3–1C

Breakfast or brunch is "a real treat" at this all-day bar-brasserie just north of Oxford Street in Fitzrovia, which provides "a fantastic choice" in a "lovely open setting". There's little feedback on dining options later in the day, despite a recent revamp and the introduction of a five-course tasting menu. / W1W 7PQ; www.ridinghousecafe.co.uk; @ridinghousecafe; Mon-Fri 10 pm, Sat & Sun 4 pm; closed Sat & Sun D.

The Rising Sun NW7 £65 3 3 3
137 Marsh Ln 020 8959 1357 1–1B

This Mill Hill gastropub is "fast becoming a 'place to be seen' in north London" for its cute, Grade-II-listed 17th-century good looks and its "exceptional", "innovative Italian cooking" from an "ever-changing menu". "Run by the popular Delnevo brothers (Luca and Matteo), it's a place "you come away from feeling uplifted by the happiness of the staff". / NW7 4EY; www.therisingsunmillhill.com; @therisingsunpub; Tue-Sat 9.30 pm, Sun 8 pm; closed Tue, Wed L, closed Mon.

Ristorante Frescobaldi W1 £86 3 3 2
15 New Burlington Pl   020 3693 3435   4–2A

This grand Mayfair Italian serves "beautiful" Tuscan dishes and boasts "a top outdoor space" in the shape of a newly extended 50-seat terrace. It's the first foray into London restaurant ownership by an ancient Florentine dynasty with a long record of doing business with England – the Frescobaldis provided banking services to Edwards I & II and wine to Henry VIII. The family currently owns 11 Italian wine estates, which feature prominently on the restaurant's list. The downbeat view is that a meal here is "nice enough… but not if you're paying for yourself!" / W1S 5HX; www.frescobaldirestaurants.com; @Frescobaldi_LDN; Mon-Sat 10 pm; closed Sun.

Rita's Soho W1 NEW
49 Lexington Street   4–2C

On the dead cute Soho site that was for years Aurora (RIP) – just opposite Andrew Edmunds and with a tiny courtyard to the rear – this autumn 2021 newcomer from Missy Flynn and Gabe Pryce is the latest site for a brand that started as a pop-up in 2012 in Hackney, and has landed here via Bodega Rita's (the Coal Drops Yard spot that closed in 2020, but has since relaunched on Cowcross Street in Clerkenwell). On the menu, a fairly eclectic assortment of modern bistro dishes with Mexican and US influences. / W1F 9AP; www.ritasdining.com; Sun-Thu 10.30 pm, Fri & Sat 11 pm.

The Ritz,
Palm Court W1 £124 3 4 5
150 Piccadilly   020 7493 8181   3–4C

"Exceptionally good afternoon tea" is rightly renowned at this "elegant and traditional" gilded chamber – still the gold standard for the ceremony after all these years and an "all-round special occasion" where you are very well looked after. "Always our Christmas and birthday treat: expensive, but worth it!" / W1J 9BR; www.theritzlondon.com; @theritzlondon; Mon-Sun 9 pm; Jacket & tie required.

The Ritz W1 £116 3 4 5
150 Piccadilly   020 7493 8181   3–4C

"By far the most attractive dining room in London" is a regularly made claim for this uniquely "romantic" Louis XVI chamber: "one of the last places in the country (sadly) where proper silver service of the traditional, gueridon variety is delivered; and with faultless aplomb; and also (mostly) without pomposity". Even those who say "the food is ultimately secondary to the amazing ambience of the room" often note "it's still very delicious"; and quite a few reporters feel John Williams's "classic French cuisine with top quality ingredients and superb sauces" unfairly risks being overlooked ("super-refined and exceptionally beautiful – my guest was a little less excited by the flavour combinations than I was, but, on the whole, dishes lived up to their appearance, and I felt it was almost worthy of a second Michelin star"). "Not cheap, but you get what you pay for!" (and that includes the weekend dinner dances). / W1J 9BR; www.theritzlondon.com; @theritzlondon; Mon-Sun 9.30 pm; Jacket & tie required; Take bookings all week via phone and/or online; SRA-Food Made Good – 2 stars.

Riva SW13 £65 3 4 2
169 Church Rd   020 8748 0434   11–1A

A foodie mecca for more than 30 years, Andreas Riva's understated northern Italian specialist in Barnes "feels like a second home" to its uber-loyal fan club. "The focus is on depth of flavour that's true to their roots, not Instagrammability" – with a "wide choice of specials using ultra-fresh ingredients". "We simply love it – as good as the best in Italy (although the closure of Hammersmith Bridge makes it difficult to get there!)" In past times, there have been gripes from some reporters that a visit can feel like a regulars' party to which they were not invited, but this year there was nothing but praise for the "polite and easy going" staff. / SW13 9HR; Tue-Sun 10 pm; closed Mon.

The River Café W6 £114 🎖️🎖️🎖️
Thames Wharf, Rainville Rd   020 7386 4200   8–2C

"Yes, the food is simply presented, yes, there are paper tablecloths, yes, it's expensive… but it's worth every penny!!" That's still the winning verdict on Ruth Rogers' world-famous canteen, where it's "so difficult to get a table", despite a hard-to-find location in a Hammersmith backstreet, and relatively humble – albeit "slightly starry" – premises. (The site started life as the staff canteen for husband, Richard Rogers' architectural practice). That "this is the restaurant that pioneered the idea of produce first", further enthuses its devotees, many of whom are longtime regulars ("we've been coming for 25 years and have never been disappointed"). And yet, despite all the positives, many diners just can't stomach a bill that can seem "terrifying", or even plain "ludicrous". Hence, for the umpteenth year, it's voted London's most overpriced restaurant by the sizeable minority who feel "it may be absolutely exceptional every time, but on occasion, you do think they're just taking the piss". Is there a way of reconciling these two competing camps? A fair middle view is as follows: "£540 for four people with one bottle of cheapish wine and a couple of gins. Can a basic Italian meal be worth that much? Well, on a beautiful summer evening on the terrace by the Thames, it feels like being on holiday: so overpriced it may be… but worth every penny!" / W6 9HA; www.rivercafe.co.uk; @RiverCafeLondon; Mon-Sat 11 pm, Sun 5.30 pm.

Roast SE1 £79 🎖️🎖️🎖️
Stoney St   0845 034 7300   10–4C

"It's a lovely room, and fantastically well located, but the food never quite lives up to expectations" at this Borough Market fixture, picturesquely perched above the market in a glazed portico that was once part of the Royal Opera House. The culinary theme is British, er, roasts, and even though most diners do actually like the results, "the prices are a bit of a fantasy". Top Tip – breakfast here gives you all the benefit of the location, and is better value. (There were plans a couple of years ago for a spin-off near Broadcasting House, but these seem to have hit the backburner.) / SE1 1TL; www.roast-restaurant.com; @roastrestaurant; Mon-Sat 10.30 pm, Sun 6.30 pm; closed Sun D.

Rocca £45 🎖️🎖️🎖️
73 Old Brompton Rd, SW7   020 7225 3413   6–2B
75-79 Dulwich Village, SE21   020 8299 6333   1–4D

This "good, dependable local Italian" duo in South Kensington and Dulwich Village can be relied on for plates of "excellent pizza" and "freshly made pasta" at sensible prices. There's a "great atmosphere when they're busy", and "children are made very welcome". The South Ken branch, formerly part of Christie's auction house, has a useful heated terrace for dining al fresco. / www.roccarestaurants.com.

The Roebuck W4 £50 🎖️🎖️🎖️
122 Chiswick High Rd   020 8995 4392   8–2A

This "spacious" late-Victorian tavern on Chiswick's main drag is thriving under "very impressive new management" who have installed a new pizza kitchen and revived the "lovely garden" with a large covered terrace. "They took over just before the first lockdown and worked their socks off to get it right – and boy, have they succeeded" with its "honest and reliable" food offer. / W4 1PU; www.theroebuckchiswick.co.uk; @the_roebuck; Wed-Sat 10 pm, Sun 7 pm.

Roka £90 4|3|4
30 North Audley St, W1   020 7305 5644   3–2A
37 Charlotte St, W1   020 7580 6464   2–1C
Aldwych House, 71-91 Aldwych, WC2   020 7294 7636   2–2D
Unit 4, Park Pavilion, 40 Canada Sq, E14   020 7636 5228   12–1C
"The original Charlotte Street site is the best", but, in fairness, all the branches are superb when it comes to Arjun Waney and Rainer Becker's sleek Japanese-inspired group, where "a visit always feels like a treat: from the slick service to the buzzy atmosphere to the consistently good food". Sushi and luxurious bites (for example black cod, yellowtail with ponzu and truffle oil), mostly from the robata grill, are the backbones of the menu. The odd report was slightly downbeat of late ("it was less good than normal, but to be fair they had just reopened post-lockdown with new staff"), but the dominant view remains that a trip is "always a lovely, fun experience" (and some regulars tip a stool at the counter as the best perches). / www.rokarestaurant.com.

Roketsu W1 NEW
12 New Quebec Street   2–2A
Set to be one of 2021's more ambitions openings – chef Daisuke Hayashi's new kaiseki restaurant in Marylebone will draw on his 20 years under Yoshihiro Murata at the three-Michelin-starred Kikunoi Honten in Kyoto (his London CV includes Tokimeite and Chrysan near Broadgate). It will offer a kaiseki-only menu, so the presumption is that you will need to melt your credit card to go... / W1H 7RP; www.roketsu.co.uk; Mon-Thu 9.30 pm, Fri & Sat 10 pm, Sun 9.15 pm.

Romulo Café W8 £63 3|4|3
343 Kensington High Street   020 3141 6390   8–1D
"Personal service from a family-owned business" adds to the appeal of this Kensington fixture (owned by the grandchildren of a famous general), whose menu offers a good introduction to Filipino cuisine. / W8 6NW; www.romulocafe.co.uk; @romulolondon; Tue-Thu 9.30 pm, Fri-Sun 10.30 pm; closed Tue-Thu L, closed Mon.

Roof Garden at Pantechnicon SW1 NEW £77 3|3|5
19 Motcomb St   020 7034 5426   6–1D
"Fun in the sun" is to be had at the Cubitt Group's new fifth-floor haunt. As glam rooftops go, few in London are lovelier than this luxurious perch atop the group's gorgeous – expense-be-damned! – redevelopment of Belgravia's Pantechnicon building, whose September 2020 opening was hampered by the pandemic. With a fully retractable, electric glass roof, the 130-seat roof garden with an expansive south-facing terrace is a local hot ticket whatever the weather (evidently, "it's lovely when it's fine and when the weather's not good you still feel like you're outside with lots of glass"). Food includes an all-day small plates menu with main dishes at lunch and dinner, served from the kitchen at Eldr (see also). Early reports say "steak tartare is to die for, and the smörgåsbord and small plates are better than the large plates". If you ever trouble yourself by glancing at your credit card bills, then exercise some caution before deciding to visit... / SW1X; www.pantechnicon.com; Tue-Sat 10 pm, Sun 4 pm; closed Sun D, closed Mon; Take bookings all week via phone and/or online.

Rose & Crown SW19 £50 2|3|3
55 High Street Wimbledon   020 8947 4713   11–2A
"Good outdoor facilities" boost the appeal of this handsome period inn, near the edge of Wimbledon Village. Run by Youngs, the food receives the odd bum rep, but for the most part is recommended as being good for a pub. / SW19 5BA; www.roseandcrownwimbledon.co.uk; @rosencrownsw19; Mon-Sat midnight, Sun 11 pm.

The Rosendale SE21 £53   3|3|3
65 Rosendale Rd   020 8761 9008   1–4D

"The best local gastropub you could imagine", say devotees of this modernised Victorian coaching inn in West Dulwich. It's *"very jolly outside under a generous canopy"*, has *"great indoor space"*, *"the food is consistently excellent and the service cheery"*. / SE21 8EZ; www.therosendale.co.uk; @threecheerspubs; Mon-Thu 11 pm, Fri & Sat 12am, Sun 10.30 pm; no Amex.

Roti Chai W1 £47   3|3|2
3 Portman Mews South   020 7408 0101   3–1A

"A great place to relish the street food of India", this two-storey operation near Selfridges was ahead of the curve in championing the cooking of the subcontinent's street hawkers, roadside stalls and station canteens, when it first opened. / W1H 6AY; www.rotichai.com; @RotiChai; Mon-Sat 10 pm, Sun 9 pm; booking D only.

Roti King NW1 £25   5|3|2
40 Doric Way   020 7387 2518   9–3C

"The best authentic roti in town" – and fans think *"the best Malaysian food in Britain"* – means you usually have to queue for a perch at this packed and extraordinarily good-value basement near Euston station. *"You won't regret it"*: the roti canai, flatbread served with curry, is *"beyond belief"* and well worth the discomfort. For the less intrepid, *"sister locations Gopal's Corner in Market Halls Victoria and Market Halls West End are just as good"*. / NW1 1LH; www.rotiking.co.uk/; @Rotiking; Mon-Sun 10.30 pm; No bookings.

Rotunda Bar & Restaurant, Kings Place N1 £60   2|2|3
90 York Way   020 7014 2840   9–3C

A *"great location on a quiet stretch of the Regent's Canal"* – which runs past the King's Place arts centre – is one selling point of this modern British restaurant, which is on the ground floor of the complex. With beef and lamb from its own farm in Northumberland, it is *"definitely a place for the serious meat eater"*. There's a feeling, though, that *"the Rotunda has never quite reached its potential, despite years of trying"*. Top Tip: *"be warned: if you choose a canalside table and it rains, you'll be handed an umbrella"*. / N1 9AG; www.rotundabarandrestaurant.co.uk; @rotundalondon.

Roux at the Landau, The Langham W1 £95
1c Portland Pl   020 7965 0165   2–1B

'Exciting concept changes' are promised at this elegant Roux-branded dining room, within the luxurious five-star opposite Broadcasting House. Democratised in style in 2018, then closed for much of the pandemic and beyond, the presumption is that it will take another move to a less formal (perhaps brasserie?) style when it reopens in 2022. Just the other side of the wall is The Wigmore – a pub created from spare space at the hotel and launched with its own entrance and Roux input in 2017. A hint at what's to come? / W1B 1JA; www.rouxatthelandau.com; @Langham_London; Tue-Sat 10.30 pm, Sun 11 am, Mon 10.30am; closed Sun & Mon D; No trainers.

ROVI W1 £67   4|2|3
59-65 Wells Street   020 3963 8270   3–1D

"The full Ottolenghi experience" – with a marvellous selection of dishes at amazing value prices – is to be found at the celebrated chef's *"foodie heaven"* in Fitzrovia. *"Unusual ingredients are beautifully combined in a varied array of options"* which put vegetables to the forefront. *"It's great fun too – bustling and chic, with a great sense of intimacy."* / W1A 3AE; www.ottolenghi.co.uk/rovi; @rovi_restaurant; Mon-Sat 10.30 pm, Sun 4 pm; closed Mon-Wed L closed Sun D; Take bookings all week via phone and/or online.

Rowley's SW1 £80 ②②🄷

113 Jermyn St   020 7930 2707   4–4D

"Good steak 'n' chips" (with unlimited top-ups on the latter) in "pleasing surroundings" still win fans for this classic St James's fixture, which dates from the 1970s, and whose characterful premises were the home of the Wall's sausages empire in Victorian times. It's "not cheap", but this occasioned fewer complaints this year. / SW1Y 6HJ; www.rowleys.co.uk; Mon-Sat 11 pm; closed Sun.

Royal China £57 🄷①②

24-26 Baker St, W1   020 7487 4688   2–1A
805 Fulham Rd, SW6   020 7731 0081   11–1B
30 Westferry Circus, E14   020 7719 0888   12–1B

"Like Rick's in Casablanca, everybody looking for dim sum in London comes to the Royal China" – whose well-established venues (decorated along the lines of an '80s disco) in Baker Street, Canary Wharf, Fulham and Harrow deliver the proper Cantonese experience. They "never disappoint" (although "main dishes can be less successful"), but, "given the well-known robotic efficiency of their approach, if you want ambience, you have to bring your own". One big loss this year, though – their most popular branch, on Queensway – has bitten the dust. / www.royalchinagroup.co.uk.

Royal China Club W1 £77 ④②②

38-42 Baker St   020 7486 3898   2–1A

The luxurious Marylebone flagship of the smart Royal China group is known for the "exceptional standard" of its dim sum during the day and its Cantonese classics, including seafood, in the evening. But while its food ratings are consistently high, marks for service and ambience have dipped, despite a refurb a few years back. / W1U 7AJ; www.royalchinagroup.co.uk; @RoyalChinaGroup; Mon-Sun 9 pm; booking weekdays only.

Royale at
East London Liquor Company E3 NEW £39

Bow Wharf, 221 Grove Road   020 3011 0980   14–2C

Born of necessity but now here to stay – this pandemic pop-up from the team behind Leroy turned permanent in June 2021. Within Bow Wharf's East London Liquor Co – and with a large outside terrace – it aims to bring some easy going Provençal good times to E3, in the form of rotisserie chicken and other 'comforting' dishes, plus gluggable wines. / E3 5SN; www.royalelondon.com; @royale_ldn; Thu-Sun 10 pm; closed Thu & Fri L, closed Mon & Tue & Wed.

Rucoletta EC2 £45 ④②②

6 Foster Lane   020 7600 7776   10–2B

A "family-run trattoria" three minutes' walk from St Paul's that rates highly for its "varied Italian menu" – and it's notably well priced for the City, too. / EC2V 6HH; www.rucoletta.co.uk; @RucolettaLondon; Mon-Wed 10 pm, Thu & Fri 10.30 pm; closed Sat & Sun; no Amex.

Rudy's W1 NEW

80-82 Wardour St   020 7734 0195   4–2D

This smash hit from Manchester's hip Ancoats enclave finally arrived in the Big Smoke (via Liverpool, Leeds and Birmingham) in mid-2021, taking over the heart-of-Soho premises that till recently housed a branch of Wahaca. There's nowt fancy about the pizza selection (marinara, margherita...) – the craft is in the Naples-imported ingredients (tomatoes grown on the slopes of Vesuvius, yada, yada). No survey feedback as yet, but the social buzz about the place suggests it's well worth trying. / W1; www.rudyspizza.co.uk/soho/; Sun-Thu 10 pm, Fri & Sat 11 pm; closed Mon-Fri L.

Rudy's Vegan Diner £35 3 3 2

206a Upper Street, N1 07547 832545 9–2D **NEW**
729-731 Camden Stables Market, NW1 07384 342144 9–2B
London's first all-vegan diner serves up plant-based versions of classic American diner food, 'from meat-free burgers and giant seitan hot dogs, to dairy-free milkshakes and 'pastrami'-packed sandwiches'; and opened a second branch in Islington's Upper Street in early 2021, next door to their vegan butcher's shop. Feedback is relatively limited, but says the brand is "a good performer in this challenging segment". / rudysvegan.com; @rudysDVD.

Rules WC2 £83 2 3 5

35 Maiden Ln 020 7836 5314 5–3D
For a "quintessentially British" meal, it's hard to beat this Dickensian icon in Covent Garden (London's oldest restaurant to operate continuously on the same site – since 1798), which has a "beautiful" Victorian interior; and which delivers an archetypal mix of grills, game and stodgy puds. To an impressive extent, it has avoided pure Tourist Trap status; and many regulars have "so many happy memories here, going back decades" thanks to its "comforting" formula. No denying, however, that it has become "very overpriced" in recent years and increasingly risks "living on its old reputation". But, for the time being, the overall verdict remains that "it's one of a kind and the world would be poorer without it". / WC2E 7LB; www.rules.co.uk; @RulesRestaurant; Mon-Sat 11.30 pm, Sun 5 pm; closed Sun D; No shorts.

Rye by the Water TW8 £35 3 2 3

Catherine Wheel Road 020 8560 9512 1–3A
"An excellent waterside spot for brunch" – this bakery and grill (from Ben Rand, ex-head chef at The Dairy, and Janine Edwards, former head pastry chef at Little Bread Pedlar) occupies part of a new development, with a large outside decked area, where the Grand Union Canal meets the Thames in Brentford. / TW8 8BD; www.ryebythewater.com; @ryebythewater; Wed & Thu 10 pm, Fri & Sat 8 pm, Sun 4 pm.

Sabor W1 £62 5 4 3

35 Heddon St 020 3319 8130 4–3A
"Seats at the bar provide both theatre and delicious bites" at Nieves Barragan and José Etura's smash hit, tucked off Regent Street, which is now four years old. You can also eat on communal tables upstairs in the 'El Asador' dining room. The "superb, modern tapas" ("focussed on seafood, with some Spanish-sourced specialities") are "heavenly", it's well-known for its suckling pig, and the "atmosphere is energetic and warm". (A shout-out also to their Dine At Home nationwide delivery: "the most innovative during lockdown" for numerous reporters.) / W1B 4BP; www.saborrestaurants.co.uk; @sabor_ldn; Tue-Sat 10.30 pm; closed Sun & Mon.

Sachi at Pantechnicon SW1 **NEW** £29

18 Motcomb St 020 7034 5425 6–1D
Occupying the barrel-vaulted lower-ground floor of this stunning Belgravia food and retail emporium, this sizeable (130-cover) mid-2021 arrival is complemented by private vaulted booths set in a Japanese garden, a sushi chef's table, and a late-night bar. On the menu (from head chef Collin Hudson, ex-Dinings and Roka), a distinctive brand of Nordic-influenced, Japanese regional cuisine promising dishes never before seen in London. / SW1X; www.pantechnicon.com; Tue-Sat 10 pm; closed Tue-Sat L, closed Sun & Mon.

Le Sacré-Coeur N1 £48 3 4 3

18 Theberton St 020 7354 2618 9–3D
"A delightful, charming slice of la vie Parisienne in N1", this "lovely friendly local bistro" off Islington's Upper Street "can't be faulted, especially on price". / N1 0QX; lesacrecoeurbistro.co.uk; @lesacre_coeur; Sun & Mon 10 pm, Tue-Thu 10.30 pm, Fri & Sat 11 pm.

Sacro Cuore £43 5 3 2
10 Crouch End Hill, N8 020 8348 8487 1–1C
45 Chamberlayne Rd, NW10 020 8960 8558 1–2B
Celebrating its 10th anniversary this year, this high-quality, independent
Neapolitan pizzeria in Kensal Rise and its Crouch End spin-off continue to
win the highest scores for their "excellent" and "moreish" pizzas. Top Tip:
"the Nutella dessert pizza is a speciality (to share)". / www.sacrocuore.co.uk;
@SacroCuorePizza.

Sagar £38 3 2 2
17a Percy St, W1 020 7631 3319 3–1D
31 Catherine St, WC2 020 7836 6377 5–3D
157 King St, W6 020 8741 8563 8–2C
"Great-value South Indian vegetarian food at its best" is served at this long-
running group with venues in Covent Garden, Fitzrovia, Hammersmith and
Harrow. "Not at all your typical Indian restaurants", they serve "food to
convince that vegetarian and vegan cooking is good", made with "fresh
ingredients, lightly spiced and producing great flavours – so "don't let the
decor put you off!". Top Tip: "the dosas are a must". / www.sagarveg.co.uk.

Saint Jacques SW1 NEW £80 4 4 4
5 St James's St 020 7930 2030 3–4D
"A useful addition to St James's", on the attractive former site of Boulestin
and L'Oranger, which benefits from a light-filled main dining room, and a cute
adjoining terrace in summer ("a fascinating and enchanting hidden corner").
It was opened in July 2020 by Frenchman Richard Weiss, who worked at
Brasserie St Jacques (long RIP) down the road, before it became Café
Murano, and thrives on its "accomplished French cuisine and helpful
service". You can push the boat out pricewise if you want to, but there's an
unusually good range of more modestly priced items here if you are on a
budget. / SW1; www.saintjacquesrestaurant.com; Sun-Thu midnight, Fri & Sat 1 am.

St John Bread & Wine E1 £65 3 2 3
94-96 Commercial St 020 7251 0848 13–2C
"The food is typical St John" – although the 'nose-to-tail' eating is in a small
plates format – at this "noisy and crowded", characteristically austere
Spitalfields canteen: the long-running offshoot of Fergus Henderson's iconic
Smithfield venue. "My go-to venue for when I don't know where else I fancy
– more accessible and casual than its big sibling, with 'big' St John the pick
for a celebration or blow out". Top Tip: "the madeleines remain unbeatable.
Always order half a dozen on your way out". / E1 6LZ;
www.stjohngroup.uk.com/spitalfields; @sjrestaurant; Thu-Sun, Wed 10 pm; closed
Wed L, closed Mon & Tue.

St John Smithfield EC1 £75 5 4 4
26 St John St 020 7251 0848 10–1B
"Uncompromising in all respects… and worth a visit" – "the original nose-
to-tail restaurant" has become "a pure London institution" for very many of
those who take part in our annual diners' survey: "timeless… fabulous!" The
top draw is the "hearty", offal-filled menu ("dem bones, dem bones are to
die for!") which is "heaven on a plate" for more adventurous palates. But the
masochistic appeal of its "stark, white, industrial interior" has also achieved
iconic status over the years – the atmosphere it creates being pepped up
considerably by the very professional and personable service. / EC1M 4AY;
stjohnrestaurant.com; @SJRestaurant; Mon-Sat 10.30 pm, Sun 4 pm; closed Sun D.

St Johns N19 £60 3 3 5
91 Junction Rd 020 7272 1587 9–1C
"Our absolute favourite" is a typical verdict on this handsome Archway
tavern, well-known across north London for its atmospheric interior (the
dining annexe is a converted period ballroom), "imaginative menu and
friendly service". About the worst that anybody says is that it "can be noisy".
/ N19 5QU; www.stjohnstavern.com; @stjohnstavern; Mon-Sat 10 pm, Sun 6 pm; closed
Mon-Thu L closed Sun D; no Amex; booking max 12 may apply.

St Moritz W1 £57 **3** **3** **4**
161 Wardour Street 020 7734 3324 4–1C
"The next best thing to visiting Switzerland" – this chalet-style Soho veteran
(est. 1974) offers an unchanging, cosy escape. Fondues, bratwurst and rosti
are menu mainstays, with venison available in season – it's all better than
you might expect. / W1F 8WJ; www.stmoritz-restaurant.co.uk.

Sake No Hana SW1 £91 **4** **3** **3**
23 St James's St 020 7925 8988 3–4D
This contemporary take on Japanese cuisine occupies one of London's most
designer-y restaurant sites – a curved Modernist building next to The
Economist in St James's, accessible via a single escalator and with a bamboo-
and-cypress interior by Kango Kuma, the architect who designed Tokyo's
Olympic stadium. While it has never achieved the fame of its siblings in the
glitzy Hakkasan group, it continues to win consistently high ratings for its
"beautiful" food. / SW1A 1HA; www.sakenohana.com; @sakenohana; Tue, Wed
10 pm, Thu-Sat 11 pm; closed Sun & Mon.

Sakonis £32 **3** **2** **1**
127-129 Ealing Rd, HA0 020 8903 9601 1–1A
330 Uxbridge Road, HA5 020 8903 9601 1–1A
This family-run Wembley veggie stalwart with "great East African[a] / Indian
food" has expanded over almost 40 years from a market stall to a full-scale
restaurant, featuring dishes from across India and Indochina and an
unlimited buffet with 45 choices. There are now menu-only branches in
Hounslow and Hatch End. / sakonis.co.uk; @sakonis.

Salaam Namaste WC1 £46 **3** **3** **2**
68 Millman Street 020 7405 3697 2–1D
For a "really delicious" curry in the vicinity of Russell Square, head to Sabbir
Karim's affordable Indian fixture. / WC1N 3EF; www.salaam-namaste.co.uk;
@SalaamNamasteUK; Sun-Thu 10 pm, Fri & Sat 10.30 pm; closed Mon-Thu L.

Sale e Pepe SW1 £77 **3** **5** **3**
9-15 Pavilion Road 020 7235 0098 6–1D
"Unchanged forever", this old-school trattoria a few steps from Harrods
shows remarkable staying power as it closes in on its half-century. With its
impeccably "noisy Italian atmosphere", regulars are happy to rate it "my
favourite restaurant in London" – "it always makes for a wonderful evening,
with delicious food and perfect, attentive service". / SW1X 0HD;
www.saleepepe.co.uk; Sun-Thu 10 pm, Fri & Sat 10.30 pm; Take bookings all week via
phone and/or online.

Salloos SW1 £67 **3** **3** **3**
62-64 Kinnerton St 020 7235 4444 6–1D
Hidden away in a Belgravia mews townhouse for over 40 years, this posh
Pakistani haunt has a "charming" if slightly dated ambience, boosted by its
"discreet", professional service. The food "always delivers an exceptional
taste sensation" – not least the superb lamb chops. / SW1X 8ER;
www.salloos.co.uk; Mon-Sat 10 pm; closed Sun; May need 5+ to book.

Salon Brixton SW9 £72 **4** **4** **3**
18 Market Row 020 7501 9152 11–2D
In Brixton Village market, Nicholas Balfe's interesting spot is worth
discovering, with its downstairs bar (snacks and sharing dishes) and upstairs
dining room (a set menu of either four or seven courses). "Passionate and
knowledgeable staff deliver lovely food and some really interesting and
unusual wines." / SW9 8LD; www.salonbrixton.co.uk; @Salon_Brixton; Tue-Sat
11 pm; closed Tue-Thu L, closed Sun & Mon.

Le Salon Privé TW1 £53 3 2 3
43 Crown Rd 020 8892 0602 1–4A

This cute and characterful independent bistro offers a "lovely neighbourhood dining experience" in suburban St Margaret's, with "very good cooking and presentation" from chef-patron Gianluca di Monaco, who learned his trade under Pierre Koffmann, doyen of French chefs in London. A favoured pit-stop before the rugby at nearby Twickenham – or to celebrate afterwards. Top Tip: "Chateaubriand to die for!" / TW1 3EJ; lesalonprive.net; @lesalon_tweet; Tue-Sat 21.30 pm, Sun 4 pm; closed Sun D, closed Mon.

Salt Yard W1 £58 3 3 3
54 Goodge St 020 7637 0657 2–1B

With its quality mix of Spanish and Italian tapas, this cosy bar/restaurant near Goodge Street was a foodie trailblazer when it opened in 2005. The buzz has moved on over the years, but it's a worthwhile, well-run venue with interesting food. / W1T 4NA; www.saltyard.co.uk; @SaltYardGroup; Mon-Sat 11 pm, Sun 10 pm; booking max 8 may apply.

Sam's Café NW1 NEW £25 3 3 3
40 Chalcot Road 020 7916 3736 9–3B

Not every café is opened by Helena Bonham Carter, but in other respects actor Sam Frears and Andrew O'Hagan's Primrose Hill newcomer has relatively ordinary aims ('French corner bistro' meets 'traditional British café'), albeit tailored to suit the local luvvies of NW1 (it has a 'legendary vintage jukebox', for instance). A long-established business that moved from nearby Regent's Park Road, it's on the tricky split-level corner-site that was once L'Absinthe (long RIP) and has had a laundry list of former occupants. Perhaps as a neighbourhood hangout for consuming all-day breakfast it's finally found its niche; early feedback hails it as "an excellent Primrose Hill greasy spoon… without the grease". / NW1 8LS; www.samscafeprimrosehill.com; Mon & Tue, Thu-Sun 10 pm, Wed 5 pm; closed Wed D.

Sams Riverside W6 £73 4 4 5
1 Crisp Walk 020 8237 1020 8–2C

"A wonderful addition to this part of London" – Sam Harrison's "sparkling" recent arrival (it opened in late 2019) is a real "class act". "Beautifully designed" for somewhere outside the centre of town, it sits at the back of the newly revamped Riverside Studios, with Hammersmith Bridge in the background and a cute covered terrace to the side. The deluxe brasserie fare is "carefully sourced" and "intelligently cooked" but it's the all-round experience created, not least, by the unusually "genuine and warm welcome" that seals the "fun atmosphere", and which makes it "a great choice for a special night out". "It just puts a smile on my face…" / W6 9DN; samsriverside.co.uk; @samsriversideW6; Mon-Sat 10 pm, Sun 6 pm; closed Sun D.

Sambal Shiok N7 £41 4 3 3
171 Holloway Road 020 7619 9888 9–2D

"Spiced, zingy laksa to die for!" – Kuala Lumpur-born Mandy Lin's "bustling" Malaysian street food bar on Holloway Road bar provides "an object lesson in how to keep people happy by doing one thing and doing it well". "Authentic, delicious laksa arrives with different levels of spiciness", hitting the spot "when you need a laksa fix". Sambal to Go has replaced the short-lived Nasi Economy Rice next door, leaving the main restaurant focused on a slightly less high-turnover eating experience, with greater 'table time' and more extensive menus, including rice bowls and noodle salads. / N7 8LX; www.sambalshiok.co.uk; @SambalShiok; Tue-Sat 10 pm; closed Sun & Mon; booking online only.

San Carlo SW1 £77 **3**2**4**
2 Regent Street Saint James's   020 3778 0768   4–4D
"A diverse age range and all family members voted it a top meal" – the San Carlo group's traditional Italian, on the lower half of Regent Street, provides a versatile and comfortable destination suited to many occasions. Like others in the chain it can sometimes seem pricey, but most reports are upbeat.
/ SW1Y 4AU; sancarlo.co.uk/restaurants/san-carlo-london/; @SanCarlo_Group; Tue-Sun 11 pm, Mon 10 pm.

San Carlo Cicchetti £62 **333**
215 Piccadilly, W1   020 7494 9435   4–4C
30 Wellington St, WC2   020 7240 6339   5–3D
A "vibrant atmosphere (especially good for a group)" helps underpin the appeal of these "glitzy and lively" spin-offs from the San Carlo national chain of glam Italians, whose most central branch – just off Piccadilly Circus – is decked out with "marble tables and stylish chandeliers". "Very tasty small plates" that are inspired by Venetian "cicchetti" are "served speedily". In late 2021, they are due to open a second Knightsbridge branch, just across the road from Harrods. / www.sancarlocicchetti.co.uk/; @SanCarlo_Group.

San Pietro W8 £51 **333**
7 Stratford Road   020 7938 1805   6–1A
In a very quiet Kensington backwater, this small Italian occupies the cute site that was for years Chez Patrick (RIP) – it's more stylish nowadays, serving high-quality fish and seafood either at the downstairs counter, or upstairs main dining room. / W8 6RF; www.san-pietro.co.uk; Mon, Thu-Sun 10 pm; closed Tue & Wed.

Santa Maria £46 **433**
160 New Cavendish St, W1   020 7436 9963   2–1B
92-94 Waterford Road, SW6   020 7384 2844   6–4A
11 Bond Street, W5   020 8579 1462   1–3A
Hailed as among "the best Neapolitan pizzerias in town", this Ealing-based chain has made slow but steady progress since its launch by Pasquale Chionchio and Angelo Ambrosio in 2010, with offshoots in Fitzrovia, Fulham Broadway, Brentford's Duke of London pub and most recently Islington, on the former site of Baba Boom in Upper Street. The Ealing branch has moved to a new address nearby – "stylish, but not as fun as the original" – making way for a new vegan pizzeria, Vergine Maria, on the St Mary's Road site (see also). / www.santamariapizzeria.com; @SantaMariaPizza.

Santa Maria del Sur SW8 £57 **333**
129 Queenstown Rd   020 7622 2088   11–1C
"Tremendous steaks" are the focus of this 15-year-old Argentinian steakhouse in Battersea – so "don't go for anything else!" Add "friendly staff and a good neighbourhood vibe" to the equation, and no wonder it's a popular spot. / SW8 3RH; www.santamariadelsur.co.uk; @StaMariadelSur; Mon-Sun 10 pm.

Santini SW1 £107 **2**3**4**
29 Ebury St   020 7730 4094   2–4B
This chic old-timer in Belgravia is still hanging in there with a "wonderful atmosphere" and "superb Italian dishes". "Long favoured by Frank Sinatra, Roger Moore and Joan Collins, it's not as dated or stuffy as that might make it sound, but it is expensive." Founded in 1984 by Gino Santini, it is now run by his daughter Laura. Top Tip: "you can't beat the outside terrace in summer". / SW1W 0NZ; www.santini-restaurant.com; @santinirest; Mon-Sat 10.30 pm; closed Sat L, closed Sun.

Santo Remedio £70 **3** **3** **2**
152 Tooley Street, SE1   020 7403 3021   10–4D
55 Great Eastern Street, EC2   13–1B **NEW**
Edson and Natalie Diaz-Fuentes again win mostly good, if slightly up-and-down reports for their 'real food of Mexico', mixing tacos and tostadas with a few more substantial dishes. In autumn 2021, the couple return to Shoreditch (site of their first restaurant, which closed in 2016) with a new opening to join their existing Bermondsey venture. It's on a corner site that was formerly a grab-and-go pitstop, Pod.

Santore EC1 £53 **3** **2** **2**
59-61 Exmouth Mkt   020 7812 1488   10–1A
"Really enjoyable" rustic Italian in Exmouth Market, which serves authentic Neapolitan cuisine, including pizza served 'al metro' and panuozzi – a variation from Gragnano, further down the coast next to Pompeii. / EC1R 4QL; www.santorerestaurant.london; @Santore_london; Mon-Sun 11 pm.

Saravanaa Bhavan HA0 £46 **3** **3** **1**
531-533 High Rd   020 8900 8526   1–1A
"Dosa vegetarian heaven" – "great vadas and idlis", too – wins the veggie vote for this Wembley outfit with seven branches across the capital (Croydon, East Ham, Harrow, Ilford, Leicester Square, Southall and Tooting). "Everything is totally on point and you'll be hard-pressed to pay more than £15 for more food than you can really eat". The Chennai-based franchise has expanded around the world in the past 20 years; founder, P Rajagopal, died of a heart attack in 2019 after being imprisoned for the murder of an employee whose wife he wanted to marry. / HA0 2DJ; saravanabhavanlondon.com; Sun-Thu 10.30 pm, Fri & Sat 11 pm; Take bookings all week via phone and/or online.

Sartoria W1 £84 **3** **3** **3**
20 Savile Row   020 7534 7000   4–3A
"A great, traditional Italian with real style", whose name references its location, amongst London's most famous tailors, and whose "well-spaced tables" help make it a "discreet and useful Mayfair location" for business lunches hosted by those wearing the bespoke products of its neighbours. Owned by D&D London, the kitchen is run by ex-Anima chef Francesco Mazzei, and it has put in a very solid performance of late. "I go when I want a special treat – I don't eat meat, but I'll always find a beautiful and flavourful vegetable-based dish or risotto, and the fish is excellent." There's a strong Italian wine list, where – for example – "you can usually find a Marche or Umbrian bottle of good vintage that doesn't appear on anyone else's list". / W1S 3PR; www.sartoria-restaurant.co.uk; @SartoriaRest; Mon-Sat 10 pm; closed Sun; Take bookings all week via phone and/or online.

Satay Street Cafe E1 **NEW**
15 Goulston Street   020 7426 0017   10–2D
Originally a stall on Brick Lane (which started in 2009), this 20-seater, a short walk north of Aldgate, is the first permanent home of this experienced Bangkok-style street food vendor. Enjoy dishes (with lots of choice for vegans) on a bed of rice, wrapped tight in a tortilla, or accompanied with salad. / E1 7TP; sataystreet.co.uk; @SatayStreetUK; Mon-Fri 8 pm; closed Sat & Sun.

The Savoy Hotel, Savoy Grill WC2 £116 2️⃣2️⃣3️⃣

Strand   020 7592 1600   5–3D

"You never go to The Savoy Grill just for the food" and that's been true since this panelled chamber first opened over a century ago. In its heyday, it was THE venue for power dining and – even if it's no longer packed with captains of industry – its "well spaced tables and great atmosphere" still earn numerous tips as a place to impress a client, aided by a "comprehensive wine list". Run by Gordon Ramsay since 2003, the "traditional" food has had its ups and downs and has stuck in recent times in a perhaps overpriced, "not exceptional" but tolerable mould. / WC2R 0EU; www.gordonramsayrestaurants.com/savoy-grill; @savoygrill; Mon-Wed midnight, Thu-Sat 1 am, Sun 11.30 pm.

The Savoy Hotel, Thames Foyer WC2 £93 2️⃣4️⃣4️⃣

The Savoy, The Strand   020 7420 2111   5–3D

"Amazing liveried service and beautiful setting" help captivate fans of this elegant, light-filled foyer space, set beneath a glass dome, and whose interior gazebo and pianist further up the tone. "No matter how many sandwiches they give you… it's not enough!" / WC2R 0ER; www.thesavoylondon.com/restaurant/thames-foyer-restaurant/; @TheSavoyLondon; Wed-Sun 5 pm; closed Wed-Sun D, closed Mon & Tue.

The Savoy Hotel, River Restaurant WC2 NEW

91 The Strand   020 7836 4343   5–3D

It's 'Back to the Future' at this fine chamber, whose window seats have majestic views over the River Thames. It has traded since 2013 as Kaspar's Seafood Bar & Grill (RIP), but is now going back to its original (1890–2013) identity as 'The River Room'. Gordon Ramsay Holdings – who already run The Savoy Grill – will relaunch it in autumn 2021. / WC2R 0EU; www.fairmont.com/savoy/; Sun-Thu 10.30 pm, Fri & Sat 11 pm; No trainers.

Scalini SW3 £92 3️⃣3️⃣3️⃣

1-3 Walton St   020 7225 2301   6–2C

Studiously old-school trattoria in the backstreets near Harrods, which "pleases a glitzy crowd with huge portions of yummy old-fashioned Italian fare" and "waiters who are always friendly and ready with a smile and a joke: it's always packed". "You'll also be surprised how many celebs have visited", as the dozens of colour snaps pasted to the wall testify. The formula is still thriving after more than three decades, to the extent that a Dubai spin-off launched in 2018. "Just know that it's not cheap"… as no doubt you've already guessed. / SW3 2JD; www.scalinilondon.co.uk; Mon-Sun 10.45 pm; No shorts.

Scott's W1 £91 3️⃣3️⃣4️⃣

20 Mount St   020 7495 7309   3–3A

"Oozing class", this "classic Mayfair dining room" (James Bond's favourite) offers "a true five-star meal"; a "consummate experience" combining "glamourous", "traditional" surroundings populated by "ever-obliging staff" and "an interesting clientele, featuring many well-known faces". Owned by Caprice Holdings, it is locked in a perpetual battle with its stablemate J Sheekey to top our poll for best London's fish (the latter, as usual, edges it this year). However, even those who acknowledge "superb seafood" often note "the hefty price tag", and there was the odd concern this year (supported by ratings) that "standards have slipped a bit" from their usual heady heights. In summer, the pavement tables are a big draw. In August 2021, Richard Caring announced that Scott's is the latest of his landmark properties to get the spin-off treatment with the announcement of Scott's on the River in Richmond – see also. / W1K 2HE; www.scotts-restaurant.com; Mon-Sat 1 am, Sun 12.30 am; booking max 6 may apply.

Scott's on the River TW9 NEW
Whittaker Avenue   1–4A

Post-pandemic, Richmond is the new mecca for restaurant openings and Richard Caring, never a man to miss a trend, has secured a site that was previously a branch of vodka bar brand Revolution for his expansion within the Caprice Group of Mayfair's famous fish veteran, Scott's. Apparently the new opening will borrow from the ethos of Sexy Fish. Sounds overpriced and good looking… so should go down a storm in Richmond! / TW9 1EH; caprice-holdings.co.uk; Mon-Sun 4 pm.

Scully SW1 £89 543
4 St James's Market   020 3911 6840   4–4D

"So innovative! 10/10" – "the menu reads like a jumble, but is bangin'" at this St James's Market four-year-old whose "unique fusion food" "still knocks it out of the park with its originality of flavours and technique". Few restaurants attract such consistently upbeat feedback, which extends to the slick service and stylish room. "The experience comes at a price, but it's COMPLETELY justified!" / SW1Y 4QU; www.scullyrestaurant.com; @scully_ldn; Tue-Sat 10.30 pm; closed Tue-Thu L, closed Sun & Mon; booking online only.

Sea Containers, Mondrian London SE1 £76 334
20 Upper Ground   020 3747 1000   10–3A

"It's such a treat to sit next to the Thames, with a great view" at this "sleek" hotel dining room near Blackfriars Bridge, designed by Tom Dixon. Its range of eating possibilities – bottomless Bloody Mary or Prosecco brunch, especially – were rated well this year. Even fans, though, say "it is pricey – so come prepared to spend!" / SE1 9PD; www.seacontainerslondon.com; @SeaContainers_; Tue-Sat 11 pm, Sun 5.30 pm; closed Mon; Take bookings all week via phone and/or online.

Seabird at The Hoxton, Southwark SE1 £80 435
The Hoxton, 40 Blackfriars Road   020 7903 3000   10–4A

"You feel like you are on holiday" at this 'it-could-be-Manhattan' rooftop location – a "gorgeous" 14th-floor perch which, despite the name of the hotel, is located in Southwark. Order some "really mouthwatering" seafood from the raw bar (including a wide range of oysters), sip a sundowner, and catch a few rays. There's a lovely high-ceilinged interior for inclement weather. "Some diners are more interested in looking good for Insta than eating, but that's all part of the entertainment!" / SE1 8NY; thehoxton.com/london/southwark/hotels; @thehoxton; Sun-Thu midnight, Fri & Sat 1 am.

Seafresh SW1 £56 322
80-81 Wilton Rd   020 7828 0747   2–4B

This veteran Pimlico fish specialist has just celebrated its 60th year, under the founder's son, Marios Leonidou, whose "attentive and friendly service" ensures satisfied customers. Classic fish 'n' chips are complemented by more upmarket options on the menu, from fresh Dorset oysters and mussels steamed in Guinness to grilled Canadian lobster and whole Dover sole. / SW1V 1DL; www.seafresh-dining.com; @SeafreshLondon; Mon-Sun 10.30 pm.

Searcys St Pancras Grand NW1 £75 233
The Concourse   020 7870 9900   9–3C

Afternoon tea ("try Champagne as well as tea!") is a highlight at this stylishly appointed brasserie inside St Pancras Station, whose popular exterior bar overlooks the Eurostar tracks. The food doesn't always impress everyone ("like a trip back to the days of British Rail catering") but most reports this year were uniformly favourable. / NW1 2QP; www.searcys.co.uk; @SearcyStPancras; Mon-Sat 11 pm, Sun 6 pm; Take bookings all week via phone and/or online.

The Sea Shell NW1 £54 🄸🄱🄼
49 Lisson Grove   020 7224 9000   9–4A
"Top-quality fish and chips" have emerged from the fryer at this acclaimed Lisson Grove establishment for a century or so, making it a firm *"cabbies' favourite"*. Ratings are particularly strong in our latest survey, perhaps reflecting a taste for comfort eating in the face of the epidemic, during which the staff provided *"welcoming and efficient service in difficult circumstances"*. / NW1 6UH; www.seashellrestaurant.co.uk; @SeashellRestaur; Tue-Fri 10.30 pm, Sat 7 pm; closed Tue-Fri L, closed Sun & Mon.

SeaSons W1 NEW
6-10 Bruton Street   020 3725 7700   3–2C
"We are Fish. We are Fresh Fish". That's the mission statement for the high-end fishmongers' chain (of the same name) which has taken over this illustrious Mayfair basement site that once housed The Square (RIP). With retail branches in Notting Hill, Kensington and Fitzrovia (and coming soon in St John's Wood and Regent's Park), this is the business's first restaurant venture (although at its other stores you can eat in, with simple fish bistro dishes on offer). Originally set to open in May 2021, it still had not arrived as we went to press in September 2021. / W1J 6PU; seasonsdream.com; Tue-Sat 11.30 pm.

Sessions Arts Club EC1 NEW £58
22 Clerkenwell Green   020 3793 4025   10–1A
Name-checked in Oliver Twist by Dickens – and until the 1920s one of the largest courthouses in the UK – this Grade-II listed Clerkenwell pile now incorporates an events space and a restaurant on the fourth floor; a 60-seater with a 20-seat terrace and rooftop pool. Planned since 2019 and open from September 2021, both the lofty, distressed Victorian interior and the Med-inspired food from chef Florence Knight (ex-head chef of Polpetto, et al) have delighted early press reviewers. / EC1R 0NA; sessionsartsclub.com; Wed-Fri 10 pm; closed Mon & Tue, Sat & Sun.

Seven Park Place SW1 £155 🄱🄱🄱
7-8 Park Pl   020 7316 1621   3–4C
"Quirky and eclectic", the dining room at this boutique hotel *"tucked away from the maelstrom of Piccadilly"* *"never fails to excel"* under its long-time chef, the highly skilled William Drabble. *"The food remains consistent year in, year out"*, *"hitting lots of high notes"*, and is frequently *"stunning"*. Marks would have been even higher, but for a minority this year who felt their meal was *"good, but didn't quite hit excellent"*. / SW1A 1LS; www.stjameshotelandclub.com; @SevenParkPlace; Tue-Sat 10 pm; closed Sun & Mon; No trainers; Take bookings all week via phone and/or online.

7 Saints W11 £63 🄼🄼🄼
7 All Saints Road   020 7460 8566   7–1B
Off Portobello Road, this *"cosy"* and *"convivial"* spot is *"perfect for date night"*. *"The owner, James (Gummer, former maître d' at The Wolseley), runs front-of-house and makes every guest feel at home."* He's also put together a *"fantastic wine list of Old World classics as well as Greek, Lebanese and Romanian options, plus some amazing, well-priced, single bottles"*. The *"uncomplicated modern European menu is cooked to perfection"* – *"absolutely first rate bistronomie, as they say in France"*. / W11 1HA; 7saints.co.uk; Tue-Sat 10 pm, Sun 4 pm; closed Tue L closed Sun D, closed Mon.

1771 SW1 NEW
18 Holbein Place   020 7881 0886   6–2D
On the site near Sloane Square that was very briefly Liv (RIP) – and for aeons previously Como Lario (long RIP) – this site is to be relaunched in October 2021 by Anglo chef Mark Jarvis, who took over as chef-director at Liv in late 2020. Now it looks like it's going to be his show, which – on his past record – should be good news. / SW1W 8NL; www.livrestaurant.co.uk; Tue-Sat 9.30 pm; closed Tue-Sat L, closed Sun & Mon.

Sexy Fish W1 £95 1️⃣2️⃣3️⃣
1-4 Berkeley Sq   020 3764 2000   3–3B

"Like stepping into the sort of reality TV series where people apply tons of make-up and not so many clothes", Richard Caring's Mayfair seafood scene has an "amazing ambience", although it can be "incredibly loud – perfect if you want to eat in a nightclub" ("my teenage daughters love it!") On the downside, the luxurious sushi and seafood is "by numbers" and prices are "stratospheric" ("shocking really, are they having a laugh?") In autumn 2021, the brand crossed the Atlantic with an opening in its true spiritual home – Miami – where the USP is the largest collection of Dom Perignon in the US. / W1J 6BR; www.sexyfish.com; @sexyfishlondon; Mon-Sat 11 pm, Sun 10.30 pm; booking max 6 may apply.

Shackfuyu W1 £47 3️⃣3️⃣3️⃣
14a Old Compton St   020 3019 3492   5–2A

Limited, but good-all-round reports again this year on this funky Japanese in Soho – part of the Bone Daddies stable – which serves an eclectic mix of dishes inspired by 'Yoshoku' food (the Western-influenced cooking style popular in Japan): well-known examples include Mentaiko mac and cheese, prawn toast and everyone's favourite pudding: Kinako French toast with soft-serve ice cream. / W1D 4TJ; bonedaddies.com/shack-fuyu/; @shackfuyu; Mon-Sat 10 pm, Sun 9 pm; no booking.

Shahi Pakwaan N2 £34 4️⃣4️⃣2️⃣
25 Aylmer Parade, Aylmer Road   020 8341 1111   1–1B

"Fresh, zinging flavours", inspired by the royal cuisine of Hyderabad, set this four-year-old Indian in East Finchley "way above run-of-the-mill competitors". The converted shop site is "not the sexiest location", but the "high-quality, genuine Indian fare" attracts diners from beyond the immediate area. / N2 0PE; www.shahipakwaan.co.uk; Sun & Mon 10 pm, Tue-Sat 10.30 pm; closed Mon-Sat L.

Shampers W1 £55 3️⃣4️⃣4️⃣
4 Kingly St   020 7437 1692   4–2B

This old-school Soho wine bar, est. 1977, has real character and is "a great favourite" of both regular and more occasional visitors, drawn by its "good, down-to-earth" bistro cooking, "wide range of wines at decent prices" and by Simon Pearson, who bought the business 30 years ago. "The patron is always present – and it shows." "This place is really consistent – I first visited in 1987 and have never been disappointed." / W1B 5PE; www.shampers.net; @Shampers_Soho; Mon-Sat 11 pm; closed Sun; No bookings.

The Shed W8 £64
122 Palace Gardens Ter   020 7229 4024   7–2B

Quirky, small place, off Notting Hill, that oldies will recall as The Ark (long RIP) and which – like its long-deceased predecessor – doesn't always inspire much feedback due to its small size and out-of-the-way location. For the last few years it's been part of the Gladwin Bros' stable of field-to-fork eateries (Rabbit, Nutbourne) with a similar, faux-rustique theme. More reports, please! / W8 4RT; www.theshed-restaurant.com; @theshed_resto; Tue-Sat, Mon 12.30 am; closed Mon L, closed Sun.

J Sheekey WC2 £88 3️⃣3️⃣4️⃣
28-34 St Martin's Ct   020 7240 2565   5–3B

"Still a favourite over many years", this heart-of-Theatreland veteran (est. 1896) yet again topped our poll for serving London's best fish and seafood: "amazing seafood platters", "the freshest fish, simply served, and a wondrous fish pie". Tucked-away down a quirky alley, just off St Martin's Lane, it occupies a "club-like" series of old-fashioned parlours, enhanced – from June 2021 – by a major refurb, with a new all-year-round terrace (fully enclosed, with a retractable roof), plus a new central crustacean bar. That said, its ratings were not at their usual heights this year. Was it the pandemic closure of theatres (for which it is treasured for pre- and post-show meals)? Was it teething troubles with the new set-up? Whatever the reason, it lost

the slot it's occupied for many years as London's most-mentioned venue. It also inspired some mixed reports from both before and after its revamp. As a result, both ratings for both food and service slipped a notch ("What's happened here?! I know we're being generous to relatively newly re-opened restaurants, but they've hired a lot of people who don't know what they're doing, and the food was good, but nothing special, especially given the prices.") / WC2N 4AL; www.j-sheekey.co.uk; @JSheekeyRest; Mon-Sat 12.30 am, Sun 11.30 pm; booking max 6 may apply.

J Sheekey Atlantic Bar WC2 £88 4 3 5
28-34 St Martin's Ct   020 7240 2565   5–3B
"There's something about eating sweet, delicious oysters from the half shell and listening to jazz....such a relaxing experience after a hard day" – Sheekey's adjacent seafood bar is more chilled (you eat at the bar) than in the neighbouring dining rooms, but "lovely", and higher rated than the rest of the operation this year. / WC2N 4AL; www.j-sheekey.co.uk; @JSheekeyRest; Mon-Sat 11.15 pm, Sun 10 pm; booking max 3 may apply.

Shikumen, Dorsett Hotel W12 £69 5 3 3
58 Shepherd's Bush Grn   020 8749 9978   8–1C
"The freshly made dumplings are almost perfect" at this smart, modern hotel restaurant overlooking gentrifying Shepherd's Bush Green. Since opening in 2014, it has been the unlikely venue for "some of the best dim sum in London". "This standard of Chinese food is hard to find here – it's where I take friends from Singapore when they visit – and they're impressed." / W12 5AA; www.shikumen.co.uk; @ShikumenUK; Mon-Sun 11 pm.

Shilpa W6 £35 4 3 1
206 King St   020 8741 3127   8–2B
"The ambience isn't great", but this inconspicuous South Indian café on Hammersmith's busy King Street is "still a top, no-frills performer in a crowded local market". "Service is very friendly" and it serves "gorgeous Keralan fare" that's "always of the highest standard" and "finely spiced", especially the "fresh vegetables". / W6 0RA; shilpahammersmith.co.uk; Sun-Wed 11 pm, Thu-Sat midnight; Take bookings all week via phone and/or online.

Shoryu Ramen £54 3 2 2
9 Regent St, SW1   no tel   4–4D
3 Denman St, W1   no tel   4–3C
5 Kingly Ct, W1   no tel   4–2B
84 New Oxford Street, WC1   5–1B
35 Great Queen Street, WC2   5–1D
45 Great Eastern Street, EC2   13–1B
Broadgate Circle, EC2   no tel   13–2B
"Quick, warm and tasty" is the verdict on Japan Centre owner Tak Tokumine's "very busy", "authentic ramen" noodle group, based in the West End but expanding fast via delivery-only kitchens. "The tonkotsu soup stock is a wonder" and the "side dishes are great, too".

Showaken Tokyo Shitamachi Ramen SW1 NEW
Japan Centre, 35b Panton Street   5–4A
Just west of Leicester Square, the Japan Centre launched this new outlet at the start of 2020. It's a no-nonsense ramen café serving soupy snacks, and the decor offers a nostalgic trip back to '70s Tokyo (Showaken denotes the Showa period, which spanned the reign of Emperor Hirohito from 1926 to 1989). / SW1Y 4EA; www.japancentre.com/en/stores; Fri & Sat 11 pm, Mon-Thu 9.30 pm, Sun 9 pm.

The Sichuan EC1 £51 4 3 2
14 City Road   020 7588 5489   13–2A

The famously mouth-numbing tastes of southwest China are celebrated at this "great value" joint between Barbican and the City. Chef Zhang Xiao Zhong (ex-Bar Shu and Hutong) is from Chengdu, the home of Sichuan cooking, and his grandfather was personal chef to Sichuan-born Deng Xiaoping, China's supreme leader in the 1980s. / EC1Y 2AA; www.thesichuan.co.uk; Mon-Sun 11 pm.

Sichuan Folk E1 £50 4 3 2
32 Hanbury St   020 7247 4735   13–2C

Sichuan hot pot is a big deal at this often "outstanding" Brick Lane café – an excellent "cheap 'n' cheerful choice". / E1 6QR; www.sichuan-folk.co.uk; Fri & Sat 10.45 pm, Mon-Thu 10 pm, Sun 10.30 pm; no Amex; booking online only.

Sidechick W1 NEW
56 James Street   020 7935 4957   3–1A

The team behind Patty & Bun started up a roast chicken delivery service during lockdown, but its new bricks-and-mortar incarnation in Marylebone feels more than just a quick fix. The roast birds are served alongside flatbreads and interesting veg, with natural wines and cocktails. All this, in an attractive two-floor setting (seating 50) from the designers behind Padella and Trullo. (It opened too late for much in the way of survey feedback, but David Ellis of The Evening Standard was very upbeat on his August 2021 trip.) / W1U 1HF; www.sidechick.co.uk; Mon-Sat 10 pm.

Signor Sassi SW1 £69 3 3 3
14 Knightsbridge Green   020 7584 2277   6–1D

"Timeless (if slightly jaded) Italian" that's been part of the nationwide San Carlo group for the last few of its 35 years. If you are looking for a lively, affordable bite near Harrods, you could do very much worse. / SW1X 7QL; www.signorsassi.co.uk; @SignorSassi.

Silk Road SE5 £25 5 2 2
49 Camberwell Church St   020 7703 4832   1–3C

The "fabulous, flavour-packed, spicy 'Chinese' food from China's Muslim northwest" (Xinjiang, home of the Uighurs) "never fails to hit the spot" at this "canteen-style" pit-stop in Camberwell. It's an absolute "byword for value", too ("and now accepts card payment"). / SE5 8TR; Mon-Sun 11 pm; closed Mon-Sun L; cash only; No bookings.

Silo E9
Unit 7 Queens Yard, White Post Lane   020 8533 3331   14–1C

Douglas McMaster's zero-waste project in grungily groovy Hackney Wick opened at a tough time and although it's attracted awards and adulatory reviews (e.g. from Jimi Famurewa in The Evening Standard) in its early days, there's very little survey feedback (or indeed social buzz on other sites). It's a place no eco-warrior should miss, though, churning its own butter, milling ancient grains, making crockery and tables from reconstituted materials, etc. His Brighton site used to do well – more reports, please. / E9 5EN; silolondon.com; @londonsilo; Wed-Sat 11 pm; closed Wed-Fri L, closed Mon & Tue & Sun.

The Silver Birch W4 NEW £61 3 4 3
142 Chiswick High Road   020 8159 7176   8–2A

"A brilliant addition to the neighbourhood" – this Chiswick site was formerly a branch of Brew (next to W4's thriving Franco Manca), and, despite opening in tricky times (October 2020), wins enthusiastic local praise. The first solo project from Kimberley Hernandez (previously head chef at XU and Kym's), it's a relatively ambitious neighbourhood restaurant for this chain-filled high street, with "competent", "flavoursome" modern European cooking. / W4 1PU; silverbirchchiswick.co.uk; Wed-Sun 10 pm; closed Mon & Tue.

Simpson's in the Strand WC2   £85   2️⃣2️⃣**3**
100 Strand   020 7420 2111   5–3D

"Buzzing with tradition and gravitas", London's most famous dining room is fast approaching its bicentenary. Prized nowadays by locals only for business breakfasts, it is sometimes noted as "an excellent place to take an overseas guest for succulent roast beef" carved from domed trolleys, but the real surprise is how very little feedback it generates nowadays. By September 2021, Simpson's remains 'temporarily closed' – presumably awaiting a revival of the tourist trade? Could Corbin & King please take it over in the interim? / WC2R 0EW; www.simpsonsinthestrand.co.uk; @simpsons1828; No trainers.

Simpson's Tavern EC3   £48   2️⃣2️⃣**4**
38 1/2 Ball Ct, Cornhill   020 7626 9985   10–2C

This "brilliant old-style chophouse" in a City courtyard is "absolutely unique" – and has served classic roasts, grills and a signature "stewed cheese" pudding to a besuited clientele for more than 250 years (although its claim that Samuel Pepys was a customer is stretching it: the diarist had been dead for half a century by the time Thomas Simpson opened for business in 1757!). It is only open for lunch and breakfast – so it's naturally the "best location for a full English". / EC3V 9DR; www.simpsonstavern.co.uk; @SimpsonsTavern; Tue-Fri, Mon 3.30 pm; closed Tue-Fri, Mon D, closed Sat & Sun.

Sinabro SW11   £72   **4**3️⃣3️⃣
28 Battersea Rise   020 3302 3120   11–2C

"Such a treat to have this on the doorstep" – the four-course, no-choice, 'menu unique' (£39) changes every two weeks and draws enthusiastic praise for this 20-seater in Battersea. / SW11 1EE; www.sinabro.co.uk; @sinabrorestaurant; Tue-Sat 11 pm; closed Tue-Thu L, closed Sun & Mon.

Singapore Garden NW6   £55   **4**2️⃣2️⃣
83a Fairfax Rd   020 7624 8233   9–2A

"Reliably delicious food" – "with choices from all over Asia" including "incredible laksa" and other Singaporean/Malaysian specialities – ensure that it's perennially "hard to get a table" at this modest-looking veteran in a shopping parade near Swiss Cottage. It has "very reasonable prices too – what's not to like?" Giles Coren, restaurant critic at The Times, spends his own money here as a long-time regular. / NW6 4DY; www.singaporegarden.co.uk; @SingaporeGarden; Mon-Sun 10 pm; closed Mon-Fri L; Take bookings all week via phone and/or online.

Singburi Royal Thai Café E11   £25   **4**3️⃣3️⃣
593 Leytonstone High Rd   020 8281 4801   1–1D

"Delicious, authentic Thai food at low prices", with a "frequently changing list of specials", draw an appreciative crowd to this Leytonstone BYO canteen. Top Tip: "try the moo krob (deep-fried pork belly) and razor clams with fresh peppercorns and chilli". / E11 4PA; @SingburiThaiCaf; Wed-Sun 8.30 pm; closed Wed-Sun L, closed Mon & Tue; cash only.

Six by Nico   £61   **4****4****4**
33-41 Charlotte Street, W1   020 7580 8143   2–1C **NEW**
6 Chancellor Passage, E14   12–1C **NEW**

Chef Nico Simeone's "amazing-value set-meal" concept, launched in Glasgow in 2017, has now opened in Fitzrovia and Canary Wharf, offering "a six-course tasting menu for only £37" – a "clever formula" with "well thought-out feasts that entice a bubbly audience". "The menu changes every six weeks", and is "themed around an experience" – 'the circus', 'the Amalfi coast' and 'the chippie' have all featured – with the cooking winning high praise for "variety, skill and quality". / www.sixbynico.co.uk; @SixbyNico.

Six Portland Road W11 £78 **4 4 2**
6 Portland Road   020 7229 3130   7–2A
This "smart neighbourhood restaurant" in Holland Park is "great value for some quite elevated cooking", with menus that change daily. It's "very small" (36 seats), "very friendly", and has a "super wine list". It sees itself as a 'smarter, smaller and more mature relative of Parlour', the highly rated gastropub in Kensal Green. Top Tip: "well-priced lunch menu". / W11 4LA; www.sixportlandroad.com; @SixPortlandRoad; Mon-Sun 10 pm.

Skal Nordic Dining N1 NEW £34 **4 4 3**
149 Upper Street   07308 031151   9–2D
With a name meaning 'cheers' in Swedish, this Islington restaurant took over the Grade II site vacated by Rok (RIP) in late 2019, and continues the Scandi theme set by its predecessor. 'Traditional Nordic recipes but with a modern twist' are underpinned – they say – by the term 'husmanskost' meaning 'traditional home-cooked food' (yes, there are meatballs…). "We tried this place after months of walking past. So glad we did. Great Nordic fish dishes, and on Sundays a surprising and delicious take on the classic British roast. Friendly and knowledgeable staff, in a bijou dining room which is nevertheless larger than it looks." / N1 1RA; www.skalnordicdining.co.uk; Tue-Sat 11 pm; closed Tue-Fri L, closed Sun & Mon.

Sketch,
Lecture Room at Library W1 £221 **3 4 5**
9 Conduit St   020 7659 4500   4–2A
"Glitz and completely OTT surroundings make this an experience that will be remembered" – there's all-round applause for this "fabulous and very romantic" dining room, on the top floor of a Mayfair palazzo of fairy tale grandeur. For the most part, despite the terrifying pricing, this praise also extends beyond the "magnificent" setting to the "superb" cuisine, which is overseen (from afar) by star chef Pierre Gagnaire. Meals "come with so many bits and bobs, so you don't really know where to start" but on nearly all accounts it's "superb". Whether Michelin should really have awarded it three stars, though, is debatable. A fair summary: "Grade A for effort, but it's all a bit too much". / W1S 2XG; sketch.london; @sketchlondon; Wed-Sun 9 pm; closed Mon & Tue; No trainers; Booking max 6 may apply.

Sketch,
Gallery W1 £98 **2 2 4**
9 Conduit St   020 7659 4500   4–2A
If you want to visit this "fantastical location" within Mourad Mazouz's lavish Mayfair palazzo – a vision in pink from designer David Shrigley – then afternoon tea is the way to go: "it's one of the more expensive options in town", but "fabulous". For dinner, however, this wacky chamber often seems "overpriced", although – to be fair – this appears to be of absolutely no concern to the fashionista crowd it perennially attracts. Go once, anyway, to visit the egg-shaped loos! / W1S 2XG; sketch.london; @sketchlondon; Mon-Sun 10 pm; Take bookings all week via phone and/or online.

Skewd Kitchen EN4 £64 **4 3 3**
12 Cockfosters Parade   020 8449 7771   1–1C
"Great Turkish food" draws an enthusiastic and sometimes "noisy" crowd to this modern grill 'with attitude' in Cockfosters, at the furthest northern reaches of the Piccadilly line. All the usual Anatolian cuts of meat are available, with a few surprises on the specials list. / EN4 0BX; www.skewd.com; @SkewdKitchen; Mon-Sat 11 pm, Sun 10 pm; closed Mon-Fri L.

Skylon,
South Bank Centre SE1 £78 2 2 3
Belvedere Rd 020 7654 7800 2–3D

An airy, light-filled space, with vast picture windows overlooking the Thames – this large dining room (once known as The People's Palace) showcases the 1950s Brutalist architecture of the South Bank arts centre at its best, and that inherent appeal keeps business ticking over at this D&D London venue. Too many reporters, however, say the food is merely "decent" or "not too bad", which makes the whole enterprise feel like a "missed opportunity". / SE1 8XX; www.skylon-restaurant.co.uk; @skylonsouthbank; Mon-Sat 9 pm, Sun 5 pm; closed Sun D; No trainers.

Slice SE1 NEW £32
Royal Festival Hall, Belvedere Road 020 4524 9409 2–3D

Grab and go at this new brand from Pizza Pilgrims where you can order New-York-style 12-inch pizza – available whole or in slices (in five flavours) – or pizza by the metre. Wash them down with alcoholic slushies and to kill any spare time there are '80s-style arcade games. / SE1 8XX; www.pizzapilgrims.co.uk/venues/slice/; @pizzapilgrims; Mon-Sun 10 pm.

Smith & Wollensky WC2 £109 2 2 3
The Adelphi Building, 1-11 John Adam St 020 7321 6007 5–4D

The first international branch of a famous New York steakhouse brand (there's now also a second, in Taipei), this grandiose dining room off The Strand is notably "pricey" and some reporters "have never quite gotten over the expense of the trip". Fans of its USDA dry-aged steaks and high-end cuts from the British Isles say it's "worth every penny" – they insist "the hanging tomahawk steak (to share for two people) is unbelievable". But there are also significant gripes, which do not relate to cost. "Grotesque US-style portions" is one (although, admittedly, some might see that as praise). Others are that the food – other than steak – is just "standard fayre and nothing special" and that "NY is much better". / WC2N 6HT; www.smithandwollensky.co.uk; @sandwollenskyuk; Mon-Thu 11.30 pm, Fri & Sat 12.30 am, Sun 8.30 pm; closed Mon L; Take bookings all week via phone and/or online.

Smith's Wapping E1 £72 4 3 4
22 Wapping High St 020 7488 3456 12–1A

"Super views over the river, Tower Bridge and The Shard" add to the atmosphere at this rather glam brasserie, "right on the river" in Wapping (the offshoot of the well-known Ongar veteran). You can get a "decent steak" here, but it is primarily recommended for its "excellent fish and seafood", "beautifully cooked". / E1W 1NJ; www.smithsrestaurants.com; Mon-Sat 10 pm, Sun 9 pm; No trainers.

Smiths of Smithfield,
Top Floor EC1 £79 3 3 4
67-77 Charterhouse St 020 7251 7950 10–1A

With fine views from the fringes of the City, this (slightly pricey) rooftop venue on top of a four-floor Smithfield destination is well-known as a "business-focused" venue, but it has broadened its appeal in recent times – there's less focus on steak and a new rooftop brunch. / EC1M 6HJ; www.smithsofsmithfield.co.uk; @thisissmiths; Mon-Wed 11 pm, Thu & Fri midnight, Sat 10 pm, Sun D; booking max 10 may apply.

Smoke & Salt SW17 £49 5 4 4
115 Tooting High St no tel 11–2C

"This crew started in Pop Brixton and now have opened up a new tasting menu venture in Tooting!" Remi Williams and Aaron Webster's new site was formerly an outpost of Dip & Flip, but the cuisine continues to celebrate 'the ancient techniques of smoking, curing and preserving, combined with bold, global flavours and modern influences'. The result is "an excellent value tasting menu" – "absolutely delicious combinations that keep you coming back for more!" and "divinely paired with drinks options". / SW17; www.smokeandsalt.com; @SmokeandSaltLDN; Tue-Sat 10 pm; closed Sun & Mon.

Smokehouse Islington N1 £60 443
63-69 Canonbury Rd   020 7354 1144   9–2D

"You can't beat the roast dinner – the meat is always perfect and with delicious side dishes too" – at this Canonbury gastropub, which provides a *"great carnivorous treat"*. Ingredients are taken seriously: meat is brought in weekly (whole carcasses, butchered in-house) and Cornish fish is delivered daily. The pub side of the operation is not neglected either, with 80 beers in stock (20 on tap) and a list of wines only from small family-owned vineyards. It's one of four in the Noble Inns chain. / N1 2RG; www.smokehouseislington.co.uk; @smokehouseN1; Mon-Sat 10.30 pm, Sun 10 pm; closed Mon-Thu L.

Smokestak E1 £47 533
35 Sclater Street   020 3873 1733   13–1C

David Carter's *"industrial-chic BBQ restaurant"* off Brick Lane, is inspired by the southern US grill-house tradition. The high-ceilinged room is *"dominated by a vast smoker"* which sends out a succession of outstanding and *"well-priced smoked meats"*, alongside dishes like grilled hispi cabbages and roast aubergines in red miso. Sides, desserts and drinks are similarly no-nonsense. / E1 6LB; www.smokestak.co.uk; @smokestakUK; Mon-Fri 11 pm, Sat & Sun 10 pm.

Smoking Goat E1 £56 443
64 Shoreditch High Street   no tel   13–1B

"If you don't like chilli, this place is not for you!" – Ben Chapman's well-known *"mecca for spice and heat"* in Shoreditch has won a major name for its *"brilliant, sharp and exotic ('real') Thai dishes"*, particularly amongst local hipsters, and it's a *"fun"* place too with *"friendly and accurate service"*. Tip Tip: *"fish sauce chicken wings to die for"*. / E1 6JJ; www.smokinggoatsoho.com; @thesmokinggoat; Mon-Sat 11 pm, Sun 10 pm.

Smokoloko E1 £15 53–
Old Spitalfields Market, Bethnal Green Road   07508 675363   13–2B

"Consistently great meat at a very reasonable price, given the quality of product" again wins the highest marks for Cleo Vizioli's street market hit, known for its rolls loaded with smoked cuts. Just look out for the old steam locomotive, and you can watch your meal roasting away in the boiler! / E1 6GY; smokoloko.uk; @smokolokoBBQ; Mon-Sun 3 pm; closed Mon-Sun D.

So LA W1 NEW £139 444
64 Dean Street   020 7734 8428   5–2A

"Superb in every way!" – Victor Garvey's decision to close his *"small"* tapas restaurant Rambla (RIP) and to transform it in late 2019 into a highly *"original"* top-end venue has paid off. The idea is to celebrate 'the modern cuisine of America's Pacific West Coast, bringing a taste of California to Soho, via LA' (hence the SO|LA name, geddit). In practice, this means a plant-filled interior; a strong, well-priced list of Californian wine; and high priority placed on *"exceptional ingredients"* (with an emphasis on seafood). *"It delivers all you could want from a top-end London restaurant whilst still feeling like you're dining in a small local bistro"*. The *"creative"* cooking is *"freshly seasonal"* (e.g. *"exceptional tomato salad"*) – *"the only drawback is the £139 tasting menu price tag, with no £89 prix fixe option available to weekend diners"*. In January 2021, it earned the first Michelin star for an American-cuisine restaurant outside of the US. / W1D 4QQ; solasoho.com; @SOLAsoho; Wed-Sat 11 pm; closed Mon & Tue & Sun.

Soane's Kitchen W5 £48 2️⃣2️⃣4️⃣

Pitzhanger Manor, Walpole Park   020 8579 2685   1–3A

"A great setting in Walpole Park with an amazing terrace" is a highpoint at this all-day café in the walled garden of Ealing's fine Pitzhanger Manor (designed by Sir John Soane). It's been on a bit of a rollercoaster ride in recent times, closing, changing operators, re-opening, and then with another change of chef in August 2021 (Andre Rhone from Richmond's Bingham). Most recommended for breakfast, so that seems a good way of dipping your toe in the water here. / W5 5EQ; soaneskitchen.co.uk; @SoanesKitchen; Wed-Sun 10 pm; closed Mon & Tue.

Social Eating House W1 £98 3️⃣3️⃣4️⃣

58-59 Poland St   020 7993 3251   4–1C

Jason Atherton's casual Soho venue maintains its "informal but enjoyable atmosphere" in large part thanks to its "warm and welcoming" approach to service. The food is well-rated too (if not quite at the heights it once was), with numerous reporters describing their best meal of the year here – you can indulge in a "wonderful chef's counter experience" or stick with the prix fixe menu. Hidden away upstairs is Atherton's speakeasy, The Blind Pig. / W1F 7NR; www.socialeatinghouse.com; @Socialeathouse; Tue-Sat 10 pm; closed Sun & Mon.

Soif SW11 £64 3️⃣3️⃣3️⃣

27 Battersea Rise   020 7223 1112   11–2C

A "consistently imaginative menu" of rustic French plates, both small and large, combines with a global list of organic and biodynamic wines at this "fabulous local" on Battersea Rise. It is part of the Terroirs group operated by natural wine pioneer Les Caves de Pyrène, which has lost some of its rarity value now that so many have followed its lead. / SW11 1HG; www.soif.co; @Soif_SW11; Wed-Sat 11 pm, Sun 5 pm; closed Sun D, closed Mon & Tue.

Sollip SE1 NEW £98 5️⃣4️⃣3️⃣

8 Melior Street   020 7378 1742   10–4C

"Who would have thought a French/Korean fusion of cuisines would be so successful?" This "tranquil and calm" (bordering on low-key) newcomer, in the unlovely environs of London Bridge, opened just a few days before lockdown in March 2020, and "deserves to do very well". Behind it are husband-and-wife team Woongchul Park (ex-The Ledbury) and Bomee Ki (previously pastry chef at The Arts Club); their whimsical culinary approach – 'haute' European cuisine, but with subtle Korean influences and ingredients – wins utter raves: "a super-clean clash between French elegance and Korean ingredients using very original methods and executed beautifully". "Every dish is like a love letter to your stomach… so pure, with pastry like a magic trick". "I felt relaxed, curious, delighted… and departed light yet sated". ('Sollip' is the Korean word for pine needles, which are used to control flames and smoke in traditional Korean cuisine.). Top Tip – "the Instagrammable daikon tarte Tatin is a savoury revelation, the gougeres moreish, but the deceptively simple cassoulet with kimchi you could feast on for the rest of days!" / SE1 3QQ; www.sollip.co.uk; Tue-Thu 11 pm, Fri & Sat 11.30 pm; closed Tue-Sat L, closed Sun & Mon; cards only.

Som Saa E1 £52 4️⃣2️⃣3️⃣

43a Commercial St   020 7324 7790   13–2C

"Food just like you get in Thailand" – "the quality and the range of flavours are superb" – can be found at this "amazing and very cool" five-year-old in a former factory near Spitalfields Market. "Zingy and authentic", "each dish looks and tastes like it's comprised of ingredients you'd be hard-pressed to source yourself". "Vegan options are plentiful", and "one price for 'eat as much rice as you want' feels generous". There's also a serious list of drinks that can cope with such highly flavoured cooking – including a "great Riesling menu". / E1 6BD; www.somsaa.com; @somsaa_london; Tue, Wed 10 pm, Thu-Sat 11 pm; closed Tue-Sat L, closed Sun & Mon; Take bookings all week via phone and/or online.

Sông Quê E2 £40 3 2 2
134 Kingsland Rd   020 7613 3222   14–2A
"The food is superb" at this Vietnamese canteen with a high reputation against strong competition on Shoreditch's Kingsland Road 'Pho Mile'. "You don't come here for the service, but for the great pho." / E2 8DY; www.songque.co.uk; Mon-Sat 11 pm, Sun 10.30 pm; no Amex.

Sorella SW4 £61 4 3 3
148 Clapham Manor Street   020 7720 4662   11–1D
Robin Gill's "excellent neighbourhood restaurant" – with "a delicious menu of top-quality Italian dishes" inspired by the Amalfi coast – is nowadays his only Clapham venue since the closure of the nearby Dairy (RIP). "The wonderful service and top-class food make this a local go-to." Top Tip: "amazing arancini" (truffle or beef short rib and black garlic). / SW4 6BX; www.sorellarestaurant.co.uk; @sorellaclapham; Wed-Sat 10 pm, Sun 2.45 pm; closed Wed L closed Sun D, closed Mon & Tue; no Amex.

Soutine NW8 £61 2 3 3
60 St John's Wood High Street   020 3926 8448   9–3A
"A great addition to St John's Wood" – Corbin & King's "easygoing" (if "noisy") brasserie is already something of an "instant classic", thanks not least to its "romantic interior, which – even though it's brand new – looks as if it hasn't changed in a hundred years". "The food is never really the main thing at C&K places: you go for the whole package", and that's true here too – the "simple" classic French fare, though "OK" is often "uninspiring". To fans, though, "it's less a meal, more a warm Gallic embrace!" / NW8 7SH; soutine.co.uk; @SoutineStJohn; Mon-Sat 10 pm, Sun 9 pm.

Sparrow SE13 £55 4 4 3
Rennell Street   020 8318 6941   1–4D
"What a find!" – "this little neighbourhood restaurant" in Lewisham is "difficult to compartmentalise: pan-Asian + Mediterranean + French + Indian, and always something to intrigue". Husband-and-wife team Terry Blake and Yohini Nandakumar have pooled their experiences and heritages to assemble "an ever-changing menu of inspired dishes which will accommodate all ages and tastes". Their place "doesn't look promising from the outside but the food is exceptional and the service perfect". / SE13 7HD; sparrowlondon.co.uk; @sparrowlondon; Wed-Sat 10 pm, Sun 5 pm; closed Sun D, closed Mon & Tue.

Spring Restaurant WC2 £82 4 4 5
New Wing, Lancaster Place   020 3011 0115   2–2D
"Brilliant, beautifully presented combinations of fresh ingredients", elegantly served "in a lovely space in Somerset House", show a restaurant really hitting its stride – with chef Skye Gyngell now matching in central London the accolades she earned over a decade ago at Petersham Nurseries in Richmond, with "fabulous, simple Italian-themed food". Top Tip: it's a romantic venue, too: "recommended this restaurant to my son for an early date – he's now happily married and we have a grandson!" / WC2R 1LA; www.springrestaurant.co.uk; @Spring_LDN; Wed-Sat 9.30 pm; closed Sat L, closed Mon & Tue & Sun; credit card required to book.

Sri Suwoon SW1 £43 3 4 3
44 Hugh Street   020 7828 0321   2–4B
This "lovely neighbourhood Thai" behind Victoria station has a strong following in Pimlico and beyond. / SW1V 4EP; www.srisuwoon.com/; @sri_suwoon; Mon-Sat 10 pm; closed Mon-Sat L, closed Sun.

St Clair SW4 NEW £57
22 The Pavement   020 7498 2636   11–2D

A sun-drenched terrace on Clapham's 'Pavement' overlooking the Common adds further lustre to this elegant (lots of marble) Clapham venture from Jorge Baumhauer da Silva, the former head chef of Ceviche restaurants. It's a haven for fish lovers – a restaurant, 'fish boutique' and cevicheria – serving Nikkei cuisine, fusing Peruvian and Japanese inspirations. / SW4 0HY; www.stclairuk.com; Mon-Sat 11 pm, Sun 10 pm.

Stanley's SW3 NEW 3 3 4
151 Sydney Street   020 7352 7664   6–3C

Opening in late 2020 – between lockdowns – the "lovely outdoor seating" at this large newcomer set around a Chelsea courtyard quickly came into its own. It's the debut restaurant for Hugh Stanley, with Olivia Burt (ex-Claridge's and MasterChef: The Professionals winner) at the stoves, and although some sceptics feel it "doesn't live up to Liv Burt's performance on TV", the majority of reports are of food with "exceptional quality and presentation". / SW3 6NT; www.stanleyschelsea.co.uk; Mon-Sat 11.30 pm, Sun 7.30 pm.

Stem & Glory EC1 £49 3 2 2
60 Bartholomew Close   020 3969 9392   10–2B

"Vegan food that is actually moreish and delicious" is the governing principle at this campaigning two-year-old near Barts Hospital, which launched after a £600k Crowdcube fundraiser and sited five minutes' walk from Smithfield meat market (the original also just re-launched in Cambridge). Plant-based versions of popular dishes dominate the menu, from dirty burgers and pizzas through to pho and katsu curry. / EC1A 7BF; www.stemandglory.uk; @stemandglory; Tue-Thu 10 pm, Fri & Sat 11 pm; closed Sun & Mon.

Steven Edwards
Bingham Riverhouse TW10 £73 4 3 4
61-63 Petersham Road   020 8940 0902   1–4A

"A really romantic setting with stunning views over the river" – this boutique hotel dining room in Richmond features "delicious, refined dining" from chef Steven Edwards (owner of Brighton's etch and a former winner of MasterChef: The Professionals) from Thursday dinner to Sunday lunch. It's "pricey, but a great treat!". A simpler menu is available for the dining room and verandah Monday-Wednesday. / TW10 6UT; www.binghamriverhouse.com; @BRiverhouse; Fri & Sat 8 pm, Thu 8 pm, Sun 1.30 pm; closed Thu L closed Sun D, closed Mon & Tue & Wed; No trainers.

Stick & Bowl W8 £20 3 4 2
31 Kensington High Street   020 7937 2778   6–1A

"You get no airs and graces and wouldn't spend hours here", but this Chinese dive on Kensington's main drag provides "great value food that has luckily survived in an expensive area" since the 1950s. "Long may it continue!" / W8 5NP; stickandbowl.has.restaurant/contact/; Mon-Fri 10.45 pm; closed Sat & Sun; cash only; no booking.

Sticks'n'Sushi £70 4 3 3
3 Sir Simon Milton Sq, Victoria St, SW1   020 3141 8810   2–4B
40 Beak Street, W1   020 3141 8191   4–2C NEW
11 Henrietta St, WC2   020 3141 8810   5–3D
113-115 King's Road, SW3   020 3141 8181   6–3C
1 Nelson Road, SE10   020 3141 8220   1–3D
58 Wimbledon Hill Rd, SW19   020 3141 8800   11–2B
1 Crossrail Place, E14   020 3141 8230   12–1C

"Absolutely top-notch food" – "pricey but great!" – is the key to the steady growth enjoyed by this Copenhagen-based Japanese group, whose most recent (2019) openings in Soho and Chelsea join established venues across

London. It's "an interesting concept, well executed" – "fresh and delicious sushi", yakitori skewers, and "colourful, almost art-directed salads", delivered in dining rooms that combine clean, Japanese minimalism with Danish hygge. / www.sticksnsushi.com; @sticksnsushi_UK.

Sticky Mango at RSJ SE1   £57   2️⃣2️⃣2️⃣
33 Coin Street   020 7928 4554   10–4A

"Freshness of flavours in the varied SE Asian dishes" all "at sensible prices" provides endorsement of Peter Lloyd's transformation of RSJ (RIP), the classic French restaurant that formerly graced the South Bank for 30 years. "They found their feet quickly after lockdown", too. On the debit side, the famous "Loire wines inherited from RSJ seem to have been exhausted, and noise levels are still as high as ever". And oddly, given the proximity to the Festival Hall and Old and Young Vics, "there's no pre-theatre menu". / SE1 9NR; www.stickymango.co.uk; @stickymangoldn; Mon-Sat 10.30 pm; closed Sun.

Stockwell Continental SW8   £51   3️⃣4️⃣3️⃣
169 South Lambeth Road   020 3019 0757   11–1D

"A really classic Italian cafe-pizzeria" – this Vauxhall venture is something of a departure for the gastropub experts behind the vaunted Canton Arms and Anchor & Hope – serving "excellent pizza" ("of the doughy, fluffy variety rather than thin and crispy, but the base is delicious and the range of toppings varies with the seasons") plus "a bunch of great small plates that some even prefer". What it has in common with its stablemates is "good value", "quality produce" and "excellent, friendly service". It's also "the kind of place you can easily go to on a regular basis". / SW8 1XW; www.stockwellcontinental.com.

Stork Restaurant W1   £90
13-14 Cork Street   020 3973 9307   4–4A

When it opened in April 2019, this heart-of-Mayfair restaurant aimed for a blend of British Modern cuisine with accents of West Africa, but nowadays a more confident Pan-African narrative is dominant, both in the styling and cooking. No survey reports as yet; online feedback has its ups and downs, but – for anyone interested in African cuisine – this is London's most poshly located destination. / W1S 3NS; www.storkrestaurant.com; @storkrestaurant; Mon-Thu midnight, Fri & Sat 2 am, Sun 10.30 pm.

Story SE1   £197   4️⃣4️⃣3️⃣
199 Tooley St   020 7183 2117   10–4D

"Story never fails to surprise and delight, and isn't that what eating out is all about?" – so say fans of Tom Sellers's "creative, clever and delicious" cuisine at his "special" venue near Tower Bridge. "The menu is a puzzle and you only know what it means when the food arrives. Presentation is awesome. And the paired wines are impressive too." "It's not cheap… but it's an adventure that keeps you on your toes." / SE1 2UE; www.restaurantstory.co.uk; @Rest_Story; Thu-Sun 8.30 pm; closed Mon & Tue & Wed; No shorts.

Straits Kitchen,
Pan Pacific London EC3 NEW   £69
80 Houndsditch   020 7118 6888   10–2D

A short walk from Liverpool Street station, this towering, new, luxury hotel from a Singapore-based chain was slated to open in 2020, but opened post-lockdown in May 2021. Straits is the flagship dining room for the hotel, where ex-Sheraton Saigon chef, British-born Lorraine Sinclair, presides over an Asian-inspired menu. In the Orchid Lounge, Cherish Finden – judge on Channel 4's Bake Off: The Professionals – has been announced as executive pastry chef. / EC3A 7AB; www.panpacificlondon.com; @PanPacific; Mon-Sat 10 pm, Sun 9.30 pm.

Street Burger

13-14 Maiden Lane, WC2   020 7592 1214   5–3D **NEW**
24 Charing Cross Road, WC2   020 7592 1361   5–4B **NEW**
222 Kensington High Street, W8   020 7592 1612   8–1D **NEW**
341 Upper Street, N1   020 7592 1355   9–3D **NEW**
Entertainment District, The O2, SE10   020 7352 2512   1–4D **NEW**
One New Change, EC4   020 7592 1217   10–2B **NEW**

Gordon Ramsay's Byron might be a better name for Big Sweary's new burger chain, which – in its first year of operation – has already taken three of Byron's former branches into its own stable. Launched in the City at the One New Change development in December 2020, after trials at several pop-ups: it's run along similar lines to his Street Pizza brand – all burgers cost £15, and include fries and unlimited soft drinks. (One New Change also houses GR's decade-old Bread Street Kitchen, for which a national roll-out is planned). It didn't take long before more branches came along, on the former Byron branch on Charing Cross Road; on High Street Kensington, in Islington and – biggest of all – an 175-seater in the O2.
/ www.gordonramsayrestaurants.com/street-burger; @GordonRamsayGRR.

Sucre London W1 **NEW**   £80

47b Great Marlborough Street   020 3988 3329   4–1B
Fernando Trocca (a star Latino chef) has imported the colour and tastes of Buenos Aires to this 120-seat, summer 2021 newcomer, and breathless, early online reports say the room is absolutey knock-out, with its glam chandeliers, and the high drama of its central open kitchen and fire pit. It occupies a Soho site of historical interest, too – the concert hall inside the 300-year-old building that once was the HQ of the Royal College of Music (currently emerging from being redeveloped). Downstairs is a moody, nightclubby bar, Abajo, from Renato Giovannoni, who is involved with one of BA's top bars: Floreria Atlantico. / W1F 7HS; www.sucrerestaurant.com; Mon-Sat 1 am, Sun 11 pm.

Sukho Fine Thai Cuisine SW6   £54   5 5 3

855 Fulham Rd   020 7371 7600   11–1B
"The best Thai restaurant ever" applaud the dedicated fan club of this long-established, tightly packed Thai in a Fulham shop conversion, which provides "consistently high-quality and delicious food with excellent, attentive service". / SW6 5HJ; www.sukhogroups.com; Mon-Sat 10.30 pm, Sun 9.30pm.

Sumak N8   £42   3 4 2

141 Tottenham Lane   020 8341 6261   1–1C
"Far superior to the vast majority of Turkish/Kurdish eateries on the nearby Haringey Green Lanes" – this "really reliable neighbourhood spot" sits "on the border of Crouch End and Hornsey" and keeps its devoted regulars happy with "generous portions of tasty food". It's "not the cheapest, but the cooking is right up there". / N8 9BJ; www.sumakrestaurants.co.uk; Mon-Sun 11 pm.

Sumi W11 **NEW**   £86   4 4 3

157 Westbourne Grove   020 4524 0880   7–1B
On the Notting Hill fringe site that was Andina Picanteria (RIP), Endo Kazutoshi – the man behind White City's ultra-luxe sushi mecca, Endo at Rotunda – launched this elegant new sushi haunt (named after his mum!) in December 2020, before Covid-19 altered his plans. Morphed quickly into a click-and-collect operation, it's since returned to being the upmarket neighbourhood perch that was originally intended. On early reports, even those who find it "rather expensive" say it's "very good" and others would go further – "sublime!" / W11 2RS; www.sushisumi.com; Tue-Sat 10 pm; closed Sun & Mon; booking online only.

The Summerhouse W9   £66   3 3 5
60 Blomfield Rd   020 7286 6752   9–4A
With its "spectacular setting by the Regent's Canal", this "lovely, tranquil restaurant" in Little Venice is "very special for a fine spring or summer evening" – supping on "generous platters of yummy fish or mezze" while "paddleboards float by". / W9 2PA; www.thesummerhouse.co; @FRGSummerhouse; Mon-Sat 11 pm, Sun 10.30 pm; no Amex.

Sumosan Twiga SW1   £73   2 1 4
165 Sloane Street   020 3096 0222   6–1D
On a strip of Sloane Street south of Harvey Nicks that has lacked its natural international passing trade in recent times, this outpost of the Moscow-based Sumosan empire serves a luxurious mix of Italian and Japanese dishes, often to the backing of live entertainment. Yet again, the level of expense is the main sticking point (and service can have its off days, too), but it has its fans for a glam night out. / SW1X 9QB; www.sumosan.com; @sumosantwiga; Mon-Sun 2 am.

Sunday N1   £34   4 3 3
169 Hemingford Rd   020 7607 3868   9–2D
This aptly-named, all-day café in Barnsbury is the local hot-spot for weekend brunch – "if you can get in before the queues". "Courgette fritters, pancakes, banana bread" all get a shout-out, along with a "seriously good Virgin Mary". It's less frenetic during the week, when they take bookings. / N1 1DA; @sundaybarnsbury; Tue-Sun 7 pm; closed Mon; no Amex.

Sunday in Brooklyn W2 NEW   £61
98 Westbourne Grove   020 7630 1060   7–1B
'Sunday in Bayswater?' Another NYC staple arrives in town; the original Stateside venture was launched in 2016 by chef Jaime Young and, as the name hints, is a hit for brunch and burgers. This summer 2021, London spin-off is on the W2 fringes of Notting Hill, aiming to be a weekend magnet for ostentatiously hungover local trustafarians. / W2 5RU; sundayinbk.co.uk; Mon-Wed 11 pm, Thu-Sat midnight, Sun 10 pm; cards only.

Supawan N1   £50   4 4 3
38 Caledonian Road   020 7278 2888   9–3D
"A gem" in King's Cross, this "cosy, flower-filled space" serves some of the "most delicious Thai food in North London". Wichet Khongphoon, the "friendly and charming owner", is from Phuket in southern Thailand, and his "small, beautifully executed menu" reflects the cuisine of the region. / N1 9DT; www.supawan.co.uk; @EatSupawan; Mon-Sat 11 pm, Sun 10 pm; closed Mon-Wed L; Take bookings all week via phone and/or online.

Sushi Atelier W1   £56   5 4 3
114 Great Portland Street   020 7636 4455   2–1B
"Very-high-quality sushi and sashimi" win high esteem for this contemporary Japanese near Oxford Circus, from the Chisou group: "the raw fish is of dream-like quality with intelligent little toppings, while the other dishes on the menu are straight from Japan and effortlessly delicious". Top Tip – "sit at the bar for superb and informative service from the chefs". / W1W 6PH; www.sushiatelier.co.uk; @sushiatelierlondon; Tue-Sat 11 pm; closed Sun & Mon; Take bookings all week via phone and/or online.

Sushi Bar Makoto W4   £35   4 3 1
57 Turnham Green Terrace   020 8987 3180   8–2A
"An unassuming place in Turnham Green Terrace" – this basic, family-run Japanese café delivers "some really excellent sushi and sashimi": "a wonderful selection at a reasonable price". / W4 1RP; www.sushibarmakoto.co.uk; Mon-Fri 3 pm, Sat & Sun 10 pm; closed Mon-Fri D.

Sushi Marasaki W9 £55 5 4 2
12 Lauderdale Road 020 3417 8130 7–1C

Lucky Maida Vale residents have this "wonderful local Japanese" on their doorsteps. "Top-quality ingredients are skilfully prepared and service is lovely", delivering "sublime sashimi – fresh, cut just right and accompanied by just enough lime, shredded vegetables and shiso to make it shine. Tempura is sweet yet crisp and the signature rolls are a textural treat of mildly spicy dressing, popping fish eggs, sweet yet savoury rice and fresh fish!" / W9 1LU; sushi-murasaki.co.uk; @sushimurasakiuk; Tue-Thu midnight, Fri & Sat 1 am.

Sushi Masa NW2 £44 3 3 2
33b Walm Lane 020 8459 2971 1–1A

"Great sushi without a schlep into town!" wins strong local praise for this "minimal-looking" Japanese in Willesden Green (on a site many still remember as Sushi Say, RIP). "The food is so fresh as it's prepared to order, the anticipation as you sip on some hot sake is so worth the wait". "I am so lucky to have this place on my doorstep". / NW2 5SH; Mon-Sat 10 pm; closed Sun.

Sushi on Jones N1 NEW £56
Goods Way, 11 Goods Way 020 3179 2800 9–3C

This NYC sushi sensation (from Derek Feldman) opened its first London branch in March 2020, occupying the upstairs at Goods Way: a street-food market and entertainment venue whose lively styling contrasts with the ever-more corporate surroundings of King's Cross's new Pancras Square development. (Google's shiny new HQ is just around the block). It's famous for its 12-piece omakase delivered in 45 minutes. / N1C 4PW; www.sushionjones.com; @sushionjones; Wed-Sun 10 pm; closed Wed-Sun L, closed Mon & Tue.

Sushi Revolution SW9 NEW £30
240 Ferndale Road 020 4537 4331 11–1D

Aidan Bryan and Tom Blackshaw (who worked together at Sticks 'n' Sushi) have taken a unit in the poshly converted ex-department store complex that's nowadays HQ to Squire & Partners (architects on many of London's super-luxe landmark projects, like Chelsea Barracks). Here, you are invited to, er, 'rebel against the establishment' – apparently that means ordering some of their non-traditional sushi options. No survey feedback as yet, but good word-on-the-street vibes. / SW9 8FR; www.sushirevolution.co.uk; Mon-Sat 10 pm, Sun 9 pm; cards only.

Sushi Show £25 4 3 2
28 Camden Passage, N1 020 7354 1329 9–3D
136 Bethnal Green Road, E2 020 7613 1926 13–1D NEW

"Tiny and friendly sushi cafe", tucked away in the heart of Islington, where "the freshest fish are expertly prepared" (it's "run by a local fish supplier"). "All the usual options are present on the menu, but there are also some interesting daily specials". Take-away only during social-distancing times, but eat in is likely to return. There is also a spin-off in Shoreditch. / www.sushishowlondon.com.

Sushi Tetsu EC1 £100 5 4 4
12 Jerusalem Passage 020 3217 0090 10–1A

"The best sushi in London bar none" is not a ludicrous claim for Toru Takahashi's Clerkenwell fixture where "the freshest fish and seafood is superbly prepared" and "its quality is at a level matched only by multi-starred places in the capital". "During lockdown, their takeaway service was a shining light", and – as we go to press – his 7-seat restaurant has yet to re-open. When it does, "you truly have a sense you are sharing something special", but "it's ridiculous trying to get a booking", with phones open for five hours once a week. / EC1V 4JP; @SushiTetsuUK; no Amex.

Sushisamba £99 ②②③
Opera Terrace, 35 The Market, WC2 020 3053 0000 5–3D
Heron Tower, 110 Bishopsgate, EC2 020 3640 7330 10–2D
"A fun night out" is not in doubt at this glitzy (if ever-so slightly "impersonal") duo: be it on the 38th floor of the City's Heron Tower (accessed via western Europe's fastest lifts); or perched at the top of Covent Garden market, overlooking the back of the Royal Opera House. You get superb views in either location (particularly in the Square Mile, with its über-glam rooftop bars), plus "loud party music and great cocktails". And, in fact, the Japanese/South American fusion food is yummy too. It's just so "horrendously overpriced" that for a large proportion of folks it's just "not really worth it". The US-based group is an international one, with venues in Las Vegas and (scheduled for late 2021) Dubai. / sushisamba.com; @SUSHISAMBA.

Sussex W1 NEW £52 ③③②
63-64 Frith Street 020 3923 7770 5–2A
The Gladwin Brothers – behind The Shed, Rabbit and Nutbourne – graduated to the West End in autumn 2019, with the opening of this new 'local and wild' venture, on the site of Arbutus (long RIP). It's a U-shaped space, with a bar at the entrance, and tables for eating tucked around the corner. (In the basement, there's a chef's table for 20). Produce is from the family farm on the South Downs, but the menu here is less sharing plates focused than at its siblings. The odd reporter feels the results from an "appealing menu" are "OK but not memorable", but most feedback says it's "very good". / W1D 3JW; www.sussex-restaurant.com; Tue-Sat 10.30 pm; closed Sun & Mon.

Suzi Tros W8 £63 ③③③
18 Hillgate Street 020 7221 2223 7–2B
"A great addition to Notting Hill" – Adrien Carre and Christina Mouratoglou's "modern take on Greek tapas-style food" has gone down well since they opened it in summer 2019, next door to their enduring taverna Mazi. In truth, the food's not that Greek: for example 'grilled calamari, yuzu and jalapeno broth', or 'Scottish langoustines, lime and lemon zest, verbena'. / W8 7SR; www.suzitros.com; Tue-Sun, Mon 10.30 pm; closed Mon L.

The Swan W4 £54 ③③③
1 Evershed Walk, 119 Acton Ln 020 8994 8262 8–1A
"Rustic yet accomplished" sums up the appeal of this "reliable local" on the Acton-Chiswick border – and refers to both its "stylish pub food with an Italian twist" and to its "lovely garden". "Love the honest food, good service and great ambience" – the Art Deco green tiles and wood panelling are further distinguishing features. / W4 5HH; www.theswanchiswick.co.uk; @SwanPubChiswick; Mon-Fri 11 pm, Sat 10 pm, Sun 9.30 pm; closed Mon-Thu L.

The Swan at the Globe SE1 £75 ③③④
21 New Globe Walk 020 7928 9444 10–3B
"Fab food, awesome views and ambience" make this modern recreation of an Elizabethan tavern – part of the Shakespeare's Globe theatre complex on the South Bank – a "real delight", far superior to most tourist-site pit stops. The restaurant features contemporary British cooking, while the bar serves "great high-end pub fare, beautifully presented and in a stunning room overlooking the river". It's perfect for pre-theatre dining, naturally, but also works for full meals – thinning out when the audience is called in for the show. / SE1 9DT; www.swanlondon.co.uk; @swanglobe; Mon-Sat 10 pm, Sun 3 pm; closed Sun D.

Sweet Thursday N1 £47 3️⃣2️⃣2️⃣
95 Southgate Rd   020 7226 1727   14–1A
"Good chewy pizza" – *"made by Italians, owned by a Brit"* – *is the reason for the popularity of this De Beauvoir Town local with attached bottle shop. Portuguese superchef, Nuno Mendes of Chiltern Firehouse fame, is behind the small list of Roman-style 'pizzette'.* / N1 3JS; www.sweetthursday.co.uk; @Pizza_and_Wine; Mon-Thu 10 pm, Fri & Sat 10.30 pm, Sun 9 pm.

Sweetings EC4 £84 3️⃣3️⃣4️⃣
39 Queen Victoria St   020 7248 3062   10–3B
"A unique institution for fish, not to be missed" – *this timewarped Victorian curio has been part of life in the Square Mile for as long as anyone can remember (it was founded on a different site in the 1830s and has been here since the 1920s). Seating is fairly crammed and higgledy-piggledy – be it at the counter or in the rear dining room – but that's all part of its appeal for a besuited clientele who don't begrudge the daunting prices for simple seafood dishes and proper puds, washed down by the most ardent traditionalists with Black Velvet in pewter tankards.* / EC4N 4SA; sweetingsrestaurant.co.uk/; @SweetingsLondon; Mon-Fri 3 pm; closed Mon-Fri D, closed Sat & Sun; Booking lunch only.

Sycamore Vino Cucina,
Middle Eight Hotel WC2 NEW £65 4️⃣4️⃣3️⃣
Middle Eight Hotel, 66 Great Queen Street   020 7309 9300   5–1D
If it hadn't originally launched on 28 October 2020, days before the UK's second national lockdown, this expensively designed Covent Garden hotel would have attracted more attention. In its all-day bar and restaurant occupying much of the ground floor (there's also a mezzanine), executive chef Paul Robinson (ex-Temper and The Coal Shed) serves food from Northern Italy using British produce. Pizza and cicchetti feature alongside small plates, pasta and secondi. Early reports praise the "excellent food and service", although there's some dispute as to whether the setting is "a bit too much like an hotel" or "lovely and chic". / WC2B 5BX; www.middleeight.com; Mon-Sat 11 pm, Sun 4 pm; closed Sun D.

Tab X Tab W2 £35 5️⃣4️⃣4️⃣
Westbourne House, 14-16 Westbourne Grove   020 7792 3445   7–1B
Mathew and Charmain Tabtabai continue to serve caffeine highs alongside brunch, breakfasts and yummy baked goods at their award-winning (including from Harden's!) three-year-old Bayswater brew-stop, with beans from the excellent Kiss the Hippo. / W2 4UJ; tabxtab.com; @TABxTABLondon; Mon-Sun 3 pm; closed Mon-Sun D; cards only; booking online only.

Taberna Etrusca EC4 £61 2️⃣3️⃣2️⃣
9 -11 Bow Churchyard   020 7248 5552   10–2C
This 55-year-old City trattoria is a popular, lunchtime rendezvous spot on account of its "huge" helpings of classic dishes; its terrace by Bow churchyard for al fresco eating; and its good regional list of Italian wines. / EC4M 9DQ; www.etruscarestaurants.com; Tue-Fri 10 pm, Mon 3.30 pm; closed Mon D, closed Sat & Sun.

Table Du Marche N2 £57 3️⃣3️⃣2️⃣
111 High Road   020 8883 5750   1–1B
This "good-quality neighbourhood bistro" in Finchley has secured a solid reputation in the area for its "very tasty" and "very French" cooking over the past five years. Top Tip: "the lunch deal is amazing" (two courses £15, three courses £19). / N2 8AG; tabledumarchelondon.co.uk; @TableDuMarche; Mon-Sat 11 pm, Sun 10 pm.

Taka Marylebone W1 NEW £109
109 Marylebone High Street   020 3637 4466   2–1A
With the demise of the original Mayfair Taka, this October 2020 spin-off – on the Marylebone site of Providores (RIP) – is now the sole survivor of the duo. Amidst a scene set by low-key woody decor, it serves a more-than-just-sushi menu also incorporating Japanese-style tapas, robata dishes and mochi flatbreads. / W1U 4RX; takalondon.com; Fri & Sat 10.30 pm, Tue-Thu 10 pm; closed Tue-Thu L, closed Sun & Mon.

Takahashi SW19 £55 5 5 3
228 Merton Road   020 8540 3041   11–2B
This "sensational local Japanese" is lost in a suburban shopping parade near South Wimbledon tube station. Owned and run by Taka, a former Nobu chef, and his wife Yuko, it has consistently won our survey's highest-possible food ratings since its launch six years ago. "With only 12 covers a night you're guaranteed the chef's full attention is on every plate he serves" – including "high-quality sushi, beautifully presented with elegant service". This "attention to detail" matches anything you might find at far more expensive places in the West End. / SW19; www.takahashi-restaurant.co.uk; @takahashi_sw19; Wed-Sat 10.30 pm, Sun 8 pm; closed Wed-Sat L, closed Mon & Tue.

Talad SW10 NEW £20
533 Lots Road   020 7351 6969   6–4B
Natalie Tangsakul grew up in Thailand, and her distant-Chelsea café serves Northern Thai food with influences from Laos, Myanmar and China. She opened it in April 2020, having worked in banking and subsequently working her way around the restaurant industry, including as a chef. / SW10 0TZ; www.taladeatery.com; @talad_eatery; Mon-Fri 9.30 pm; closed Sat & Sun.

Tamarind W1 £80 4 3 3
20 Queen St   020 7629 3561   3–3B
"Beautiful and elegant Indian food of a rare quality" is the hallmark of this "refined" Mayfair basement, which shrugged off the 'curry house' label to pioneer "modern-style presentation of the best traditional tastes" at its launch in 1995. The first Indian restaurant in the world to bag a Michelin star in 2001, it suffered a dip in standards thereafter, but has revived in recent years, by doing "everything an Indian restaurant should to make you feel at home and appreciate the cuisine". The "subterranean location" was much improved by a refurb a few years back, and it's nowadays often praised as a "lovely setting". / W1J 5PR; www.tamarindrestaurant.com; @TamarindMayfair; Mon-Sat 10.15 pm, Sun 9.15 pm; No trainers.

Tamarind Kitchen W1 £59 4 3 3
167-169 Wardour St   020 7287 4243   4–1C
This spin-off from Mayfair's Tamarind has a "really good buzz" and "an unusual take on Indian food", serving "delicious and aromatic small plates", many of them "inspired by street food". With its "great decor and good, friendly service", it's "not super cheap, but the prices are consistent with the area". / W1F 8WR; tamarindkitchen.co.uk; @TamarindKitchen; Sat, Wed-Fri 10.30 pm, Sun 9.30 pm; closed Wed-Fri L, closed Mon & Tue.

Tamp Coffee W4 £25 3 3 4
1 Devonshire Road   no tel   8–2A
"A bizarre concept – coffee and empanadas – but it works. Who knew?!" This small Chiswick coffee bar, just off the high road, is "a great spot to while away an hour on the sunny terrace… and there's top coffee, too". / W4; www.tampcoffee.co.uk; @TAMPCOFFEE; Mon-Sun 4 pm; closed Mon-Sun D; No bookings.

Tandoor Chop House £56 4 3 3
8 Adelaide Street, WC2   020 3096 0359   5–4C
30 Uxbridge Street, W8   020 3535 8300   7–2B **NEW**

The "incredibly tasty food" at this Anglo-Indian hybrid, in "small but lovely" premises near Trafalgar Square (with a newer offshoot in Notting Hill), draws an appreciative crowd. "It doesn't have curries, but specialises in tandoori-baked meat". Top Tip: "you have to order the lamb chops, they're brutal!" / tandoorchophouse.com.

Tapas Brindisa SW7 £52 3 2 3
7-9 Exhibition Rd   020 7590 0008   6–2C

Providing "tasty tapas on the well-trodden path between South Ken tube and the museums" means the well-known Spanish food importers can hardly go wrong with this "cheap and cheerful" fixture. There's plenty of pavement seating to go with the "friendly staff and a really nice tapas menu with all the faves" – plus "great Spanish wines". / SW7 2HE; www.brindisatapaskitchens.com/restaurant/casa-brindisa-south-kensington/; @Brindisa; Mon-Sat midnight, Sun 11 pm; booking max 8 may apply.

Tapas Brindisa £66 3 3 3
46 Broadwick St, W1   020 7534 1690   4–2B
18-20 Southwark St, SE1   020 7357 8880   10–4C

The tapas bar operated by this Spanish food importer greets arrivals at the main entrance to Borough Market – and "on a bustling summer day, sitting outside with a glass of simple red, a table full of tapas on the go, chatting convivially with friends, it's great – just what one would expect". The newer branches around town match the quality, and can be a little easier to nab a table. The group is scheduled to open its sixth site in Richmond – the first located in the suburbs – in late 2021 (it will be on the striking riverside site that was formerly Jackson & Rye (RIP) complete with 150 covers and a 60-seat outside terrace). / www.brindisakitchens.com; @Brindisa.

Taqueria W11 £45 3 2 3
141-145 Westbourne Grove   020 7229 4734   7–1B

"Really delicious and varied tacos and tostadas" plus "killer margaritas" ensure a "busy atmosphere (and sometimes haphazard service)" at this Westbourne Grove cantina, which was a pioneer of the Mexican street food boom when it graduated from market stall to bricks and mortar in 2005. It's now spreading its wings, with a new spin-off in Exmouth Market under Adam Pawlak, who has been in the W11 kitchen for a dozen years. / W11 2RS; www.taqueria.co.uk; @TaqueriaUK; Mon-Sat 11 pm, Sun 10.30 pm; no Amex.

Tarantella Ristorante Pizzeria W4 £52 3 4 3
4 Elliot Rd   020 8987 8877   8–2A

A "lovely local" near Turnham Green, this "family-owned Italian" is "tiny but with terrific food and atmosphere". There's a good range of pizzas but the Puglian dishes are what makes it special. / W4 1PE; www.latarantella.london/; Mon-Sun 10 pm.

Taro £37 3 2 2
61 Brewer St, W1   020 7734 5826   4–3C
414 Kennington Road, SE11   020 7735 7772   1–3C
193 Balham High Rd, SW12   020 8675 5187   11–2C
44a Cannon St, EC4   020 7236 0399   10–3B

"No frills but great food" is the deal at this small group of basic Japanese canteens, which has pushed south and east after more than 20 years in Soho, with branches now in the City, Balham and Kennington. They serve a wide range of sushi, noodle and rice dishes, with the best value to be found in the bento boxes and 'set' meals. / www.tarorestaurants.co.uk.

Tas Pide SE1 £38 3 3 3
20-22 New Globe Walk   020 7928 3300   10–3B
"Good value and tasty food that never disappoints" is the reason to list this offshoot from the Turkish mezze chain, which is brilliantly positioned on the South Bank, right next to Shakespeare's Globe. The decor is on a comforting Anatolian theme, as is the cuisine which majors in 'pide' – stuffed Turkish flatbread 'pizzas'. / SE1 9DR; www.tasrestaurants.co.uk; @TasRestaurants; Sun & Mon 10.30 pm, Tue-Sat 11.30 pm.

Tatale SE1 NEW
66 Great Suffolk Street   020 8004 6436   10–4B
African cuisine has come a long way in London since Calabash – the capital's first African restaurant in the basement of the former Africa Centre in Covent Garden – opened in 1964. On the site of the new Africa Centre, in a repurposed Southwark office block, this January 2022 50-seater will be run by Ghanaian-British restaurateur Akwasi Brenya-Mensa. Named after a form of plantain pancake, Tatale aims to reflect the spirit of busy African roadside 'chop bars'. On the menu: omo tuo nkatenkwan sesame (mashed rice with groundnut, peanut soup); and buttermilk chicken burger topped with shito chilli, citrus yogurt and basil oil. / SE1 0BL; Thu-Sat 9 pm, Sun 4 pm.

Tate Modern, Kitchen & Bar, Level 6 SE1 £51 2 2 4
Level 6 Boiler House, Bankside   020 7401 5108   10–3B
"Decent food with a stunning view – if you're lucky enough to get a window table" overlooking the Thames and City rooftops, is the uncontested verdict on the 'Kitchen and Bar' in the Boiler House part of the gallery. / SE1 9TG; www.tate.org.uk/visit/tate-modern/kitchen-and-bar; @TateFood; Mon-Sun 6 pm; closed Mon-Sun D.

Tattu London WC2 NEW
The Now Building, Denmark Street   5–1A
The largest deployment of video screens in the world will make it hard to ignore The Now Building – a new landmark venue, near Centrepoint – and its anchor restaurant will be this first London branch of the well-known northern chain, which provides a contemporary and extremely glossy Chinese experience that promises 'a sensory journey from East to West'. In short, probably not a particularly foodie hotspot, but somewhere to go with Instagram at the ready. / WC2H 8LH; tattu.co.uk; Thu-Sun 6 pm.

Tavernaki W11 NEW £27
222 Portobello Road   07510 627752   7–1A
Chef Harris Mavropoulos opened this cosy modern taverna in the heart of Portobello at the start of 2020. It's yet to garner much in the way of profile, but early feedback is encouraging and suggests it's a cut above both the standard taverna experience, and also the often-disappointing standards of this chichi 'hood. (If you want to suss it out first, head to the downstairs Mykonos Bar). / W11 1LJ; www.tavernakiportobello.co.uk/; Mon-Sun 11 pm.

Tavolino SE1 NEW £48 3 4 4
Unit 1, 2 More London Place   020 8194 1037   10–4D
"Given its location, with a fantastic view of Tower Bridge" – not to mention a big outside terrace – *"you would expect this to be a tourist trap"*, but reports are upbeat on this large, *"classy-feeling"* two-floor newcomer in the More London development by City Hall (which opened in July 2020 on the site that was formerly a Strada). Chef Louis Korovilas previously headed up the kitchen at Bancone, making pasta the best choice here from the fairly traditional Italian menu. Early reports suggest it's proving a very worthwhile addition – *"not perhaps worth a trip, but – if you are in the area – well worth a visit"*. / SE1 2JP; www.tavolino.co.uk; @tavolinokitchen; Sun-Wed 10 pm, Thu-Sat 11 pm.

Tayyabs E1 £33 4 1 2
83 Fieldgate St 020 7247 6400 10–2D
"An institution and rightly so." "You don't come to this 500-seat BYO in the East End for the dining experience: you come for the amazing Punjabi food." "Still up there with the best" – the lamb chops in particular "are to die for". "Terrible service but great buzz and great food." "Such a brilliant place to take out-of-towners. Not fussy: fully authentic." / E1 1JU; www.tayyabs.co.uk; @1tayyabs; Mon-Sun 11.30 pm.

The Telegraph SW15 £50 3 3 4
Telegraph Road, Putney Heath 020 8194 2808 11–2A
"In the serene location of Putney Heath", this beautifully situated pub "was closed for a while before lockdown 1.0" to be rebuilt by new owners – Chester-based pub group, Brunning & Price – and "has come out as a great addition to Putney". "Spacious but humming", it now has "great outside dining" too. True to the chain's restaurant DNA, the food's not very foodie, but rated consistently well and there's a "good choice of beers and wines". / SW15 3TU; www.brunningandprice.co.uk/telegraph; Sun-Thu 11 pm, Fri & Sat 11.30 pm.

temper £54 4 3 4
25 Broadwick Street, W1 020 3879 3834 4–1C
5 Mercers Walk, WC2 020 3004 6669 5–2C
Angel Court, EC2 020 3004 6984 10–2C
Neil Rankin's trio of venues all centre on cooking over fire – with fire pits more and less on display – and the choice of an array of steaks (rare breed, from UK farms), fish and other meats, backed up by a selection of tacos. Sunday roast, bottomless brunch and steak supper clubs also feature in their list of attractions. All reports are positive this year, although even those who consider the food "outstanding" can quibble over the pricing. A "lovely new outdoor space" in WC2 has been a great addition. / temperrestaurant.com; @temperldn.

The 10 Cases WC2 £68 3 3 2
16 Endell St 020 7836 6801 5–2C
"Great French-style bistro" – "a bit of a squeeze" with "lots of hustle and bustle" – close to the Royal Opera House in Covent Garden. The "interesting if slightly limited menu" is overshadowed by the "amazing wines" on a constantly changing list. Only 10 cases of each are bought at a time – hence the name (but you can also "order from the much lengthier list at their wine bar next door, which always includes interesting options at various price points, as well as classics"). / WC2H 9BD; www.the10cases.co.uk; Mon-Thu 10 pm, Fri & Sat 11 pm; closed Sun.

10 Greek Street W1 £64 4 2 2
10 Greek St 020 7734 4677 5–2A
"The food is one star turn" (the wine is the other) at this "small and spartan" Soho wine bar, frequented by wine-trade insiders. There's an "interesting menu, short but imaginative", with "beautiful combinations of textures and flavours that make a very special meal". Ask the "knowledgeable front-of-house staff" for tips on the day's handwritten 'Black Book' list of fine wines. / W1D 4DH; www.10greekstreet.com; @10GreekStreet; Wed-Sat, Tue 10.30 pm; closed Tue L, closed Sun & Mon; No jeans; booking L only.

Tendido Cero SW5 £58 4 3 4
174 Old Brompton Road 020 7370 3685 6–2B
This "buzzy neighbourhood stalwart" in South Ken has long been known as a good bet for "top tapas". Its older sibling, directly across the road, is Cambio de Tercio, a leading light of Hispanic cuisine in London. / SW5 0BA; www.cambiodetercio.co.uk; @CambiodTercio; Mon-Sat 11.30 pm, Sun 11 pm.

Tendril W1 NEW £52
21 Great Pulteney Street   07842 797541   4–2C

Celebrating his journey from 'hardcore carnivore' to committed vegetarian, Rishim Sachdeva (whose CV includes Chiltern Firehouse and The Dairy) launched this 'mostly vegan' Indian as a 2021 residency in Soho's well-known Sun & 13 Cantons pub. Next stop is a permanent HQ, which is aimed for the end of 2021 or in 2022. / W1F 9NG; www.tendrilkitchen.co.uk; Wed-Fri, Tue, Sat 10 pm, Sun 5.30 pm; closed Tue L, closed Mon.

Terra Rossa N1 £61   3 3 3
139 Upper Street   020 7226 2244   9–3D

A "very good local Italian" serving "cheering, and honest food" – this modest-looking Puglian close to Islington's Almeida Theatre is named after the red earth of the Salento peninsula, the 'heel' of southern Italy. It's "much more than a pizza place", and prepares its own "home-made pasta" along with "dishes you won't find in a standard UK Italian". / N1 1QP; terrarossa-restaurant.co.uk; @terrarossa-restaurant; Mon-Sat 10.30 pm, Sun 9.30 pm.

Terroirs SE22 £60
38 Lordship Lane   020 8693 9021   1–4D

The East Dulwich branch (alongside sibling Soif, see also) is now the sole representative of this natural wine bar chain, whose original branch (which opened in 2008, off The Strand) introduced London to the joyful formula of natural wines and hearty small plates. Reasonable, but very limited, feedback on it nowadays. / SE22 8HJ; terroirswinebar.com; @TerroirsWineBar; Tue-Sun 11 pm.

Thali SW5 £45   4 3 3
166 Old Brompton Rd   020 7373 2626   6–2B

With a menu "based on the family recipes of the owner, from northern India", this smart little South Kensington spot is "welcoming and casual, making it perfect for focusing on the delicious flavours and aromas". / SW5 0BA; @ThaliLondon; Mon-Sat midnight; closed Mon-Sat L, closed Sun.

The Dusty Knuckle £20   4 2 2
429 Green Lanes, N4   9–2B NEW
Car Park, Abbot Street, E8   020 3903 7598   14–1A

Delicious breads and "lovely interesting sandwiches" have won acclaim for this hipster bakery in a Dalston car park, which helps get young offenders onto the straight and narrow. You can also book for eat-in pizza (Thu-Sat evenings only). In summer 2021, a second café and bakery opened on Haringey's Green Lanes. / www.thedustyknuckle.com; @thedustyknuckle.

The Petersham Restaurant TW10 £73   2 2 4
Nightingale Lane   020 8003 3602   1–4A

Stunning views across Petersham Meadows to the Thames are the highlight of any meal in the dining room of this rather stately Richmond hotel, built in 1865. The cooking is generally competent, if some would say "overpriced", but has its fans: "we love it for family get-togethers", while "afternoon tea here is perfect for catching up with friends". / TW10 6UZ; petershamhotel.co.uk/restaurant; @thepetersham; Mon-Sun 9 pm.

The Sea, The Sea £71   3 3 4
174 Pavilion Road, SW3   020 7824 8090   6–2D
337 Acton Mews, E8   14–2A NEW

"Fishmonger by day and intimate restaurant by night" – this "unique" two-year-old in a quiet mews near Sloane Street is pioneering "innovative techniques such as ageing fish". The result is a "very interesting tasting menu – expensive but well executed". Created by the team behind Bonnie Gull in Fitzrovia (RIP), it was joined in summer 2021 by a bigger branch next to Berber & Q in Hackney – a base for their wholesale fish and seafood processing business, with an 'immersive dining counter' under chef Leo Carreira. The aim is to create 'somewhere between art installation, restaurant, laboratory and factory!' / www.theseathesea.net.

Theo Randall at the InterContinental
London Park Lane W1 £81 ③③②

1 Hamilton Place 020 7318 8747 3–4A

"Sublime" Italian cooking of "the highest quality" – not least from the "fantastic, regional four-course menu and wine pairing" – inspires a large and devoted fan club to return time and again to Theo Randall's long-established dining room, just off Park Lane. And, alongside the "charming and friendly" service, the main man is regularly in evidence and "a real gent as well as an exceptional chef". The catch? The "large" space is windowless and "though it's an enjoyable evening, it's hard to forget that you are eating just off the lobby of a hotel". / W1J 7QY; www.theorandall.com; @theorandall; Tue-Sat 10 pm, Mon 10.30 , Sun 11 am; closed Sun & Mon D; Take bookings all week via phone and/or online.

Theo's SE5 £43 ③③②

2 Grove Ln 020 3026 4224 1–3C

"A real neighborhood gem", this Camberwell independent wins enthusiastic praise for its "great sourdough pizza, simply topped. What's not to like?" "Good house wines" complete the deal. There's also a (less commented on) outpost in Elephant & Castle. / SE5; www.theospizzeria.com; @theospizzaldn; Sun-Thu 10 pm, Fri & Sat 11 pm; no Amex; May need 6+ to book.

34 Mayfair W1 £117 ③④③

34 Grosvenor Sq 020 3350 3434 3–3A

This lavish take on an American grill from Richard Caring's Caprice group, near the former US Embassy in Mayfair, excelled this year with its "well-prepared food", "extensive wines list" and "superb service". The only real complaint? It can seem "just ridiculously expensive". But this complaint was less in evidence this year. / W1K 2HD; www.34-restaurant.co.uk; @34_restaurant; Mon-Sun 11 pm.

The Thomas Cubitt Pub Belgravia SW1 £67 ②②③

44 Elizabeth St 020 7730 6060 2–4A

This "comfortable and attractive pub" on a prime corner of Belgravia's smart Elizabeth Street is a "pleasant place for lunch, with good pub food". If you want something "more formal", the upstairs restaurant fits the bill. / SW1W 9PA; www.thethomascubitt.co.uk; @TheThomasCubitt; Mon-Sat 10 pm, Sun 9.30 pm.

Tila SE8 NEW £44

14 Deptford Broadway 020 8692 8803 1–3D

Worth finding – especially if you live in Deptford – Dan Doherty's year-old venture is a casual neighbourhood haunt, complete with bare brick walls, polished floors and picture windows. It's open all day from breakfast and is most popular for weekend brunch / lunch. / SE8 4PA; www.tiladeptford.com; Wed-Fri 11 pm, Sat 10 pm, Sun 5 pm; closed Wed-Fri L closed Sun D, closed Mon & Tue.

TING SE1 £102 ②③④

Level 35, 31 St Thomas St 020 7234 8108 10–4C

Incredible vistas are a given from the 35th floor of the Shard and this all-day restaurant and lounge doesn't disappoint with a 360° panorama of the capital. It perennially attracts some criticism for being overpriced, but significant criticism was absent this year and most aspects of the experience are rated good to outstanding. The menu hedges its bets – although predominantly focused on 'time-honoured Asian cuisine', there is also a section devoted to 'classic British gastronomy' (plus options for breakfast and afternoon tea). / SE1 9RY; www.ting-shangri-la.com; @TheShardLondon; Mon-Sun 10.30 pm; No trainers; credit card required to book.

Tish NW3 £88 🔳3️⃣4️⃣4️⃣
196 Haverstock Hill   020 7431 3828   9–2A
David Levin's Belsize Park brasserie boasts gorgeous interior design and a large attractive terrace out front. The food is kosher, but you wouldn't know it from the choice of European dishes on the large menu. And although one or two reporters find the food here a little pricey, more are heartily impressed by this three-year-old venture. / NW3 2AG; www.tish.london; @tish_london; Sun-Thu midnight; closed Fri & Sat.

Titu W1 £58 4️⃣4️⃣4️⃣
1A Shepherd Street   020 7493 8746   3–4B
Tiny, 15-seater, luxury fusion gyoza bar in Mayfair's cute and quirky Shepherd Market, where ex-Novikov head chef Jeff Tyler, a Kiwi, stuffs gyoza (Japanese dumplings) with such prime ingredients as foie gras and wagyu beef, and tempts the palate with other mouthwatering morsels. / W1J 7HJ; www.titurestaurant.com; @titulondon; Mon-Sat 11 pm; closed Sun.

Toff's N10 £51 3️⃣3️⃣2️⃣
38 Muswell Hill Broadway   020 8883 8656   1–1B
"A Muswell Hill institution with frequent queues" – "Toff's is a fantastic fish 'n' chip restaurant run by a Greek Cypriot family, which has been doing a roaring trade for decades". It's known for its "friendly welcome and the fantastic quality of its fish" – "there are other fish 'n' chip shops in the area, but Toff's is tops". Sadly, George Georgiou, the co-owner with his brother Costas, died of Covid in April 2020; his widow Giga and son Christopher have stepped in to continue his legacy. Now in its 54th year, Toff's is named after a former owner, Andreas Ttofalli. / N10 3RT; www.toffsfish.co.uk; @toffsfish; Mon-Sat 10 pm; closed Sun.

TOKii W1 NEW £86
The Prince Akatoki Hotel
50 Great Cumberland Place   020 7724 0486   2–1A
The first international branch of an expanding Japan-based group of five-star luxury hotels – this two-year-old Marylebone venture (opened in autumn 2019) is on the site near Marble Arch fka Hunter 486 at The Arch (and inherited some of its personnel, including in the kitchen). The menu is Japanese-inspired (think Zuma, etc) rather than being particularly traditional – not perhaps one for purists, but feedback suggests it's a calming oasis and one with good-value cooking. / W1H 7FD; www.tokii.co.uk; Mon-Sun 10 pm.

Tokimeite W1 £93 3️⃣2️⃣2️⃣
23 Conduit St   020 3826 4411   3–2C
'High-grade wagyu, supplied by Zen-Noh, Japan's agricultural cooperative' was an important part of the raison d'être for this Mayfair five-year-old, set up by the organisation as a showcase for Japanese ingredients. It continues to be a central menu feature, but – with the involvement of London importers Atariya Foods Group in the restaurant's management since 2020 – there's now more emphasis on the sushi and sashimi for which Atariya is known. Even those who say a meal here is "incredibly expensive" rate it as "good all-round". / W1S 2XS; www.tokimeite.com; @tokimeitelondon; Tue-Sat 10.30 pm; closed Sun & Mon.

Toklas WC2 NEW
180 Strand   2–2D
Aside from its nondescript location near Aldwych, this autumn 2021 newcomer is strong on fashionable credentials. In a Soho House property (yes); backers are famous in the art world (the duo behind art fair, Frieze – yes); large al fresco terrace (yes); cooking over open fire (yes); on-site baker and food shop (yes). Here's hoping it's as good off paper as on it. / WC2R 1EA; Mon-Sun midnight.

Tokyo Sukiyaki-Tei & Bar SW3
85 Sloane Avenue   020 3583 3797   6–2C

Tucked away off Sloane Avenue, this comfortable Japanese sells a lot of wagyu beef, alongside sushi and other classics like shabu-shabu and, of course, sukiyaki (meat slowly cooked or simmered). Survey feedback was too limited for a rating, but it looks like an interesting arrival of relatively recent times (it opened in 2019). / SW3 3DX; www.tokyosukiyakitei.com; @TokyoSukiyakiT; Mon-Sat 11 pm, Sun 10 pm; closed Mon L; No shorts; Take bookings all week via phone and/or online.

Tomahawk Steakhouse N1 NEW   £72
15 Westland Place   020 3972 0180   13–1A

Hailing originally from North Yorkshire and the North East, this branch of steakhouses opened in London in December 2020, on the former site of Jamie O's once-famous Fifteen (RIP) in Hoxton. A furore during furlough – when staff were asked to pay their own National Insurance – did nothing for the press profile of the chain's management. Perhaps now it's back to business as usual, folks will just concentrate on the steak and cocktails? / N1 7LP; tomahawk-steakhouse.co.uk; Mon-Sun 11 pm.

Tommi's Burger Joint   £33   3 3 2
30 Thayer St, W1   020 7224 3828   3–1A
37 Berwick Street, W1   020 7494 9086   4–2D

Tómas Tómasson, creator of two burger chains in his native Iceland, can now celebrate 10 years at his "straightforward and affordable" Marylebone venue, which these days has "nice outdoor seating". He also has outlets in Soho and Oxford. / www.burgerjoint.co.uk; @BurgerJointUk.

Tomoe SW15   £41   4 2 2
292 Upper Richmond Road   020 3730 7884   11–2B

An "extremely busy" little corner of Tokyo transported to Putney – "so book ahead" – this owner-operated café comes "damn close to the full 5 stars for food – we had the toro maki, okonomiyaki and plaice karaage, all somewhere between very good and excellent". / SW15; Wed & Thu 9 pm, Fri & Sat 9.30 pm; closed Mon & Tue & Sun.

Tonkotsu   £49   4 3 2
Selfridges, 400 Oxford St, W1   020 7437 0071   3–1A
63 Dean St, W1   020 7437 0071   5–2A
7 Blenheim Cr, W11   020 7221 8300   7–1A
14 New Broadway, W5   020 8810 1414   1–3A
133 Rye Lane, SE15   020 7732 5256   1–4D NEW
4 Canvey St, SE1   020 7928 2228   10–4B
Battersea Power Station Arches, SW8   020 7720 7695   11–1C
Unit 1, Endeavour Square, E20   020 8534 6809   14–1D
382 Mare St, E8   020 8533 1840   14–1B
Arch 334, 1a Dunston St, E8   020 7254 2478   14–2A
New Inn Yard, 1 Anning Street, EC2   020 7732 5256   13–1B NEW

"Casual and inexpensive, but no compromise on the standards" – this Japanese noodle chain has become a firm favourite in London's "competitive" ramen market, with 14 branches (and counting). "I can't speak highly enough of the quality of ramen here, absolutely packed full of flavour and at a really good price." The name is taken from the pork broth used, and the noodles are made daily in-house and cooked, it is said, for precisely 32 seconds. / www.tonkotsu.co.uk; @TonkotsuSoho.

Top Cuvee N5   £63   3 4 3
177b Blackstock Road   020 3294 1665   9–1D

This "buzzy" Highbury wine bar specialises in hip low-intervention wines, backed up by "great food and service". The menu is predominantly small-plate bites to accompany the interesting bottles being quaffed, so "they could do with more main course options – but the atmosphere is fantastic". / N5 2LL; www.topcuvee.com; Wed-Sat 11 pm, Sun 9 pm; closed Wed-Fri L, closed Mon & Tue.

Toulouse Lautrec SE11 £68 343
140 Newington Butts 020 7582 6800 1–3C
This long-running outfit just south of Elephant & Castle combines a very Gallic brasserie based on Paris in the 1920s with, upstairs, an excellent jazz club. / SE11 4RN; www.toulouselautrec.co.uk/; @tlvenue; Mon-Sat midnight, Sun 10.30 pm.

Townsend @ Whitechapel Gallery E1 NEW £38 333
77-82 Whitechapel High St 020 7539 3303 10–2D
"Lovely food and fantastic staff" feature in many reports on this – the latest in a series of impressive incumbents at Grade-II listed Whitechapel Gallery, which has (since early 2020), seen Nick Gilkinson (ex-Anglo and Lambeth's Garden Museum café) and Joe Fox (ex-head chef at Petersham Nurseries) create 'a modern British dining room' whose thoughtfully conceived dishes have also won it solid plaudits in the press. It's a smallish but sympathetic space, whose name references the gallery's architect, Charles Harrison Townsend. / E1; www.whitechapelgallery.org/townsend; @TheWhitechapel; Tue, Sun 6 pm, Wed-Sat 11 pm; closed Tue & Sun D, closed Mon.

Tozi SW1 £57 333
8 Gillingham St 020 7769 9771 2–4B
This "cracking" venue near Victoria station wins high praise for its Venetian cicchetti – small plates that "never fail to please and surprise". There's disagreement on the atmosphere – to many it's "so warm and welcoming", but there's also a view that "it suffers from being part of a hotel". / SW1V 1HN; www.tozirestaurant.co.uk; @ToziRestaurant; Tue-Sat 9.30 pm; closed Sun & Mon.

Trawlerman's Fish Bar N1 NEW £17
205 Upper Street 020 7088 1777 9–2D
Returning in early 2020 to an Islington site its owners used to run in the 1980s (and unconnected with Trawler Trash which recently closed on this site, RIP), this somewhat modernised but relatively traditional chippy provides a proper fish 'n' chip fix for those times when the many more rarefied options available locally just won't hit the spot. / N1 1RQ; Mon-Sun 10 pm.

Trinity SW4 £105 554
4 The Polygon 020 7622 1199 11–2D
Prince Charles was one of the first post-lockdown visitors to Adam Byatt's "sophisticated and unhurried" Clapham HQ – a further hint that this "exceptional" venture in Clapham (complete with "tables outside on newly paved area") is "so much more than a neighbourhood local" and "one of the best south of the river". His "wonderfully inventive" (but not over-fussy) cooking, is served with notable "professionalism and charm", alongside a "beautifully curated" and "fairly priced wine list". "Tables outside on a newly paved area are fun" and add another dimension to a meal here. See also Upstairs at Trinity and Charlie's at Browns. / SW4 0JG; www.trinityrestaurant.co.uk; @TrinityLondon; Mon-Sun 8 pm; Take bookings all week via phone and/or online.

Trinity Upstairs SW4 £60 434
4 The Polygon 020 3745 7227 11–2D
"A perennial favourite" in Clapham – this small-plates alternative to the more formal Trinity downstairs is "a favourite place to enjoy fantastic quality food in an unstuffy, relaxed environment", while overall, chef Adam Byatt is "still flying the flag for the best food in South London". Top Tip: it enjoys "the added benefit of access to the superb Trinity wine list". / SW4 0JG; www.trinity-upstairs.co.uk; @trinityupstairs; Tue-Sat 8.30 pm, Sun 4 pm; closed Tue-Sat L closed Sun D, closed Mon.

Trishna W1 £69 5 4 3
15-17 Blandford St 020 7935 5624 2–1A
"Simply brilliant food that just blows your socks off" – "posh curry, but not
too mucked about with" – continues to wow at JKS restaurant's original
Marylebone venture, which remains one of London's top destinations for "top
notch" Indian cuisine. ("Excellent home delivery meal boxes" are also a
feature.) Its modestly sized, U-shaped premises are slightly constrained by
their layout, but for most reporters the effect is "lovely and intimate".
/ W1U 3DG; www.trishnalondon.com; Mon-Sat 10.15 pm, Sun 9.45 pm; closed
Mon-Thu L.

Trivet SE1 £109 4 3 3
36 Snowsfields, Melior Street 020 3141 8670 10–4C
"What a cellar of joy!" Alumni of the Fat Duck, head chef Jonny Lake and
sommelier Isa Bal opened this Bermondsey venture in late 2019, in the new
Snowsfields Yard development, and it has become a favourite for many
reporters, thanks to its "brilliant but not OTT cuisine" and also to the
veritable "tomb" of a wine list ("they must have a huge cavern somewhere
to store it all") – that "goes deep on surprising regions – like the Greek
Islands – and is, in itself, a journey through the history and love of wine".
There's only one drawback – it's "flipping pricey". / SE1 3SU;
trivetrestaurant.co.uk; Wed-Sat midnight; closed Mon & Tue & Sun.

La Trompette W4 £98 4 4 3
5-7 Devonshire Rd 020 8747 1836 8–2A
"Somewhat more formal than Chez Bruce (like a sterner sister!) – but still
fabulous!" This sibling to the south London phenomenon may hide in a Zone
3 sidestreet, just off Chiswick's main drag, but it features in London's Top 20
most-mentioned restaurants thanks to "a quality of experience usually found
only in central London". Rob Weston's cuisine has been "consistently
wonderful" over many years and it is "skillfully served" by "friendly" staff in
rather "elegant" surroundings. Very uncharacteristically, though, ratings came
slightly off the boil this year amidst reports of "amateur" service,
"substantially increased prices" and "a few courses recently that have let the
side down". That's still a minority view as yet, though, and for the majority it's
still "always top notch" (and was "a beacon through the tedious days of the
pandemic" – "it kept us sane!") / W4 2EU; www.latrompette.co.uk;
@LaTrompetteUK; Wed & Thu, Sun 9 pm, Fri & Sat 10 pm; closed Mon & Tue.

Truffle W1 NEW £13 3 2 2
22 Bateman Street 020 7998 7787 5–2A
"Burgers with a luxurious twist – but at reasonable prices": this mid-2020
newcomer replaced Bonnie Gull's Seafood Shack (RIP) in central Soho, to
create the brand's first dedicated, eat-in outlet (its first outlet was in Kerb's
Seven Dials Market). A no-frills, minimally decorated space, it only sells
burgers, and – as the name hints – truffle everywhere is the key USP: truffle
mayo, truffle sauce, truffle and Parmesan fries... / W1D 3AN;
www.truffle-london.co.uk; Tue-Sun 11 pm; closed Tue-Fri L, closed Mon.

Trullo N1 £71 3 3 3
300-302 St Paul's Rd 020 7226 2733 9–2D
Tim Siadatan and Jordan Frieda's neighbourhood Italian near Highbury
Corner remains one of north London's most commented-on destinations. The
"simple but extremely well-executed dishes" are "authentic" and served with
a "real sense of gusto". (They can, however, "sometimes seem a bit pricey",
and this was a caveat that cropped up more this year.) Its "intimate" style
also makes it a romantic favourite: "choose a table in the light and airy
upstairs for a date in summer, or a booth downstairs for a steamy tryst in
winter!" / N1 2LH; www.trullorestaurant.com; @Trullo_LDN; Mon-Sat 10.30 pm, Sun
9.30 pm; no Amex.

Tsunami SW4 £51 4 3 3
5-7 Voltaire Rd 020 7978 1610 11–1D

With its "great selection of fresh, authentic and interesting Japanese fusion cuisine", this high-grade local in Clapham continues to wow reporters, even though what was super-innovative when it was launched 21 years ago by a trio of ex-Nobu chefs is now found all over London. "It's great to have an off-West End restaurant with reasonable prices and top-quality food." "Every year it's my favourite – nothing in London can compare with the grilled scallops and black cod washed down with an Electric Kamikaze buzz-button cocktail!" / SW4 6DQ; www.tsunamirestaurant.co.uk; @TsunamiRest; Sun-Thu 9.30 pm, Fri & Sat 10.30 pm; closed Mon-Fri L; no Amex.

Turnips
with Tomas Lidakevicius SE1 NEW £106 4 3 4
43 Borough Market, Off Bedale Street 020 7357 8356 10–4C

Out of challenging times can come genius solutions – this "unique" venture "tucked inside a greengrocer's shop/stall in Borough Market" was an off-the-cuff collaboration in July 2020 between the well-known 'Turnips' fruit 'n' veg business and Tomas Lidakevicius from Jason Atherton's City Social. In May 2021 it announced that it was going permanent. It provides two dining options, both within the stand, which inspire not only rave press reviews but also excellent early feedback from reporters. "Tables are well laid-out, the ambience is soothing, and all courses on the excellent and innovative tasting menu are exceptional, both in taste and presentation, with the chef explaining each course. Very good wine selection too". There's a fine dining menu (at £65m served Wed-Sat 5pm-9pm) and a more casual 'small plates' operation and cocktail bar (Wed-Sat noon-10pm). / SE1 9AH; www.turnipsboroughmarket.com/restaurant; @TurnipsBorough; Wed & Thu, Sat, Fri midnight, Sun 8 pm; closed Mon & Tue.

Turul Project N15 NEW £36 3 4 2
1 Turnpike Parade 020 8888 9886 1–1C

"The Best Hungarian in Turnpike Lane!" is to damn with faint praise this interesting May 2021 newcomer. Situated in a 1930s Art Deco building – part of the Grade II listed modernist tube station – this restaurant, wine bar and deli started out as a pop-up and series of supper clubs in 2018 by István Ruska, and aims to showcase Hungarian cuisine within a modern fine dining setting. Much of its appeal stems from a "superb" (we'd guess unrivalled) "all Hungarian selection" of white, red and dessert wines, as well as rosés and sparkling vintages, many of which have never been represented before in the UK. / N15 3LA; www.turulproject.com; Tue-Sat 10 pm, Sun 5 pm; closed Sun D, closed Mon.

12:51 by chef James Cochran N1 £51 4 3 3
107 Upper Street 07934 202269 9–3D

"Superb, really unique combinations and presentation" brings some welcome pizzazz to Islington's Upper Street, by courtesy of chef James Cochran, formerly of The Ledbury (RIP) and a Great British Menu winner. Raised in Whitstable, he mines his Caribbean-Scottish dual heritage to produce a "fantastic value" five-course tasting menu. Top Tip: "the roast on Sundays is also delicious – and the truffle cauliflower cheese is the stuff of dreams!" / N1 1QN; www.1251.co.uk; @restaurant_1251; Tue-Sat 11 pm, Sun 8 pm; closed Tue-Thu L, closed Mon; cards only; booking online only.

28 Church Row NW3 £53 4 4 4
28 Church Row 020 7993 2062 9–2A

This atmospheric Hampstead basement bar serves some of the "better tapas" in town, winning high praise for its changing Spanish menu and international wines. Bookings are only taken for lunch on Fridays to Sundays, but you can wait for a table in the pub opposite and they'll text you. / NW3 6UP; www.28churchrow.com; @28churchrow.com; Mon-Sat 10.30 pm, Sun 9.30 pm; closed Mon-Thu L.

28-50
£82   **3 3 2**
15-17 Marylebone Ln, W1   020 7486 7922   3–1A
10 Upper St Martin's Lane, WC2   020 7420 0630   5–3B **NEW**
300 King's Road, SW3   020 7349 9818   6–3C **NEW**
96 Draycott Ave, SW3   020 7581 5208   6–2C **NEW**

"The sort of handy local that everyone needs" – with "good food and a particularly interesting wine list" – this modern wine bar chain has expanded with investment from its new owner, Alpine holiday supremo Richard Green, and now has branches in Marylebone, Covent Garden, South Ken and Chelsea. "The wine is what you come for", "from a list that is both surprising and well understood by the staff" – with a range available by the glass as well as some "fabulous but expensive" 'Collectors' bottles.

24 The Oval SW9
£50   **3 4 3**
24 Clapham Road   020 7735 6111   11–1D

"This relaxed upmarket bistro delivers excellent cuisine with style" in a pocket of South London that has lacked cooking of any ambition. There's "always a buzz about the place", which is a partnership between successful operators down the road in Clapham – Andrew and Kelsey Bradford of Knife steakhouse and Matt Wells, co-owner of The Dairy. / SW9 0JG; www.24theoval.co.uk; @24theoval; Wed-Sat 9.30 pm, Sun 4.30 pm; closed Wed-Sat L closed Sun D, closed Mon & Tue; No shorts; Take bookings all week via phone and/or online.

26 Grains
1 Neal's Yard, WC2   5–2C
2-3 Stoney Street, SE1   020 3489 5657   10–3C **NEW**

In late 2019, the team from well-known café, 26 Grains of Neal's Yard, opened a big sister over the road from Borough Market. It's a casual, tastefully decorated haunt serving simple food; and where at night, the vibe is less café, more wine bar. In late 2020, Tom Cenci (the ex Duck & Waffle head chef, whose own Loyal Tavern venture did not survive the pandemic) took over what has become an extended residency. The cooking (by him and one other chef) centres on sustainability, and less-used cuts of meat (particularly Irish beef).

Twist Connubio W1
£61   **4 3 2**
42 Crawford St   020 7723 3377   2–1A

"Really enjoyable" is the general verdict on Amalfi-born chef Eduardo Tuccillo's "creative" (if "slightly cramped") Marylebone tapas bar with a 'twist' – the twist being that the dishes are not Spanish but a marriage, 'connubio' in Italian, of different cuisines – hence the recent re-launch (it was founded seven years back as Twist at Crawford). / W1H 1JW; www.twistconnubio.com; Sun-Wed-Sat 11 pm; closed Sun-Wed L; Take bookings all week via phone and/or online.

Two Brothers N3
£35   **3 2 2**
297-303 Regent's Park Rd   020 8346 0469   1–1B

"Absolutely delicious, simply cooked, very fresh fish" has made this chippy a Finchley favourite for over 25 years. "It's great for a special meal for someone who likes fish". Top Tip: the monthly free-entry Fish'n'Chips'n'Jazz features some top live jazz to perk up a Monday night. / N3 1DP; www.twobrothers.co.uk; Tue-Sun 10 pm; closed Mon.

222 Veggie Vegan W14
£45   **3 3 2**
222 North End Rd   020 7381 2322   8–2D

If you've ever been stuck in a traffic jam near the gyratory on the North End Road, you may have noticed this small, long-standing vegan and vegetarian café. It doesn't inspire a huge volume of feedback, but such as there is still says it's a "good" choice for an "original" meal. / W14 9NU; www.222vegan.com; @222VeganCuisine; Wed-Sun 9 pm; closed Mon & Tue.

2 Veneti W1 £53 2 3 2
10 Wigmore Street   020 7637 0789   3–1B

"Genuine Venetian specialities" are the highlight of the menu at this *"rustic"* Italian near the Wigmore Hall. *"Prices are reasonable for the area"*, and even those diners who find the cuisine *"unexceptional"* are impressed by the *"intriguing all-Italian wine list"*, again leaning heavily to the Veneto.
/ W1U 2RD; www.2veneti.com; @2veneti; Mon-Fri 9.45 pm, Sat 10.15pm; closed Sat L, closed Sun.

Uli W11 £65 2 3 3
5 Ladbroke Road   020 3141 5878   7–2B

"A good all-rounder" known for its *"great atmosphere"* – Michael Lim's *"wonderful Singaporean-style"* operation has been a Notting Hill fixture for 25 years, first in All Saints' Road and now at a smart new location with an outdoor terrace in Ladbroke Grove. *"Michael always makes it a special occasion with his helpful and friendly style"*. See also Huo. / W11 3PA; www.ulilondon.com; @ULILONDON; Mon-Sat midnight, Sun 11 pm.

Umu W1 £151 4 4 4
14-16 Bruton Pl   020 7499 8881   3–2C

One of London's most accoladed Japanese restaurants, this bijou venue in a quiet Mayfair mews was formerly part of Marlon Abela's M.A.R.C. group – it was sold as a going concern by the administrators when the group collapsed financially in 2020. Feedback is limited over the intervening period, but remains highly enthusiastic, and we've rated the restaurant on the basis that both its luxurious Kyoto-inspired kaiseki cuisine, and the bill that accompanies it, remain at a formidable level. / W1J 6LX; www.umurestaurant.com; Tue-Sat 22 pm; closed Sun & Mon; No trainers; booking max 14 may apply.

Unwined SW17 £32 3 4 4
21-23 Tooting High Street   020 3583 9136   11–2C

"What a find" in Tooting Market – Laura Aitkin and Kiki Evans have maintained the *"fun"* pop-up vibe of their 'Grape Night In' wine tasting sessions at their permanent shop and wine bar, where guest chefs cook meals to accompany their *'off-the-beaten-track'* bottles. They have a second bar in a shipping container beside Waterloo Station. / SW17 0SN; www.unwinedbars.co.uk/tooting; @UnwinedSW17; Wed-Sat 11 pm; closed Wed L, closed Mon & Tue & Sun; booking online only.

Le Vacherin W4 £71 3 3 3
76-77 South Parade   020 8742 2121   8–1A

All stylish white tablecloths and *"romantic, old-school"* atmosphere – this Acton Green fixture serves *"really good French bistro cuisine"* to a happy crowd of regulars. *"So consistent for so long"*, it *"gets very busy at weekends"* – *"long may Le Vacherin last – there are far too few places like it"*. The one muted criticism, voiced by a minority of reporters, is that it *"never quite delivers on expectations – we always leave wanting just a bit more"*. / W4 5LF; www.levacherin.com; @Le_Vacherin; Mon-Sat 10.30 pm, Sun 9 pm.

Vardo SW3 £25 3 3 5
9 Duke of York Square   020 7101 1199   6–2D

Looking a bit like a spaceship that's beamed down next to the old Duke of York barracks, this *"buzzy"* and architecturally stunning all-day café – cylindrical and complete with public roof garden and mobile glass wall – opened in late 2019. Run by the team behind Caravan, it exhibits a lot of their DNA, scoring well as a *"cheap 'n' cheerful"* option in pricey Chelsea and also for its superb breakfasts and brunches: *"the people watching is great, as is the obviously high quality food (unusual, fresh and delicious) and coffee"*. / SW3 4LY; vardorestaurant.co.uk; Mon-Sun 10.30 pm.

Vasco & Piero's Pavilion W1 £70
11 D'Arblay St 020 7437 8774 4–1C

This endearing Soho veteran escaped closure during the pandemic by vacating its home of decades standing to find these new premises just around the corner. Much of its former appeal lay in its pleasing, old-fashioned approach – here's hoping they keep the best of its traditional virtues on re-opening in mid October 2021. (Founded in 1971, this latest relocation is actually the second in the history of the restaurant, which shifted to Poland Street from above the Academy Cinema in Oxford Street in 1989). / W1F 8DT; www.vascosfood.com; @Vasco_and_Piero; Mon-Sat 10 pm; closed Sat L, closed Sun; Take bookings all week via phone and/or online.

Veeraswamy W1 £87 3 3 3
Victory Hs, 99-101 Regent St 020 7734 1401 4–4B

At 95 years old – the same age as the Queen – London's oldest Indian restaurant, near Piccadilly Circus, continues to send out "delicious, beautifully presented food drawing on Mughal recipes with a modern twist". Unlike Her Majesty, however, its styling is rather contemporary nowadays, giving next to no hint at its long heritage. "Sitting at a table overlooking Regent's Street, with the mouth-watering fragrance of Indian spices, swish decor and professional yet understated service. you could almost do without the food! But the food is superb." / W1B 4RS; www.veeraswamy.com; @theveeraswamy; Sun-Wed 9.30 pm, Thu-Sat 10 pm; closed Mon L; booking max 12 may apply.

Vergine Maria W5 NEW £20
15 Saint Mary's Road 020 8579 1462 1–3A

From the Santa Maria team – and on the characterful original site of the smash hit Ealing branch (which has since shifted to Bond Street in W5) – a new vegan pizzeria concept, which is set to open in October 2021. / W5 5RA; www.santamariapizzeria.com; @santamariapizza; Sun-Thu 10.30 pm, Fri & Sat 11 pm.

Vermuteria N1 £51
Coal Drops Yard 020 3479 1777 9–3C

A "top Negroni" is to be had at Anthony Demetre's all-day bar/café in ever-more-happening Coal Drops Yard. We've had little feedback on the food this year, though – hence no rating – whose stated aim is to gather the best bar bites of Italy, France and Spain. More reports please. / N1C 4AB; vermuteria.cc; Mon & Tue, Sun 9 pm, Wed-Sat 10 pm.

Via Emilia N1 £47 3 2 2
37a Hoxton Square 020 7613 0508 13–1B

Pasta made with ingredients from Emilia-Romagna is the specialty at this 40-seater Italian, just off Hoxton Square, praised by fans for its splendid, "simple" dishes of excellent quality. / N1 6NN; www.via-emilia.com; Mon-Sat 11 pm, Sun 10.30 pm; Take bookings all week via phone and/or online.

Il Vicolo SW1 £61 3 3 3
3-4 Crown Passage 020 7839 3960 3–4D

An archetypal "hidden gem" set "in tiny Crown Passage" – this "lovely, little, family-run Italian in the heart of St James's" has served "authentic" Calabrian-based dishes for almost 30 years – at "great value" too, considering the area. Regulars mourned the death of its owner, Giacomo Bonavita, in 2020, but "the family have really stepped up – the food is better than ever and they're super-generous with the truffle!" "The sisters run a tight ship, providing a good range of food with friendly service". / SW1Y 6PP; www.ilvicolorestaurant.co.uk; Mon-Sat 10 pm; closed Sun.

The Victoria SW14 £59 2 2 3
10 West Temple Sheen 020 8876 4238 11–2A
This "charming gastropub", a short walk from Richmond Park's Sheen Gate, "keeps its standards", as set in the dozen years it has been run by chef Paul Merrett. A substantial Victorian building, it has six hotel rooms and a large, family-friendly conservatory along with garden tables. / SW14 7RT; victoriasheen.co.uk; @TheVictoria_Pub; Wed-Sun 10.30 pm; closed Mon & Tue; no Amex.

Viet Food W1 £38 3 3 2
34-36 Wardour St 020 7494 4555 5–3A
"So tasty" – ex-Hakkasan chef Jeff Tan's spacious Chinatown restaurant is a good choice for "very reasonably priced Vietnamese food". Top Tip: "the upstairs is lovely and you really feel you're in another country". / W1D 6QT; www.vietnamfood.co.uk; @vietfoodlondon; Sun-Thu 10.30 pm, Fri & Sat 11 pm.

Viet Garden N1 £33 3 3 2
207 Liverpool Rd 020 7700 6040 9–3D
This "local standby Vietnamese" in Islington, with "food cooked by the family", is now "much more stylish after a recent refurbishment". "Our daughter who's been to Vietnam says the food is authentic – and the staff are lovely". It's "great for vegetarians and vegans, and good value – watch you don't over-eat!" / N1 1LX; www.vietgarden.co.uk; Mon-Sun 10.30 pm; no Amex.

Vijay NW6 £40 3 4 1
49 Willesden Ln 020 7328 1087 1–1B
Grunge-tastic Kilburn institution that lays claim to being Britain's first South Indian restaurant, opening in 1964. TBH, it's not clear if there has been a decor rethink at any time since, so "don't be surprised if it looks a bit basic". For reasons it's hard to discern, it draws quite a cool crowd, and has over the years hosted celebrities as diverse as Harrison Ford, Kylie, Diana Ross and the Indian cricket team. Presumably, they too were drawn by its "great choice of Keralan dishes for vegans, vegetarians or carnivores" at prices that are decidedly "not expensive". / NW6 7RF; www.vijayrestaurant.co.uk; @vijayindiauk; Sun-Thu 10.45 pm, Fri & Sat 11.45 pm; no booking.

Villa Bianca NW3 £60 2 2 2
1 Perrins Ct 020 7435 3131 9–2A
The dead cute location, off Hampstead High Street, and trattoria interior – with a "nice and old-fashioned feel" – has changed little in three decades at this enduring Italian. Some reporters are mightily impressed by the "delicious" traditional fare; for others it's only average, with other gripes including "noise levels that make meaningful conversation difficult" or slightly "attitude-y" service. / NW3 1QS; villabiancagroup.com/villabianca; @VillaBiancaNW3; Mon-Sat 11.30 pm, Sun 10.30 pm.

Villa Di Geggiano W4 £78 3 3 4
66-68 Chiswick High Road 020 3384 9442 8–2B
"The next best thing to going on holiday to Italy" (well, nearly) – this "little piece of Tuscany in Chiswick" has become one of west London's better-known dining destinations, despite a tricky no-man's-land location between Chiswick and Hammersmith (which music buffs may recognise as being next to Metropolis Studios). Assets include its "elegant interior" and "gorgeous outdoor space", plus "good, traditional Tuscan food" chosen to accompany the "exceptionally good wines from the owners' own vineyards" (a 500-year-old Chianti estate). "Lovely staff" help ensure "a meal at the Villa is always an event". / W4 1SY; www.villadigeggiano.co.uk; @VilladiGeggiano; Tue-Sat 10.30 pm, Sun 9 pm; closed Mon.

The Vincent Rooms,
Westminster Kingsway College SW1 £38 3 3 2
76 Vincent Sq   020 7802 8391   2–4C
In an attractive building on Westminster's leafy Vincent Square, this catering
college dining room offers you the chance to be cooked for and served by
future hospitality industry workers at a price reflecting your 'guinea pig'
status. "It's a great place to enjoy very good food, prepared and served by
the students. Have never been disappointed. The price is very good for the
Tasting Menu and we have introduced friends to it. Not the best dining room
but good enough." / SW1P 2PD; www.thevincentrooms.co.uk; @thevincentrooms;
Mon, Fri 3 pm, Tue–Thu 9 pm; closed Mon & Fri D, closed Sat & Sun; no Amex.

Vinoteca £67 2 2 2
15 Seymour Pl, W1   020 7724 7288   2–2A
18 Devonshire Rd, W4   020 3701 8822   8–2A
One Pancras Sq, N1   020 3793 7210   9–3C
7 St John St, EC1   020 7253 8786   10–1B
Bloomberg Arcade, Queen Victoria Street, EC2   awaiting tel   10–3C
This modern take on the wine bar "sets the benchmark for an imaginative,
indeed educational, wine list" – with "constantly surprising selections from
far-flung places alongside the old-world classics". There are "good choices by
the glass, though prices can start quickly to move upwards", and the "food is
generally surprisingly good, with good-value set-lunch options". The ultra-
handily situated King's Cross branch draws some flak for being "just too
popular", while branches in the City, Faringdon, Marylebone and Chiswick all
have their fans. A new branch is scheduled to open by Borough Market in
late 2021. / www.vinoteca.co.uk.

Vivat Bacchus £66 3 3 3
4 Hay's Ln, SE1   020 7234 0891   10–4C
47 Farringdon St, EC4   020 7353 2648   10–2A
Limited but positive feedback for this duo of South-African-owned venues in
Farringdon and London Bridge. The appeal at both is straightforward: simple
fare, majoring in steaks from the Surrey Hills, are matched with excellent SA
wines (picked from a visit to the walk-in cellar), and – if you still have space
– cheese from the special walk-in cheese room. / www.vivatbacchus.co.uk.

Volta do Mar WC2 NEW £63 4 3 3
13-15 Tavistock Street   020 3034 0028   5–3D
High-quality Portuguese cooking – rare in London – is the aim of this heart-
of-tourist-Covent-Garden venture: opened in November 2019 by Salt Yard
founder, Simon Mullins and his Portugal-born wife Isabel Almeida Da Silva.
The aim is to celebrate the cuisine's diversity "with influences from all the
places around the world where Portugal had a colonial presence", from
South America to Africa and Asia. "The wines are all from Portugal, covering
all areas and containing some real gems." All early survey reports suggest it's
well worth a visit. / WC2E 7PS; voltadomar.co.uk; @voltadomar_ldn; Wed-Sat
10.30 pm; closed Wed & Thu L, closed Mon & Tue & Sun.

VQ £50 2 3 3
111a Great Russell Street, WC1   020 7636 5888   5–1A
325 Fulham Rd, SW10   020 7376 7224   6–3B
9 Aldgate High St, EC3   020 3301 7224   10–2D
"Reliable, whatever the hour" – this small group of upscale diners has grown
from its long-established Chelsea base, although – with closures in recent
times – its only two siblings now are within midtown hotels in Aldwych and
Bloomsbury. Aldwych is the only one actually open 24/7 (VQ = 'Vingt
Quatre', i.e. 24-hour), but both its siblings are open for most of the wee
hours, which is when they come into their own as a pick-me-up post
clubbing. "It's a very cosmopolitan menu, but drink may dull the senses of
fussier gastronomes…" / www.vingtquatre.co.uk; @VQRESTAURANTS.

Vrisaki N22 £40 **3**3**2**
73 Middleton Rd   020 8889 8760   1–1C

This Greek-Cypriot taverna in Bounds Green has earned a wide following across north London over 50 years for its generous 'Special Mezze': various cold starters followed by charcoal-grilled meats and fish specialities. Family-run by Adreas and Anthony Antoniou, it has recently been given a modern revamp. / N22 8LZ; vrisakirestaurant.co.uk; @vrisakiuk; Tue-Sat 11 pm, Sun 9 pm; closed Mon; no Amex.

VyTA WC2 NEW £64
21 The Market   020 7654 3030   5–3D

In the heart of tourist Covent Garden – on the corner of the market itself, near The Punch & Judy pub – this large (200-seat) Italian arrived in late 2019. It's the first venture outside Italy for Nicolo Marzotti, who has 13 restaurants back home. The jury is still out on whether or not it transcends its tourist trap location (including some seating on a balcony over the main market square). / WC2E 8RD; vytacoventgarden.co.uk; Wed-Sun 10 pm; closed Mon & Tue.

Wagamama £47 **2**2**2**
"Reliable, fun and fast, with a nice range of healthy food" – this Japanese-inspired chain celebrates its 30th anniversary this year from a position of strength, with 42 branches across the capital and another 100 or so scattered across Britain and 21 other countries. Founded by Alan Yau, the restaurant guru who also launched Hakkasan, the chain cost The Restaurant Group more than half a billion pounds when it last changed hands in 2018. "You can't go wrong here", fans say – "the Wagas have always seemed to get the fast-food experience about right, so they're absolutely reliable" – "every meal tastes the same, a bit like McDonalds" – "and if you're not happy they'll correct promptly and without a drama". They cater for a wide range of occasions: from "a quick slurp of noodles over business"; via "a great (and efficient) place for families"; to branches close to theatres such as the South Bank arts centre ("perfect when you're in a hurry before a concert"). There are muted complaints: branches can be "charmless" and "soft drink/small bottle prices are a rip off" – but a legion of regulars are happy that "you get what you pay for". / www.wagamama.com.

Wahaca £41 **2**3**3**
"Tasty Mexican street food" at this "buzzing" chain still wins over plenty of supporters, who swear by its "fresh, wholesome, family-friendly" grub (ideal for "when you're on the hoof"). Others, though, complain that "the menu is getting a bit tired" and the "flavours can be a bit hit and miss outside the standard dishes". Financial losses during the pandemic forced the chain to close nearly half its branches and sell a majority stake to South African billionaire Dick Enthoven, owner of Nandos. Founded in 2007 by former MasterChef winner Thomasina Miers and Mark Selby, it now has 10 remaining branches in London as well as venues in Brighton, Cardiff and Edinburgh. / www.wahaca.com; @wahaca.

The Wallace,
The Wallace Collection W1 £40 **2**2**4**
Hertford Hs, Manchester Sq   020 7563 9505   3–1A

"An absolute treat of a covered courtyard nestled behind one of London's oddest museums" – the Wallace Collection, off Oxford Street, which mixes fabulous Old Master paintings with fine furniture and armour from the age of chivalry. But despite the "polished" setting, "the menu is unenterprising" – "a shame because it is a very lovely space to eat in". Top Tip – go in the afternoon – "there's a wide selection of teas" and the cakes are fine. / W1U 3BN; www.peytonandbyrne.co.uk; @peytonandbyrne; Mon-Sun 5 pm; closed Mon-Sun D; no Amex; booking max 10 may apply.

The Water House Project E2 NEW — £115 — 4 3 3
1 Corbridge Crescent   07841 804119   14–2B

On the move again… chef Gabriel Waterhouse (ex-Galvin La Chapelle) opened his first permanent HQ, perched by the canal in Hackney in January 2020, after four years of running a supper club. Now – having closed in Hackney in June 2021 – he's reopening in Bethnal Green in autumn 2021. The format will be similar, with only one option: a 9-course tasting menu (with paired wines optional). We've rated the new venture on the basis that it scores similarly to the last, which won praise for "a fantastic tasting menu, with innovative and precise dishes". The only critical comment? – "some delicate and well-conceived dishes but some (such as the heralded pheasant doughnut) came out as confused and incoherent". / E2 9DS; www.thewaterhouseproject.com; Wed-Sat 11 pm; closed Wed-Sat L, closed Mon & Tue & Sun.

The Watermans TW9 NEW — £78 — 3 3 4
10-12 Water Lane   020 3638 9160   1–4A

"A lovely pub on Water Lane leading down to the Thames: now more of a restaurant than a pub" – a smart refit now lends a brasserie vibe to the dining room at this traditional boozer, off Richmond's picturesque waterfront. The makeover – in late 2019 – was by the Ram Pub Co, which is part of Youngs. Few reports as yet on the rather posh-for-a-pub menu (they serve a selection of oysters, for example), but early feedback says it's "the food is good, especially the fish", and for a comfy yet relaxed get-together you could do much worse than a trip here. / TW9 1TJ; www.watermansrichmond.co.uk/; @watermansrich; Sun-Wed 11 pm, Thu-Sat midnight.

The Wells Tavern NW3 — £63 — 3 3 4
30 Well Walk   020 7794 3785   9–1A

"A traditional but varying menu" and "very consistently good cooking" are prime reasons why this handsome Georgian tavern has become a Hampstead institution in the 20-odd years since it was taken over by Beth Coventry, sister of veteran restaurant critic Fay Maschler (who's been known to give it the occasional plug). "Upstairs always pleases", with no fewer than three different dining rooms, and there's an "excellent Sunday lunch". / NW3 1BX; thewellshampstead.london; @WellsHampstead; Mon-Sat 10 pm, Sun 9.30 pm.

West 4th SW6 NEW
175 New King's Road   11–1B

Canadian-inspired brunch is coming to Parson's Green at this October 2021 newcomer. Friends Livia Boumeester and Louisa Stevenson-Hamilton will launch the 1,800 square foot venue with 60 covers serving brunch through the day and wine and charcuterie in the evening, the aim being to 'emulate Vancouver's relaxed, convivial hospitality scene'. / SW6 4SW; Thu-Sat 9 pm, Sun 4 pm.

Westerns Laundry N5 — £62 — 3 4 2
34 Drayton Park   020 7700 3700   9–2D

A hipster hit of recent years, Jeremie Cometto-Lingenheim and David Gingell's "lively", hard-surfaced operation off the Holloway Road has built a strong following for its zeitgeisty style, matched with "inventive and well-presented" fish and seafood cooking, with ingredients from 'regenerative producers', and an "interesting" list of low-intervention wines. "I'm not a great fan of small plates but we decided to have every dish on the menu – and it has to be said they were all excellent." / N5 1PB; www.westernslaundry.com; @WesternsLaundry; Tue-Sat 10.30 pm, Sun 9 pm; closed Tue-Fri L, closed Mon.

The Wet Fish Café NW6 £54 🔳🔳🔳

242 West End Lane 020 7443 9222 1–1B

"A dream local that never disappoints"; this all-day café and brasserie in West Hampstead provides *"lovely service"* and *"some cool tunes create a nice vibe"*. Set in a converted 1930s fishmonger – hence the name – it majors in *"delicious fresh fish from Cornwall, cooked to perfection"*, which is also available as, yes, wet fish for home consumption. *"Love it any time of day – brunch, coffee, lunch or dinner"*. *"Prices are reasonable, too"*. *"It's on my doorstep – jealous yet?"* / NW6 1LG; www.thewetfishcafe.co.uk; @thewetfishcafe; Mon-Sun 11 pm; Booking evening only.

Whitcomb's at The Londoner WC2 NEW £87

The Londoner, 38 Leicester Square 020 7451 0102 5–4A

This 300-room landmark hotel – from the Edwardian Group – just off Leicester Square had been set to open in 2020 as the pandemic hit, and finally launched in September 2021. As well as incorporating two Odeon luxe cinemas and a rooftop bar with fire pits, it offers six concept eateries, bars and a tavern. The main event is Whitcomb's, an all-day bar/brasserie. Other possibilities include The Stage (for breakfast, tea and caviar, with Champagne a-go-go); and 8 at The Londoner (on the rooftop, serving Japanese dishes and cocktails). / WC2H 7DT; www.thelondoner.com; @TheLondonerHotel; Tue-Sat 11 pm, Sun & Mon 10 pm.

The White Onion SW19 £69 🔳🔳▨

67 High St 020 8947 8278 11–2B

"A local treat in the heart of Wimbledon Village", this offshoot from Eric and Sarah Guignard's highly rated French Table in Surbiton has long been known for its *"consistently high-quality modern European cooking"*. Many folks like the interior, but its look is a tad *"subdued"* for some tastes, and it can be *"noisy"*. / SW19 5EE; www.thewhiteonion.co.uk; @thewhiteonionSW; Wed & Thu 10 pm, Fri & Sat 10.30 pm, Sun 2.30 pm; closed Wed & Thu L closed Sun D, closed Mon & Tue; Take bookings all week via phone and/or online.

The Wigmore, The Langham W1 £55 🔳🔳🔳

15 Langham Place, Regent Street 020 7965 0198 2–1B

"The perfect London pub," say fans of Michel Roux's *"sophisticated"* bar with *"exceptional food"* near Oxford Circus. It's not really a pub, of course; it's been converted from part of the historic five-star Langham hotel. But there's an undeniable buzz around this latest incarnation: *"How can you make the humble cheese toastie taste this good?"* / W1B 3DE; www.the-wigmore.co.uk; @Wigmore_London; Tue-Sat 11 pm; closed Sun & Mon; Take bookings all week via phone and/or online.

Wild Honey St James SW1 £87 🔳🔳🔳

Sofitel, 8 Pall Mall 020 7389 7820 2–3C

"Refined, classic cuisine is well-presented and served with grace" at Anthony Demetre's *"classy"* hotel dining room, near Trafalgar Square (to which he shifted from Mayfair a couple of years ago). Even fans can find the experience rather *"expensive"* in its new quarters, but – especially for a hotel – it's *"a beautiful venue"* and one that's very conveniently situated for business or pre-theatre. / SW1Y 5NG; www.wildhoneystjames.co.uk; @WildHoneySJ; Tue-Sat 9.30 pm, Mon 10.30 , Sun 11am; closed Sun & Mon D.

Wild Tavern SW3 NEW £107 2|3|3
2 Elystan Street   020 8191 9885   6–2C

The casually luxurious DNA of Goodmans and Burger & Lobster is evident at this two-year-old venture (opened in December 2019), overlooking Chelsea Green. What is essentially a surf 'n' turf menu with seafood and USDA steaks sold by the 100g is bolstered by Italian dishes and pasta, all served in an elegant, vaguely Alpine setting, complete with fire pit and wooden ceiling. For the most part reports are all good – "a very welcome addition" – but, on the downside, ratings are dragged down by the fact that it's "soooo expensive". / SW3 3NS; www.wildtavern.co.uk; Mon-Sat 10 pm, Sun 9.30 pm.

Wildflower NW1 NEW £85 4|3|3
180-188 Camden High Street   07799 357396   9–2B

"It's amazing how much fun you can have dining in a shipping container!!" – Irish chef Adrian Martin's July 2020 newcomer may be thus housed in Camden Town's new eco market on Buck Street, but – with its incongruously posh decor and £65 eight-course menu (£110 if you go for the wine matching) – it's certainly not in the grungy, street food category (even if you do have to go outside to the loos in the market). As the name hints, the focus is on seasonality and foraged food, but early press reviews – while not writing the enterprise off – have given it a slightly bumpy ride. Some of our early reporters are much more upbeat, though, hailing "inspirational and outstanding cuisine" that its most ardent supporters would put "in the same class as Aulis and Story". / NW1 8QP; wildflowerrestaurant.co.uk; @wildflowerrest; Wed-Sat 11 pm; closed Mon & Tue & Sun; no Amex; Take bookings all week via phone and/or online.

Wiltons SW1 £101 3|5|4
55 Jermyn St   020 7629 9955   3–3C

"With a menu well-suited to any Edwardian gourmet" ("wonderful Dover sole" and other "excellent fish dishes", plus game in season), this "very civilised" and "wonderfully traditional" St James's bastion (London's oldest restaurant, established in 1742, albeit not on this site) "just has a certain class about it" and is "ideal for taking someone on business who you want to impress" – "whether it's for schmoozing or to seal a deal". A particular highlight is the "old-style service" – "staff are wonderfully discreet" and there's an "unwavering dedication to customer service". Just one thing... "you need a very healthy expense account" before setting out, as the final reckoning can be terrifying. ("It is an icon, but if it was half the price, I'd double the score!") / SW1Y 6LX; www.wiltons.co.uk; @wiltons1742; Mon-Sat 10.30 pm; closed Sat L, closed Sun; Take bookings all week via phone and/or online.

The Windmill W1 £61 3|3|3
6-8 Mill St   020 7491 8050   4–2A

"I could have bathed in the sauce smothering the devilled kidneys", eulogises one poetic fan of this "sparkling pub with excellent food" in poshest Mayfair. It's a proper pub, too, with "well-kept beer" and a "great selection of pies". "A pint of Young's bitter and a great pie takes some beating – and only a hop from Oxford Circus." Upstairs, there's a smarter restaurant. / W1S 2AZ; www.windmillmayfair.co.uk; @windmillpubW1; Wed-Sat 9 pm.

The Wine Library EC3 £44 2|2|4
43 Trinity Sq   020 7481 0415   10–3D

A Victorian vaulted wine cellar near Tower Hill offering a "unique service": a "fascinating and wide-ranging list" of 300+ wines "sold at off-licence prices with a modest corkage charge" (£9.50), to enjoy with a "tasty selection" of French cheeses, game pâtés, rillettes and charcuterie. / EC3N 4DJ; www.winelibrary.co.uk; Tue-Fri 8 pm, Mon 6 pm, Sat 5.30 pm; closed Sat D, closed Sun.

The Wolseley W1 £62 [2][3][5]

160 Piccadilly   020 7499 6996   3–3C

"The place to go to impress anybody!" – Corbin & King's "elegant classic" next to The Ritz remains a superb choice for most kinds of rendezvous, including a business meal for which it is yet again the survey's No.1 choice. A "sumptuous-looking" chamber – originally built as an Edwardian car showroom (whose brand survives only in the restaurant's name) – it is styled as a Continental "Grand Café", and the "large open space has an old-world glamour", whose "buzz makes for a very memorable occasion". Despite the pressures of such a big venue, service typically is "smart and crisp" and immaculately besuited owner "Jeremy King walks the floor and has a wonderful memory for regulars" (many of whom are famous faces). "So long as you don't expect haute cuisine", the brasserie fare is "generally sound", and at its best is "comfort food done really well". (Do not go anticipating any culinary fireworks!). An archetypal London experience – it offers "the epitome of all-day dining", from its "classic old-school breakfast" onwards (for which it's also the survey's No. 1 choice) and is "just the place to take an out-of-towner for brunch". "Afternoon tea is an absolute bargain too – particularly as they will bring you more cakes if you ask!" ("Crikey, we missed The Wolseley during lockdown. It feels even more special now!") / W1J 9EB; www.thewolseley.com; @TheWolseley; Mon-Sat 11 pm, Sun 10 pm.

Wong Kei W1 £35 [3][1][1]

41-43 Wardour St   020 7437 8408   5–3A

"Service is as efficient and as unfriendly as ever, and the interior has looked the same for over 20 years now" (i.e. with precious little in terms of atmosphere) at this notorious Chinatown veteran – "certainly not a place for romance". The legendary brusque service is "an acquired taste" and all part of the fun ("was staff rudeness toned down in the past year? Not something I'm happy with!"), but what keeps this place going are the "plates heaped with tasty food for a very good price". / W1D 6PY; www.wongkeilondon.com; Mon-Sat 11.30 pm, Sun 10.30 pm; cash only.

Wright Brothers £75 [3][2][3]

56 Old Brompton Rd, SW7   020 7581 0131   6–2B
11 Stoney St, SE1   020 7403 9554   10–4C
26 Circus Road West, SW8   020 7324 7734   11–1C
Frederick's Place, EC2   10–2C NEW

"Amazing seafood" – "really fresh and full of taste" – is the headliner at this oyster supplier turned producer turned "bustling" seafood bar at Borough Market, from brothers-in-law Ben Wright and Robin Hancock (now also with offshoots at Battersea Power Station and South Ken). In March 2021, acclaimed chef Henry Harris joined as group chef, adding his knowledge of classic meat dishes and fine wines to the Wright Bros' traditional oysters, crustaceans and seafood platters. Top Tip: "curried oysters sounds awful and sacrilegious but is stunning – a real tasting experience".

Wulf & Lamb £55 [3][3][2]

243 Pavilion Road, SW1   020 3948 5999   6–2D
66 Chiltern Street, W1   020 8194 0000   2–1A NEW

Despite the ironically red-blooded name, this pair of 'plant-based' cafés in smart Chelsea and Marylebone are "favourites for vegetarian food so well prepared you hardly notice the lack of meat". Their "tasty food covers all bases", including vegan versions of such comfort-food classics as burgers and mac'n'cheese, with borrowings from Mediterranean, Middle Eastern and Oriental cuisines.

Wun's W1 £45 3 3 2

24 Greek Street   020 8017 9888   5–2A

"A great find" – Z He and Alex Peffly's Soho 60s-style 'tea room and bar' in Soho is "not your standard Chinese". Instead, it serves turbocharged versions of Cantonese classics, such as char sui using Iberico pork, alongside ambitious cocktails and house-made rice wine. The couple's Bun House, originally on this site, moved to Chinatown two years ago. / W1D 4DZ; tearoom.bar; Tue-Thu 10 pm, Fri & Sat 11 pm, Sun 8 pm; closed Tue-Sat L, closed Mon; booking online only.

Xi'an Impression N7 £42 4 2 1

117 Benwell Rd   020 3441 0191   9–2D

"The hand-pulled noodles are so moreish and unctuous – really off the chart", at this basic "hole in the wall" opposite Arsenal's Emirates stadium, serving unusual dishes from Xi'an in central China. "The tables full of Chinese customers vouch for the authenticity of dishes such as black fungus and pig's ear in soy sauce". / N7; www.xianimpression.co.uk; @xianimpression; Mon-Sun 10 pm; No bookings.

Yama Momo SE22 £67 3 2 2

72 Lordship Ln   020 8299 1007   1–4D

"Consistently high-quality food and cocktails" set the tone at this Japanese izakaya in East Dulwich, from the ex-Nobu team behind Clapham's well-known Tsunami. "Occasionally you get the sense that some of the staff don't really know what they're doing" – but most reporters are more than happy with the sushi, sashimi, tempura and other delicacies on the menu. / SE22 8HF; www.yamamomo.co.uk; @YamamomoRest; Mon-Thu 10 pm, Fri & Sat 10.30 pm, Sun 9.30 pm; closed Mon-Thu L.

Yard Sale Pizza £46 3 2 2

54 Blackstock Road, N4   020 7226 2651   9–1D
46 Westow Hill, SE19   020 8670 6386   NEW
39 Lordship Lane, SE22
63 Bedford Hill, SW12   020 8772 1100
622 High Road Leytonstone, E11   020 8539 5333   1–1D
15 Hoe Street, E17   020 8509 0888   1–1D
184 Hackney Road, E2   020 7739 1095
105 Lower Clapton Rd, E5   020 3602 9090   14–1B

"Yummy, doughy crusts" and "unusual but great topping combinations" have built a growing following for this "too cool for school" east London pizza multiple, founded in 2016 in Clapton. It now has eight outlets following a fast roll-out south of the river, with openings in East Dulwich, Balham and most recently Crystal Palace. Most of them are "small, busy crowded"… for good reason. / yardsalepizza.com; @YardSalePizza.

Yardarm E10 3 4 3

238 Francis Road   020 8556 2444   1–1D

Leyton deli and bottle shop that's a fave rave for anyone living within striking distance (but we also received a very good report on it from a reporter living in SW19!). In autumn 2019, they opened an adjoining café serving snacks and small plates. / E10 6NQ; yardarm.london/; @yardarm_leyton; Thu-Sat 11 pm, Sun 5 pm; closed Sun D, closed Mon & Tue & Wed.

Yashin £109 3 2 3

117-119 Old Brompton Rd, SW7   020 7373 3990   6–2B
1a Argyll Rd, W8   020 7938 1536   6–1A

Despite designer interiors and posh locations (the ten-year-old original in a Kensington backstreet; the 'Ocean House' spin-off in South Kensington, in a quirky building built as Brompton Library), this off-radar duo perennially inspire surprisingly little feedback. Not only that, such reports as we do get typically say something like "one of the most delicious Japanese restaurants in town". Perhaps it's because they are not cheap?

Yauatcha **£98** 3 2 3
Broadwick Hs, 15-17 Broadwick St, W1   020 7494 8888   4–1C
Broadgate Circle, EC2   020 3817 9888   13–2B
"The venison puffs are the best things ever", the "prawn cheung fun with
tofu is inspired" and desserts are "dainty and exciting looking" at these
stylish and very successful spin-offs from the Hakkasan chain, whose
formula is well summarised as "lovely dim sum in a buzzy location". The two
sites are quite different in character: the smaller, two-floor Soho original
incorporates a ground-floor tea rooms and moody basement – the
Broadgate branch boasts an outside cocktail terrace, but is much glossier,
bigger and altogether more "corporate". "There's surprising attention to
detail in each item of the menu" but the feeling that prices are "good but
high for the portions" limits its food score; and "every now and again the
service seems a tad chaotic". Despite these quibbles, though, serious criticism
was entirely absent this year. / www.yauatcha.com.

The Yellow House SE16 **£55** 3 4 3
126 Lower Rd   020 7231 8777   12–2A
SE16 is not the centre of the universe for restaurant-going, so it's particularly
worth knowing about this cosy local near Surrey Quays station, where wood-
fired pizza (including take away) is a highlight. / SE16 2UE;
www.theyellowhouse.eu; @Theyellowhouse_; Tue-Fri 11.30 pm, Sat midnight; closed
Tue-Sat L, closed Sun & Mon.

Yi-Ban E16 **£47**
Dockside Rd, Royal Albert Dock   020 7473 6699   12–1D
No feedback this year on this distant Chinese restaurant, near Royal Albert
Dock DLR. If you are looking to eat in these parts though – while watching
the take-offs and landings at nearby London City Airport – it is worth
knowing about. / E16 2QT; www.yi-ban.co.uk; Tue-Sat 11 pm, Mon 10 pm, Sun
10.30 pm; Take bookings all week via phone and/or online.

Yipin China N1 **£57** 4 2 1
70-72 Liverpool Rd   020 7354 3388   9–3D
"The atmosphere is downbeat but the food is addictive" at this Chinese
canteen near Angel, which serves "tasty, spicy food with lots and lots of
pepper". "Try and avoid the more conventional Chinese restaurant dishes for
an authentic regional treat." / N1 0QD; @YipinChina; Tue-Thu, Sun 10 pm, Fri &
Sat 10.30 pm; closed Tue L, closed Mon; cash only.

Yming W1 **£52** 4 4 3
35-36 Greek St   020 7734 2721   5–2A
Christine Lau's "enduring" Soho "institution" (just north of the melee of
Chinatown) is noted for its "excellent food" at "very reasonable prices" and
particularly for its "warm service" – "and they never rush customers". "The
regulars are just that – regular, and for very good reason: "I always head
here when in the West End"; "it's a place I can always go and feel the world
is somewhere else!" / W1D 5DL; www.yming.co.uk; Mon-Sat 11 pm; closed Sun.

Yopo W1 **£76**
20-21 Newman Street   020 3146 8880   3–1D
Impress your friends on Instagram with enviable scenes from the lush
outside terraces at this very good-looking boutique hotel in Fitzrovia. Not as
many reports as we'd like on its interesting restaurant – where the cuisine
comes with a South American accent – hence, for this year, we've left it
unrated. / W1T 1PG; www.themandrake.com; @MandrakeHotel; Mon & Tue 11 am,
Wed-Sat 11 pm, Sun 10 pm; closed Mon & Tue D.

York & Albany NW1 £60
127-129 Parkway 020 7592 1227 9–3B

This imposing Regency tavern where Camden Town meets Regent's Park is part of Gordon Ramsay's portfolio, and impresses some visitors with its cooking. Too many, though, reckon it makes a "poor choice" for a meal, and sleb-chef ownership may be its only real attraction. / NW1 7PS; www.gordonramsayrestaurants.com/york-and-albany; @yorkandalbany; Mon-Fri 11 pm, Sat 11.30 pm, Sun 10 pm.

Yoshino W1 £60
3 Piccadilly Pl 020 7287 6622 4–4C

This tranquil veteran hidden away in an alleyway just off Piccadilly Circus has provided one of London's "best Japanese experiences" for nearly 40 years. It's "run by the nicest people" – "the welcome from Lisa is always amazing" – and if you sit downstairs near the counter, she'll choose a wonderful meal for you from the sushi, sashimi and cooked dishes on offer. Upstairs, there's waitress service at tables. / W1J 0DB; www.yoshino.net; @Yoshino_London; Tue-Sat 10.30 pm; closed Sun & Mon.

Zafferano SW1 £95
15 Lowndes St 020 7235 5800 6–1D

"Nothing changes" at this "expensive but classy" Italian near Knightsbridge, although it has lost some of its celeb-pulling-power over the years – Giorgio Locatelli was the founding chef in 1995, with the likes of Madonna and Mick Jagger among the diners. But even those who find it "overpriced" are won over by "the wonderful pasta". / SW1X 9EY; zafferanorestaurant.com; Mon-Sat 11 pm, Sun 10.30 pm.

Zaffrani N1 £52
47 Cross St 020 7226 5522 9–3D

This "good, family-run local Indian" near Islington's Almeida Theatre serves a welcome range of seafood and vegetarian options as well as carnivore classics from across the subcontinent. / N1 2BB; www.zaffrani.co.uk; Mon-Sun 10.30 pm; closed Mon-Sun L.

Zahter W1 NEW
30-32 Foubert's Place 4–1B

Ex-Spitalfields Ottolenghi chef, Esra Muslu is finally opening her own London restaurant (rumours of which have been circulating for years) in Autumn 2021. A four-floor site off Carnaby Street will incorporate a ground floor with counter and al fresco seating, plus a dining room, events space and cookery school on upper floors. The cuisine? 'Istanbulite'. / W1F 7PS; Sun-Thu 11.30 pm, Fri & Sat 12.30 am.

Zaibatsu SE10 £33
96 Trafalgar Rd 020 8858 9317 1–3D

In an "unlikely location" on the edge of Greenwich, this "unassuming" outfit serves "incredible" Japanese fusion dishes in "very generous portions" (notable sushi and "perfect tempura, with light batter"). Given its basic interior, the name is surely ironic ('zaibatsu' are the vast – and far from unassuming – conglomerates that dominate the Japanese economy, such as Mitsubishi, Mitsui and Nissan). / SE10 9UW; www.zaibatsufusion.co.uk; @ong_teck; Tue-Sat 11 pm, Sun 9 pm; closed Mon; cash only.

Zaika of Kensington W8 £69
1 Kensington High Street 020 7795 6533 6–1A

This plush modern venue occupies a "lovely space" – a former banking hall near Kensington Palace Gardens – and is the less well-known stablemate of the vaunted Tamarind in Mayfair. It serves "beautiful" and "innovative" dishes inspired by the historic cuisines developed for royalty in Lucknow, northern India. / W8 5NP; www.zaikaofkensington.com; @ZaikaLondon; Mon-Sat 10.30 pm, Sun 9.45pm; closed Wed-Sun L; No trainers; credit card required to book.

Zelman Meats **£71** **3**|**2**|**3**
Harvey Nichols, Fifth Fl…, Knightsbridge, SW1 020 7201 8625 6–1D
"Always enjoyable steaks" still win acclaim for Misha Zelman's steakhouse brand, but – with the closure in March 2021 of its St Anne's Court branch – it's down to a single outlet now, on the fifth floor of Harvey Nicks.
/ zelmanmeats.com.

Zeret SE5 **£44** **4**|**4**|**3**
216-218 Camberwell Road 020 7701 8587 1–3C
"Splendid flavours, lovely service, and reasonable prices" are, say fans, a "perfect combination" at this affordable Ethiopian restaurant in Camberwell.
/ SE5 0ED; zeretkitchen.co.uk; @zeret_kitchen; Mon-Thu 10 pm, Fri & Sat 11 pm; closed Mon-Fri L, closed Sun; no Amex.

081 Pizzeria SE15 NEW
5th Floor, Peckham Levels, 95a Rye Lane 1–4D
From Andrea Asciuti of Streatham's Bravi Ragazzi – this 2021 opening features ten of the traditional, Neapolitan-style pizzas that have created a buzz about his Streatham venture, as well as smaller bites, described as 'Neapolitan tapas'. / SE15 4ST; www.081pizzeria.com; @081pizzeria; Mon-Sun 10.30 pm.

Zheng SW3 **£61** **3**|**2**|**2**
4 Sydney St 020 7352 9890 6–2C
A "delicious range of Malay-Chinese food" on the menu at this smart Chelsea outfit is the reason why "a lot of Asians eat here". This London offspring of a successful Oxford restaurant has taken on a tricky site in Sydney Street where others have failed to last the distance. / SW3 6PP; www.zhengchelsea.co.uk; @zhengchelsea; Mon, Wed-Sun 11 pm; closed Mon, Wed-Fri L, closed Tue.

Zia Lucia **£40** **4**|**3**|**3**
61 Blythe Road, W14 020 7371 4096 8–1C
Boxpark Wembley, 18 Olympic Way, HA9 020 3744 4427
157 Holloway Road, N7 020 7700 3708 9–2D
65 Balham High Road, SW12 NEW
356 Old York Road, SW18 020 3971 0829 11–2B NEW
12a Piazza Walk, E1 020 7702 2525 10–2D NEW
"The stunning sourdough pizzas are a proper treat" at these "fast and delicious local favourites" which are a "great addition to the burgeoning London real pizza scene". There's a "particularly interesting menu with a variety of crusts including charcoal (looks burnt, tastes like chewy pizza heaven)". The original Islington branch now has an adjoining home-made pasta specialist, Berto, from founders Claudio Vescovo and Gianluca D'Angelo, while the group's sixth pizzeria opened on Balham High Road in autumn 2021. / zialucia.com; @zialuciapizza.

Ziani's SW3 **£68** **2**|**2**|**4**
45 Radnor Walk 020 7351 5297 6–3C
"There's a real buzz and warmth" to this tiny but "intimate" Venetian trattoria off the King's Road, which packs in well-heeled Chelsea locals and their families. Roberto Colussi, who founded it in 1984, died four years ago, but its regulars continue to recommend it as "great for a night with good friends". "The cooking is amazing given its minute kitchen", but overall "you don't really go to Ziani's for the food". / SW3 4BP; www.ziani.co.uk; Mon-Sun 10 pm.

Zoilo W1 £84 **4** **3** **3**

9 Duke St   020 7486 9699   3–1A

Argentinian chef/patron Diego Jacquet's Marylebone ten-year-old again won high marks this year. There's quite a menu selection, of which the mainstays are the grills and steaks – the latter includes both UK-reared options and those imported from Argentina – and there's also an interesting selection of Argentinean wines to interest all budgets (including large ones!) Both meat and wine are now available mail order. / W1U 3EG; www.zoilo.co.uk; @Zoilo_London; Tue-Sat 10 pm; closed Tue, Wed L, closed Sun & Mon.

Zuma SW7 £83 **4** **3** **4**

5 Raphael St   020 7584 1010   6–1C

"Even in these troubled times, it never fails to deliver" – Rainer Becker and Arjun Waney's "fantastic fusion" scene, a short walk from Harrods, wins impressive support as ever, despite the absence for much of the year of the supercar-driving international crowd for which it's known (and it "can still be an OTT scene at times"). It helps that the "beautifully presented", Japanese-inspired cuisine is reliably "fantastic". / SW7 1DL; www.zumarestaurant.com; Mon-Sat 11 pm, Sun 10.30 pm; booking max 8 may apply.

AREA OVERVIEWS

CENTRAL

Soho, Covent Garden & Bloomsbury
(Parts of W1, all WC2 and WC1)

£170+	Aulis London	*British, Modern*	5 5 4
£130+	So LA	*American*	4 4 4
£110+	Park Row	*British, Modern*	– – –
	The Savoy Hotel, Savoy Grill	*British, Traditional*	2 2 3
	Kebab Queen	*Turkish*	4 4 3
£100+	Evelyn's Table	*British, Modern*	5 5 3
	Smith & Wollensky	*Steaks & grills*	2 2 3
£90+	Fallow at 10 Heddon Street	*British, Modern*	4 4 4
	Social Eating House	"	3 3 4
	L'Escargot	*French*	3 3 4
	Frenchie	"	3 3 2
	Louie	"	3 3 4
	Otto's	"	4 5 3
	Sushisamba	*Fusion*	2 2 3
	The Petersham	*Italian*	2 2 4
	Decimo	*Spanish*	3 3 5
	Hawksmoor	*Steaks & grills*	3 3 2
	Oscar Wilde Lounge	*Afternoon tea*	3 3 5
	Savoy, Thames Foyer	"	2 4 4
	Cecconi's Pizza Bar	*Pizza*	2 2 4
	Yauatcha	*Chinese*	3 2 3
	Roka, Aldwych House	*Japanese*	4 3 4
£80+	Christopher's	*American*	2 2 3
	28-50	*British, Modern*	3 3 2
	Balthazar	"	2 2 3
	Bob Bob Ricard	"	2 4 5
	Frog by Adam Handling	"	5 4 3
	The Ivy	"	2 3 3
	Quo Vadis	"	3 3 5
	Spring Restaurant	"	4 4 5
	Rules	*British, Traditional*	2 3 5
	Simpson's in the Strand	"	2 2 3
	J Sheekey	*Fish & seafood*	3 3 4
	J Sheekey Atlantic Bar	"	4 3 5
	Clos Maggiore	*French*	2 2 5
	Margot	*Italian*	2 4 4
	Whitcomb's at The Londoner	*Mediterranean*	– – –
	Sucre London	*Argentinian*	– – –
	aqua kyoto	*Japanese*	2 2 4
£70+	NoMad London	*American*	3 3 5
	Dean Street Townhouse	*British, Modern*	2 3 4
	Ducksoup	"	3 3 3
	The French House	"	3 4 5
	L'Oscar Restaurant	"	– – –

	Noble Rot	"	3 5 5
	Holborn Dining Room	British, Traditional	3 2 2
	Fishworks	Fish & seafood	2 2 2
	Café Murano	Italian	2 3 2
	Nopi	Mediterranean	4 4 3
	Cakes and Bubbles	Spanish	3 4 4
	Heritage	Swiss	– – –
	Dalloway Terrace	Afternoon tea	2 3 4
	Gauthier Soho	Vegan	3 4 3
	Chotto Matte	Japanese	4 3 4
	Sticks'n'Sushi	"	4 3 3
£60+	Big Easy	American	3 2 3
	Andrew Edmunds	British, Modern	3 3 5
	Coopers Restaurant & Bar	"	3 4 3
	Cora Pearl	"	3 3 3
	Ham Yard Restaurant	"	2 2 4
	Heliot Steak House	"	3 3 3
	The Ivy Market Grill	"	2 3 4
	10 Greek Street	"	4 2 2
	The Ivy Soho Brasserie	British, Traditional	2 3 4
	The Delaunay	East & Cent. European	2 4 4
	The Oystermen	Fish & seafood	4 3 3
	Parsons	"	4 3 2
	Randall & Aubin	"	4 4 5
	Blanchette	French	4 3 3
	The 10 Cases	International	3 3 2
	Bocca di Lupo	Italian	5 3 3
	Da Mario	"	2 3 3
	Dehesa	"	2 2 3
	Luce e Limoni	"	4 4 3
	San Carlo Cicchetti	"	3 3 3
	Sycamore Vino Cucina	"	4 4 3
	VyTA	"	– – –
	Volta do Mar	Portuguese	4 3 3
	Barrafina	Spanish	4 4 5
	Tapas Brindisa Soho	"	3 3 3
	Burger & Lobster	Burgers, etc	3 2 2
	Ceviche Soho	Peruvian	4 3 4
	The Barbary	North African	5 4 4
	The Palomar	Middle Eastern	4 4 3
	Berenjak	Persian	4 3 3
	Nutshell	"	3 2 2
	The Duck & Rice	Chinese	3 3 3
	Fatt Pundit	"	3 3 2
	Darjeeling Express	Indian	4 5 2
	Fatt Pundit	"	3 3 2
	Flesh and Buns	Japanese	3 3 3
	Jinjuu	Korean	4 3 3
	Patara Soho	Thai	3 3 2
£50+	Joe Allen	American	3 3 3
	Café Deco	British, Modern	3 2 2
	Double Standard	"	3 4 4
	Noble Rot Soho	"	4 4 5
	Shampers	"	3 4 4

Sussex	"	3 3 2
VQ, St Giles Hotel	"	2 3 3
Cork & Bottle	British, Traditional	2 3 5
Cigalon	French	3 4 4
Le Garrick	"	3 3 4
Mon Plaisir Restaurant	"	3 3 4
Relais de Venise L'Entrecôte	"	3 2 2
La Fromagerie Bloomsbury	International	3 3 3
Ave Mario	Italian	– – –
Bancone	"	4 4 3
Ciao Bella	"	3 3 4
Fumo	"	3 3 3
La Goccia	"	3 3 4
Mele e Pere	"	2 2 3
Pastaio	"	3 3 3
Opera Tavern	Spanish	3 3 3
Blacklock	Steaks & grills	4 4 4
Macellaio RC	"	4 3 3
St Moritz	Swiss	3 3 4
Mildreds	Vegetarian	3 3 3
North Sea Fish	Fish & chips	3 3 2
Poppies	"	3 3 2
L'Antica Pizzeria da Michele	Pizza	5 3 4
temper Covent Garden	"	4 3 4
temper Soho	BBQ	4 3 4
Casita Andina	Peruvian	– – –
Le Bab	Middle Eastern	4 2 3
Lahpet	Burmese	3 3 3
Four Seasons	Chinese	4 1 1
Yming	"	4 4 3
Cinnamon Bazaar	Indian	4 3 4
Kricket	"	5 4 4
Tamarind Kitchen	"	4 3 3
Tandoor Chop House	"	4 3 3
Hoppers	Sri Lankan	3 2 3
Tendril	Vegan	– – –
Bisushima	Japanese	– – –
Inko Nito	"	3 3 4
Oka, Kingly Court	"	3 2 2
Shoryu Ramen	"	3 2 2
£40+ Breakfast Club	American	3 3 3
The Norfolk Arms	British, Modern	3 3 3
Brasserie Zédel	French	2 3 5
Prix Fixe	"	3 2 2
Gordon's Wine Bar	International	2 2 5
Lina Stores	Italian	4 3 3
Haché	Burgers, etc	3 2 2
50 Kalò di Ciro Salvo	Pizza	5 4 3
Homeslice	"	3 2 3
Pizza Pilgrims	"	3 3 3
Chick 'n' Sours	Chicken	3 3 3
El Pastor Soho	Mexican/TexMex	3 3 4
Golden Dragon	Chinese	3 2 2
Wun's	"	3 3 2
Dishoom	Indian	3 4 5

	Name	Cuisine			
	Malabar Junction	"	3	3	2
	Punjab	"	3	2	3
	Salaam Namaste	"	3	3	2
	Paradise	Sri Lankan	4	3	3
	Bone Daddies	Japanese	3	3	3
	Kanada-Ya	"	5	2	2
	Koya-Bar	"	4	4	4
	Shackfuyu	"	3	3	3
	Tonkotsu	"	4	3	2
	Hare & Tortoise	Pan-Asian	3	3	2
	Kiln	Thai	5	4	4
	Cay Tre	Vietnamese	3	3	3
	Bao Soho	Taiwanese	3	4	4
£35+	The Black Book	British, Modern	2	3	4
	Bar Italia	Italian	2	3	5
	Flat Iron	Steaks & grills	3	4	4
	Chilli Cool	Chinese	4	2	1
	Wong Kei	"	3	1	1
	Din Tai Fung	Chinese, Dim sum	3	3	3
	Hankies	Indian	4	2	2
	Sagar	"	3	2	2
	Club Mexicana Taqueria	Vegan	4	4	3
	Kolamba	Sri Lankan	4	3	3
	Eat Tokyo	Japanese	3	2	2
	Humble Chicken	"	5	3	3
	Taro	"	3	2	2
	Bibimbap Soho	Korean	3	2	2
	Lao Cafe	Thai	3	2	2
	Viet Food	Vietnamese	3	3	2
£30+	Café in the Crypt	British, Traditional	2	2	4
	Patty and Bun Soho	Burgers, etc	4	3	3
	Tommi's Burger Joint	"	3	3	2
	Baozi Inn	Chinese	3	3	3
	Master Wei	"	3	3	2
	Baozi Inn	Chinese, Dim sum	3	3	3
	C&R Café	Malaysian	4	3	2
£25+	Coqfighter	Chicken	5	3	2
	India Club	Indian	3	3	2
	Heddon Yokocho	Japanese	4	2	3
£20+	The Kati Roll Company	Indian	3	2	2
£15+	Mr Ji	Fusion	3	3	2
	Bageriet	Sandwiches, cakes, etc	4	2	2
	Imad's Syrian Kitchen	Syrian	4	4	3
£10+	Nordic Bakery	Scandinavian	3	3	2
	Truffle	Burgers, etc	3	2	2
	Flat White	Sandwiches, cakes, etc	–	–	–
£5+	Maison Bertaux	Afternoon tea	4	4	5
	Monmouth Coffee Company	Sandwiches, cakes, etc	3	4	4

Mayfair & St James's (Parts of W1 and SW1)

			Rating		
£380+	The Araki	*Japanese*	5	4	4
£220+	Alain Ducasse	*French*	2	3	3
	Sketch, Lecture Room	*"*	3	4	5
£210+	Ikoyi	*International*	4	3	2
£170+	Hélène Darroze	*French*	3	3	2
	Maru	*Japanese*	5	4	4
£160+	Davies and Brook	*British, Modern*	3	3	3
	Above at Hide	*"*	3	4	3
£150+	Seven Park Place	*French*	3	3	3
	Umu	*Japanese*	4	4	4
£140+	Le Gavroche	*French*	4	5	4
	Promenade, The Dorchester	*Afternoon tea*	2	4	4
	Park Chinois	*Chinese*	2	2	3
£120+	The Connaught Grill	*British, Modern*	–	–	–
	Hide Ground	*"*	4	4	4
	Pollen Street Social	*"*	4	4	4
	Le Comptoir Robuchon	*French*	4	4	3
	Galvin at Windows	*"*	2	3	4
	Novikov (Italian restaurant)	*Italian*	2	2	2
	The Ritz, Palm Court	*Afternoon tea*	3	4	5
	Hakkasan Mayfair	*Chinese*	3	2	3
	Cubé	*Japanese*	–	–	–
£110+	Corrigan's Mayfair	*British, Modern*	3	3	3
	The Game Bird	*British, Traditional*	3	3	2
	The Ritz	*"*	3	4	5
	LPM (fka La Petite Maison)	*French*	4	3	4
	Giannino Dal 1899	*Italian*	3	4	3
	Murano	*"*	4	4	3
	34 Mayfair	*Steaks & grills*	3	4	3
	Kai Mayfair	*Chinese*	3	4	3
	Novikov (Asian restaurant)	*Pan-Asian*	3	3	4
£100+	Colony Grill Room	*American*	–	–	–
	The Grill at The Dorchester	*British, Modern*	4	4	4
	Ormer	*"*	4	4	3
	Wiltons	*British, Traditional*	3	5	4
	Estiatorio Milos	*Fish & seafood*	3	2	4
	Bar des Prés	*French*	3	3	3
	Bocconcino Restaurant	*Italian*	2	3	3
	The Guinea Grill	*Steaks & grills*	3	4	4
	China Tang	*Chinese*	3	3	4
	Benares	*Indian*	4	4	4
	Ginza Onodera	*Japanese*	2	2	2
	Jean-Georges	*Pan-Asian*	3	3	3

£90+					
Charlie at Brown's	British, Modern	3	4	3
Hush	"	2	2	3
Stork Restaurant	"	–	–	–
Bentley's	Fish & seafood	3	2	2
Scott's	"	3	3	4
Sexy Fish	"	1	2	3
Sketch, Gallery	French	2	2	4
Amazonico	International	3	3	4
Cecconi's	Italian	2	2	4
Chucs Dover Street	"	2	3	4
Aquavit	Scandinavian	3	3	2
Goodman	Steaks & grills	3	3	2
Hawksmoor	"	3	3	2
Ella Canta	Mexican/TexMex	–	–	–
Coya	Peruvian	3	3	4
Kanishka	Indian	3	3	2
Nobu, Metropolitan Hotel	Japanese	4	3	3
Roka	"	4	3	4
Sake No Hana	"	4	3	3
Tokimeite	"	3	2	2

£80+					
45 Jermyn St.	British, Modern	3	3	3
Quaglino's	"	2	2	5
Wild Honey St James	"	3	3	3
GBR	British, Traditional	3	3	4
Maison Francois	French	4	4	4
Saint Jacques	"	4	4	4
Scully	International	5	4	3
Franco's	Italian	3	3	4
Ristorante Frescobaldi	"	3	3	2
Sartoria	"	3	3	3
Theo Randall	"	3	3	2
The American Bar	Mediterranean	2	3	4
Rowley's	Steaks & grills	2	2	3
Diamond Jubilee Tea S…	Afternoon tea	3	3	4
Momo	Moroccan	–	–	–
Chutney Mary	Indian	3	3	3
Gymkhana	"	4	3	3
Jamavar	"	5	4	4
Tamarind	"	4	3	3
Veeraswamy	"	3	3	3
Lucky Cat	Pan-Asian	2	2	2

£70+					
Kitty Fisher's	British, Modern	3	3	4
Langan's Brasserie	"	–	–	–
Little Social	"	3	3	3
Native at Browns	"	5	4	3
Fishworks	Fish & seafood	2	2	2
Café Murano	Italian	2	3	2
San Carlo	"	3	2	4
Brown's, Drawing Room	Afternoon tea	3	4	4
MiMi Mei Fair	Chinese	–	–	–
Chisou	Japanese	3	2	2

£60+					
The Avenue	American	–	–	–
Bellamy's	British, Modern	3	4	4

267

	116 at the Athenaeum	"	2	4	2
	The Wolseley	"	2	3	5
	The Windmill	British, Traditional	3	3	3
	Al Duca	Italian	3	2	2
	Il Vicolo	"	3	3	3
	Sabor	Spanish	5	4	3
	Burger & Lobster	Burgers, etc	3	2	2
	Delfino	Pizza	3	3	3
	Bombay Bustle	Indian	4	3	3
	Manthan	"	–	–	–
	Yoshino	Japanese	3	4	2
	The Ivy Asia	Pan-Asian	2	4	3
	Patara Mayfair	Thai	3	3	2
£50+	123V	Vegan	4	4	2
	El Pirata	Spanish	2	3	3
	O'ver	Pizza	3	3	3
	Shoryu Ramen	Japanese	3	2	2
	Titu	Pan-Asian	4	4	4
£40+	Le Deli Robuchon	Sandwiches, cakes, etc	3	3	3
	Bindas Eatery	Indian	–	–	–
£35+	Queens of Mayfair	British, Modern	–	–	–
£30+	Frank's	French	–	–	–
£20+	BiBi	Indian	–	–	–

Fitzrovia & Marylebone (Part of W1)

£320+	Kitchen Table	British, Modern	4	5	4
£140+	Akoko	Afro-Caribbean	4	4	4
£130+	Hot Stone	Japanese	4	4	4
£120+	Kol	Mexican/TexMex	3	3	4
	Hakkasan	Chinese	3	2	3
£110+	Pied à Terre	French	5	4	4
	Beast	Steaks & grills	2	2	2
£100+	The Chiltern Firehouse	American	1	2	3
	The Berners Tavern	British, Modern	2	2	5
	Mere	East & Cent. European	4	5	4
	Arros QD	Spanish	2	2	3
	Nobu Portman Square	Japanese	3	2	2
	Taka Marylebone	"	–	–	–
£90+	Portland	British, Modern	5	5	3
	Roux at the Landau	"	–	–	–
	Noizé	French	4	5	3

	Locanda Locatelli	*Italian*	**3** **4** **3**
	Roka	*Japanese*	**4** **3** **4**
£80+	AOK Kitchen	*British, Modern*	**3** 2 **4**
	Clipstone	"	**4** **4** **3**
	28-50	"	**3** **3** 2
	Clarette	*French*	**3** **3** **3**
	Les 110 de Taillevent	"	**3** **3** **3**
	Orrery	"	2 2 2
	The Ninth London	*Mediterranean*	**5** **4** **3**
	Palm Court, The Langham	*Afternoon tea*	**3** **3** **4**
	Zoilo	*Argentinian*	**4** **3** **3**
	Pachamama	*Peruvian*	2 2 **3**
	1947 London	*Indian*	– – –
	Defune	*Japanese*	**4** **4** 2
	Dinings	"	**5** **3** 2
	TOKii	"	– – –
£70+	Brasserie of Light	*British, Modern*	2 2 2
	Fishworks Marylebone	*Fish & seafood*	2 2 2
	Yopo	*Fusion*	– – –
	Meraki	*Greek*	**3** **3** **4**
	Opso	"	**3** 2 2
	Carousel	*International*	– – –
	Caffè Caldesi	*Italian*	2 2 2
	Norma	"	**3** **4** **4**
	The Bright Courtyard	*Chinese*	**3** 2 2
	Royal China Club	"	**4** 2 2
	Jikoni	*Indian*	**4** **3** **4**
£60+	Caravan	*British, Modern*	2 2 2
	The Ivy Café	"	**1** 2 **3**
	The Lore of the Land	"	**3** **3** **4**
	108 Brasserie	"	**3** 2 **3**
	Vinoteca Seymour Place	"	2 2 2
	Fischer's	*East & Cent. European*	2 2 **4**
	Twist Connubio	*Fusion*	**4** **3** 2
	Ampéli	*Greek*	**3** **4** **3**
	Six by Nico	*International*	**4** **4** **4**
	Briciole	*Italian*	**3** 2 2
	Harry's Bar	"	2 2 **3**
	Blandford Comptoir	*Mediterranean*	**3** **3** **3**
	Ottolenghi	"	**4** **3** **3**
	Riding House Café	"	2 **3** **3**
	ROVI	"	**4** 2 **3**
	Ibérica	*Spanish*	**3** 2 2
	Lurra	"	**4** **3** **3**
	Burger & Lobster	*Burgers, etc*	**3** 2 2
	Daylesford Organic	*Sandwiches, cakes, etc*	2 2 2
	Honey & Co	*Middle Eastern*	**4** 2 2
	Honey & Smoke	"	**5** **4** 2
	Ishtar	*Turkish*	**3** **3** **3**
	Trishna	*Indian*	**5** **4** **3**
	Flesh and Buns Fitzrovia	*Japanese*	**3** **3** **3**

£50+	Passyunk Avenue	*American*	2	2	4
	Gunmakers	*British, Modern*	–	–	–
	The Wigmore, The Langham	*British, Traditional*	3	4	5
	RAW - Fish & Cocktails	*Fish & seafood*	4	3	2
	Foley's	*International*	3	3	2
	La Fromagerie Café	*"*	3	3	3
	Circolo Popolare	*Italian*	3	3	4
	Italian Greyhound	*"*	–	–	–
	2 Veneti	*"*	2	3	2
	Barrica	*Spanish*	3	3	3
	Donostia	*"*	4	4	3
	Salt Yard	*"*	3	3	3
	Boxcar Bar & Kitchen	*Steaks & grills*	4	4	3
	Le Relais de Venise	*"*	3	2	2
	The Gate	*Vegetarian*	4	2	2
	Madera	*Mexican/TexMex*	–	–	–
	Reubens	*Kosher*	3	2	2
	Royal China	*Chinese*	3	1	2
	Pali Hill	*Indian*	3	3	2
	Hoppers	*Sri Lankan*	3	2	3
	Wulf & Lamb	*Vegan*	3	3	2
	Sushi Atelier	*Japanese*	5	4	3
	Laksamania	*Malaysian*	3	2	2
	Oka	*Pan-Asian*	3	2	2
£40+	The Wallace	*French*	2	2	4
	Isola by San Carlo	*Italian*	–	–	–
	MEATLiquor	*Burgers, etc*	4	2	3
	Golden Hind	*Fish & chips*	3	2	2
	Homeslice	*Pizza*	3	2	3
	Pizzeria Mozza	*"*	–	–	–
	Santa Maria	*"*	4	3	3
	Delamina	*Middle Eastern*	3	3	3
	Roti Chai	*Indian*	3	3	2
	Bone Daddies	*Japanese*	3	3	3
	Sushiology by Atari-Ya	*"*	3	3	2
	Tonkotsu, Selfridges	*"*	4	3	2
	Bao Fitzrovia	*Taiwanese*	3	4	4
£35+	Cin Cin	*Italian*	–	–	–
	Flat Iron Marylebone	*Steaks & grills*	3	4	4
	Hankies Marble Arch	*Indian*	4	2	2
	Ragam	*"*	4	3	2
	Sagar	*"*	3	2	2
£30+	Patty and Bun	*Burgers, etc*	4	3	3
	Tommi's Burger Joint	*"*	3	3	2
£25+	Kiss the Hippo	*Sandwiches, cakes, etc*	3	3	3
£20+	Icco Pizza	*Italian*	4	3	2
£15+	Kaffeine (Eastcastle Street)	*Sandwiches, cakes, etc*	3	5	4

Belgravia, Pimlico, Victoria & Westminster (SW1, except St James's)

£170+	Muse	British, Modern	5 4 4
	Nusr-Et Steakhouse	Steaks & grills	– – –
£150+	Marcus, The Berkeley	British, Modern	3 3 3
£140+	Dinner	British, Traditional	2 2 1
£130+	Celeste at The Lanesborough	British, Modern	2 2 5
£120+	The Collins Room	Afternoon tea	3 3 4
	Imperial Treasure	Chinese	3 2 2
£110+	Kerridge's Bar & Grill	British, Modern	2 2 3
	Pétrus	French	3 3 2
	Harrods Social	International	3 4 4
	Hunan	Chinese	5 3 1
£100+	Goring, Dining Room	British, Traditional	4 5 4
	Santini	Italian	2 3 4
£90+	Chucs	Italian	2 3 4
	Zafferano	"	3 2 2
	Al Mare	Mediterranean	– – –
	Crystal Moon, Corinthia	Afternoon tea	3 4 4
	Amaya	Indian	5 3 3
£80+	Olivomare	Fish & seafood	3 3 2
	Olivocarne	Italian	3 3 2
	Boisdale of Belgravia	Scottish	2 2 3
	M Victoria	Steaks & grills	3 2 3
	Parlour, Gt Scotland Yd	Afternoon tea	– – –
£70+	Alfred Tennyson	British, Modern	3 2 3
	Hans' Bar & Grill	"	3 3 3
	Lorne	"	5 5 3
	Harrods Dining Hall	International	3 4 4
	Caraffini	Italian	3 4 3
	Enoteca Turi	"	3 5 3
	Olivo	"	3 3 2
	Sale e Pepe	"	3 5 3
	Eldr at Pantechnicon	Scandinavian	3 3 4
	Roof Gdn at Pantechnicon	"	3 3 5
	Zelman Meats	Steaks & grills	3 2 3
	Oliveto	Pizza	4 3 2
	The Cinnamon Club	Indian	3 3 4
	Kahani	"	4 4 3
	Quilon	Indian, Southern	5 4 2
	Sticks'n'Sushi	Japanese	4 3 3
	Sumosan Twiga	"	2 1 4
£60+	Daylesford Organic	British, Modern	2 2 2
	The Ivy Victoria	"	2 3 4

	Thomas Cubitt	"	2	2	3
	Colbert	French	2	2	3
	La Poule au Pot	"	2	2	5
	Motcombs	International	2	2	4
	Il Convivio	Italian	3	3	3
	Signor Sassi	"	3	3	3
	Ottolenghi	Mediterranean	4	3	3
	Ibérica, Zig Zag Building	Spanish	3	2	2
	Burger & Lobster	Burgers, etc	3	2	2
	A Wong	Chinese	5	5	3
	Ken Lo's Memories	"	2	2	2
	Salloos	Pakistani	3	3	3
£50+	Granger & Co	Australian	2	2	2
	The Jones Family Kitchen	British, Modern	4	3	4
	The Orange	"	2	2	3
	Gustoso	Italian	3	3	3
	Tozi	"	3	3	3
	Wulf & Lamb	Vegetarian	3	3	2
	Seafresh	Fish & chips	3	2	2
	Kazan (Café)	Turkish	3	3	2
£40+	Grumbles	International	3	3	3
	Goya	Spanish	3	2	3
	Pizza Pilgrims	Pizza	3	3	3
	Morena	South American	–	–	–
	Cyprus Mangal	Turkish	3	2	2
	Bone Daddies, Nova	Japanese	3	3	3
	Kanada-Ya	"	5	2	2
	Sri Suwoon	Thai	3	4	3
£35+	The Vincent Rooms	British, Modern	3	3	2
	Hankies Haymarket	Indian	4	2	2
£30+	Ganymede	British, Modern	–	–	–
£25+	Sachi at Pantechnicon	Japanese	–	–	–
£20+	Bleecker Burger	Burgers, etc	4	2	1
£15+	Regency Cafe	British, Traditional	3	3	5

WEST

Chelsea, South Kensington, Kensington, Earl's Court & Fulham (SW3, SW5, SW6, SW7, SW10 & W8)

£170+	Gordon Ramsay	*French*	3	3	2
£160+	The Five Fields	*British, Modern*	5	5	4
£140+	Bibendum	*French*	4	3	4
£100+	No. Fifty Cheyne	*British, Modern*	3	3	4
	Wild Tavern	*Italian*	2	3	3
	Yashin Ocean House	*Japanese*	3	2	3
£90+	Clarke's	*British, Modern*	5	4	4
	Elystan Street	"	4	4	3
	Launceston Place	"	4	4	4
	Medlar	"	3	4	3
	Chucs	*Italian*	2	3	4
	Lucio	"	3	2	2
	Scalini	"	3	3	3
	Hawksmoor Knightsbridge	*Steaks & grills*	3	3	2
	Min Jiang	*Chinese*	4	3	5
£80+	Bluebird	*British, Modern*	2	3	4
	Kitchen W8	"	4	3	2
	28-50 Chelsea	"	3	3	2
	Restaurant at The Capital	*British, Traditional*	–	–	–
	Bibendum Oyster Bar	*Fish & seafood*	3	4	4
	Le Colombier	*French*	3	3	3
	Daphne's	*Italian*	2	2	3
	Manicomio Chelsea	"	2	2	3
	Hot May Pot Pot	*Chinese*	–	–	–
	Bombay Brasserie	*Indian*	3	3	2
	Dinings	*Japanese*	5	3	2
	Koji	"	3	3	4
	Zuma	"	4	3	4
£70+	The Abingdon	*British, Modern*	3	3	4
	Harwood Arms	"	4	3	3
	The Sea, The Sea	*Fish & seafood*	3	3	4
	Wright Brothers	"	3	2	3
	Mazi	*Greek*	3	3	4
	Myrtle	*Irish*	5	4	3
	La Famiglia	*Italian*	2	2	3
	Il Portico	"	3	4	3
	Cambio de Tercio	*Spanish*	4	4	4
	Chicama	*Peruvian*	3	2	3
	Akira at Japan House	*Japanese*	3	3	3
	Chisou	"	3	2	2
	Sticks'n'Sushi	"	4	3	3

£60+					
Big Easy	American		3	2	3
Brinkley's	British, Modern		2	2	3
Brook House	"		3	2	3
The Builders Arms	"		3	3	3
Daylesford Organic	"		2	2	2
The Enterprise	"		2	3	4
The Ivy Chelsea Garden	"		2	3	4
Rabbit	"		3	2	3
The Shed	"		–	–	–
Suzi Tros	Greek		3	3	3
Frantoio	Italian		3	4	4
Pino	"		4	4	3
Ziani's	"		2	2	4
Maroush	Lebanese		3	2	2
Good Earth	Chinese		3	3	2
Romulo Café	Filipino		3	4	3
Kutir	Indian		4	4	4
Zaika of Kensington	"		3	3	3
Zheng	Malaysian		3	2	2
Huo	Pan-Asian		2	3	4
The Ivy Asia	"		2	4	3
Patara South Kensington	Thai		3	3	2

£50+					
The Cadogan Arms	British, Modern		–	–	–
FENN	"		5	4	3
The Fox and Pheasant	"		3	3	4
The Hunter's Moon	"		3	4	4
Manuka Kitchen	"		3	2	3
Megan's	"		2	3	3
VQ	"		2	3	3
Maggie Jones's	British, Traditional		2	2	4
The Admiral Codrington	International		3	3	4
Jolie	"		–	–	–
Chelsea Cellar	Italian		4	4	4
Made in Italy	"		3	2	2
Riccardo's	"		3	2	3
San Pietro	"		3	3	3
The Atlas	Mediterranean		4	3	4
Pascor	"		–	–	–
Daquise	Polish		3	3	3
Ognisko Restaurant	"		3	3	5
Tapas Brindisa	Spanish		3	2	3
Tendido Cero	"		4	3	4
Macellaio RC	Steaks & grills		4	3	3
Royal China	Chinese		3	1	2
Flora Indica	Indian		4	3	4
Malabar	"		–	–	–
Noor Jahan	"		3	3	2
Tandoor Chop House	"		4	3	3
Oka	Japanese		3	2	2
Sukho Fine Thai Cuisine	Thai		5	5	3

£40+					
Churchill Arms	British, Traditional		3	3	4
Los Mochis	Fusion		–	–	–
Mona Lisa	International		2	3	2
Aglio e Olio	Italian		3	3	2

	Da Mario	"	3 3 4
	L'Artigiano	"	– – –
	Haché	Steaks & grills	3 2 2
	Rocca	Pizza	2 2 3
	Santa Maria	"	4 3 3
	Best Mangal	Turkish	3 4 2
	Dishoom	Indian	3 4 5
	Pure Indian Cooking	"	3 4 3
	Thali	"	4 3 3
	Bone Daddies, Whole Foods	Japanese	3 3 3
	Mien Tay	Vietnamese	3 3 3
£35+	Ceru	Middle Eastern	4 4 4
	Addie's Thai Café	Thai	4 2 2
	Phat Phuc	Vietnamese	3 2 2
£25+	Vardo	International	3 3 5
	Big Fernand	Burgers, etc	– – –
£20+	Stick & Bowl	Chinese	3 4 2
	Talad	Thai	– – –

Notting Hill, Holland Park, Bayswater, North Kensington & Maida Vale (W2, W9, W10, W11)

£170+	The Ledbury	British, Modern	– – –
£130+	Core by Clare Smyth	British, Modern	5 5 4
£90+	Julie's	British, Modern	2 2 4
	104 Restaurant	"	4 4 3
	Chucs Westbourne Grove	Italian	2 3 4
£80+	Caractère	Mediterranean	4 4 3
£70+	Six Portland Road	British, Modern	4 4 2
	London Shell Co.	Fish & seafood	3 3 4
	Assaggi	Italian	3 4 3
	Osteria Basilico	"	3 3 3
	Portobello Ristorante	"	3 3 5
	E&O	Pan-Asian	3 3 3
£60+	Sunday in Brooklyn	American	– – –
	Daylesford Organic	British, Modern	2 2 2
	Gold	"	2 2 4
	The Hero of Maida	"	3 3 3
	The Ladbroke Arms	"	3 2 3
	7 Saints	"	4 4 4
	The Summerhouse	Fish & seafood	3 3 5
	The Cow	Irish	3 3 3
	Edera	Italian	3 3 3
	Mediterraneo	"	3 2 3
	The Oak W2	"	3 2 3
	Ottolenghi	Mediterranean	4 3 3

			Rating		
	Farmacy	*Vegetarian*	4	4	4
	Pizza East Portobello	*Pizza*	4	3	4
	Maroush	*Lebanese*	3	2	2
	Bombay Palace	*Indian*	5	4	3
	Flat Three	*Japanese*	4	3	3
	Uli	*Pan-Asian*	2	3	3
£50+	Granger & Co	*Australian*	2	2	2
	Fiend	*British, Modern*	–	–	–
	The Frontline Club	*"*	3	3	4
	Hereford Road	*British, Traditional*	4	4	3
	Orasay	*Scottish*	5	4	4
	Four Seasons	*Chinese*	4	1	1
	Mandarin Kitchen	*"*	4	3	2
	Pearl Liang	*"*	3	3	2
	Noor Jahan	*Indian*	3	3	2
	Maguro	*Japanese*	4	4	2
	Sushi Marasaki	*"*	5	4	2
£40+	Bertie Blossoms	*British, Modern*	–	–	–
	MEATliquor	*Burgers, etc*	4	2	3
	Buvette	*French*	3	3	4
	Taqueria	*Mexican/TexMex*	3	2	3
	Cha Cha x Sister Jane	*South American*	–	–	–
	Gold Mine	*Chinese*	3	2	2
	Durbar	*Indian*	3	2	2
	Tonkotsu	*Japanese*	4	3	2
£35+	Hankies	*Sri Lankan*	4	2	2
	Tab X Tab	*International*	5	4	4
	Ceru	*Middle Eastern*	4	4	4
	Eat Tokyo	*Japanese*	3	2	2
£30+	Ayllu	*Fusion*	–	–	–
	Patty and Bun	*Burgers, etc*	4	3	3
	Sumi	*Japanese*	4	4	3
£25+	Tavernaki	*Greek*	–	–	–
	Fez Mangal	*Turkish*	5	4	3
£20+	The Cheese Barge	*British, Traditional*	2	3	3
£15+	Normah's	*Malaysian*	4	3	2

Hammersmith, Shepherd's Bush, Olympia, Chiswick, Brentford & Ealing (W4, W5, W6, W12, W13, W14, TW8)

£270+	Endo at Rotunda	*Japanese*	5	5	5
£110+	The River Café	*Italian*	3	3	3
£90+	La Trompette	*French*	4	4	3

£70+			
Sams Riverside	British, Modern		4 4 5
Michael Nadra	French		4 4 2
Le Vacherin	"		3 3 3
Villa Di Geggiano	Italian		3 3 4

£60+			
The Anglesea Arms	British, Modern		4 4 4
City Barge	"		3 3 3
The Duke of Sussex	"		2 2 3
High Road Brasserie	"		1 2 2
The Silver Birch	"		3 4 3
Vinoteca	"		2 2 2
Annie's	International		3 3 4
The Oak W12	Italian		3 2 3
Pentolina	"		4 4 4
The Carpenter's Arms	Mediterranean		3 3 3
Shikumen, Dorsett Hotel	Chinese		5 3 3

£50+			
Brackenbury Wine Rooms	British, Modern		2 3 3
The Crabtree	"		3 3 4
The Dartmouth Castle	"		3 4 4
The Havelock Tavern	"		3 2 3
Megan's… Flower Market	"		2 3 3
The Roebuck	"		3 2 3
The Hampshire Hog	British, Traditional		3 3 3
Albertine	French		3 3 5
Le Petit Citron	"		3 4 4
The Andover Arms	International		2 3 4
L'Amorosa	Italian		4 4 3
Cibo	"		4 4 3
Pastaio	"		3 3 3
Tarantella Ristorante Pizzeria	"		3 4 3
The Swan	Mediterranean		3 3 3
The Gate	Vegetarian		4 2 2
Indian Zing	Indian		4 3 2
Kiraku	Japanese		4 3 3

£40+			
The Prince of Wales	British, Modern		– – –
The Princess Victoria	"		3 3 4
Soane's Kitchen	"		2 2 4
Homeslice	Pizza		3 2 3
Oro Di Napoli	"		3 4 2
Pizza Pilgrims	"		3 3 3
Santa Maria	"		4 3 3
Zia Lucia	"		4 3 3
Angie's Little Food Shop	Sandwiches, cakes, etc		3 2 2
222 Veggie Vegan	Vegan		3 3 2
Best Mangal	Turkish		3 4 2
North China	Chinese		4 3 3
Bindas Eatery	Indian		– – –
Patri	"		3 4 3
Potli	"		3 4 3
Republic	"		– – –
Kanada-Ya	Japanese		5 2 2
Tonkotsu	"		4 3 2
Hare & Tortoise	Pan-Asian		3 3 2
101 Thai Kitchen	Thai		3 1 2

£35+	Base Face Pizza	Pizza	3 3 3
	Prairie Fire	BBQ	– – –
	Adams Café	Moroccan	3 4 3
	Abu Zaad	Syrian	3 3 3
	Copper Chimney	Indian	– – –
	Sagar	"	3 2 2
	Shilpa	Indian, Southern	4 3 1
	Eat Tokyo	Japanese	3 2 2
	Sushi Bar Makoto	"	4 3 1
£30+	The Hawk's Nest	Pizza	3 3 4
	The Phoenix	"	– – –
£25+	Rhythm & Brews	Sandwiches, cakes, etc	3 4 5
	Tamp Coffee	"	3 3 4
	Poppy's Thai Eatery	Thai	3 2 4
£20+	Vergine Maria	Vegan	– – –
	Bleecker Burger	Burgers, etc	4 2 1
	Ngon	Vietnamese	4 2 2
£5+	Bears Ice Cream	Ice cream	3 3 2

Hampstead, West Hampstead, St John's Wood, Regent's Park, Kilburn & Camden Town (NW postcodes)

Price	Name	Cuisine	Ratings
£160+	PLU	*French*	5 4 4
£90+	The Landmark	*British, Modern*	2 3 5
£80+	L'Aventure	*French*	3 4 4
	Wildflower	*Irish*	4 3 3
	Lume	*Italian*	3 4 3
	Tish	*Kosher*	3 4 4
£70+	Odette's	*British, Modern*	3 3 3
	Searcys St Pancras Grand	*"*	2 3 3
	Holly Bush	*British, Traditional*	2 2 3
	Michael Nadra	*French*	4 4 2
	Oslo Court	*"*	3 4 4
	Bull & Last	*International*	3 3 3
	La Collina	*Italian*	3 2 3
	Kaifeng	*Chinese*	3 3 2
£60+	Bradley's	*British, Modern*	2 2 2
	The Clifton	*"*	3 3 3
	Ham	*"*	3 3 2
	The Ivy Café	*"*	1 2 3
	The Wells Tavern	*"*	3 3 4
	York & Albany	*British, Traditional*	2 2 2
	Soutine	*International*	2 3 3
	Morso	*Italian*	3 3 3
	The Rising Sun	*"*	3 3 3
	Villa Bianca	*"*	2 2 2
	Cinder	*BBQ*	3 2 2
	Maroush Park Royal	*Lebanese*	3 2 2
	Delicatessen	*Middle Eastern*	3 2 2
	Skewd Kitchen	*Turkish*	4 3 3
	Good Earth	*Chinese*	3 3 2
	Phoenix Palace	*"*	3 2 2
	Patara	*Thai*	3 3 2
£50+	Parlour Kensal	*British, Modern*	4 3 4
	The Wet Fish Café	*"*	4 4 4
	The Farrier	*British, Traditional*	– – –
	Lemonia	*Greek*	1 3 3
	Anima e Cuore	*Italian*	5 3 2
	28 Church Row	*Spanish*	4 4 4
	The Gate	*Vegetarian*	4 2 2
	Mildreds	*"*	3 3 3
	Poppies Camden	*Fish & chips*	3 3 2
	The Sea Shell	*"*	4 3 2
	L'Antica Pizzeria da Michele	*Pizza*	4 3 4
	Crocker's Folly	*Lebanese*	4 4 4
	Bonoo	*Indian*	4 4 3

	Jin Kichi	*Japanese*	5	4	3
	Oka	"	3	2	2
	Singapore Garden	*Malaysian*	4	2	2
	Bang Bang Oriental	*Pan-Asian*	2	2	2
£40+	Lure	*Fish & seafood*	3	3	2
	Authentique Epicerie & Bar	*French*	3	3	3
	Greenberry Café	*Fusion*	3	4	4
	L'Artista	*Italian*	2	4	3
	Giacomo's	"	3	3	2
	Quartieri	"	4	3	3
	Haché	*Steaks & grills*	3	2	2
	Nautilus	*Fish & chips*	3	3	2
	East West	*Pizza*	–	–	–
	Pizza Pilgrims Academy	"	3	3	3
	Sacro Cuore	"	5	3	2
	Zia Lucia	"	4	3	3
	Chameleon	*Israeli*	–	–	–
	Saravanaa Bhavan	*Indian*	3	3	1
	Vijay	"	3	4	1
	Atari-Ya	*Japanese*	3	3	2
	Sushi Masa	"	3	3	2
£35+	Rudy's Vegan Diner	*Vegan*	3	3	2
	Philippe Conticini	*French*	–	–	–
	Paradise Hampstead	*Indian*	3	5	3
	Ravi Shankar	"	3	2	2
	Asakusa	*Japanese*	4	3	2
	Eat Tokyo G2 (Shabu-Shabu)	"	3	2	2
£30+	Ali Baba	*Egyptian*	3	2	2
	Diwana Bhel-Poori House	*Indian*	4	2	2
	Sakonis	"	3	2	1
	Anjanaas	*Indian, Southern*	3	3	2
£25+	At Feast	*British, Modern*	–	–	–
	Sam's Café	*British, Traditional*	3	3	3
	Balady	*Middle Eastern*	3	2	2
	Roti King	*Malaysian*	5	3	2
£20+	Icco Pizza	*Pizza*	4	3	2
	E Mono	*Turkish*	4	3	2
	Chutneys	*Indian*	3	3	2
£10+	Ginger & White Hampstead	*Sandwiches, cakes, etc*	3	2	4

Hoxton, Islington, Highgate, Crouch End, Stoke Newington, Finsbury Park, Muswell Hill & Finchley (N postcodes)

£130+	Hot Stone	*Japanese*	4	4	4
£70+	Perilla	*British, Modern*	4	4	3
	Radici	*Italian*	2	2	2

280   FSA Ratings: from **1** (Poor) to **5** (Exceptional)

	Trullo	"		3 3 3
	Coal Office	Mediterranean		4 4 4
	Parrillan	Spanish		3 3 4
	Tomahawk Steakhouse	Steaks & grills		– – –
	Casa Pastór & Plaza Pastór	Mexican/TexMex		3 2 3
£60+	The Bull	British, Modern		2 3 3
	Caravan King's Cross	"		2 2 2
	The Drapers Arms	"		3 3 4
	Frederick's	"		3 3 4
	Hicce	"		2 2 3
	Humble Grape	"		3 4 3
	Jolene	"		3 2 3
	Pig & Butcher	"		3 3 3
	Rotunda	"		2 2 3
	Top Cuvee	"		3 4 3
	Westerns Laundry	"		3 4 2
	St Johns	British, Traditional		3 3 5
	Prawn on the Lawn	Fish & seafood		5 3 2
	German Gymnasium	German		2 2 3
	The Nook	International		– – –
	Terra Rossa	Italian		3 3 3
	Ottolenghi	Mediterranean		4 3 3
	Vinoteca	"		2 2 2
	Barrafina	Spanish		4 4 5
	Smokehouse Islington	Steaks & grills		4 4 3
£50+	Granger & Co	Australian		2 2 2
	The Lighterman	British, Modern		2 2 3
	Megan's at the Sorting Office	"		2 3 3
	The Red Lion & Sun	"		3 3 4
	12:51 by chef James Cochran	"		4 3 3
	Kipferl	East & Cent. European		3 3 3
	Lyon's	Fish & seafood		4 4 3
	Bellanger	French		3 4 5
	Table Du Marche	"		3 3 2
	Banners	International		2 3 3
	The Flask	"		3 3 4
	La Fromagerie	"		3 3 3
	FKABAM (Black Axe Mangal)	"		4 3 3
	Primeur	"		3 4 3
	500	Italian		3 4 3
	Il Guscio	"		3 3 3
	Osteria Tufo	"		4 4 2
	Bar Esteban	Spanish		3 3 3
	Camino King's Cross	"		3 3 2
	Vermuteria	"		– – –
	Mildreds	Vegetarian		3 3 3
	Toff's	Fish & chips		3 3 2
	Fink's Salt and Sweet	Sandwiches, cakes, etc		3 4 3
	Arabica KX	Middle Eastern		3 3 2
	Yipin China	Chinese		4 2 1
	Hoppers	Indian		3 2 3
	Zaffrani	"		3 2 2
	Sushi on Jones	Japanese		– – –
	Supawan	Thai		4 4 3

£40+					
	Breakfast Club Angel	American	3	3	3
	Chriskitch	British, Modern	4	3	3
	Granary Square Brasserie	"	2	2	3
	Le Sacré-Coeur	French	3	4	3
	Vrisaki	Greek	3	3	2
	Frank's Canteen	International	3	4	3
	Lina Stores	Italian	4	3	3
	Via Emilia	"	3	2	2
	Cut + Grind	Burgers, etc	3	3	3
	MEATLiquor Islington	"	4	2	3
	Sacro Cuore	Pizza	5	3	2
	Sweet Thursday	"	3	2	2
	Yard Sale Pizza	"	3	2	2
	Zia Lucia & Berto	"	4	3	3
	Chick 'n' Sours	Chicken	3	3	3
	Plaquemine Lock	Cajun/creole	3	3	3
	Gallipoli	Turkish	2	3	3
	Gem	"	3	4	2
	Sumak	"	3	4	2
	Kaki	Chinese	3	2	2
	Xi'an Impression	"	4	2	1
	Dishoom	Indian	3	4	5
	Rasa	Indian, Southern	4	3	3
	Kanada-Ya	Japanese	5	2	2
	Sambal Shiok	Malaysian	4	3	3
	Farang	Thai	4	3	3
	Mien Tay	Vietnamese	3	3	3
	Cafe Bao	Taiwanese	3	4	4
£35+	Rudy's Vegan Diner	Vegan	3	3	2
	The Clock N8	British, Modern	–	–	–
	Two Brothers	Fish & seafood	3	2	2
	Le Mercury	French	2	2	3
	Turul Project	Hungarian	3	4	2
	Pizzeria Pappagone	Italian	3	4	3
	Flat Iron	Steaks & grills	3	4	4
	Olympus Fish	Fish & chips	3	4	2
	Indian Rasoi	Indian	3	2	2
	Jashan	"	3	4	2
£30+	The Clarence Tavern	British, Modern	–	–	–
	Sunday	"	4	3	3
	Jiji	Fusion	–	–	–
	Skal Nordic Dining	Scandinavian	4	4	3
	Chuku's	West African	–	–	–
	Afghan Kitchen	Afghani	3	3	2
	Delhi Grill	Indian	3	3	2
	Shahi Pakwaan	"	4	4	2
	Bund	Pan-Asian	–	–	–
	Viet Garden	Vietnamese	3	3	2
£25+	Big Jo Bakery	British, Modern	–	–	–
	The Duke of York	"	–	–	–
	Sushi Show	Japanese	4	3	2

£20+	The Dusty Knuckle	*Sandwiches, cakes, etc*	🄸 2 2
£15+	Trawlerman's Fish Bar	*Fish & chips*	– – –

SOUTH

South Bank (SE1)

£190+	Story	British, Modern	4 4 3
£120+	Oblix	British, Modern	2 1 3
	Hannah	Japanese	4 3 2
£110+	Aqua Shard	British, Modern	2 2 4
£100+	TING	British, Modern	2 3 4
	Trivet	"	4 3 3
	Turnips	International	4 3 4
	Hutong, The Shard	Chinese	2 2 5
£90+	Oxo Tower, Restaurant	British, Modern	1 1 1
	Le Pont de la Tour	French	2 2 2
	Sollip	"	5 4 3
	Hawksmoor	Steaks & grills	3 3 2
£80+	Oxo Tower, Brasserie	British, Modern	1 1 3
	Butlers Wharf Chop House	British, Traditional	2 2 4
	Seabird	Fish & seafood	4 3 5
	La Barca	Italian	3 3 3
	Andanza	Spanish	– – –
£70+	Sea Containers	British, Modern	3 3 4
	Skylon, South Bank Centre	"	2 2 3
	The Swan at the Globe	"	3 3 4
	Roast	British, Traditional	2 2 4
	Applebee's Fish	Fish & seafood	3 3 2
	fish!	"	4 3 3
	Wright Brothers	"	3 2 3
	Cafe Murano	Italian	2 3 2
	The Coal Shed	Steaks & grills	3 3 3
	Santo Remedio	Mexican/TexMex	3 3 2
	Mei Mei	Malaysian	5 3 2
£60+	Caravan Bankside	British, Modern	2 2 2
	Elliot's	"	3 3 4
	Flor	"	5 4 4
	The Garrison	"	3 2 3
	House, National Theatre	"	2 2 2
	The Ivy Tower Bridge	"	2 3 4
	Casse-Croute	French	4 4 3
	Borough Market Kitchen	International	– – –
	Vivat Bacchus	"	3 3 3
	Pizarro	Spanish	3 3 3
	Tapas Brindisa	"	3 3 3
	Pique Nique	Chicken	4 3 3
	Antillean	Afro-Caribbean	– – –
	Rabot 1745	"	2 2 3
	Bala Baya	Middle Eastern	3 2 2

£50+	The Anchor & Hope	British, Modern	3 4 3
	40 Maltby Street	"	3 3 4
	Garden Museum, Café	"	3 2 3
	Lupins	"	4 2 2
	Tate Modern, L6	"	2 2 4
	BOB's Lobster	Fish & seafood	3 4 3
	Macellaio RC	Italian	4 3 3
	José	Spanish	5 3 5
	LOBOS Meat & Tapas	"	3 2 2
	O'ver	Pizza	3 3 3
	Paladar	South American	4 4 4
	Arabica Bar and Kitchen	Lebanese	3 3 2
	Gunpowder	Indian	4 3 3
	Sticky Mango at RSJ	Pan-Asian	2 2 2
£40+	Baccala	Fish & seafood	3 4 3
	Legare	Italian	4 4 3
	Tavolino	"	3 4 4
	Bar Douro	Portuguese	4 4 4
	Casa do Frango	"	4 3 4
	Mar I Terra	Spanish	3 4 3
	Meson don Felipe	"	3 3 3
	El Pastór	Mexican/TexMex	3 3 4
	Tonkotsu Bankside	Japanese	4 3 2
	Bao Borough	Taiwanese	3 4 4
£35+	Flat Iron	Steaks & grills	3 4 4
	Masters Super Fish	Fish & chips	3 2 2
	Erev	Israeli	– – –
	Tas Pide	Turkish	3 3 3
£30+	Padella	Italian	5 4 3
	Patty and Bun	Burgers, etc	4 3 3
	Slice	Pizza	– – –
	Baozi Inn	Chinese	3 3 3
£25+	Mercato Metropolitano	Italian	3 3 4
£20+	Bermondsey Larder	British, Modern	3 4 3
£5+	Monmouth Coffee Company	Sandwiches, cakes, etc	3 4 4

Greenwich, Lewisham, Dulwich & Blackheath
(All SE postcodes, except SE1)

£80+	Copper & Ink	British, Modern	5 4 3
£70+	Peckham Cellars	British, Modern	4 5 3
	Sticks'n'Sushi	Japanese	4 3 3
£60+	Bobo Social	British, Modern	– – –
	Llewelyn's	"	3 3 2
	Terroirs	"	– – –
	Toulouse Lautrec	French	3 4 3

	Coal Rooms	Steaks & grills	4	4	4
	Yama Momo	Japanese	3	2	2
£50+	The Alma	British, Modern	3	2	4
	The Camberwell Arms	"	4	3	3
	The Crooked Well	"	3	3	3
	The Guildford Arms	"	3	4	3
	Levan	"	5	3	3
	Louie Louie	"	3	3	3
	The Rosendale	"	3	3	3
	Sparrow	"	4	4	3
	Peckham Bazaar	Greek	4	3	3
	Joanna's	International	3	4	4
	The Yellow House	"	3	4	3
	Con Gusto	Italian	3	4	4
	Luciano's	"	4	4	3
	Le Querce	"	5	4	3
	Dulwich Lyceum	Mediterranean	–	–	–
	Kudu	South African	5	4	4
	Babur	Indian	5	4	3
	Heritage	"	4	3	3
	Kennington Tandoori	"	3	4	3
	The Begging Bowl	Thai	3	3	3
£40+	Peachy Goat	Vegan	3	3	3
	Tila	British, Modern	–	–	–
	Brookmill	International	3	3	3
	Artusi	Italian	4	3	3
	Forza Wine	"	3	4	4
	Marcella	"	3	4	3
	Naifs	Vegetarian	–	–	–
	MEATliquor ED	Burgers, etc	4	2	3
	Mamma Dough	Pizza	4	3	2
	Mike's Peckham	"	4	3	3
	Rocca	"	2	2	3
	Theo's	"	3	3	2
	Yard Sale Pizza	"	3	2	2
	Zeret	Ethiopian	4	4	3
	Kudu Grill	South African	–	–	–
	FM Mangal	Turkish	3	3	2
	Dragon Castle	Chinese	3	3	3
	Everest Inn	Indian	3	2	2
	Ganapati	"	4	3	3
	Bone Daddies	Japanese	3	3	3
	Tonkotsu	"	4	3	2
	Bánh Bánh	Vietnamese	3	3	2
£35+	Olley's	Fish & chips	3	4	3
	500 Degrees	Pizza	4	3	2
	Taro	Japanese	3	2	2
£30+	Larry's	American	3	3	3
	400 Rabbits at The Lido	British, Modern	3	3	3
	400 Rabbits	Pizza	3	3	3
	Zaibatsu	Japanese	4	3	2
	Mr Bao	Taiwanese	4	3	3

£25+	The Perry Hill	British, Modern	3 2 4
	Bando Belly	International	– – –
	Silk Road	Chinese	5 2 2
	Paranhodu	Korean	3 3 3
£20+	Goddards At Greenwich	British, Traditional	3 4 3
	Mama's Jerk	Afro-Caribbean	4 3 2
£10+	Kappacasein	Sandwiches, cakes, etc	4 3 3
	La Chingada	Mexican/TexMex	5 4 3

Battersea, Brixton, Clapham, Wandsworth Barnes, Putney & Wimbledon (All SW postcodes south of the river)

£100+	Trinity	British, Modern	5 5 4
£90+	Chez Bruce	British, Modern	5 4 3
£80+	Rick Stein	Fish & seafood	2 2 4
£70+	Black Radish	British, Modern	4 5 3
	Hatched	"	5 3 3
	Only Food and Courses	"	– – –
	Salon Brixton	"	4 4 3
	Sinabro	"	4 3 3
	Wright Brothers	Fish & seafood	3 2 3
	Darby's	Irish	3 3 4
	Fiume	Italian	3 2 4
	Knife	Steaks & grills	4 4 3
	Sticks'n'Sushi	Japanese	4 3 3
£60+	Bistro Union	British, Modern	3 2 3
	The Brown Dog	"	3 2 3
	Brunswick House Café	"	3 2 5
	Church Road	"	4 4 3
	Humble Grape	"	3 4 3
	The Ivy Café	"	1 2 3
	Nutbourne	"	2 2 2
	The Oak SW11	"	3 2 3
	Trinity Upstairs	"	4 3 4
	Soif	French	3 3 3
	The White Onion	"	3 3 2
	Brinkley's Kitchen	International	3 3 3
	Osteria Antica Bologna	Italian	4 3 3
	Riva	"	3 4 2
	Sorella	"	4 3 3
	Lusitania	Portuguese	3 3 2
	Good Earth	Chinese	3 3 2
	Cinnamon Kitchen Battersea	Indian	3 2 2
	Kibou London	Japanese	3 4 3
	Patara	Thai	3 3 2

£50+				
	The Abbeville	British, Modern	3	3	3
	Hood	"	4 3 3
	Megan's at the Power Station	"	2 3 3
	Olympic, Olympic Studios	"	2 2 3
	The Plough	"	2 2 4
	Rose & Crown	"	2 3 3
	The Telegraph	"	3 3 4
	24 The Oval	"	3 4 3
	The Victoria	"	2 2 3
	Canton Arms	British, Traditional	4 3 3
	Fox & Grapes	"	3 2 2
	Augustine Kitchen	French	4 4 3
	Gazette	"	2 3 3
	St Clair	Fusion	– – –
	The Light House	International	3 3 3
	Cent Anni	Italian	3 3 3
	Made in Italy	"	3 2 2
	Maremma	"	4 4 4
	Pizza Metro	"	3 3 3
	Stockwell Continental	"	3 4 3
	Bellefields	Mediterranean	– – –
	Boqueria	Spanish	3 3 3
	Macellaio RC	Steaks & grills	4 3 3
	Naughty Piglets	"	4 4 4
	Dynamo	Pizza	3 3 3
	Santa Maria del Sur	Argentinian	3 3 3
	Oka	Japanese	3 2 2
	Takahashi	"	5 5 3
	Tsunami	"	4 3 3

£40+				
	London Stock	British, Modern	– – –
	Smoke & Salt	British, Traditional	5 4 4
	Numero Uno	Italian	3 2 3
	Little Taperia	Spanish	3 3 3
	Haché	Burgers, etc	3 2 2
	MEATliquor	"	4 2 3
	Mamma Dough	Pizza	4 3 2
	Pizza da Valter	"	3 3 3
	Yard Sale Pizza	"	3 2 2
	Zia Lucia	"	4 3 3
	Chishuru	West African	4 4 3
	Kashmir	Indian	3 3 2
	Ma Goa	"	3 3 3
	Hashi	Japanese	3 4 2
	Nanban	"	4 2 2
	Tomoe	"	4 2 2
	Tonkotsu Battersea	"	4 3 2
	Hare & Tortoise	Pan-Asian	3 3 2
	Bánh Bánh	Vietnamese	3 3 2
	Mien Tay	"	3 3 3

£35+				
	Dip & Flip	Burgers, etc	3 2 2
	Dirty Burger	"	3 2 2
	Orange Pekoe	Sandwiches, cakes, etc	3 3 4
	Chicken Shop	Chicken	3 2 2
	Meza Trinity Road	Lebanese	3 2 3

	BabaBoom	*Middle Eastern*	3 3 2
	Indian Moment	*Indian*	3 3 2
	Taro	*Japanese*	3 2 2
	Awesome Thai	*Thai*	3 3 2
£30+	Amrutha	*Vegan*	4 5 2
	Nue Ground	*British, Modern*	– – –
	Unwined	*Mediterranean*	3 4 4
	Munal Tandoori	*Indian*	4 4 2
	Sushi Revolution	*Japanese*	—
	Daddy Bao	*Taiwanese*	4 3 3
£25+	Indian Ocean	*Indian*	3 3 3
	Mirch Masala	*Pakistani*	4 2 2
	Kaosarn	*Thai*	4 3 3
£20+	Jaffna House	*Sri Lankan*	4 2 2
	Dropshot Coffee	*British, Modern*	3 4 4
	Bravi Ragazzi	*Pizza*	5 2 2
	Party Store Pizza	*"*	– – –
£15+	Joe Public	*Pizza*	3 3 2
	Milk	*Sandwiches, cakes, etc*	3 2 3
	Other Side Fried	*Chicken*	– – –
	Indian Room	*Indian*	4 3 3
£10+	Black Bear Burger	*Burgers, etc*	5 3 3

Outer western suburbs
Kew, Richmond, Twickenham, Teddington

£90+	The Glasshouse	*British, Modern*	4 4 2
£80+	The Dysart Petersham	*British, Modern*	3 3 4
	Petersham Nurseries Cafe	*"*	2 2 5
	M Bar & Grill Twickenham	*Steaks & grills*	3 2 3
£70+	Steven Edwards, Bingham	*British, Modern*	4 3 4
	The Petersham Restaurant	*"*	2 2 4
	The Watermans	*"*	3 3 4
£60+	The Ivy Café	*British, Modern*	1 2 3
	Bacco	*Italian*	3 3 2
£50+	Black Dog Beer House	*British, Modern*	4 3 3
	Petit Ma Cuisine	*French*	3 3 3
	Le Salon Privé	*"*	3 2 3
	A Cena	*Italian*	3 3 3
£40+	The Black Horse	*British, Modern*	3 3 3
	Dastaan	*Indian*	5 5 3
	Matsuba	*Japanese*	4 3 2

| £35+ | Rye by the Water | *British, Modern* | 3 2 3 |
| £25+ | Kiss the Hippo | *Sandwiches, cakes, etc* | 3 3 3 |

EAST

Smithfield & Farringdon (EC1)

£180+	The Clove Club	*British, Modern*	5 4 4
£130+	Club Gascon	*French*	4 3 3
£110+	The Drunken Butler	*French*	4 4 4
£100+	Sushi Tetsu	*Japanese*	5 4 4
£90+	Luca	*Italian*	4 3 4
£80+	Anglo	*British, Modern*	5 3 2
	The Quality Chop House	*British, Traditional*	3 5 4
£70+	St John Smithfield	*British, Traditional*	5 4 4
	Daffodil Mulligan	*Irish*	3 4 3
	Moro	*Spanish*	4 3 3
	Smiths of Smithfield	*Steaks & grills*	3 3 4
£60+	Caravan	*British, Modern*	2 2 2
	The Coach	"	2 2 2
	The Jugged Hare	"	3 2 3
	Vinoteca	"	2 2 2
	Bleeding Heart Bistro	*French*	3 3 5
	Comptoir Gascon	"	3 2 3
	Apulia	*Italian*	2 2 2
	Palatino	"	4 3 2
	Ibérica	*Spanish*	3 2 2
	Burger & Lobster	*Burgers, etc*	3 2 2
	Ceviche Old St	*Peruvian*	4 3 4
£50+	Granger & Co	*Australian*	2 2 2
	Sessions Arts Club	*British, Modern*	– – –
	Café du Marché	*French*	3 3 5
	Macellaio RC	*Italian*	4 3 3
	Santore	"	3 2 2
	The Eagle	*Mediterranean*	4 2 4
	Fare	"	3 3 3
	Morito	*Spanish*	3 3 4
	The Gate	*Vegetarian*	4 2 2
	Le Bab	*Middle Eastern*	4 2 3
	Berber & Q Shawarma Bar	"	4 3 4
	The Sichuan	*Chinese*	4 3 2
	Pham Sushi	*Japanese*	4 3 3
£40+	Bleeding Heart Tavern	*British, Modern*	3 3 3
	Trattoria Brutto	*Italian*	– – –
	Homeslice	*Pizza*	3 2 3
	Pizza Pilgrims	"	3 3 3
	Stem & Glory	*Vegan*	3 2 2
	Breddos Tacos	*Mexican/TexMex*	3 2 2
	Bone Daddies, The Bower	*Japanese*	3 3 3

291

	On The Bab	Korean	3	2	2
	Cây Tre	Vietnamese	3	3	3
£35+	Fish Central	Fish & seafood	3	3	2
£10+	Prufrock Coffee	Sandwiches, cakes, etc	3	3	3

The City (EC2, EC3, EC4)

£130+	La Dame de Pic London	French	5	4	3
£120+	Nobu Shoreditch	Japanese	–	–	–
£100+	City Social	British, Modern	3	3	3
	Angler, South Place Hotel	Fish & seafood	4	3	3
	Lutyens Grill, The Ned	Steaks & grills	3	2	4
£90+	Duck & Waffle	British, Modern	2	2	3
	Fenchurch Restaurant	"	3	3	4
	Coq d'Argent	French	2	2	3
	Cecconi's, The Ned	International	2	2	4
	Goodman City	Steaks & grills	3	3	2
	Hawksmoor Guildhall	"	3	3	2
	Coya	Peruvian	3	3	4
	Yauatcha City	Chinese	3	2	3
	Sushisamba	Japanese	2	2	3
£80+	14 Hills	British, Modern	3	3	4
	Helix, Gherkin	"	3	3	5
	Sweetings	Fish & seafood	3	3	4
	Manicomio City	Italian	2	2	3
	Boisdale of Bishopsgate	Scottish	3	2	2
	M Threadneedle	Steaks & grills	3	2	3
	Pachamama East	Peruvian	2	2	3
£70+	Bread Street Kitchen	British, Modern	2	2	3
	Darwin Brasserie	"	3	3	5
	Fortnum's Bar & Rest...	"	2	3	3
	Parlour, The Ned	"	–	–	–
	Princess of Shoreditch	"	4	3	3
	Wright Brothers	Fish & seafood	3	2	3
	Cabotte	French	4	5	4
	Bibo by Dani García	Spanish	–	–	–
	Hispania	"	3	4	4
	Santo Remedio	Mexican/TexMex	3	3	2
	Barboun	Turkish	–	–	–
	Oklava	"	4	4	3
£60+	Caravan	British, Modern	2	2	2
	High Timber	"	4	4	3
	Humble Grape	"	3	4	3
	The Ivy City Garden	"	2	3	4
	Leroy	"	3	4	3
	The Mercer	"	3	2	3

	1 Lombard Street	"	2️⃣2️⃣2️⃣
	Vinoteca City	"	2️⃣2️⃣2️⃣
	Paternoster Chop House	British, Traditional	2️⃣2️⃣2️⃣
	Vivat Bacchus	International	3️⃣3️⃣3️⃣
	Caravaggio	Italian	3️⃣2️⃣2️⃣
	Piazza Italiana	"	– – –
	Taberna Etrusca	"	2️⃣3️⃣2️⃣
	José Pizarro	Spanish	3️⃣3️⃣2️⃣
	Aviary	Steaks & grills	2️⃣3️⃣4️⃣
	Burger & Lobster	Burgers, etc	3️⃣2️⃣2️⃣
	Brigadiers	Indian	5️⃣4️⃣4️⃣
	Cinnamon Kitchen	"	3️⃣2️⃣2️⃣
	Mint Leaf Lounge	"	3️⃣3️⃣4️⃣
	The Ivy Asia	Pan-Asian	2️⃣4️⃣3️⃣
	Straits Kitchen	"	– – –
£50+	The Anthologist	British, Modern	2️⃣2️⃣2️⃣
	VQ	"	2️⃣3️⃣3️⃣
	Gloria	Italian	3️⃣3️⃣5️⃣
	Popolo	"	5️⃣4️⃣3️⃣
	Ekte Nordic Kitchen	Scandinavian	3️⃣2️⃣2️⃣
	Camino Shoreditch	Spanish	3️⃣3️⃣2️⃣
	Blacklock	Steaks & grills	4️⃣4️⃣4️⃣
	Relais de Venise L'Entrecôte	"	3️⃣2️⃣2️⃣
	temper City	BBQ	4️⃣3️⃣4️⃣
	Maya	Mexican/TexMex	– – –
	Haz	Turkish	2️⃣3️⃣2️⃣
	Shoryu Ramen	Japanese	3️⃣2️⃣2️⃣
£40+	The Bow Wine Vaults	British, Traditional	3️⃣3️⃣4️⃣
	Simpson's Tavern	"	2️⃣2️⃣4️⃣
	The Wine Library	International	2️⃣2️⃣4️⃣
	Eataly	Italian	3️⃣2️⃣2️⃣
	Rucoletta	"	4️⃣2️⃣2️⃣
	Casa do Frango	Portuguese	4️⃣3️⃣4️⃣
	Haché	Burgers, etc	3️⃣2️⃣2️⃣
	Homeslice	Pizza	3️⃣2️⃣3️⃣
	Pizza Pilgrims	"	3️⃣3️⃣3️⃣
	Ozone Coffee Roasters	Sandwiches, cakes, etc	3️⃣4️⃣4️⃣
	Baraka	Turkish	– – –
	Koya	Japanese	4️⃣4️⃣4️⃣
	Tonkotsu	"	4️⃣3️⃣2️⃣
	On The Bab	Korean	3️⃣2️⃣2️⃣
	Hare & Tortoise	Pan-Asian	3️⃣3️⃣2️⃣
£35+	Epic Pies	British, Traditional	– – –
	Flat Iron	Steaks & grills	3️⃣4️⃣4️⃣
	Taro	Japanese	3️⃣2️⃣2️⃣
£30+	Padella Shoreditch	Italian	5️⃣4️⃣3️⃣
	Patty and Bun	Burgers, etc	4️⃣3️⃣3️⃣
£20+	Bleecker Burger	Burgers, etc	4️⃣2️⃣1️⃣
£15+	Cincinnati Chilibomb	American	– – –
	Halo Burger	Burgers, etc	3️⃣3️⃣2️⃣

East End & Docklands (All E postcodes)

£200+	Māos	*British, Modern*	5	5	4
£170+	Da Terra, Town Hall Hotel	*Fusion*	5	4	4
£110+	The Water House Project	*British, Modern*	4	3	3
£100+	Galvin La Chapelle	*French*	3	4	5
£90+	Brat at Climpson's Arch	*British, Modern*	4	2	2
	Lyle's	"	5	3	2
	Cecconi's Shoreditch	*Italian*	2	2	4
	Goodman	*Steaks & grills*	3	3	2
	Hawksmoor	"	3	3	2
	Roka	*Japanese*	4	3	4
£80+	Bright	*British, Modern*	4	4	3
	Cornerstone	*Fish & seafood*	5	5	4
	The Melusine	"	4	3	3
	Plateau	*French*	2	2	3
	Brat	*Fusion*	5	4	3
	Brick Lane Beigel Bake	*Sandwiches, cakes, etc*	4	1	1
£70+	The Light Bar	*British, Modern*	–	–	–
	Mama Shelter Restaurant	"	–	–	–
	Pidgin	"	5	3	3
	Smith's Wapping	"	4	3	4
	Behind	*Fish & seafood*	5	4	4
	The Sea, The Sea	"	3	3	4
	Casa Fofó	*International*	5	4	4
	The Laughing Heart	"	3	4	3
	Canto Corvino	*Italian*	3	3	3
	Brawn	*Mediterranean*	5	3	3
	Sticks'n'Sushi	*Japanese*	4	3	3
£60+	Big Easy	*American*	3	2	3
	The Culpeper	*British, Modern*	3	2	3
	Elliot's	"	3	3	4
	Humble Grape	"	3	4	3
	Jones & Sons	"	3	3	4
	Madame Pigg	"	4	4	4
	The Narrow	"	2	2	3
	The Marksman	*British, Traditional*	3	2	3
	St John Bread & Wine	"	3	2	3
	Chez Elles	*French*	4	4	4
	Galvin Bistrot & Bar	"	3	4	4
	Six by Nico	*International*	4	4	4
	Oren	*Mediterranean*	4	2	2
	Ottolenghi	"	4	3	3
	Boisdale of Canary Wharf	*Scottish*	3	3	4
	Ibérica	*Spanish*	3	2	2
	Burger & Lobster	*Burgers, etc*	3	2	2
	Pizza East	*Pizza*	4	3	4
	Café Spice Namaste	*Indian*	–	–	–

	Grand Trunk Road	"		4 4 3
£50+	Passyunk Avenue	American		2 2 4
	Corner Room	British, Modern		3 3 3
	Duke of Richmond	"		3 2 3
	The Empress	"		3 3 3
	The Gun	"		2 2 4
	Mare Street Market	"		3 2 5
	No 35 Mackenzie Walk	"		– – –
	P Franco	"		4 3 3
	Angelina	Fusion		4 4 3
	Il Bordello	Italian		3 3 3
	Campania & Jones	"		4 3 3
	Morito	Spanish		3 3 4
	Mildreds	Vegetarian		3 3 3
	Poppies	Fish & chips		3 3 2
	Le Bab at Kraft Dalston	Middle Eastern		4 2 3
	Berber & Q	"		4 3 4
	Haz	Turkish		2 3 2
	Lahpet	Burmese		3 3 3
	Royal China	Chinese		3 1 2
	Sichuan Folk	"		4 3 2
	Gunpowder	Indian		4 3 3
	Smoking Goat	Thai		4 4 3
	Som Saa	"		4 2 3
£40+	Breakfast Club	American		3 3 3
	Homestead	British, Modern		– – –
	NEST	"		4 4 3
	Provender	French		4 4 3
	Joan	Mediterranean		– – –
	Burger & Beyond	Burgers, etc		4 3 2
	Ark Fish	Fish & chips		3 3 2
	Pizza Pilgrims	Pizza		3 3 3
	Yard Sale Pizza	"		3 2 2
	Zia Lucia Aldgate	"		4 3 3
	Ozone Coffee Roasters	Sandwiches, cakes, etc		3 4 4
	Chick 'n' Sours	Chicken		3 3 3
	Smokestak	BBQ		5 3 3
	Bubala	Middle Eastern		4 4 3
	Delamina East	"		3 3 3
	Lucky & Joy	Chinese		4 3 3
	Yi-Ban	"		– – –
	Dishoom	Indian		3 4 5
	Tonkotsu	Japanese		4 3 2
	Mien Tay	Vietnamese		3 3 3
	Sông Quê	"		3 2 2
	Bao Noodle Shop	Taiwanese		3 4 4
£35+	Townsend @ Whitechapel	British, Modern		3 3 3
	Royale	French		– – –
	Flat Iron	Steaks & grills		3 4 4
	Dirty Burger Shoreditch	Burgers, etc		3 2 2
	Crate Brewery and Pizzeria	Pizza		3 2 4
	Mangal 1	Turkish		5 2 2

£30+	Pergola on the Wharf	*International*	– – –
	Figo	*Italian*	– – –
	Patty and Bun	*Burgers, etc*	4 3 3
	My Neighbours The Dum…	*Chinese, Dim sum*	3 2 2
	Mio Yatai	*Japanese*	– – –
	Lahore Kebab House	*Pakistani*	4 2 2
	Tayyabs	*"*	4 1 2
£25+	A Slice of Blue	*Pizza*	3 3 3
	Nebula Pizza	*"*	– – –
	Sushi Show	*Japanese*	4 3 2
	Singburi Royal Thai Café	*Thai*	4 3 3
£20+	E Pellicci	*Italian*	3 5 5
	Bleecker Burger	*Burgers, etc*	4 2 1
	The Dusty Knuckle	*Sandwiches, cakes, etc*	4 2 2
	Attawa	*Indian*	3 3 2
£15+	The Duck Truck	*Burgers, etc*	5 4 2
	Smokoloko	*BBQ*	5 3 –
	The Halal Restaurant	*Indian*	– – –
£10+	Black Bear Burger	*Burgers, etc*	5 3 3
	The Rib Man	*"*	5 3 –
£5+	Dumpling Shack x Fen N…	*Chinese*	5 3 2

MAPS

MAP I – LONDON OVERVIEW

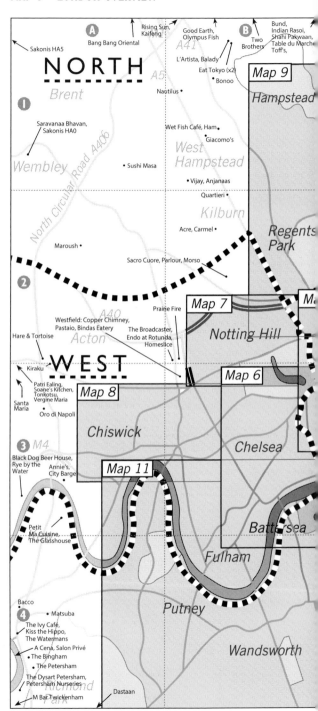

Ⓐ Bang Bang Oriental

Rising Sun, Kaifeng

Good Earth, Olympus Fish

Ⓑ Bund, Indian Rasoi, Shahi Pakwaan, Table du Marche, Toff's,

Sakonis HA5

L'Artista, Balady

Two Brothers

NORTH

A41

Eat Tokyo (x2)

Map 9

A5

Bonoo

Brent

Ⓘ

Nautilus •

Hampstead

Saravanaa Bhavan, Sakonis HA0

Wet Fish Café, Ham •

• Giacomo's

West Hampstead

Wembley

North Circular Road A406

• Sushi Masa

• Vijay, Anjanaas

Quartieri •

Kilburn

Acre, Carmel •

Regents Park

• Maroush •

Sacro Cuore, Parlour, Morso

Ⓜ

Ⓜ

Map 7

Prairie Fire

Westfield: Copper Chimney, Pastaio, Bindas Eatery

A40

Notting Hill

Acton

The Broadcaster, Endo at Rotunda, Homeslice

Hare & Tortoise

WEST

Map 6

Map 8

• Kiraku

Patri Ealing, Soane's Kitchen, Tonkotsu, Vergine Maria

Santa Maria

Chiswick

• Oro di Napoli

Chelsea

Ⓜ M4

Black Dog Beer House, Rye by the Water

Annie's, City Barge •

Map 11

Ⓒ

Petit Ma Cuisine, The Glasshouse

Battersea

Fulham

Bacco •

• Matsuba

Putney

The Ivy Café, Kiss the Hippo, The Watermans

Wandsworth

A Cena, Salon Privé

• The Bingham

• The Petersham

The Dysart Petersham, Petersham Nurseries

M Bar Twickenham

Richmond Park

Dastaan

MAP 1 – LONDON OVERVIEW

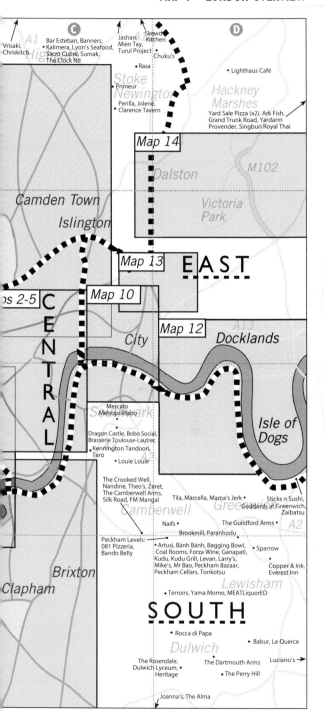

C

A1 High...

Vrisaki, Chriskitch

Bar Esteban, Banners, • Kalimera, Lyon's Seafood, Sacro Cuore, Sumak, The Clock N8

Jashan, Mien Tay, Turul Project •

Skewd Kitchen
• Chuku's

Stoke Newington

• Primeur

Perilla, Jolene, • Clarence Tavern

• Rasa

D

• Lighthaus Café

Hackney Marshes

Yard Sale Pizza (x2), Ark Fish, Grand Trunk Road, Yardarm Provender, Singburi Royal Thai

Map 14

Dalston

M102

Camden Town

Islington

Victoria Park

Map 13

E A S T

os 2-5

C E N T R A L

Map 10

City

Map 12

A13

Docklands

Isle of Dogs

Mercato Metropolitano

Southwark

• Dragon Castle, Bobo Social, Brasserie Toulouse-Lautrec
• Kennington Tandoori, Taro

• Louie Louie

A2

The Crooked Well, Nandine, Theo's, Zéret, The Camberwell Arms, Silk Road, FM Mangal

Tila, Marcella, Mama's Jerk •

Sticks n Sushi, Goddards at Greenwich, Zaibatsu

Camberwell

Greenwich

Naifs •

The Guildford Arms •

A2

Brookmill, Paranhodu

Peckham Levels: 081 Pizzeria, Bando Belly

• Artusi, Bánh Bánh, Begging Bowl, Coal Rooms, Forza Wine, Ganapati, Kudu, Kudu Grill, Levan, Larry's, Mike's, Mr Bao, Peckham Bazaar, Peckham Cellars, Tonkotsu

• Sparrow

Copper & Ink, Everest Inn

Brixton

Lewisham

• Terroirs, Yama Momo, MEATLiquorED

Clapham

S O U T H

• Rocca di Papa

Dulwich

• Babur, Le Querce

The Rosendale, Dulwich Lyceum, • Heritage

The Dartmouth Arms

Luciano's →

• The Perry Hill

Joanna's, The Alma

MAP 2 – WEST END OVERVIEW

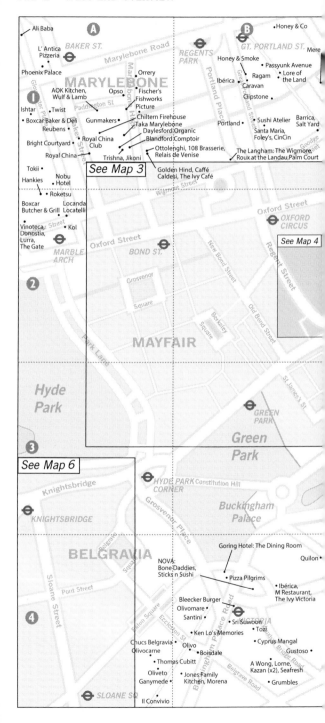

A

B

Ali Baba

Honey & Co

L' Antica Pizzeria

BAKER ST.

GT. PORTLAND ST.

Mere

Phoenix Palace

Marylebone Road

REGENTS PARK

Honey & Smoke

Passyunk Avenue

Orrery

Ibérica

Ragam

Lore of the Land

MARYLEBONE

Caravan

AOK Kitchen, Wulf & Lamb

Opso

Fischer's Fishworks

Clipstone

Ishtar

Twist

Picture

Boxcar Baker & Deli

Chiltern Firehouse

Reubens

Gunmakers

Taka Marylebone

Portland

Sushi Atelier

Barrica, Salt Yard

Daylesford Organic

Santa Maria, Foley's, CinCin

Bright Courtyard

Royal China Club

Blandford Comptoir

Royal China

Ottolenghi, 108 Brasserie, Relais de Venise

The Langham: The Wigmore, Roux at the Landau, Palm Court

Trishna, Jikoni

See Map 3

Golden Hind, Caffé Caldesi, The Ivy Café

Tokii

Hankies

Nobu Hotel

Oxford Street

OXFORD CIRCUS

Roketsu

See Map 4

Boxcar Butcher & Grill

Locanda Locatelli

Vinoteca, Donostia, Lurra, The Gate

Kol

Oxford Street

MARBLE ARCH

BOND ST.

Grosvenor

Square

MAYFAIR

Berkeley

Square

Park Lane

Old Bond Street

New Bond Street

Regent Street

St. James's St.

Hyde Park

GREEN PARK

Green Park

See Map 6

Knightsbridge

HYDE PARK CORNER

Constitution Hill

KNIGHTSBRIDGE

Grosvenor Place

Buckingham Palace

BELGRAVIA

Goring Hotel: The Dining Room

Quilon

Belgrave Square

NOVA: Bone Daddies, Sticks n Sushi

Pizza Pilgrims

Ibérica, M Restaurant, The Ivy Victoria

Sloane Street

Pont Street

Bleecker Burger

Olivomare

Santini

Sri Suwoon

Tozi

Chucs Belgravia

Ken Lo's Memories

Cyprus Mangal

Gustoso

Olivocarne

Olivo

Boisdale

A Wong, Lorne, Kazan (x2), Seafresh

Thomas Cubitt

Oliveto

Jones Family Kitchen, Morena

Grumbles

Ganymede

Belgrave Road

SLOANE SQ.

Il Convivio

MAP 2 – WEST END OVERVIEW

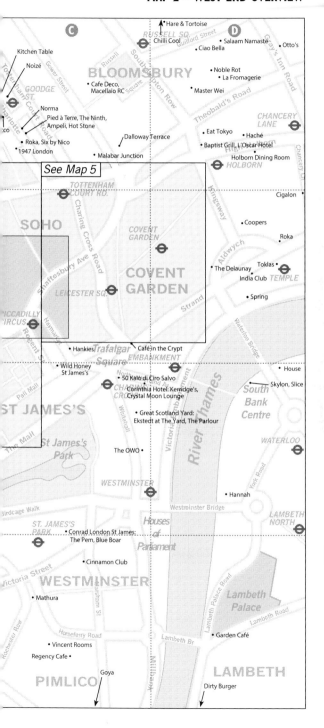

↑ Hare & Tortoise
RUSSELL SQ.
Chilli Cool
Salaam Namaste
Otto's
Ciao Bella
Kitchen Table
Noizé
GOODGE ST.
BLOOMSBURY
Noble Rot
La Fromagerie
Cafe Deco, Macellaio RC
Master Wei
co
Norma
Pied à Terre, The Ninth, Ampeli, Hot Stone
CHANCERY LANE
Eat Tokyo
Haché
Baptist Grill, L'Oscar Hotel
Holborn Dining Room
HOLBORN
Roka, Six by Nico
1947 London
Dalloway Terrace
Malabar Junction

See Map 5

TOTTENHAM COURT RD.
SOHO
Cigalon
Coopers
Roka
COVENT GARDEN
COVENT GARDEN
The Delaunay
Toklas
India Club
TEMPLE
LEICESTER SQ.
Strand
Spring
PICCADILLY CIRCUS
Hankies
Trafalgar Square
Café in the Crypt
EMBANKMENT
Wild Honey
St James's
House
50 Kalò di Ciro Salvo
Corinthia Hotel: Kerridge's, Crystal Moon Lounge
Skylon, Slice
South Bank Centre
ST JAMES'S
Great Scotland Yard: Ekstedt at The Yard, The Parlour
WATERLOO
St James's Park
The OWO
WESTMINSTER
Hannah
Birdcage Walk
Westminster Bridge
LAMBETH NORTH
ST. JAMES'S PARK
Conrad London St James: The Pem, Blue Boar
Houses of Parliament
Cinnamon Club
Victoria Street
WESTMINSTER
Lambeth Palace
Mathura
Horseferry Road
Lambeth Br
Garden Café
Vincent Rooms
Regency Cafe
PIMLICO
Goya
LAMBETH
Dirty Burger

MAP 3 – MAYFAIR, ST. JAMES'S & WEST SOHO

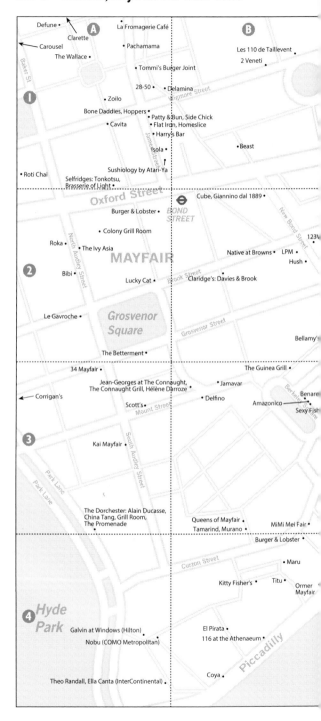

MAP 3 – MAYFAIR, ST. JAMES'S & WEST SOHO

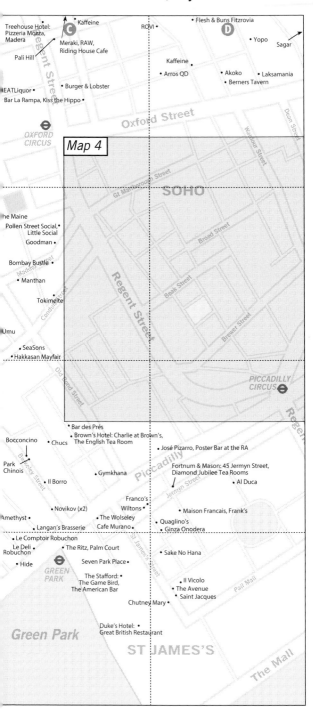

Kaffeine

Treehouse Hotel:
Pizzeria Mozza,
Madera

ROVI

Flesh & Buns Fitzrovia

Yopo

Sagar

Pali Hill

Meraki, RAW,
Riding House Cafe

Kaffeine

Arros QD

Akoko

Laksamania

Berners Tavern

EATLiquor

Bar La Rampa, Kiss the Hippo

Burger & Lobster

Oxford Street

OXFORD
CIRCUS

Map 4

SOHO

Gt Marlborough Street

Broad Street

the Maine

Pollen Street Social,
Little Social

Goodman

Berk Street

Bombay Bustle

Manthan

Regent Street

Brewer Street

Tokimeite

Conduit Street

Umu

SeaSons
Hakkasan Mayfair

Old Bond Street

PICCADILLY
CIRCUS

Bar des Prés

Bocconcino

Chucs

Brown's Hotel: Charlie at Brown's,
The English Tea Room

José Pizarro, Poster Bar at the RA

Park
Chinois

Il Borro

Gymkhana

Piccadilly

Fortnum & Mason: 45 Jermyn Street,
Diamond Jubilee Tea Rooms

Jermyn Street

Al Duca

Franco's

Novikov (x2)

Wiltons

Maison Francais, Frank's

Amethyst

The Wolseley

Langan's Brasserie

Cafe Murano

Quaglino's

Ginza Onodera

Le Comptoir Robuchon

Le Deli
Robuchon

The Ritz, Palm Court

Sake No Hana

Hide

GREEN
PARK

Seven Park Place

The Stafford:
The Game Bird,
The American Bar

Il Vicolo
The Avenue
Saint Jacques

Pall Mall

Chutney Mary

Green Park

Duke's Hotel:
Great British Restaurant

ST JAMES'S

The Mall

MAP 4 – WEST SOHO & PICCADILLY

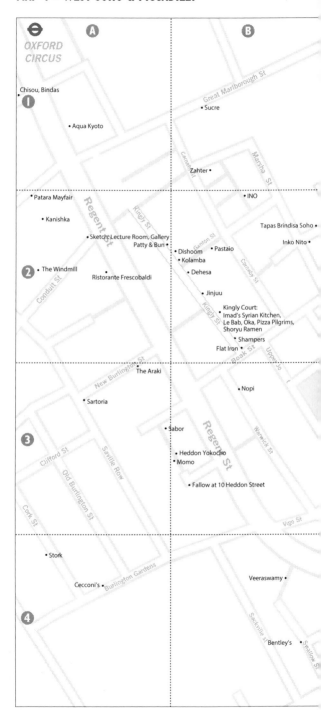

OXFORD CIRCUS

Ⓐ Ⓑ

Great Marlborough St

• Chisou, Bindas
❶

• Aqua Kyoto

• Sucre

Carnaby St

Marsha St

Zahter •

• Patara Mayfair

• INO

Regent St

• Kanishka

Kingly St

Tapas Brindisa Soho •

Inko Nito •

• Sketch: Lecture Room, Gallery
Patty & Bun •

Ganton St

• Dishoom • Pastaio
• Kolamba

Carnaby St

❷ • The Windmill

• Dehesa

Conduit St

• Ristorante Frescobaldi

• Jinjuu

Kingly St

Kingly Court:
Imad's Syrian Kitchen,
Le Bab, Oka, Pizza Pilgrims,
Shoryu Ramen
• Shampers

Flat Iron •

Beak St

Upper J

• The Araki

New Burlington St

• Nopi

• Sartoria

❸

• Sabor

Regent St

Warwick St

Clifford St

Saville Row

• Heddon Yokocho
• Momo

Old Burlington St

• Fallow at 10 Heddon Street

Cork St

Vigo St

• Stork

• Veeraswamy

Cecconi's • Burlington Gardens

❹

Sackville St

Bentley's •

Swallow St

MAP 4 – WEST SOHO & PICCADILLY

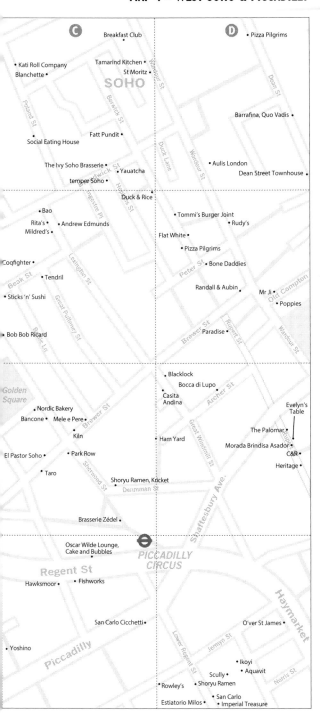

MAP 5 – EAST SOHO, CHINATOWN & COVENT GARDEN

- Bao Fitzrovia
- **A**
- VQ
- Shoryu Ramen
- New Oxford Street
- Dyott St
- Hakkasan
- Circulo Popolare, Akoko
- **B**
- Oxford Street
- Arcade at Centre Point, Din Tai Fung
- Tattu
- **1** TOTTENHAM CT. RD
- Soho St
- Flat Iron
- Charing Cross Road
- Kanada-Ya
- Soho Square
- Noble Rot Soho
- SOHO
- Shaftesbury Avenue
- Mon Plaisir
- Sussex
- Truffle
- 10 Greek Street
- Bibimbap Soho
- Patara Soho
- Monmouth Coffee
- Manzi's
- Lina Stores
- L'Escargot
- Greek St
- Frith St
- **2** Humble Chicken
- Chotto Matte
- Shackfuyu
- Eat Tokyo
- Wun's
- Patty & Bun
- Monmouth St
- Ceviche
- Hoppers, Koya Bar
- Burger & Lobster
- Bar Italia
- The Black Book
- Cambridge Circus
- Chick 'n' Sours
- So LA
- Prix Fixe
- Cecconi's Pizza
- Tonkotsu
- Ducksoup
- Maison Bertaux
- Louie
- Cay Tre
- L'Antica Pizzeria da Michele
- Berenjak
- Yming
- Dean St
- Old Compton St
- Baozi Inn
- Gauthier Soho
- Shaftesbury Avenue
- The Ivy
- 28-50
- The French House
- Relais de Venise
- Dishoom
- Hankies
- Feng Wei Shi Tang
- **3**
- Four Seasons, Little Four Seasons
- CHINATOWN
- Baozi Inn
- Il Teatro della Carne
- Plum Valley
- Viet Food
- Dumplings' Legend
- Gerrard St
- Charing Cross Road
- Cranbourn St
- Wong Kei
- Golden Dragon
- Lisle Street
- Heliot
- St Martin's Lane
- LEICESTER SQ
- Wardour Street
- Cork & Bottle
- Four Seasons
- J Sheekey, Atlantic Bar
- Street Burger
- Leicester Square
- Coventry St
- **4**
- The Londoner
- Panton Yokocho
- Haymarket
- Kanada-Ya, Showaken
- Whitcomb Street

MAP 5 – EAST SOHO, CHINATOWN & COVENT GARDEN

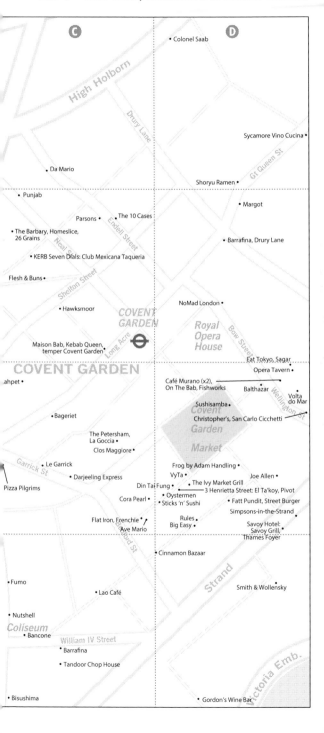

C

D

• Colonel Saab

Sycamore Vino Cucina •

High Holborn

Drury Lane

Gt Queen St

• Da Mario

Shoryu Ramen •

• Punjab

• Margot

Parsons • • The 10 Cases

Neal Street

Endell Street

• The Barbary, Homeslice, 26 Grains

• Barrafina, Drury Lane

• KERB Seven Dials: Club Mexicana Taqueria

Flesh & Buns •

Shelton Street

• Hawksmoor

COVENT GARDEN

NoMad London •

Royal Opera House

Bow Street

Long Acre

Maison Bab, Kebab Queen, temper Covent Garden •

COVENT GARDEN

Eat Tokyo, Sagar
Opera Tavern •

ahpet •

Café Murano (x2),
On The Bab, Fishworks

Wellington St

Balthazar

Volta
do Mar

• Bageriet

Sushisamba •

Covent

Christopher's, San Carlo Cicchetti

The Petersham,
La Goccia •

Garden

Clos Maggiore •

Market

Garrick St

• Le Garrick

Frog by Adam Handling •

Pizza Pilgrims

• Darjeeling Express

VyTa •

Joe Allen •

Din Tai Fung •

• The Ivy Market Grill
3 Henrietta Street: El Ta'koy, Pivot

Bedford St

Cora Pearl •

• Oystermen

• Fatt Pundit, Street Burger

• Sticks 'n' Sushi

Simpsons-in-the-Strand

Flat Iron, Frenchie •
Ave Mario

Rules •
Big Easy •

Savoy Hotel:
Savoy Grill,
Thames Foyer

• Cinnamon Bazaar

• Fumo

Strand

• Lao Café

Smith & Wollensky •

• Nutshell

Coliseum

• Bancone

William IV Street

• Barrafina

• Tandoor Chop House

Victoria Emb.

• Bisushima

• Gordon's Wine Bar

MAP 6 – KNIGHTSBRIDGE, CHELSEA & SOUTH KENSINGTON

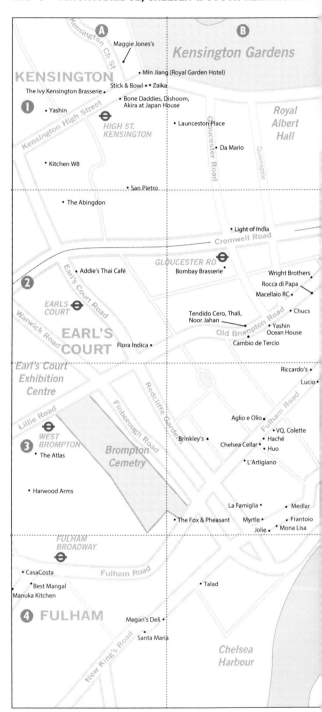

MAP 6 – KNIGHTSBRIDGE, CHELSEA & SOUTH KENSINGTON

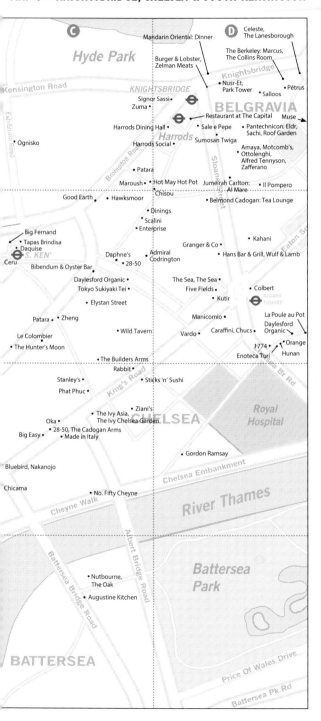

Hyde Park

Kensington Road

Mandarin Oriental: Dinner

Burger & Lobster,
Zelman Meats

Celeste,
The Lanesborough

The Berkeley: Marcus,
The Collins Room

Knightsbridge

KNIGHTSBRIDGE

Nusr-Et,
Park Tower

Salloos

Pétrus

Signor Sassi

Zuma

BELGRAVIA

Restaurant at The Capital

Muse

Harrods Dining Hall

Sale e Pepe

Pantechnicon: Eldr,
Sachi, Roof Garden

Harrods Social

Sumosan Twiga

Harrods

Ognisko

Amaya, Motcomb's,
Ottolenghi,
Alfred Tennyson,
Zafferano

Patara

Maroush

Hot May Hot Pot

Jumeirah Carlton:
Al Mare

Il Pompero

Chisou

Good Earth

Hawksmoor

Belmond Cadogan: Tea Lounge

Dinings

Scalini

Enterprise

Granger & Co

Kahani

Big Fernand

Tapas Brindisa

Daquise

Ceru

S. KEN'

Daphne's

28-50

Admiral
Codrington

Hans Bar & Grill, Wulf & Lamb

Bibendum & Oyster Bar

Daylesford Organic

Tokyo Sukiyaki Tei

The Sea, The Sea

Five Fields

Kutir

Colbert

Elystan Street

Patara

Zheng

Le Colombier

The Hunter's Moon

Wild Tavern

Manicomio

Vardo

Caraffini, Chucs

La Poule au Pot

Daylesford
Organic

1774

Orange

Enoteca Turi

Hunan

The Builders Arms

Rabbit!

Sticks 'n' Sushi

Stanley's

Phat Phuc

Ziani's:
The Ivy Asia,
The Ivy Chelsea Garden

CHELSEA

Oka

28-50, The Cadogan Arms

Big Easy

Made in Italy

Royal
Hospital

Gordon Ramsay

Bluebird, Nakanojo

Chelsea Embankment

Chicama

No. Fifty Cheyne

Cheyne Walk

River Thames

Battersea
Park

Nutbourne,
The Oak

Augustine Kitchen

BATTERSEA

Price Of Wales Drive

Battersea Pk Rd

MAP 7 – NOTTING HILL & BAYSWATER

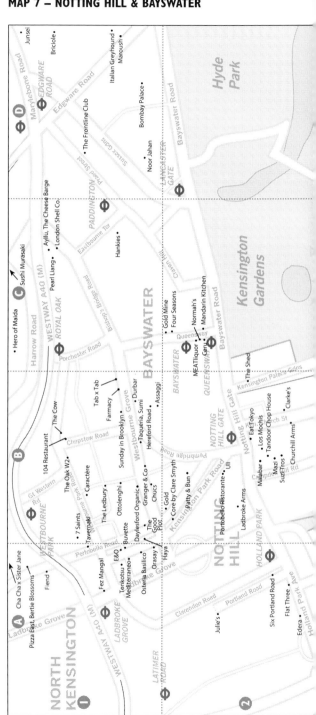

MAP 8 – HAMMERSMITH & CHISWICK

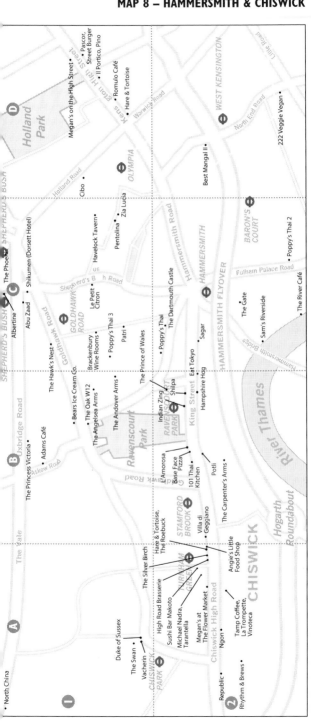

North China

Holland Park

• Pascor,
Street Burger
Eton High Street • Il Portico, Pino
Megan's on the High Street • • Romulo Café
• Hare & Tortoise

WEST KENSINGTON

Kenton Road

Warwick Road

Lillie Road

OLYMPIA

Holland Road

Cibo •

• Best Mangal II

222 Veggie Vegan •

North End Road

Havelock Tavern •

The Phoenix •
Albertine • Shkumen (Dorset Hotel)

Pentolina •
• Zia Lucia

HAMMERSMITH ROAD

HAMMERSMITH

BARON'S
COURT

• Poppy's Thai 2

Fulham Palace Road

Abu Zaad •

Shepherd's B h Road

GOLDHAWK
ROAD
Le Petit
Citron •
• The Dartmouth Castle

HAMMERSMITH FLYOVER

The Hawk's Nest •

Poppy's Thai 3 •

Brackenbury
Wine Rooms •

Patri •

• Poppy's Thai

Sagar •

The Gate •

Sam's Riverside •

• The River Café

Bears Ice Cream Co. •

The Oak W12 •
• The Angelsea Arms

The Andover Arms •

The Prince of Wales •

Eat Tokyo •

Indian Zing •
Shilpa •

Hampshire Hog •

RAVENSCOURT
PARK

King Street

River Thames

Ravenscourt
Park

Uxbridge Road

The Princes Victoria •

Adams Café •

Askew Road

L'Amorosa •
Base Face
Pizza •

101 Thai
Kitchen •

Potli •

The Carpenter's Arms •

Chiswick Road

Hogarth
Roundabout

The Vale

The Silver Birch •

Hare & Tortoise,
The Roebuck •

STAMFORD
BROOK

Villa di
Geggiano •

Angie's Little
Food Shop •

CHISWICK

Duke of Sussex •

The Swan •

Vacherin •

High Road Brasserie •

Sushi Bar Makoto •

Michael Nadra •
Tarantella •

Megan's at
The Flower Market •

Ngon •

Chiswick High Road

Tamp Coffee,
La Trompette,
Vinoteca •

CHISWICK
PARK

Republic •

Rhythm & Brews •

North China •

MAP 9 – HAMPSTEAD, CAMDEN TOWN & ISLINGTON

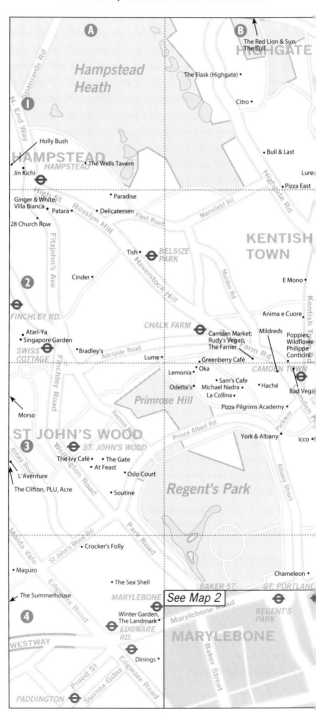

A

B

The Red Lion & Sun,
The Bull

HIGHGATE

Hampstead
Heath

The Flask (Highgate) •

Citro •

Holly Bush

• Bull & Last

HAMPSTEAD
HAMPSTEAD • The Wells Tavern

Lure

Jin Kichi •

• Pizza East

Ginger & White, • Paradise
Villa Bianca
• Patara • Delicatessen

Mansfield Rd

KENTISH
TOWN

28 Church Row

Tish • BELSIZE
PARK

E Mono •

Cinder •

Anima e Cuore •

FINCHLEY RD.

CHALK FARM

Atari-Ya •
• Singapore Garden

Camden Market: Mildreds
Rudy's Vegan,   Poppies,
The Farrier   Wildflowe
                                            Philippe
• Bradley's   Lume •   Conticini

SWISS
COTTAGE

Adelaide Road

• Greenberry Café

CAMDEN TOWN

Lemonia • Oka

Odette's •

• Sam's Cafe
Michael Nadra •   • Haché   Bad Vega
La Collina •

Primrose Hill

Pizza Pilgrims Academy •

Morso

Prince Albert Rd

ST JOHN'S WOOD

York & Albany •

Icco •

ST. JOHN'S WOOD

The Ivy Café • • The Gate
• At Feast

L'Aventure

• Oslo Court

The Clifton, PLU, Acre

Regent's Park

• Soutine

• Crocker's Folly

Chameleon •

• Maguro

• The Sea Shell

BAKER ST.   GT. PORTLAND

↙ The Summerhouse

MARYLEBONE   See Map 2

REGENT'S
PARK

Winter Garden,
The Landmark •

MARYLEBONE

EDGWARE
RD.

WESTWAY

Dinings •

PADDINGTON

MAP 9 – HAMPSTEAD, CAMDEN TOWN & ISLINGTON

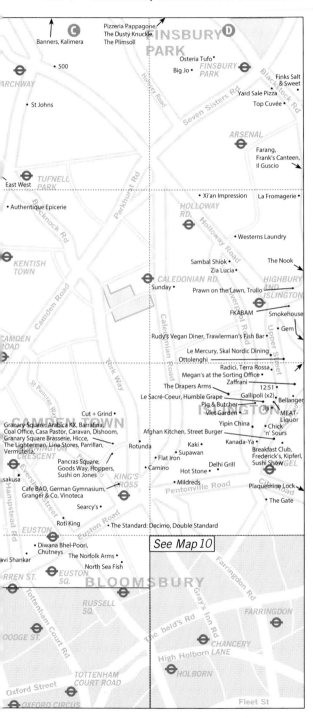

Banners, Kalimera

Pizzeria Pappagone
The Dusty Knuckle,
The Plimsoll

FINSBURY PARK

• 500

Osteria Tufo •

Big Jo •

FINSBURY PARK

Finks Salt
& Sweet

ARCHWAY

• St Johns

Seven Sisters Rd

Blackstock Rd

Yard Sale Pizza

Top Cuvée •

ARSENAL

Farang,
Frank's Canteen,
Il Guscio

TUFNELL PARK

East West

• Authentique Epicerie

Parkhurst Rd

Blackstock Rd

• Xi'an Impression

La Fromagerie •

HOLLOWAY RD.

Holloway Road

• Westerns Laundry

KENTISH TOWN

Camden Road

Sambal Shiok •

Zia Lucia •

The Nook

Sunday •

CALEDONIAN RD.

Prawn on the Lawn, Trullo

HIGHBURY AND ISLINGTON

FKABAM

Smokehouse

• Gem

York Way

Upper St

CAMDEN ROAD

St Pancras Way

Rudy's Vegan Diner, Trawlerman's Fish Bar •

Le Mercury, Skal Nordic Dining
Ottolenghi •

Radici, Terra Rossa •

Megan's at the Sorting Office •

Zaffrani

The Drapers Arms •

12:51 •

Le Sacré-Coeur, Humble Grape

Gallipoli (x2) •

Bellanger

Pig & Butcher •

Jiji •

MEAT-
Liquor

Viet Garden •

Yipin China •

Chick
'n' Sours

ISLINGTON

Cut + Grind •

Granary Square: Arabica KX, Barrafina,
Coal Office, Casa Pastor, Caravan, Dishoom,
Granary Square Brasserie, Hicce,
The Lighterman, Lina Stores, Parrillan,
Vermuteria,

Afghan Kitchen, Street Burger

Kanada-Ya •

Rotunda

Kaki •

Supawan •

Breakfast Club,
Frederick's, Kipferl,
Sushi Show

CAMDEN TOWN

ISLINGTON CRESCENT

sakusa

Pancras Square:
Goods Way, Hoppers,
Sushi on Jones

Eversholt Rd

Hampstead Rd

Cafe BAO, German Gymnasium,
Granger & Co, Vinoteca

Searcy's •

KING'S CROSS

Flat Iron •

Delhi Grill •

Camino •

Hot Stone •

Pentonville Road

• Mildreds

• Plaquemine Lock

City Road

• The Gate

Roti King

• The Standard: Decimo, Double Standard

EUSTON

See Map 10

• Diwana Bhel-Poori,
Chutneys

avi Shankar

The Norfolk Arms •

North Sea Fish

WARREN ST.

EUSTON SQ.

BLOOMSBURY

Tottenham Court Rd

RUSSELL SQ.

FARRINGDON

Farringdon Rd

Gray's Inn Rd

OODGE ST.

The bald's Rd

CHANCERY LANE

High Holborn

HOLBORN

Oxford Street

TOTTENHAM COURT ROAD

OXFORD CIRCUS

Fleet St

MAP 10 – THE CITY

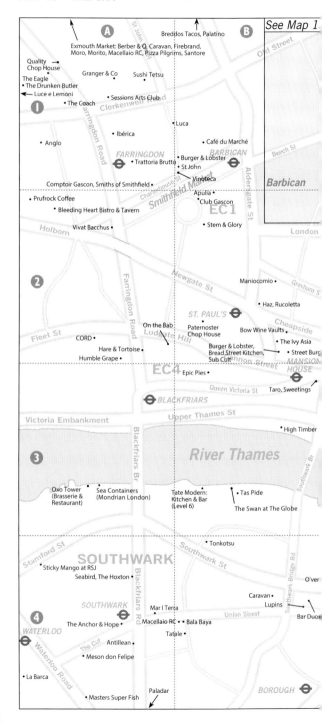

See Map 1

Breddos Tacos, Palatino

Exmouth Market: Berber & Q, Caravan, Firebrand,
Moro, Morito, Macellaio RC, Pizza Pilgrims, Santore

Quality
Chop House

The Eagle
• The Drunken Butler
← Luce e Lemoni
• The Coach

Granger & Co

Sushi Tetsu

Sessions Arts Club

Old Street

St John St

Clerkenwell Rd

• Luca

• Ibérica

FARRINGDON

• Anglo

• Café du Marché

• Burger & Lobster
• Trattoria Brutto

BARBICAN

St John

Beech St

Aldersgate St

Vinoteca

Charterhouse St

Smithfield Market

Barbican

Comptoir Gascon, Smiths of Smithfield •

Apulia

• Prufrock Coffee

• Club Gascon

EC1

London

• Bleeding Heart Bistro & Tavern

Holborn

Vivat Bacchus •

• Stem & Glory

Farringdon Road

Newgate St

Maniocomio •

Gresham S

• Haz, Rucoletta

ST. PAUL'S

Cheapside

On the Bab

Fleet St

CORD •

Ludgate Hill

Paternoster
Chop House

Bow Wine Vaults •

• The Ivy Asia

Hare & Tortoise •

Burger & Lobster,
Bread Street Kitchen,
Sub Cult

• Street Burg

MANSION
HOUSE

Humble Grape •

Cannon Street

EC4

Epic Pies •

Queen Victoria St

Taro, Sweetings

BLACKFRIARS

Upper Thames St

Victoria Embankment

Blackfriars Br

• High Timber

River Thames

Southwark Br

Oxo Tower
(Brasserie &
Restaurant)

Sea Containers
(Mondrian London)

Tate Modern:
Kitchen & Bar
(Level 6)

• Tas Pide

The Swan at The Globe

Stamford St

SOUTHWARK

• Tonktsu

Southwark St

Southwark Bridge Rd

• Sticky Mango at RSJ

Seabird, The Hoxton •

Blackfriars Rd

O'ver

Caravan •

Lupins

SOUTHWARK

Mar I Terra

Bar Duo

The Anchor & Hope •

Macellaio RC • • Bala Baya

Union Street

WATERLOO

Tatale •

The Cut

Antillean •

Waterloo Road

• Meson don Felipe

• La Barca

• Masters Super Fish

Paladar

BOROUGH

MAP 10 – THE CITY

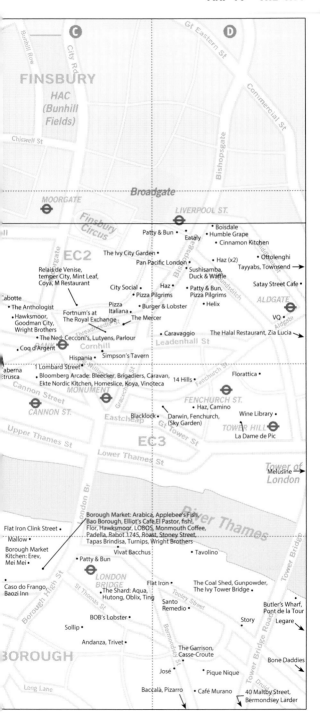

FINSBURY

HAC
(Bunhill
Fields)

Chiswell St

MOORGATE

Broadgate

LIVERPOOL ST.

EC2

Finsbury
Circus

Patty & Bun •
Eataly

• Boisdale
• Humble Grape
• Cinnamon Kitchen

The Ivy City Garden •
Pan Pacific London •

• Haz (x2)
• Sushisamba,
Duck & Waffle

• Ottolenghi

Tayyabs, Townsend →

Relais de Venise,
temper City, Mint Leaf,
Coya, M Restaurant

City Social •
• Pizza Pilgrims

Haz •
• Patty & Bun,
Pizza Pilgrims

Satay Street Cafe •

Cabotte •
• The Anthologist

Pizza
Italiana •
• Burger & Lobster

• Helix

ALDGATE

• Hawksmoor,
Goodman City,
Wright Brothers

Fortnum's at
The Royal Exchange

The Mercer

VQ •

• The Ned: Cecconi's, Lutyens, Parlour
• Coq d'Argent

Cornhill

• Caravaggio

Leadenhall St

The Halal Restaurant, Zia Lucia →

Hispania •

• Simpson's Tavern

taberna
etrusca

1 Lombard Street •
• Bloomberg Arcade: Bleecker, Brigadiers, Caravan,
Ekte Nordic Kitchen, Homeslice, Koya, Vinoteca

MONUMENT

14 Hills •

Florattica •

Cannon Street

FENCHURCH ST.

CANNON ST.

• Haz, Camino

Wine Library •

Upper Thames St

Blacklock •

Eastcheap

Darwin, Fenchurch,
(Sky Garden)

TOWER HILL

La Dame de Pic

EC3

Lower Thames St

Tower of
London

Melusine →

London Br

River Thames

Borough Market: Arabica, Applebee's Fish,
Bao Borough, Elliot's Cafe, El Pastor, fish!,
Flor, Hawksmoor, LOBOS, Monmouth Coffee,
Padella, Rabot 1745, Roast, Stoney Street,
Tapas Brindisa, Turnips, Wright Brothers

Flat Iron Clink Street •
• Mallow

Borough Market
Kitchen: Erev,
Mei Mei •

• Patty & Bun

Vivat Bacchus •

• Tavolino

LONDON
BRIDGE

Flat Iron •

The Coal Shed, Gunpowder,
The Ivy Tower Bridge •

Caso do Frango •
Baozi Inn •

The Shard: Aqua,
Hutong, Oblix, Ting

Santo
Remedio •

Butler's Wharf,
Pont de la Tour

BOB's Lobster •

Story •

Legare →

• Sollip

Andanza, Trivet •

BOROUGH

The Garrison,
Casse-Croute

Bone Daddies →

Long Lane

José •

• Pique Nique

Baccalà, Pizarro •

• Café Murano

40 Maltby Street,
Bermondsey Larder

MAP 11 – SOUTH LONDON (& FULHAM)

See Map 8

See Map 6

BARNES

- Rick Stein
- Orange Pekoe
- The Brown Dog
- The Crossing
- Riva
- Olympic
- Awesome Thai
- Oka, Church Road

The Crabtree

FULHAM

- Sukho Fine Thai Cuisine
- Fishers
- Mien Tay, Pure Indian
- Chook Chook

Fulham Palace Rd

Fulham Broadway

PUTNEY

- Munal Tandoori
- Hare & Tortoise, Ma Goa, Tomoe
- The Telegraph

Upper Richmond Road

Roehampton Lane

Richmond Park

The Victoria
The Plough SW14

The Black Horse

- Royal China
- Megan's by the Green
- West 4th
- KOJI
- Brook House
- FENN

PARSONS GREEN

Putney Bridge

- Kashmir
- Dynamo
- Gazette

East Putney

Putney Hill

- Black Radish, Patara,
The Ivy Café, Cent Anni
The Light House, Megan's
White Onion, Colette
- Takahashi,
Made in Italy
- Chicken Shop,
Dip & Flip, Sticks'n'Sushi
- Dropshot
- Amrutha
- Fox & Grapes, Hashi, Hatay,
Rose & Crown

WANDSWORTH

- Zia Lucia
- London Stock

Garratt Lane

- Kaosam, Unwined,
Jaffna House

Wandsworth Common

- Indian Ocean
- Good Earth, Pizza de Valter
- Chez Bruce,
Brinkley's Kitchen
- Kibou

Battersea Park

King's Rd
Cheyne Walk
Albert Br Rd
Battersea Br Rd

- Gazette

BATTERSEA

- Mien Tay
- Humble Grape,
Sinabro, Bababoom
- Dip & Flip
- Kaosarn
- Hatched
- Pizza Metro
- MEATliquor
- Macellaio RC
- Numero Uno
- Osteria Antica Bologna
- Sofi, Indian Moment

Chelsea Embankment
Queenstown
Queenstown Rd
Battersea Park Rd

- Santa Maria del Sur
- Boqueria

Battersea Power Station:
Cinnamon Kitchen, Fiume,
Megan's, Tonkotsu,
Wright Brothers

CLAPHAM

Clapham Common

Clapham Common Sth

Clapham South

- Trinity, Trinity
Upstairs, Megan's
Old Town
- Taro
- Milk
- Meza II

VAUXHALL

- Darby's, Oxeye

Brunswick House Café

Sth Lambeth Rd

Wandsworth Road

- Lusitania
- Tsunami
- Sorella

STOCKWELL

Stockwell

OVAL

Oval
Brixton Road
- 24 The Oval
- Stockwell Continental
- Canton Arms

BRIXTON

Brixton

- Pop Brixton: Only Food
and Courses
- Party
- Store, Pizza
- Other Side Fried

BRIXTON NORTH

- Bellefields,
Sushi Revolution
- Joe Public
- Haché
- St Clair
- Boqueria
- Knife

Acre Lane

Paynters Rd

- Haché
- The Abbeville,
Bistro Union,
Nue Ground
- Megan's on the Hill, Indian Room
- Daddy Bao, Dynamo,
Little Taperia, Smoke & Salt
- Bravi Ragazzi

Brixton Hill

- Banh Banh, Black Bear
Burger, Brixton Laundry,
Chishuru, Kaosarn,
Mamma Dough,
Nanban, Salon Brixton
- 500 Degrees
- 400 Rabbits at The Lido
- Llewelyn's, Olley's
Peachy Goat
- Maremma, Hood,
Mirch Masala,
Naughty Piglets

RIVER THAMES

MAP 12 – EAST END & DOCKLANDS

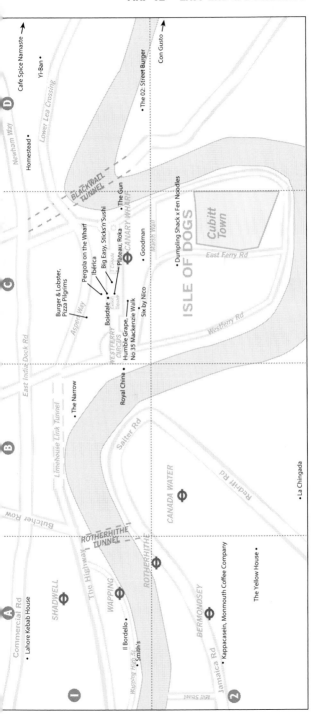

MAP 13 – SHOREDITCH & BETHNAL GREEN

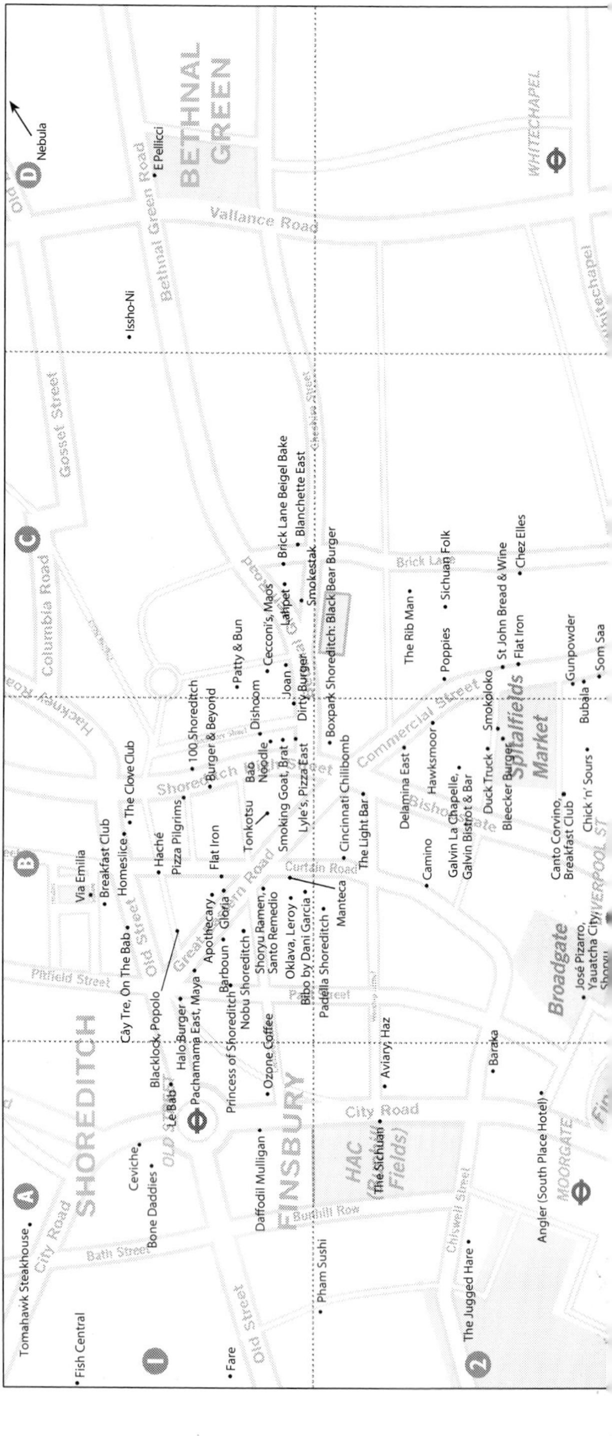

BETHNAL GREEN

WHITECHAPEL

SHOREDITCH

FINSBURY

BROADGATE

MOORGATE

Old Street

Bethnal Green Road

Vallance Road

Gosset Street

Columbia Road

Hackney Road

Brick Lane

Commercial Street

Bishopsgate

Shoreditch High Street

Curtain Road

Old Street

Great Eastern Street

City Road

Pitfield Street

Bath Street

Old Street

Bunhill Row

Chiswell Street

Whitechapel

Cheshire Street

HAC (The Artillery Fields)

Spitalfields Market

D Nebula
E Pellicci

Issho-Ni

Brick Lane Beigel Bake
Blanchette East
Ceccori's Maos
Joan Clapton
Dirty Burger
Smokestak
Boxpark Shoreditch: Black Bear Burger

Sichuan Folk
Chez Elles
The Rib Man
Poppies
St John Bread & Wine
Flat Iron
Smokoloko
Gunpowder
Bubala
Som Saa
Burger & Lobster
Duck Truck
Chick 'n' Sours
Bleecker Burger
St John Bread & Wine

Patty & Bun
Dishoom
Bao
Noodle
Smoking Goat, Brat
Lyle's, Pizza East
Cincinnati Chillibomb
The Light Bar

100 Shoreditch
Burger & Beyond
Flat Iron
Tonkotsu
Manteca

Delamina East
Hawksmoor
Camino
Galvin La Chapelle, Galvin Bistrot & Bar

Canto Corvino, Breakfast Club
José Pizarro, Yauatcha City, Shoryu

The Clove Club
Homeslice
Haché
Pizza Pilgrims

Via Emilia
Breakfast Club
Cay Tre, On The Bab
Blacklock, Popolo
Halo Burger
Pachamama East, Maya
Le Bab
Apothecary
Barboun
Gloria
Nobu Shoredtich
Princess of Shoreditch
Ozone Coffee
Shoryu Ramen, Santo Remedio
Oklava, Leroy
Bibo by Dani Garcia
Padella Shoreditch

Aviary
Haz
Baraka

Angler (South Place Hotel)

The Jugged Hare

Pham Sushi

Daffodil Mulligan

Fish Central
Ceviche
Bone Daddies
Tomahawk Steakhouse

Fare

Nebula

MAP 14 – EAST LONDON

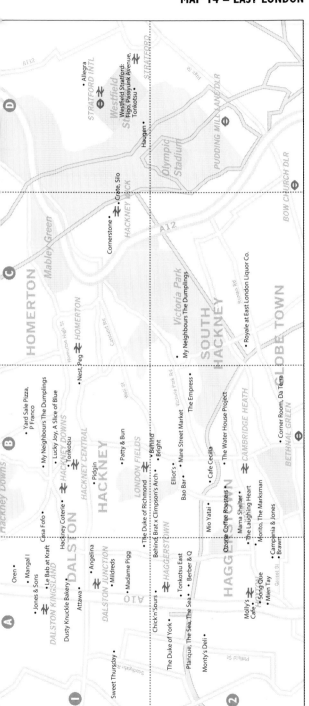